CIRCUITS, SIGNALS, AND NETWORKS

MACMILLAN SERIES IN ELECTRICAL SCIENCE

Roger F. Harrington, Editor

CIRCUITS, SIGNALS, AND NETWORKS

CYRUS W. COX

AND

WILLIAM L. REUTER

SOUTH DAKOTA SCHOOL OF MINES AND TECHNOLOGY

The Macmillan Company

NEW YORK

Collier-Macmillan Limited

LONDON

Library of Congress catalog card number: 68–15935

THE MACMILLAN COMPANY, NEW YORK
COLLIER-MACMILLAN CANADA, LTD., TORONTO, ONTARIO

PRINTED IN THE UNITED STATES OF AMERICA

290417

Preface

As is probably the case with most textbooks, this book started as class notes to provide a particular electrical engineering department with instructional material more suited to its own philosophy and to its own special needs than the texts then available. Although new books, of excellent quality, on electric circuits have appeared since the inception of this one, most of the conditions which motivated the work are with us yet. It was the feeling on the part of the authors that their own set of requirements was not a unique one, but rather one shared by instructors in many other departments, that led to the publication of this material.

The material is designed to serve students who have commenced their study of the calculus and their first course in physics. The following assumptions governed its construction: (1) It should provide a modern treatment wherein the mathematical abstractions, so much a part of modern analysis, are firmly rooted in physical considerations of the real world. (2) The engineer's viewpoint should be maintained while full use is made of the methods of the mathematician and physicist. (3) The work in networks should be preceded by just enough basic fields and materials to provide a physical description of the network parameters and of the network laws; the authors do not believe that "postulated" circuit parameters are satisfying to the neophyte engineer. (4) Every effort should be extended to produce in the mind of the student an association between the abstractions of theoretical analysis and the realities of the laboratory. (5) Generalized methods and special terminology should be delayed until the student is able to "discover" them from the vantage point of a firm foundation in the essentials of network theory. (6) Initial concepts should be expressed in the same language that will be used later by the student in his advanced courses and in his advanced readings.

It was not the intention of the authors to introduce radical new departures in the teaching of introductory circuits, but the very ingredients in the motivation of a new text naturally lead to approaches that are different from custom. For example, this text contains a significant deviation from conventional presentations of operational methods. A modified Heaviside–Jeffrey's approach has been adopted which utilizes operations on the unit impulse and includes the effects of initial conditions. Associated with this approach, as a necessary adjunct to it, is a fairly detailed study of the singularity functions, with the step function and the unit impulse considered as limiting forms of classes of regular functions with a very few prescribed properties and symmetries. We believe our experience has confirmed that this early introduction to the singularity functions is less traumatic for the student than is a late one. Furthermore, the student learns early to accept signal discontinuities as one of the facts of nature that must be faced if excited systems are to exist.

The modified Heaviside–Jeffrey's approach evolves forms identical to the Laplace transforms the student will meet later, requiring nothing more than a replacement of p in the operator technique with the s of Laplace transforms; that is, if $f(t) = F(p)\delta(t)$, then $\mathscr{L}[f(t)] = F(s)$. This similarity is carefully pointed out in Chapter 7, where the operator technique is introduced, and students who are already trained in the use of the Laplace transform can easily follow the material after Chapter 7 without an in-depth study of the chapter itself. Although the method has a significant conceptual difference from the Laplace transform method, the formalisms involved are essentially the same.

It is the belief of the authors that the adopted technique gives the neophyte a better feel for the effect of discontinuities and for the weighting of results by the past history of the system than does the transform approach. Moreover, the idea of a general linear operator is an important one in systems and signals, and it should follow naturally for the student versed in an operator technique. Best of all, we have avoided the superficial treatment of Laplace transforms which would have been necessary at this level while actually making it simpler for the student to solve with understanding complicated networks with nonzero initial conditions.

Another departure from conventional procedures is the introduction of the Thévenin and Norton equivalents and of the principle of superposition at the beginning of the material on networks. It is our feeling that the equivalents are implied anyway, in any realistic treatment of practical sources, and we have devoted more time to the nature of sources than is customary. The superposition principle must be accepted in order to discuss networks at all, and to use network equations to justify superposition makes us guilty of a "circular" proof in which the thing to be proved is implied in the beginning assumptions.

It may be that the authors will be accused of too much detail in the presentation of network topology to the student. However, it has appeared to us that when the student moves from his undergraduate text to the advanced treatments of networks, he often finds a grey area existing between the two in which important concepts have been given at most a superficial treatment. We have attempted to bridge this gap and, in addition, to give the same degree of physical significance to mesh currents that the student can readily attach to node voltages.

Other items in the text which have the flavor of innovations are the early introduction of the impedance-admittance concept during the study of classical solutions of the integro-differential equations, a little more attention than is customary to the interrelations between bandwidth and transient response, and the use of the transfer permeance in the development of mutual inductance. In the section on coupled circuits, the transformer is discussed in some detail for the benefit of those who find it missing elsewhere in their curriculum.

Some standard topics have been relegated to the problem lists to provide exercises in the development of generalized methods. For example, the development of admittance loci is assigned as a student exercise.

The authors are indebted to many people who have directly or indirectly influenced the progress of this project, including the students who have endured several drafts of varying degrees of polish and the colleagues who have taught the material and provided our toughest critics. Special acknowledgments must go to Mrs. Bonnie Bober, who has critically typed every draft, and to Mrs. Peggy Ann Nissen, who so patiently and carefully proofread the final two drafts. Their assistance has been invaluable.

C. W. C.
W. L. R.

Contents

6.   Network Analysis   225

1

The Nature of the Circuit Parameters

1.1 INTRODUCTION

Electric circuits are one class of lumped-parameter systems. Such systems are those wherein the medium through which particle or signal flow occurs is composed of discrete elements or components. These discrete elements are connected together in various ways to comprise systems which will accomplish specified goals.

When ascertaining the behavior of a given lumped-parameter system, the engineer needs to know at least the external characteristics of each of the discrete elements being used in the system. He must focus his attention on the gross *flow* of elementary *particles* through the system and must determine the associated *potential differences* that occur across the discrete elements due to flow of a specified nature through them. He must also be concerned with the resulting energy exchanges and rates of exchange. He must determine the operating condition at which each of the components deviates from the assumed characteristics, especially to the extent of its own destruction. In short, he must be adept at what is commonly called *circuit analysis*, which is the subject of this text.

When modifying an existing lumped-parameter system or trying to devise a new system that will meet certain prescribed specifications, the engineer needs to know what types of components are available. He must also be aware of which characteristic parameter magnitude for each type of component is feasible, and he should also know the approximate physical size or geometry that is associated with a particular parameter magnitude. He must gain knowledge of how external characteristics of discrete elements can be combined to achieve new characteristics. In other words, he must be proficient at what is commonly called *circuit synthesis*.

When the student is analyzing a lumped-parameter system or synthesizing a new system using discrete elements, he is often, for the sake of his own understanding of the problem, forced to delve into the inner nature of the components. In other situations he may need to look into the possibility of one component affecting some other component in the near vicinity, even though the two discrete elements are not apparently interconnected. Then he must enter the realm of distributed parameters, wherein the nature of every variable depends on the physical location of the point at which the variable is observed. It is necessary to become acquainted with the mathematical models that are used to describe the physical phenomena that occur within the discrete elements before one can be cognizant of the approximations that are employed in efforts to simplify the mathematical models. Such considerations require that the student have some minimum knowledge of what is commonly called *field theory* before he can wisely use discrete elements in circuit analysis and synthesis.

Most students beginning their study of electrical engineering have had enough prior contact with electricity to realize that there are such discrete elements as resistors, capacitors, and inductors. These components have different types of external characteristics which are described in part by the parameters resistance, capacitance and inductance. These parameters characterize the flow-potential relationships that exist within each of the components, and a true understanding of their nature can only come through a thorough study of the distributed parameter techniques used in the development of these lumped parameters.

It is the intent of this chapter to provide the briefest of glimpses into the internal nature of circuit components. Also, the chapter will provide some physical basis for the external behavior that results. The student is cautioned that the chapter is only an introduction to the problem of relating external characteristics to internal phenomena. Only an introduction is being provided into the capabilities and limitations of the mathematical models that will result. Hopefully, the student will gain some insight into the ever-used process of *approximation for simplification*—a process lined with more and more pitfalls as more and more approximations are employed.

1.2 BASIC ELECTRIC AND MAGNETIC PARTICLES

The effects of electricity observed as tangible forces were witnessed before the time of Christ. In fact, Thales (640?–546 B.C.) knew that after natural resin amber was rubbed it would attract lightweight objects, but the Greek philosopher did not conduct extensive experiments in an effort to explain this phenomenon. For that matter, this phenomenon of attraction remained insignificant until William Gilbert's (1544–1603) experimentation demonstrated that many substances developed an attractive power. These substances were termed *electrics*, which was coined from the Greek word for amber, *elektron*.

Unfortunately, Gilbert did not observe the force of repulsion between certain substances after they were rubbed together. Such a force was observed later; and an experiment which illustrated both the forces of attraction and repulsion appears in the 1891 third edition of *A Treatise on Electricity and Magnetism*, written by James Clerk Maxwell.

In Maxwell's " Electrification by Friction " experiment, a piece of glass and a piece of resin were rubbed together. Then a second piece of glass and a second piece of resin were also rubbed together. When these four pieces were suspended in the neighborhood of one another, it was observed that:

1.   The two pieces of glass repelled each other;
2.   The two pieces of resin repelled each other; and
3.   Either piece of glass attracted either piece of resin.

Thus, the bodies were said to be *electrified* or *charged with electricity*; and the electrical properties of glass were said to be opposite those of resin.

Some definitions were established from the above results. If a substance repelled glass and attracted resin after being electrified by one means or another, the substance was said to have *vitreous* or *positive* electrification because it behaved like glass in the above experiment. On the other hand, if the electrified substance attracted glass and repelled resin, the substance was said to have *resinous* or *negative.* electrification, or *charge*.

The determination of the magnitudes of the forces existing on charged bodies, such as those in Maxwell's experiment, became the objective of experiments conducted independently by Charles Augustin Coulomb (1736–1806) and Joseph Priestley (1733–1804). Both of these experimenters discovered that the force created by a concentrated charged body on another concentrated charged body was directly proportional to the magnitude of the two charges and inversely proportional to the square of the distance of separation.

The basic unit of charge is the *coulomb*. The smallest known charged particle is the *electron*, possessing a charge of -1.602×10^{-19} coulombs and having a mass of 9.11×10^{-27} kilograms. The smallest particle of matter which can be identified as one of the chemical elements is the *atom*. The central part of the atom consists of a *nucleus* containing a given number of *protons*, each having a much greater mass than the electron but a positive charge of magnitude equal to that of the negatively charged electron. The number of protons in a nucleus determines the element the atom subdivides, and it is matched by an equal number of electrons in discrete orbits about the nucleus, so that the net charge on a normal atom is zero. The nucleus may also contain bodies of nearly the same mass as the proton but having no charge. These bodies are called *neutrons*.

We have now established the basic quantity of electricity: the coulomb of charge. Electrically, a particle is described completely by its charge. Other physical attributes of a charged particle such as its mass or kinetic energy are mechanical attributes it possesses quite aside from its role as a *carrier* of electric charge. When we speak of a *point charge of q coulombs*, we are speaking loosely (but conventionally). What we really mean is *a particle of infinitesimal size carrying a charge of q coulombs*. For example, in the macroscopic (large) view, the electron above may be considered a *point charge* with a charge of -1.602×10^{-19} coulombs.

A characteristic of point charges is that the attracting or repelling force between a pair of them varies inversely as the square of the distance separating them and directly as the product of the charges, i.e.,

$$f = \frac{k_e q_1 q_2}{r^2}.$$
(1.1)

Maxwell also made note of the fact that the force of attraction or repulsion between a pair of poles on two separate long, slender magnets varies inversely as the square of the distance between them and as the product of their strengths in a manner similar to the behavior of electric charges. When magnets are long enough, their poles show no effect on each other and may each be considered to be isolated, and when magnets are slender enough, the poles may be considered concentrated. The force between such poles is of the form

$$f = \frac{k_m m_1 m_2}{r^2},$$ (1.2)

where m_1 and m_2 are the *pole strengths* of the magnets, with the units of *webers*.

The two types of particles described in this article are the basic electro-magnetic particles of our study in electromagnetism.

1.3 PROPERTIES OF UNIFORM REAL-PARTICLE FLOW

Consider a uniform flow (or *flux*, which is Old English and means *to flow*) of particles through surfaces *a* and *b*, each of area *A*, over distance *l*, as shown in Fig. 1.1. The particle quantity is designated m and its volume density ρ_m. The volume spanned by Δl contains

$$\Delta m = \rho_m A \, \Delta l \text{ particle units}$$ (1.3)

of the particles in the total volume.

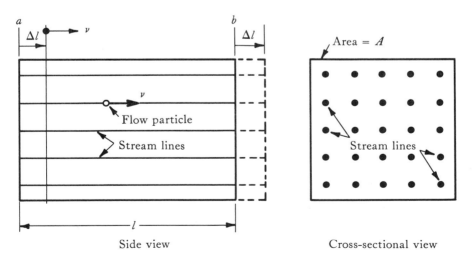

Side view   Cross-sectional view

Fig. 1.1 *Uniform flow.*

If both the particles and the plane at c are moving at velocity v, then the particle flow through the volume is

$$f = \lim_{\Delta t \to 0} \frac{\Delta m}{\Delta t} = \frac{dm}{dt}$$

$$= \rho_m A \frac{dl}{dt}$$

$$= \rho_m A v \; \frac{\text{particle units}}{\text{sec}} \; or \; \text{flux units.} \qquad (1.4)$$

The flow density is

$$\mathscr{D} = \frac{f}{A}$$

$$= \rho_m v \; \frac{\text{particle units}}{\text{meter}^2\text{-sec}} \; or \; \frac{\text{flux units}}{\text{meter}^2} \; or \; \text{flux density units.} \qquad (1.5)$$

Alternatively,

$$f = \mathscr{D} A. \qquad (1.6)$$

In real-particle flow there is usually a change in the energy content in the particles as they flow. The energy loss, in a given time, Δt, in flow through the volume is the energy lost by each particle-unit multiplied by the total number of particle units, or

$$\Delta w = \frac{dw_m}{dm} \Delta m \; \text{joules,} \qquad (1.7)$$

where, you will recall, the *joule* is the amount of energy expended by one *newton* of force acting through a distance of one meter. The *power* is the rate of energy exchange, or

$$p = \frac{dw}{dt}$$

$$= \lim_{\Delta t \to 0} \frac{\Delta w}{\Delta t} = \lim_{\Delta t \to 0} \frac{dw_m}{dm} \frac{\Delta m}{\Delta t}$$

$$= \frac{dw_m}{dm} \frac{dm}{dt}.$$

The quantity dm/dt is defined in Eq. (1.4) as the flow quantity. The quantity dw_m/dm, or the energy *loss* per particle-unit flowing through length l, is the *potential drop*,

$$v = \frac{dw_m}{dm} \frac{\text{joules}}{\text{particle units}}, \qquad (1.8)$$

and the power becomes

$$p = vf \frac{\text{joules}}{\text{sec}} \text{ or watts.} \tag{1.9}$$

According to Eq. (1.8), any discrete particle of m units in size moving through a potential drop, v, over length, l, losing a discrete amount of energy, w_m, gives rise to the relationship, for uniform flow,

$$v = \frac{w_m}{m}.$$

As the energy lost is the product of the force acting to move the particle times the distance moved, this becomes

$$v = \frac{f_m l}{m}.$$

The *field intensity* in the flow medium is defined as the loss in potential per meter of flow distance, or, again for uniform flow,

$$\mathscr{I} = \frac{v}{l} = \frac{f_m}{m}. \tag{1.10}$$

Thus, an alternate description of field intensity is the *force per unit of basic particle*. This latter definition holds even for the case of nonuniform flow, where the intensity depends on the location of the point at which it is measured.

As one would intuitively expect, the force required to move a particle depends on the rate at which one attempts to move it. In *linear media*, which will exist either exactly or approximately in the cases considered in this course, the relationship will be a proportional one. Thus, f_m becomes proportional to v and, consequently, to the flow density, $\mathscr{D}$. Therefore,

$$\mathscr{D} = k\mathscr{I}, \tag{1.11}$$

where k depends on the type of medium in which flow takes place.

Equation (1.11) may be written

$$\frac{f}{A} = k\frac{v}{l},$$

from which we have

$$f = \frac{kA}{l} v = \mathscr{G}v = \frac{v}{\mathscr{R}}. \tag{1.12}$$

Now we have a new parameter,

$$\mathscr{G} = \frac{1}{\mathscr{R}} = \frac{kA}{l}, \tag{1.13}$$

depending not only on the nature of the medium but also on its dimensions.

1.4 ABSTRACT FLOW (OR FLUX)

As we have seen, one way to detect the intensity of the field in real-particle flow is to measure the force on a basic particle in the flow. The field thus monitored is said to be a *force field*, or a *vector field*, measured by the magnitude and direction of the force on a basic particle. This idea of a field is *extended* to include *any* case in which a basic particle experiences a force, whether or not real-particle flow actually occurs in the region. Examples of such fields familiar to almost everyone are the magnetic field, as evidenced by the force on a magnetic pole, and the gravitational field, as evidenced by the force on a mass.

This extension of real flow to abstract fields includes the existence of abstract fluxes and flux densities, related to measured field intensities by Eq. (1.11). Fluxes so defined provide an artificial visualization of the interaction between basic particles and agglomerates of such particles. In fact, all equations of the previous article which do not require the consideration of particles in motion apply to the abstract fields. Equation (1.8),

$$v = \frac{dw_m}{dm},$$

now refers to the work done on a unit of *test particle* as it is moved along length, l, in the direction of the field.

As fields of the type discussed here can exist in a space with no particles in motion, or in a space with no particles at all, it is often convenient to define the characteristic constant of the field property observed as

$$k = k_o k_r, \tag{1.14}$$

where k_o is the value of the constant in free space and k_r is the *relative value* of the constant, k. Of course, in real-particle flow k_o has no meaning, since the existence of particles precludes observation of the field in free space.

1.5 ELECTRIC CIRCUIT VARIABLES

All our commonly used electric circuit variables can be defined in terms of real-particle flow, as the circuit measurements which convey information about the circuit depend on the flow of *electric charge* on real carriers. In such flow, the general flow quantity of Eq. (1.4),

$$f = \frac{dm}{dt},$$

is replaced by

$$i = \frac{dq}{dt} \quad \text{or} \quad i(t) = \frac{dq(t)}{dt} \text{ amperes (A),} \tag{1.15}$$

where the flow quantity, $i(t)$ is called the *electric current*, or, simply, the *current*. The compound units of (particle units)/sec, in this case coulombs/sec, are shortened to the single unit, the *ampere*. The function notation is introduced to emphasize that circuit variables generally have values which depend on the time, t, at which they are observed.

The potential drop between two points arises when Eq. (1.8),

$$v = \frac{dw_m}{dm},$$

is replaced by

$$v = \frac{dw_q}{dq} \quad \text{or} \quad v(t) = \frac{dw_q(t)}{dq} \text{ volts (V).} \tag{1.16}$$

In other words, the *volts* of potential drop between point a and point b is the loss in energy, in joules, by a coulomb of positive test charge moving from point a to point b.

According to general Eq. (1.9), where

$$p = vf,$$

we now have the power, or rate of energy exchange by charge flow of rate i through a potential drop of v, as

$$p = vi \quad \text{or} \quad p(t) = v(t)i(t) \text{ watts (W).} \tag{1.17}$$

This is the power *absorbed* by the section of circuit in question, which means that electrical energy is lost from the system by transformation into heat energy, mechanical energy, chemical energy, or some other form of energy. We recognize that some of these transformations may be reversible; that is, we admit the possibility of a negative sign on p.

Let us now turn to Fig. 1.2 for a clarification of the nature of these basic circuit variables. This figure shows a general electrical system with attention focused on the interconnecting region, where measurements are made relative to signal and energy transfer between two portions of the system. The region in which the measurements are made is a region of real-particle flow in a charge-neutral medium. That is, the algebraic sum of all the free charges making up current flow and the fixed charges in any region, however small, is zero.

This condition appears in the conducting media, such as the metals, plasmas, and electrolytes. It is shown in diagram form in Fig. 1.3, where free charges are shown in circles and charges not free to move are shown in squares.

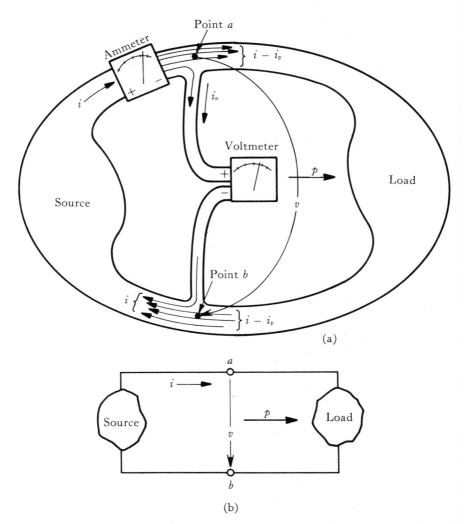

Fig. 1.2 *Illustrating the circuit variables. (a) The system and its instruments. (b) The system schematic.*

Suppose each charge is one coulomb in size, to pick a convenient, though unrealistic, number. The net charge is zero, since there are equal amounts of positive and negative charge. Positive free charges are shown in motion to the right, and whatever force tends them toward that direction will cause the opposite tendency on the negative charges, causing them to move to the left. Therefore, we have a net charge of -3 coulombs moving to the left, which is identical in effect to a charge of $+3$ coulombs moving to the right. If all

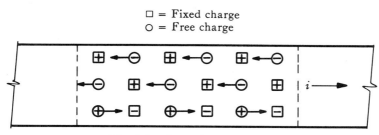

Fig. 1.3 *Illustrating current flow.*

shown mobile charges are replaced in one second, the current, i, is 3 amperes to the right.

In the region shown energy is being transferred from some source external to the region, a portion of which is lost as heat due to collisions as the carriers pass through the region. This means that, in general, there is a potential drop, v, in the positive current direction, over the length of the section shown. Sometimes such losses of potential are negligibly small when compared with other significant potential differences in the system. Then the flow approaches the lossless case, in which all points along the section may be considered to be at the same potential. The section of flow then constitutes an *ideal conductor*.

After this digression, let us return to Fig. 1.2. We show a standard laboratory instrument called an *ammeter* (pronounced, as written, without a "*p*") which indicates the current passing through it, and another laboratory instrument, the *voltmeter*, which indicates the potential drop across its *terminals*. Unfortunately, any measuring device disturbs the system to which it is attached, because energy is required to effect the change from *no indication* to *finite indication*. In the case of the instruments in Fig. 1.2(a), the evidence of such loss is the existence of a small potential drop, v_a, across the ammeter and a small current, i_v, through the voltmeter. These meters then require energy at the rates of

$$p_a = v_a i \quad \text{and} \quad p_v = v i_v$$

to maintain their indications. In general, the smaller that v_a becomes, the less the ammeter will disturb the system, and the smaller i_v becomes, the less the voltmeter disturbs the system.

Careful manufacture of instruments can reduce the above disturbances to negligibly small values for many applications, but by no means for all conceivable applications. For the purposes of the remaining discussion, we will assume that the instruments are *ideal*, i.e., they do not disturb the system at all. This means that

$$v_a = 0 \quad \text{and} \quad i_v = 0.$$

Let us now make note of the manner in which circuit variables are indicated on the diagram. The following conventions are used:

1. The current is indicated by its letter symbol along with a solid-headed arrow showing the direction *chosen* for its positive flow.

2. The potential drop is indicated by its letter symbol along with an open-headed arrow indicating the direction *chosen* for positive drops in potential.

The figure shows the same current to the left at the bottom as that to the right at the top, and the inquisitive student may be asking why this was presumed to be the case. The answer goes back to the original assumption of charge neutrality of the system. In order that there not be an accumulation of charge anywhere in the system (unless canceled by an accumulation of equal charge nearby), the real-particle flow into any charge-neutral portion of the system must be a net zero. Stated another way, the current entering a charge-neutral portion of the system must equal the current leaving.

Why has the component on the left been denoted a *source* and that on the right a *load*? The answer to this is simple if one allows one unit of the charge making up the current, i, to be a test charge. As this unit of positive charge goes from a to b through the right-hand component, it follows from the definition of potential drop that it loses v joules of its potential energy, as has every other unit of positive charge making the same trip. This energy is transformed to some other form of energy, such as heat, mechanical energy, or chemical energy, and is lost to the electrical circuit. Thus, the right-hand component acts as a *load* on the electrical system.

As the same positive charge continues on its way from b back to a through the left-hand component, it regains an amount of potential energy equal to that which it lost on the right. This increase in electrical energy must have been converted from some non-electrical form, hence the designation of the left-hand component as a *source*.

In summary: *When the voltage drop across a circuit section is positive in the same direction as the current through it, that section is a load absorbing electrical energy from the remainder of the circuit when voltage drop and current are both positive. Conversely, choosing positive voltage drop and current in opposite directions is equivalent to assuming that the circuit section is, under positive conditions, a source delivering energy to the remainder of the circuit.*

This discussion points up something else. That is the fact that the assumption of the indicated positive directions for i and v forced the indicated direction of the power or rate of electrical energy flow, p, from left to right. These interrelationships between the directions of v, i, and p should be

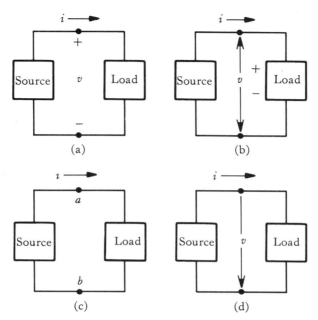

Fig. 1.4 *Schematic diagrams (models) of the system of Fig. 1.2.*

thoroughly understood by the student. They are indicated symbolically on the *schematic* diagram of Fig. 1.2(b).

In Fig. 1.4 the various equivalent schematic diagrams used as symbolic *models* of the system of Fig. 1.2 are shown. That of (d) corresponds to the notation in Fig. 1.2. In (a) and (b) we indicate that the potential difference, v, is positive when a is at a higher potential or is *more positive* than b. Generally, (a) or (d) will be used, often without the letters identifying terminal points. When the diagram is complicated, however, it will often be simpler to letter the terminals and utilize (c), in which it is not necessary to label the v's on the diagram itself. In (c) we simply associate the quantity v_{ab} with the two points, a and b. Equality between (a), (b), (c), and (d) exists only if

$$v = v_{ab} = \text{potential drop from } a \text{ to } b. \qquad (1.18)$$

The potential difference in the schematic diagrams of Fig. 1.4 can also be labeled in terms of potential rise instead of potential drop. Then the potential difference between a and b is defined as the *increase* in potential energy of a test piece, per unit of test piece size, as the test piece is moved from point a to point b. In this alternative definition the symbol e is usually used to represent the potential rise, and the notation in Fig. 1.4 becomes that shown in Fig. 1.5. It should be noted that

$$v_{ab} = e_{ba}$$
$$= -e_{ab}$$
$$= -e.$$

The mixture of the two notations in a given treatment is usually confusing to the student (and the nonstudent). Consequently, in this text we will denote potential differences as potential drops, designated by the symbol v. This choice is made simply because a survey of current texts indicates it to be the most popular. However, the student must be open-minded and prepared to chance upon literature where the opposite choice has been made.

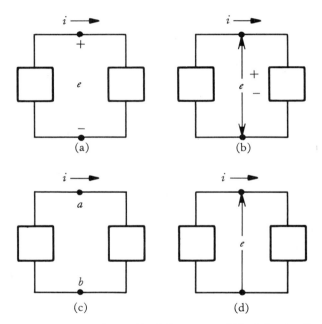

Fig. 1.5 *Schematic diagrams (models) of the system of Fig. 1.2 using the convention of potential rise.*

EXAMPLE 1.1. The source in Fig. 1.2 is a storage battery, and the load is a starting motor. On a cold winter morning the starting motor was used for 4 sec. During that time, the ammeter read 170 amperes, and voltmeter indicated 9 volts. Determine the power and the energy delivered to the starting motor.

Solution. Using Eq. (1.17),

$$p = vi$$
$$= 9 \times 170 = 1530 \text{ watts.} \qquad Ans.$$

Since power is the rate at which energy is transferred,

$$w = pt$$
$$= 1530 \times 4 = 6120 \text{ joules.} \qquad Ans.$$

1.6 THE CONDUCTIVE MEDIUM AND THE CONDUCTANCE PARAMETER

The medium in which real flow of electric particles occurs, as discussed in the previous article, is called a *conductive medium*. The conductive medium is of neutral charge in the large, but a microscopic view shows individual charged particles which are free to move about in the medium. In a *metallic* conductor, these *free charges* are outer-orbit electrons loosely attached to their atoms, which are continually replacing one another with respect to the atom they occupy. In an *electrolyte*, the charged bodies result from *ionized molecules* which have separated into positive and negative ions, as, for example, in a zinc sulphate solution which contains the positively charged zinc ion and the negatively charged sulphate radical. In a *plasma*, electrons have become disassociated from atoms, leaving the latter with a net positive charge, so that both positively and negatively charged particles are available.

In any of these conducting media, the flow, or flux, is a real one in which the free charges are in motion. The flow through a given area is that of Eq. (1.15),

$$i = \frac{dq}{dt},$$

or the time rate of positive charge flow through an area. It should again be carefully noted that a *given flow of positively charged particles to the right is equivalent to the same* (on the basis of charge) *flow of negatively charged particles to the left*. In plasmas and electrolytes, for example, both kinds of charges move in opposite directions, so that their contributions to current flow are in the same direction. In other words, the sign, and therefore the direction of flux, is a result of *both* the sign of the flowing quantity and the sign of the velocity.

The density function, J, corresponding to general Eq. (1.5) connects to the above flow quantity as follows:

$$i = JA, \qquad (1.19)$$

where J is the *current density*.

The equation corresponding to Eq. (1.11) is

$$J = \sigma E = \frac{1}{\rho} E \text{ amperes/meter}^2 \text{ (A/m}^2\text{)},\qquad (1.20)$$

relating current density to field intensity in the conductor. The constant of proportionality, σ, is the *conductivity* of the medium, and its reciprocal, ρ, *the resistivity*. The conductivity of a material is a measure of the mobility of the electrically charged particles under the influence of electric fields. Values of σ for various conducting materials are given in Table 1.1.

TABLE 1.1 CONDUCTIVITY AT 20°C

Material	Conductivity in mhos/meter
Aluminum	35.4×10^6
Copper (annealed)	57.0×10^6
Copper (hard-drawn)	56.5×10^6
Lead	4.55×10^6
Mercury	1.04×10^6
Nickel	12.8×10^6
Nichrome	0.91×10^6
Silver	61.0×10^6
Tungsten (annealed)	22.9×10^6

EXAMPLE 1.2. A 20-ampere current is flowing in an annealed copper conductor 0.0808 in. in diameter. Determine the current density, the field intensity, and the electron drift velocity assuming each atom contributes one free electron.

Solution. The cross-sectional area is

$$A = \pi r^2$$
$$= \pi(0.0404)^2(0.0254)^2$$
$$= 3.30 \times 10^{-6} \text{ m}^2.$$

Rewriting Eq. (1.19) provides

$$J = i/A$$
$$= 20/(3.30 \times 10^{-6})$$
$$= 6.06 \times 10^6 \text{ amperes/m}^2. \quad \textit{Ans.}$$

Using the conductivity from Table 1.1 in Eq. (1.20) yields

$$E = J/\sigma$$

$$= \frac{6.06 \times 10^6}{57.0 \times 10^6}$$

$$= 0.106 \text{ newtons/coulomb.} \quad \textit{Ans.}$$

To determine the electron drift velocity, the linear density of the free charge must be determined. As the density of atoms in copper is known to be 8.40×10^{28} atoms/m^3 and as it is being assumed that each atom is contributing one free electron, the free-charge linear density in coulombs/meter is

$$\frac{dq}{dl} = \rho_q A$$

$$= (8.40 \times 10^{28})(3.30 \times 10^{-6})(-1.602 \times 10^{-19})$$

$$= -44.4 \times 10^3 \text{ coulomb/m.}$$

Rewriting Eq. (1.4) then provides

$$\frac{dl}{dt} = i \Big/ \frac{dq}{dl}$$

$$= \frac{20}{-44.4 \times 10^3}$$

$$= -0.450 \times 10^{-3} \text{ m/sec.} \quad \textit{Ans.}$$

For uniform current flow, as in Fig. 1.6(a), Eq. (1.12) becomes

$$i(t) = Gv(t) = \frac{v(t)}{R}, \tag{1.21}$$

where, as in Eq. (1.13),

$$G = \frac{1}{R} = \frac{\sigma A}{l} = \frac{A}{\rho l} \text{ mhos } (\textit{or } \text{ohm}^{-1}). \tag{1.22}$$

Equation (1.21) is known as *Ohm's law*, and has the alternative form

$$v(t) = Ri(t). \tag{1.23}$$

The parameter, G, is called the *conductance*, and its reciprocal, R, the *resistance* of the circuit element described, which in turn is normally called a *resistor*.

In the case of nonuniform flow, as in Fig. 1.6(b), Ohm's law becomes the defining relationship for the G-parameter, and Eq. (1.22) does not apply. The schematic representation is the same for uniform and nonuniform *conductors* (or *resistors*).

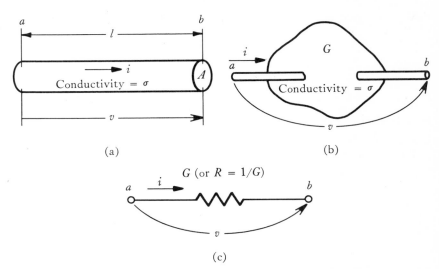

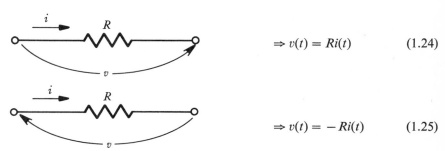

Fig. 1.6   *The conductance parameter.* (a) *Uniform flow.* (b) *Nonuniform flow.*
(c) *Standard schematic.*

It is very important to keep track of signs when using Ohm's law. Note that
v and i *have the same sign when their positive directions are the same*; that
is, when the potential drop and the current have the same positive direction. To emphasize this, let us note the following correspondences between
schematic variables and the related statement of Ohm's law.

$$\Rightarrow v(t) = Ri(t) \tag{1.24}$$

$$\Rightarrow v(t) = -Ri(t) \tag{1.25}$$

Equation (1.17) becomes for this special case

$$p(t) = \frac{dw_h(t)}{dt}$$

$$= v(t)i(t)$$

$$= Ri^2(t) \tag{1.26}$$

$$= Gv^2(t),$$

where $w_h(t)$ is the heat energy being converted from electrical energy in the resistor (conductor). This heat results primarily from the energy released on impacts between the charge-carrying bodies in the conductor.

EXAMPLE 1.3. Determine the resistance of 1000 feet of the annealed copper conductor in Example 1.2. Also calculate the potential difference between the two ends of the conductor and the power dissipated when the current is 20 amperes.

Solution. The length in meters is

$$l = (1000)(12)(0.0254)$$

$$= 305 \text{ m};$$

and from Eq. (1.22) the resistance is

$$R = l/\sigma A$$

$$= \frac{305}{(57 \times 10^6)(3.30 \times 10^{-6})}$$

$$= 1.62 \text{ ohms.} \quad Ans.$$

Using Eq. (1.23),

$$v = Ri$$

$$= 1.62 \times 20$$

$$= 32.4 \text{ volts.} \quad Ans.$$

The power dissipated as heat can be determined using any of the forms of Eq. (1.26) which provide

$$p = vi$$

$$= 32.4 \times 20$$

$$= 648 \text{ watts.} \quad Ans.$$

1.7 THE ELECTRIC MEDIUM AND THE CAPACITANCE PARAMETER

In an electric medium (sometimes called a *dielectric medium*), there are no free charges. There are either no charges at all, as in free space, or all charges must remain with a given atom or molecule of the matter making up the medium. The net charge within a given finite closed area completely within the medium is always zero.

In an electric medium the flux lines are abstract *lines of force* in the direction of the force on a positive test charge. The *electric field intensity* is defined as the force per unit of test charge, as in Eq. (1.10), but with $\mathscr{I}$ replaced by E, the electric field intensity, and m replaced by q, the electric charge. The *electric flux density* relates to field intensity in the fashion of general Eq. (1.11) as

$$D = \varepsilon E \text{ coulombs/meter}^2 \text{ (C/m}^2\text{)}, \tag{1.27}$$

where ε is the *permittivity* of the medium. Since the dielectric media includes regions of free space, general Eq. (1.14) applies, and we have

$$\varepsilon = \varepsilon_0\, \varepsilon_r \text{ coulombs}^2/(\text{newton} \cdot \text{meter}^2)[\text{C}^2/(\text{N} \cdot \text{m}^2)]$$
$$\text{or farads/meter (F/m)}, \tag{1.28}$$

where ε_0 is the electric constant or permittivity of a vacuum and ε_r is the dimensionless *relative permittivity*. Due to electric polarization in material dielectrics, a given flux density usually corresponds to a smaller field intensity than would exist in a vacuum, so that ε_r is greater than unity. Various values for ε_r are given in Table 1.2. In free space the relative permittivity is unity

TABLE 1.2 RELATIVE DIELECTRIC CONSTANTS

Material	Dielectric strength (kv/mm)		Relative permittivity	
Air	3		1.00058	
Bakelite	12 to 31		3.7 to 8.6	
Free Space			1	
Glass	8	9	3.9	10.0
Mica	14	28	2.5	8.0
Oil	10	35	2.2	
Paper (impregnated)	12	20	2.0	4.0
Polyethylene	48		2.25	
Polystyrene	20	28	2.55	
Rubber (hard)	70		2.0	3.5
Water (pure)	15		78	81

and the permittivity is

$$\varepsilon_0 = \frac{1}{36\pi \times 10^9} \text{ farads/meter.} \tag{1.29}$$

For the electric medium the general flux of Eq. (1.6) becomes the *electric flux*,

$$\psi = DA \text{ coulombs.} \tag{1.30}$$

Each unit of electric flux originates on a unit of positive electric charge. Thus, if (A) is some *closed* surface of area A (i.e., the total area of a sphere or a cube), then

$$\psi_{\text{(A)}} = q_{\text{(A)}}. \tag{1.31}$$

This is a simplified version of what is known as *Gauss's law*.

For uniform flux, as in Fig. 1.7(a), Eq. (1.12) becomes

$$\psi(t) = Cv(t), \tag{1.32}$$

where, as in the general case of Eq. (1.13), the dimension-dependent parameter is

$$C = \frac{1}{S} = \frac{\varepsilon A}{l} \text{ farads (F).} \tag{1.33}$$

The parameter, C, is called the *capacitance* (and its reciprocal, S, the elastance) of the circuit element described, which is called a *capacitor* or a *condenser*.

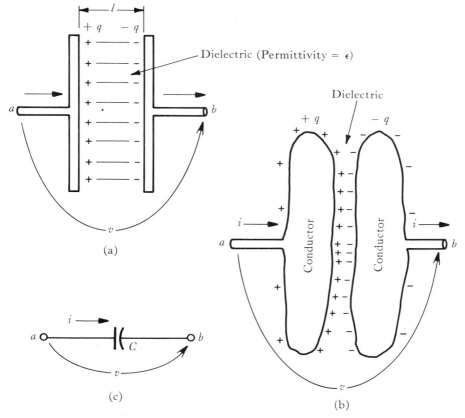

Fig. 1.7 *The capacitance parameter. (a) Uniform flux. (b) Nonuniform flux. (c) Standard schematic.*

If we enclose the positively charged conductor of the capacitor above in a closed surface and apply Gauss's law, we see that $\psi = q$, and Eq. (1.32) becomes

$$q(t) = Cv(t). \tag{1.34}$$

The dielectric separating the two conducting surfaces in a capacitor will not always carry the uniform fields we have assumed here. However, the general case, illustrated in Fig. 1.7(b), will have a capacitance defined by Eqs. (1.32) and (1.34). That is, capacitance is the accumulated charge per volt.

If charge is accumulating on the left-hand plate, we have charge entering the point *a* at the rate

$$\frac{dq(t)}{dt} = i(t), \tag{1.35}$$

which is the current indicated on the left. As the increase in positive charges on the left is matched by an increase in electric flux and in negative charges on the right, in order to satisfy Gauss's law at both plates, the charge *entering* through point *b* is

$$\frac{d}{dt}[-q(t)] = -\frac{dq(t)}{dt} = -i(t).$$

Or, we have *leaving* through point *b* the negative of the above entering current

$$\frac{dq(t)}{dt} = i(t),$$

which shows that the current entering one terminal of a capacitor is the same as the current leaving the other, even though *no conduction current is flowing through the dielectric.*

Substituting Eq. (1.35) into Eq. (1.34), after differentiating both sides of the latter with respect to time, *t*, results in

$$i(t) = C\frac{dv(t)}{dt}, \tag{1.36}$$

which relates the voltage and current of the capacitor, or condenser. Note that here, as in the case of Ohm's law for conductances, the equation is based on current and voltage drop having the same positive directions.

The charge that has accumulated on the positive plate of the condenser at time *t* is

$$q(t) = \int_0^{q(t)} dq.$$

The time at which *q* is, and has always been, zero is any time prior to the time the charging process started. We cannot go wrong if we go all the way back into the past and take $t = -\infty$ as this time. Now the above integral may be written

$$q(t) = \int_{-\infty}^{t} \frac{dq(\tau)}{d\tau} d\tau$$

$$= \int_{-\infty}^{t} i(\tau) \, d\tau, \tag{1.37}$$

where τ is introduced as a dummy variable of integration.

Substituting Eq. (1.37) into Eq. (1.34) yields the alternative form of Eq. (1.34)

$$v(t) = \frac{1}{C} \int_{-\infty}^{t} i(\tau) \, d\tau. \tag{1.38}$$

As the schematic of Fig. 1.7(c) has its circuit variables positioned as those in Fig. 1.2(b) position themselves relative to the *load*, Eq. (1.17) gives the instantaneous power into the capacitor. Thus,

$$p(t) = v(t)i(t)$$

$$= v(t)\frac{dq(t)}{dt}$$

$$= Cv(t)\frac{dv(t)}{dt}$$

$$= \frac{dw_e(t)}{dt}. \tag{1.39}$$

This may be rewritten to yield the differential of accumulated energy,

$$dw_e(t) = Cv(t) \, dv(t).$$

The total energy stored in the capacitor is the totality of all such differentials since time began at $t = -\infty$, or

$$w_e(t) = \int_{0}^{w_e(t)} dw_e(\tau)$$

$$= C \int_{v(-\infty)}^{v(t)} v(\tau) \, dv(\tau)$$

$$= C[\tfrac{1}{2}v^2(\tau)]_{v(-\infty)}^{v(t)}$$

$$= \tfrac{1}{2}C[v^2(t) - v^2(-\infty)].$$

If at $t = -\infty$, the condenser was uncharged, $v(-\infty) = 0$ and

$$w_e(t) = \tfrac{1}{2}Cv^2(t). \tag{1.40}$$

What is the physical significance of this stored energy? You will recall that unlike charges attract, and certainly the two plates of the condenser are charged with unlike charges. Therefore, the plates possess potential energy by virtue of their separation associated with an attractive force, and this potential energy must have come from the electrical system.

EXAMPLE 1.4. A capacitor is constructed using two circular plates each having a radius of 5 cm. The spacing between the plates is 2 mm, and the dielectric is air. If 360 volts of potential difference exist between the plates, determine the magnitude of the charge on each plate, the energy stored in the capacitor, and the electric field intensity in the dielectric.

Solution. Assuming a uniform distribution of electric flux between the two plates as shown in Fig. 1.7(a), Eq. (1.33) gives

$$C = \varepsilon A / l$$

$$= \frac{1}{36\pi \times 10^9} \frac{\pi(0.05)^2}{0.002}$$

$$\fallingdotseq 69.4 \times 10^{-12} \text{ farads.}$$

The magnitude of the charge on each plate, using Eq. (1.34), is

$$q = Cv$$

$$= (69.4 \times 10^{-12})(360)$$

$$= 25.0 \times 10^{-9} \text{ coulombs.} \qquad Ans.$$

The stored energy, from Eq. (1.40), is

$$w_e = \tfrac{1}{2}Cv^2$$

$$= (\tfrac{1}{2})(69.4 \times 10^{-12})(360^2)$$

$$= 4.50 \times 10^{-6} \text{ joules.} \qquad Ans.$$

The electric field intensity or potential gradient in the dielectric is

$$E = v / l$$

$$= 360/(2 \times 10^{-3})$$

$$= 180 \times 10^3 \text{ volts/m.} \qquad Ans.$$

EXAMPLE 1.5. If the current flowing to the capacitor in Fig. 1.8 varies with time as shown and if the capacitor was never used before $t = 0$, determine $v(t)$ for $t > 0$ and the maximum voltage that will exist across the capacitor.

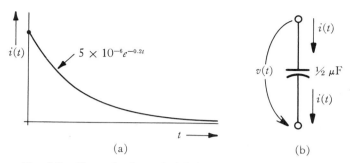

Fig. 1.8 *Figure for Example 1.5. (a) Current. (b) Schematic.*

Solution. The integral in Eq. (1.38) can be written in two parts, one for negative time and one for positive time as shown.

$$v(t) = \frac{1}{C} \int_{-\infty}^{t} i(\tau) \, d\tau$$

$$= \frac{1}{0.5 \; 10^{-6}} \left[\int_{-\infty}^{0} 0 \, d\tau + \int_{0}^{t} 5 \times 10^{-6} e^{-0.2\tau} \, d\tau \right], \qquad t > 0$$

$$= 2 \times 10^{6} \left[0 + \frac{5 \times 10^{-6}}{-0.2} e^{-0.2\tau} \Big|_{0}^{t} \right], \qquad t > 0$$

$$= 50[1 - e^{-0.2t}], \qquad t > 0 \text{ volts.} \qquad Ans.$$

The maximum voltage occurs as t approaches infinity; therefore,

$$v_{\max} = \lim_{t \to \infty} v(t) = v(\infty) = 50 \text{ volts.} \qquad Ans.$$

1.8 THE MAGNETIC MEDIUM AND THE INDUCTANCE PARAMETER

The magnetic medium also supports an abstract field rather than real flow. The test piece we shall use is the isolated concentrated north magnetic pole, though such a pole can be approached only approximately through the use of long, slim permanent magnets. Another test piece often used is the magnetic dipole, which is formed by a microscopic loop of electric current, with the torque on the dipole being a measure of the field strength.

Serving the function of m in the general case of Eq. (1.10), we have m, the strength of a concentrated north pole, which is the total flux units leaving the pole external to the long magnet of which it is a part. Then the general field intensity, $\mathscr{I}$, becomes the magnetic field intensity H, and the general flux density, $\mathscr{D}$, becomes the magnetic flux density, B. Equation (1.11) then becomes

$$B = \mu H \text{ webers/meter}^2 \text{ (tesla)}, \qquad (1.41)$$

where

$$\mu = \mu_o \mu_r \qquad (1.42)$$

is the *permeability* of the medium. The magnetic constant or permeability of a vacuum is

$$\mu_o = 4\pi \times 10^{-7} \frac{\text{webers}^2}{\text{newton} \cdot \text{meter}^2} \text{ or henries/meter (H/m)}. \qquad (1.43)$$

Ferromagnetic materials, such as iron, steel, and the other ferrites, are made up of small *magnetic dipoles* (short permanent magnets), formed by *domains* in the material. Normally, these domains are randomly oriented and make no net contribution to the flux density. However, under the influence of an externally applied field, these domains tend to rotate into alignment, thereby contributing a field of their own and increasing the flux density. The result is that the externally applied field has produced a greater flux density than it would have created in free space. Therefore, the value of μ_r for a magnetic material is normally considerably greater than unity.

Unfortunately, in the ferrites the value of μ_r depends on the completeness of the dipole alignment, and, therefore, on the flux density, so that μ_r is not truly a *constant*. This is illustrated by the typical *hysteresis curves* for a magnetic material in Fig. 1.9. The arrows indicate the direction of variable change, and we see that B is not even a *single-valued* function of H. That is, there is more than one value of B for a given value of H. Furthermore, the form of the B-H curve depends on the external (maximum and minimum) values of the variables. Consequently, a *constant* μ_r can be presumed only on

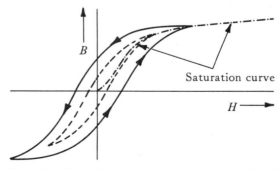

Fig. 1.9 *Magnetic hysteresis curves for a typical ferrite.*

the basis of some more or less valid straight-line approximation to the *B-H* curve, since Eq. (1.41) infers a *B-H* curve which is a straight line through the origin.

Table 1.3 lists relative permeabilities for a number of materials. Those given

TABLE 1.3 RELATIVE PERMEABILITIES

General type	Material	Relative Permeability
	Free Space	1.00000
Diamagnetic	Bismuth	0.99998
Paramagnetic	Platinum	1.00002
Ferromagnetic	Annealed Allegheny Electric Metal	27,000
	Cast Iron	380
	Cast Steel	1,350
	Sheet Steel	5,600
	Wrought Iron	41,000

for the ferromagnetic materials are representative values for relatively low flux densities. The diamagnetic and paramagnetic materials have not been discussed here and for most engineering purposes may be considered to possess a relative permeability of unity.

The *magnetic flux* corresponding to that in Eq. (1.6) for the general case is

$$\phi = BA \text{ webers.} \qquad (1.44)$$

Magnetic flux lines are continuous everywhere; that is, they close on themselves, so that they have no beginning and no end. Therefore, all lines entering a closed surface must also leave it, and no magnetic flux can originate within such a surface. The expression for magnetic fields corresponding to Eq. (1.31) for electric fields is thus

$$\phi_{\circled{A}} = 0. \qquad (1.45)$$

In the case of uniform field, we have the counterpart of Eq. (1.12)

$$\phi(t) = \mathscr{P}U(t) \text{ webers.} \qquad (1.46)$$

$U(t)$ is the magnetic potential drop (in joules per unit north pole), and the dimension-dependent parameter is

$$\mathscr{P} = \frac{1}{\mathscr{R}} = \frac{\mu A}{l} \text{ henries (H).} \qquad (1.47)$$

This parameter is called the *permeance* and its reciprocal is called the *reluctance* of the magnetic path.

These magnetic variables are tied to the electric circuit variables through two experimentally determined laws. The first of these is *Ampere's law*, which states that *the total magnetic potential drop around a closed path is equal to the net electric current enclosed by the path.* That is,

$$U\Big|_{\substack{\text{around a} \\ \text{closed path}}} = i\Big|_{\substack{\text{encircled} \\ \text{by path}}}. \qquad (1.48)$$

Relative directions are determined by the right-hand rule, which says that if the flux path is encircled by the right hand in such a way that the fingers are in the direction of current, then the thumb will point in the direction of U (and, consequently, of B and H).

In the closed uniform flux path of Fig. 1.10(a),

$$U(t) = i(t)\Big|_{\substack{\text{enclosed} \\ \text{by path}}} = Ni(t). \qquad (1.49)$$

Substituted into Eq. (1.46), this yields

$$\phi(t) = \mathscr{P}Ni(t). \qquad (1.50)$$

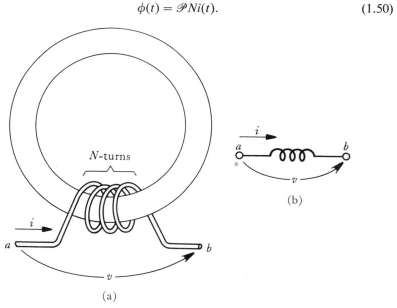

Fig. 1.10 *The inductance parameter.* (a) *Uniform flux linking coil.* (b) *Schematic.*

We shall now define an important quantity, called the magnetic *flux linkages* of the coil carrying the current, i. This is the total amount of flux threading the circuit which would be formed if the coil ends are joined at some location remote enough from the coil to not be influenced by its fields.

In this idealized case of uniform flux along the axis of the coil and all flux completely inside the coil, the flux linkages are simply

$$\lambda(t) = N\phi(t) = N^2 \mathscr{P} i(t). \tag{1.51}$$

Alternatively,

$$\lambda(t) = Li(t), \tag{1.52}$$

where we have defined the constant of proportionality between the flux linkages and current as

$$L = N^2 \mathscr{P} = \frac{\lambda(t)}{i(t)} \frac{\text{webers}}{\text{ampere}} \text{ or henries.} \tag{1.53}$$

This *constant* is called the *inductance* of the coil. The italics are to emphasize that L is a constant only when the path permeance, $\mathscr{P}$, is, which is not always the case. Equations (1.47) and (1.42) show that both μ_r and the geometry must be fixed for a constant $\mathscr{P}$. In some cases the former is a function of i (when magnetic saturation occurs) and often the latter is a function of time. However, in the *linear static* networks we shall consider in this course, $\mathscr{P}$, and therefore L, may be considered constant.

To complete the story, we need to know how the electric potential drop, v, relates to the current, i, for this case. This requires the second experimentally determined law, called *Faraday's law*, which states that

$$v(t) = \frac{d\lambda(t)}{dt}, \tag{1.54}$$

where relative positive directions are determined by the right-hand rule, i.e., if the thumb of the right hand is aligned with the center of the flux path in the direction of increasing flux, then the fingers will surround the coil in the direction of the voltage drop.

Substitution of Eq. (1.52) yields the volt-ampere relationship for constant L:

$$v(t) = L \frac{di(t)}{dt}. \tag{1.55}$$

These variables appear on the schematic representation of the coil in Fig. 1.10(b).

The development of the alternative form of the volt-ampere relationship and stored energy parallels that for the capacitive case, with the roles of voltage and current, of charge and flux linkages, and of capacitance and inductance interchanged. The student should take note of this *duality* by comparing the two developments.

The flux linkages that have accumulated in the coil by time t are

$$\lambda(t) = \int_0^{\lambda(t)} d\lambda$$

$$= \int_{-\infty}^t \frac{d\lambda(\tau)}{d\tau} d\tau$$

$$= \int_{-\infty}^t v(\tau)\, d\tau. \tag{1.56}$$

Substituting Eq. (1.52) yields

$$i(t) = \frac{1}{L} \int_{-\infty}^t v(\tau)\, d\tau, \tag{1.57}$$

or the inverse form of Eq. (1.55).

The electrical power *delivered to the inductance* is

$$p(t) = v(t)i(t)$$

$$= i(t)\frac{d\lambda(t)}{dt}$$

$$= Li(t)\frac{di(t)}{dt}$$

$$= \frac{dw_m(t)}{dt}, \tag{1.58}$$

where $w_m(t)$ is the energy stored in the inductance by the time t, or

$$w_m(t) = \int_0^{w_m(t)} dw_m(\tau)$$

$$= L \int_{i(-\infty)}^{i(t)} i(\tau)\, di(\tau)$$

$$= \tfrac{1}{2}L[i^2(t) - i^2(-\infty)].$$

But $i(-\infty) = 0$, so

$$w_m(t) = \tfrac{1}{2}Li^2(t). \tag{1.59}$$

This may be considered the energy stored in the magnetic field created by the current in the coil.

Of course, many coils do not produce the nice uniform flux that prevails in this simple example. For example, the air-cored coil of Fig. 1.11 has a nonuniform field and a different amount of flux linking each of its turns. However, Faraday's law applies to each turn, and the sum of the turn voltages will be the total coil voltage. So

$$v(t) = v_1(t) + v_2(t) + \cdots + v_N(t)$$

$$= \frac{d}{dt}[\phi_1(t) + \phi_2(t) + \cdots + \phi_N(t)]. \qquad (1.60)$$

If Eq. (1.54) is still to hold, we must set

$$\lambda(t) = \phi_1(t) + \phi_2(t) + \cdots + \phi_N(t), \qquad (1.61)$$

and Eq. (1.51) requires that the *coil flux* be

$$\phi(t) = \frac{1}{N}[\phi_1(t) + \phi_2(t) + \cdots + \phi_N(t)], \qquad (1.62)$$

which is the average of the turn fluxes. For this nonuniform case the per-meance of the *coil flux path* is defined by Eq. (1.50).

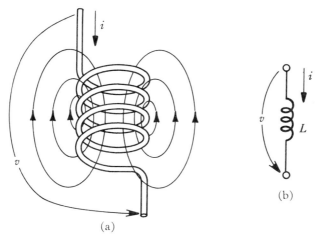

(b)

(a)

Fig. 1.11   *Coil with nonuniform field. (a) Actual coil. (b) Schematic.*

EXAMPLE 1.6. An inductor is constructed by winding 10 turns of wire around a toroid. The toroid has an average radius of 2 cm, a cross-sectional area of 0.785 cm^2, and a relative permeability of 5000. If 0.2 ampere of current is flowing in the windings, determine the inductance, the magnitude of the magnetic flux in the core, and the energy stored in the inductor.

Solution. From Eq. (1.47) we get

$$\mathscr{P} = \mu A/l$$

$$= \frac{(4\pi \times 10^{-7})(5000)(0.785 \times 10^{-4})}{2\pi(2 \times 10^{-2})}$$

$$= 3.925 \times 10^{-6} \text{ henries,}$$

and Eq. (1.53) provides

$$L = N^2 \mathscr{P}$$
$$= 10^2 \times 3.925 \times 10^{-6}$$
$$= 0.3925 \times 10^{-3} \text{ henries.} \qquad Ans.$$

The magnetic flux, from Eq. (1.50), is

$$\phi = \mathscr{P}Ni$$
$$= (3.925 \times 10^{-6})(10)(0.2)$$
$$= 7.85 \times 10^{-6} \text{ webers.} \qquad Ans.$$

The energy stored in the magnetic field is given by Eq. (1.59)

$$w_m = \tfrac{1}{2}Li^2$$
$$= (\tfrac{1}{2})(0.3925 \times 10^{-3})(0.2^2)$$
$$= 7.85 \times 10^{-6} \text{ joules.} \qquad Ans.$$

EXAMPLE 1.7. If the current flowing through the inductor in Fig. 1.12

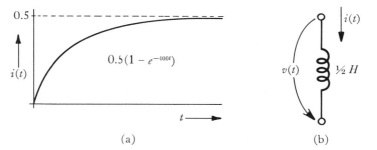

(a)   (b)

Fig. 1.12   *Figure for Example 1.7. (a) Current. (b) Schematic.*

varies with time as shown, determine $v(t)$ for $t > 0$ and the maximum voltage that exists across the inductor.

Solution. Equation (1.55) yields

$$v(t) = L \frac{di(t)}{dt}$$

$$= \frac{1}{2} \frac{d\, 0.5(1 - e^{-400t})}{dt}, \qquad t > 0$$

$$= (\tfrac{1}{2})(0.5)(-e^{-400t})(-400), \qquad t > 0$$

$$= 100\, e^{-400t} \text{ volts,} \qquad t > 0. \qquad Ans.$$

The maximum voltage across the inductor occurs when the slope of the current curve in Fig. 1.12 is the largest, or just to the right of the origin.

Hence we must take the limit of the above answer as t approaches zero from the right and

$$v_{max} = \lim_{t \to 0} v(t) = v(0^+) = 100 \text{ volts.} \qquad Ans.$$

1.9 PRIMARY AND SECONDARY UNITS

Throughout this chapter SI (International System of Units) units have been employed. This will continue to be the basic system of units, though it may be necessary from time to time to introduce other units which are customarily in use by particular groups within the engineering profession.

Table 1.4 lists electromagnetic quantities along with the associated *primary*

TABLE 1.4 ELECTROMAGNETIC QUANTITIES

Quantity	Symbol	Primary unit	Equivalent Compound units	Unit Symbol
Electric charge	q	coulomb		C
Electric flux	ψ	coulomb		C
Electric flux density	D	coulombs/meter²		C/m²
Electric field Intensity	E	volts/meter	newtons/coulomb	V/m
Magnetic flux	ϕ	weber		Wb
Magnetic flux density	B	webers/meter²		Wb/m²
Magnetic field intensity	H	amperes/meter; (ampere-turns/meter)*		A/m; (A·t/m)
Flux linkages	λ	webers; (weber-turns)		Wb; (Wb·t)
Electric current	i	ampere	coulomb/sec; joule/weber	A
Electric potential drop	v	volt	weber/sec; joule/coulomb	V
Energy	w	joule	watt-second newton-meter	J
Power	p	watt	joule/second; newton-meter/ second	W
Resistance	R	ohm	volt/ampere	Ω
Conductance	G	mho or ohm⁻¹	ampere/volt; coulomb/(volt·sec)	℧ or Ω⁻¹
Capacitance	C	farad	mho·sec; coulomb/volt	F
Inductance	L	henry	ohm·second; weber/ampere	H

*Parentheses indicate commonly used units in which "turns" has no dimensional significance.

units and their standard abbreviations. Where more than one dimension-name is listed, the first is the preferred usage unless another listed adds more physical significance to the problem at hand.

Often the primary units, listed in Table 1.4, will, in particular applications, result in numerics which are unwieldy because of their smallness or their largeness. Therefore, a system of secondary units has been adopted which is sized to specify magnitudes which are decimal fractions or decade multipliers of the primary units. Such units are indicated by prefixes to the primary

TABLE 1.5 SECONDARY UNITS

Number of primary units	Name of secondary units	Standard unit symbol
10^{-18}	attounit	aU
10^{-15}	femtounit	fU
10^{-12}	picounit	pU
10^{-9}	nanounits	nU
10^{-6}	microunit	μU
10^{-3}	milliunits	mU
10^{-2}	centiunits	cU
10^{-1}	deciunit	dU
1	unit	U
10	dekaunit	daU
10^2	hectounit	hU
10^3	kilounit	kU
10^6	megaunit	MU
10^9	gigaunit	GU
10^{12}	teraunit	TU

units. Table 1.5 carries a listing of the secondary units associated with some arbitrary primary unit, abbreviated *U*.

1.10 SUMMARY

The purpose of this chapter has been to determine the basic nature of the three circuit parameters. The important results are tabulated in Table 1.6.

TABLE 1.6 PARAMETER SUMMARY

Parameter (reciprocal)	Unit	Parameter description		Volt-ampere relationships		Energy equation
		Geometric	From basic variables	$i = f_i(v)$	$v = f_v(i)$	
Conductance (Resistance)	mho (ohm)	$G = \dfrac{1}{R} = \dfrac{\sigma A}{l} = \dfrac{A}{\rho l}$	$G = \dfrac{i}{v}$	$i(t) = Gv(t)$	$v(t) = Ri(t)$	$p(t) = \dfrac{dw_h(t)}{dt} = Ri^2(t)$ $= Gv^2(t)$
Capacitance (Elastance)	farad (farad^{-1})	$C = \dfrac{1}{S} = \dfrac{\varepsilon A}{l}$	$C = \dfrac{q}{v}$	$i(t) = C\dfrac{dv(t)}{dt}$	$v(t) = \dfrac{1}{C}\displaystyle\int_{-\infty}^{t} i(\tau)\,d\tau$	$w_e(t) = \tfrac{1}{2}Cv^2(t)$
Inductance	henry	$L = N^2\mathscr{P} = N^2\dfrac{\mu A}{l}$	$L = \dfrac{\lambda}{i}$	$i(t) = \dfrac{1}{L}\displaystyle\int_{-\infty}^{t} v(\tau)\,d\tau$	$v(t) = L\dfrac{di(t)}{dt}$	$w_m(t) = \tfrac{1}{2}Li^2(t)$

PROBLEMS

1.1   The force between two concentrated charges is 0.5 newtons at a separation of 5.0 cm. What is the force between the same two charges when the separation is reduced to 1.0 mm?

1.2   What are the units on k_e, in terms of mass, length, time, and charge, if the force is to be in newtons when the charges are measured in coulombs and the radius in meters?

In Probs. 1.3 through 8, the particle unit is the kilogram (of water). Be sure to include the units on all answers.

1.3   What is ρ_m?

1.4   If the rate of flow through a pipe ten centimeters in diameter is 15 l/min, what are f, v, and $\mathscr{D}$?

1.5   Suppose the pressure differential across 50 meters of the pipe in Prob. 1.4 is 70 newtons/cm². What is the potential difference and the power for the 50 meters?

1.6   What is the field intensity, $\mathscr{I}$, in the pipe of Prob. 1.5?

1.7   What are the parameters $\mathscr{G}$ and $\mathscr{R}$ in Prob. 1.5 for 50 meters of pipe?

1.8   What is k in Prob. 1.5?

1.9   In a region having a cross-sectional area of 4.0 mm², there are 9×10^9 C/m³ of positive charge moving to the right perpendicular to the area at a velocity of 3×10^{-4} m/sec and 3×10^{10} C/m³ of negative charge are moving to the left at 5×10^{-4} m/sec. What is the magnitude and direction of the current?

The next three problems may require reference to sources other than this text.

1.10   Determine the density of atoms in copper.

1.11   Determine the average electron drift velocity in a copper wire of 0.0808 in. in diam. when a 20-A current is flowing. Assume each atom contributes one free electron.

1.12   In Prob. 1.11, what is the average electron drift velocity if there is only one free electron for each ten atoms of copper?

1.13   In Fig. 1.2(a), $i = 10$ A, $v = 120$ V, $i_v = 0.001$ A, and $v_a = 0.02$ V.

a.   What is the rate at which energy is delivered by the source and the rate at which energy is delivered to the load?

b.   What is the power required to operate each of the instruments?

1.14   The source in Fig. 1.4 is the 12-V battery of an automobile and the load is the starting motor. Twenty percent of the energy delivered to the motor is converted to heat. The remainder is converted to mechanical energy. If the current is 100 amperes, what horsepower is the starting motor delivering?

1.15 The 12-V battery in Prob. 1.14 is capable of delivering 8 A for ten hours at an average voltage of 12 V before it becomes discharged. How much energy, in joules, can the battery deliver at this rate?

1.16 A certain electric heating element is rated at 1500 W and 120 V. What current does it require at rated voltage?

1.17 How many joules equals one kilowatt-hour?

1.18 What does it cost to operate the heater in Prob. 1.16 for 8 hours if electricity costs 3 cents per kilowatt-hour?

1.19 Find the resistance of 100 meters of annealed copper wire of circular cross-section 0.25 cm in diam.

1.20 An annealed copper bus bar is 0.5 cm thick and 6.0 cm wide. What is the resistance per meter? What is the maximum current if heat dissipation is limited to 5 W/m length of bus bar.

1.21 An electric heating element is made of nichrome wire 1.2 mm in diameter and is designed to generate heat at the rate of 800 W at 120 V. What must be the length of the nichrome wire?

1.22 In the electrical construction and power industries in the United States, cross-sectional areas of conductors are measured in circular mils (CM) and lengths are measured in feet. A circular mil is the area of a circle one mil (0.001 in.) in diam. Find the resistivity of annealed copper in $(\Omega\text{-CM})/\text{ft}$.

1.23 Find the conductivity of aluminum in $(\Omega^{-1}\text{-ft})/\text{CM}$. (see Prob. 1.22).

1.24 An AWG (American wire gage) No. 10 copper wire has a diameter of 100 mils. (See Prob. 1.22). What is its resistance per thousand feet if it is of annealed copper?

1.25 Most metals exhibit an increase in resistivity with temperature, rising from zero at zero degrees Kelvin. This is indicated in Fig. P.1.1, where resistivity is shown as a function of temperature, T. A straight line tangent to the curve at $T = T_1$ intersects the temperature axis at $T = T_0$. The resistivity

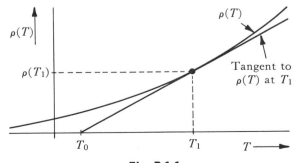

Fig. P.1.1.

at any temperature, T, in the neighborhood of the specific temperature, T_1, is

$$\rho(T) = \rho(T_1)[1 + \alpha_1(T - T_1)],$$

where α_1 is the *temperature coefficient of resistance* at temperature T_1. Express α_1 in terms of T_1 and T_0.

1.26 For copper at the standard temperature of $T_1 = 20°C$ used in Table 1.1, $T_0 = -234.5°C$. What is α_1? (See Prob. 1.25).

1.27 A copper coil has a resistance of 105 Ω at 20°C. What is its resistance at 50°C? At 0°C? (See Probs. 1.25 and 1.26.)

1.28 A copper field winding operates at 120 V. It takes 3.5 A when first energized at 15°C. After operating for an hour, the winding has heated to 55°C. What current will it take now? (See Probs. 1.25 and 1.26.) What is the power dissipated at 15°C and at 55°C?

1.29 If in Fig. P.1.2(a), $f(t)$ is the current $i(t)$ flowing through a conductance of 0.1 Ω^{-1}, plot the dissipated power, $p(t)$, and $v(t)$, the latter positive in the same direction as $i(t)$.

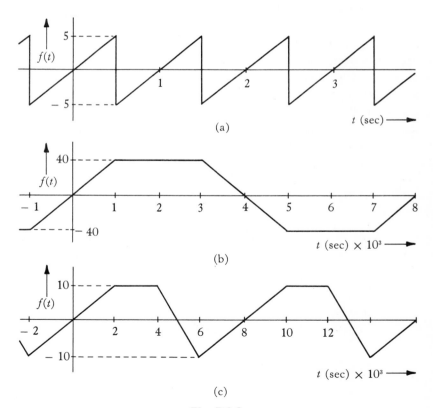

Fig. P.1.2.

1.30 Repeat Prob. 1.29 for a resistance of 2 Ω utilizing Fig. P.1.2(b) to describe $i(t)$.

1.31 In Fig. P.1.2(c), $f(t)$ is the voltage, $v(t)$, applied to a resistance of 50,000 ohms. Plot $i(t)$, positive in the same direction as $v(t)$, and the dissipated power, $p(t)$.

1.32 Based on Eqs. (1.27 through 1.31), what are the flux density and electric field intensity at the surface of a sphere, in air, of radius r with a concentrated charge q at the center? (Note: utilize the symmetries in the system.)

1.33 The voltage

$$v(t) = 50 \cos\left(10,000\, t + \frac{\pi}{6}\right)$$

is applied to a conductance of $50 \times 10^{-6}\ \Omega^{-1}$. Find $i(t)$ in the direction of $v(t)$ and the dissipated power, $p(t)$, and plot on one graph $v(t)$, $i(t)$, and $p(t)$.

1.34 Find the force tending to separate two concentrated charges, one of 15×10^{-6}C, the other of 140×10^{-6}C, 2 cm apart.

1.35 What is the electric field intensity and electric flux density 1.0 cm from a concentrated electric charge of 15×10^{-6}C? The dielectric medium is air.

1.36 Two parallel 1-m square aluminum plates are separated by 2 mm of air. What is the capacitance between the two plates?

1.37 Repeat Prob. 1.36 when the air is replaced by polyethylene.

1.38 What is the capacitance between two parallel 2-in. metal plates separated by 0.1 in. of air?

1.39 What is the maximum capacitance of the variable capacitance of Fig. P.1.3 if the dielectric is air?

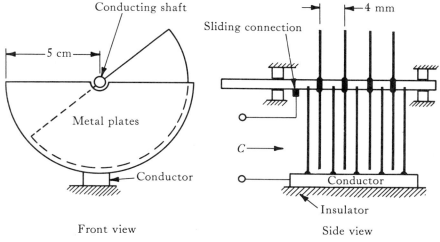

Fig. P.1.3.

1.40 Repeat Prob. 1.39 if the plates are immersed in oil.

1.41 A capacitor is formed by winding into a tight coil a long ribbon formed of two layers of metal foil separated by two alternate layers of impregnated paper of relative permittivity 4.0, as shown in cross-section in Fig. P.1.4. The ribbon is 5.0 cm in width, the impregnated paper is 0.02 mm

Heavy line−metal foil
Light line−impregnated paper

Fig. P.1.4.

in thickness, there are 3000 turns in the coil, and the average turn diameter is 1.5 cm. What is the capacitance?

1.42 A capacitance of 20×10^{-6} F, not connected into any circuit, exhibits a voltage of 300 V across its terminals. What are the charge on its plates and the stored energy?

1.43 The voltage across a 5×10^{-6}-F capacitor is increasing at the rate of 200 V/sec. At what rate is charge accumulating on the positive plate? What is the current?

1.44 Over a certain interval of time, the terminal current of a 10^{-5}-F capacitor is constant at 0.5 A. What can be said about the voltage during this same interval of time?

1.45 The current into a 2×10^{-4}-F capacitor has been zero for $t < 0$ but is 0.5 A for $t > 0$. What is the terminal voltage for $t > 0$? What is the stored energy at $t = 0.05$ sec?

1.46 The capacitor shown schematically in Fig. 1.7(c) has 6.0×10^{-6} F of capacitance. The voltage, $v(t)$, is zero for $t < 0$ and

$$v(t) = 100 \cos 1000 \, t, \qquad t > 0.$$

Find $i(t)$, $p(t)$, and $w_C(t)$, the stored energy, at time t. Plot, as functions of t, $i(t)$ and $p(t)$ on the same graph with $v(t)$.

1.47 Repeat Prob. 1.46 when

$$v(t) = 100 \sin 1000 \, t, \qquad t > 0.$$

1.48 A 0.2×10^{-6}-F capacitor has a terminal current of zero for $t < 0$ and

$$i(t) = 3.0 \cos 10^5 t, \qquad t > 0.$$

Find $v(t)$, $p(t)$ and the stored energy, $w_C(t)$.

1.49 Repeat Prob. 1.48 when

$$i(t) = 3.0 \sin 10^5 t, \qquad t > 0.$$

1.50 In a 10×10^{-6}-F capacitor,

$$i(t) = \begin{cases} 10e^{0.005t}, & t < 0 \\ 10e^{-0.001t}, & t > 0. \end{cases}$$

Find $v(t)$ for $t < 0$ and $t > 0$.

1.51 In Fig. P.1.2(a), $f(t) = v(t)$ is the voltage applied to the capacitor shown schematically in Fig. 1.7. Plot on the same graph with $v(t)$ the current $i(t)$, assuming a capacitance of 1.0 farad.

1.52 Repeat Prob. 1.51, except replace Fig. P.1.2(a) with Fig. P.1.2(b).

1.53 Repeat Prob. 1.51, except replace Fig. P.1.2(a) with Fig. P.1.2(c).

1.54 Repeat Prob. 1.51 after interchanging $v(t)$ and $i(t)$ in the problem statement.

1.55 Repeat Prob. 1.52 after interchanging $v(t)$ and $i(t)$ in the problem statement.

1.56 Repeat Prob. 1.53 after interchanging $v(t)$ and $i(t)$ in the problem statement.

1.57 In Fig. 1.10, the core is cast steel of 25 cm² cross-sectional area. The mean diameter of the toroid is 30 cm, and there are 1200 turns in the coil. Find the magnetic flux and flux density, the magnetic field intensity, the core permeance and reluctance, the coil inductance, and the flux linkages when the current is 0.4 A.

1.58 Repeat Prob. 1.57 when the core material is wrought iron.

1.59 In Fig. P.1.5, the toroidal coil has closely-packed turns uniformly

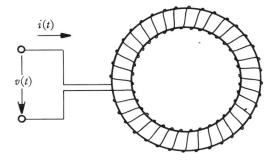

Fig. P.1.5.

distributed around the entire circumference of the toroidal core. Utilizing Ampere's law and symmetry considerations, show that all flux remains in the core, regardless of permeability.

1.60   If the toroidal core in Prob. 1.59 has a cross-sectional area of 20 cm², a mean radius of 10 cm, and 2000 turns, find the inductance if

a.   The core is air.

b.   The core is cast steel.

1.61   Repeat Part b of Prob. 1.60 when there is a 2-mm slice out of the cast-steel ring, along a radius, creating a 2-mm airgap.

1.62   What are the flux linkages and stored energy in a 2-H coil when there are 6 A flowing through it?

1.63   The current through a 0.2-H coil is increasing at the rate of 100 A/sec. What is the rate of change in flux linkages? What is the voltage across the terminals of the coil?

1.64   What can you say, quantitatively, about the current through a 1.5-H coil during an interval of time when the voltage has been constant at 250 V?

1.65   The voltage across a 4-H coil has been zero for $t < 0$ but is 80 V for $t > 0$. What are the current for $t > 0$ and stored energy at $t = 3$ sec?

1.66   The coil shown schematically in Fig. 1.11(b) has 4.0 henries of inductance. The current, $i(t)$, is zero for $t < 0$ and

$$i(t) = 10 \cos 500 \, t, \qquad t > 0.$$

Find $v(t)$, $p(t)$, and the stored energy, $w_m(t)$, at time t. Plot, as functions of t, $v(t)$, and $p(t)$ on the same graph as $i(t)$. How do these results compare with those of Prob. 1.33 for the resistor and Prob. 1.46 for the capacitor?

1.67   Repeat Prob. 1.66, except for the comparisons, for

$$i(t) = 10 \sin 500 \, t, \qquad t > 0.$$

1.68   A 5×10^{-3}-henry inductance has a terminal voltage of zero for $t < 0$ and

$$v(t) = 200 \cos 10{,}000 \, t, \qquad t > 0.$$

Find $i(t)$, $p(t)$, and the stored energy, $w_m(t)$.

1.69   Repeat Prob. 1.68 when

$$v(t) = 200 \sin 10{,}000 \, t, \qquad t > 0.$$

1.70   The voltage across a 5-H coil is

$$v(t) = \begin{cases} 30e^{3t}, & t < 0 \\ 30e^{-5t}, & t > 0. \end{cases}$$

Find $i(t)$ for $t < 0$ and for $t > 0$.

1.71 In Fig. P.1.2(a), $f(t) = i(t)$ is the current through the inductor shown schematically in Fig. 1.10. Plot on the same graph with $i(t)$ the voltage $v(t)$, assuming an inductance of 1.0 H.

1.72 Repeat Prob. 1.71 for Fig. P.1.2(b).

1.73 Repeat Prob. 1.71 for Fig. P.1.2(c).

1.74 Repeat Prob. 1.71 after interchanging $v(t)$ and $i(t)$ in the problem statement.

1.75 Repeat Prob. 1.72 after interchanging $v(t)$ and $i(t)$ in the problem statement.

1.76 Repeat Prob. 1.73 after interchanging $v(t)$ and $i(t)$ in the problem statement.

1.77 Express the stored energy in a capacitor in terms of capacitance and charge.

1.78 Express the stored energy in an inductor in terms of the inductance and the flux linkages.

1.79 Express each of the following as the smallest possible integral number of primary units or secondary units from Table 1.5 (i.e., express 2.5×10^{-5} F as 25 μF).

a.	2×10^{-6} F	**b.**	2.97×10^{-8} F
c.	25,000 W	**d.**	25×10^6 Ω
e.	349×10^6 Ω	**f.**	9.46×10^{-10} F
g.	0.035 H	**h.**	4.8×10^{-7} H

2

The Network Laws and Energy Sources

2.1 INTRODUCTION

In the last chapter the terminal characteristics of the three passive circuit elements were established. Our interest in this text is in the behavior of systems formed by interconnecting collections of such elements into *electrical networks* excited by *energy sources*. Such behavior is governed by a very few basic circuit laws, which are studied in this chapter. Then, after a look at the nature of the energy sources which may *excite* the network, the principle tasks of this text may be attacked in earnest.

2.2 THE NETWORK APPROXIMATIONS

Consider the electrical system of Fig. 2.1. On the left is an energy source in which some nonelectrical form of energy is converted to electrical energy by separating charges of opposite sign in the source. The potential

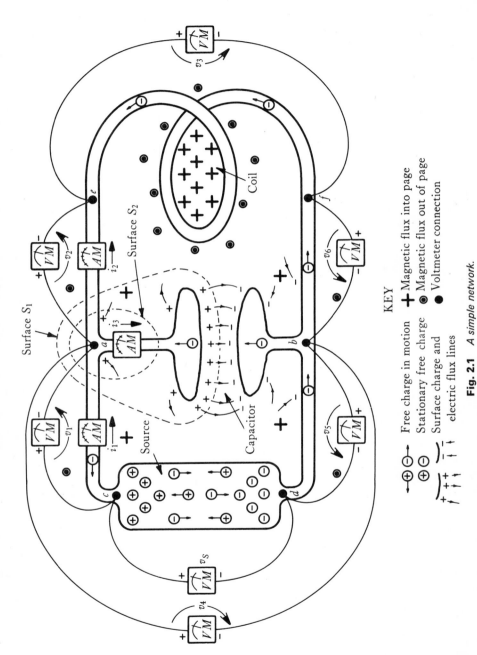

Fig. 2.1 *A simple network.*

KEY

⊕⊙→ Free charge in motion

⊕⊙ Stationary free charge

Surface charge and electric flux lines

+ Magnetic flux into page

⊙ Magnetic flux out of page

● Voltmeter connection

energy gained by each unit of positive charge moved from *d* to *c* represents the volts of potential *increase* from *d* to *c*, or, equivalently, the drop in potential from *c* to *d*. Thus, with charge motion as shown, v_{cd} is positive.

If there were no conductors connected to the source, the charge motion would cause charges to collect, as shown, until the repelling forces of the collected charges would cause charge motion to cease, and an equilibrium condition would exist. The work required to move a coulomb of positive charge from point *d* to point *c* would, in this equilibrium state, be the *open-circuit value of* v_{cd}, or the *open-circuit terminal voltage*. The equilibrium state is, in most sources, established instantaneously, for all practical purposes. It is important to note, however, that the source is, as a whole, charge neutral.

When the circuit is closed as shown, the potential energy possessed by accumulated charges in the source is transferred to the free electrons in the metal causing a general drift of electrons in the direction shown. The interior of the metal remains charge neutral, because for every electron entering the metal from the bottom of the source one leaves the metal at the top of the source to neutralize an equal-sized positive charge. The resultant reduction of potential energy in the source's charge accumulations again permits the motion of the free charges within the source, and energy is absorbed by the system. Since the source remains charge neutral, the same current flows through it as through the metallic conductor connected to it.

In the crude capacitor shown, the fact that the top is at a higher potential than the bottom causes electrons to leave the surface of the top conductor, leaving a net positive surface charge and creating a positive downward current as they leave. This is matched by an equivalent negative charge on the bottom conductor, the accumulation of which creates the same positive downward current that exists at the top.

The charges circulating around the coil produce a clockwise current around the coil which, according to the right-hand rule, produces magnetic flux downward through the coil. Most of these flux lines return near the outside of the coil as shown.

If it is assumed that the conductors between the points marked have finite resistance, the *schematic*, or *circuit model*, of the system shown is that shown in Fig. 2.2.

The system in Fig. 2.1 is an exaggerated illustration of the fact that the *lumpiness* of the system represented by the *lumped-parameter* model is a relative property. That is, instead of the parameters being nicely discrete and distinct from one another, they tend to smear together to a certain extent. In fact, if this were a modern *microcircuit*, this lack of parameter distinctness would not be an exaggeration.

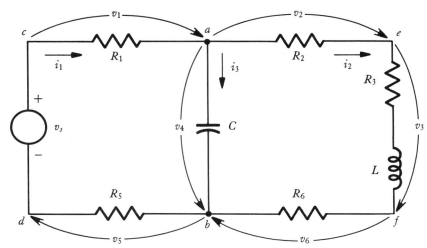

Fig. 2.2   *Circuit model of the system of Fig. 2.1.*

This lack of distinctness results from the fact that surface charges (and associated electric flux) exist at points in the network outside the part designated *capacitor*, and magnetic fluxes exist away from the neighborhood of the loop called the *coil*. For example, the entire circuit itself forms a closed loop producing a small amount of magnetic flux.

Let us now consider the closed loop *c-a-e-f-b-d-c following the conductors of the circuit*. According to Faraday's law, the potential drop around such a loop is equal to the rate of change of flux linked by it. That is,

$$v_{ca} + v_{ae} + v_{ef} + v_{fb} + v_{bd} + v_{dc} = \frac{d\phi}{dt}. \qquad (2.1)$$

Now traverse the same loop except choose paths through the voltmeters by following their leads. This selection also constitutes a conductive path. Now the path followed encloses a net flux which is approximately zero, though it can never be made exactly so with real meters. Thus, the voltages indicated by the meters will add to zero, so

$$v_1 + v_2 + v_3 + v_6 + v_5 - v_s = 0. \qquad (2.2)$$

In the work on circuit theory, it will be assumed that circuit elements are discrete enough and measurements made in such a way that voltages around loops add to zero, as in Eq. (2.2), rather than to a rate of change in flux, as in Eq. (2.1). Furthermore, by *the voltage between point a and point b* we shall mean that measured by voltmeters connected between the two points. Also, when we say *the voltage around a loop*, we shall be referring to the closed loop which traverses the voltmeters and their leads. In such a system as that of Fig. 2.1, then we shall have $v_{ca} = v_1$, $v_{ae} = v_2$, $v_{ef} = v_3$, etc.

On Fig. 2.1 we have shown two *closed* surfaces, S_1 and S_2. The surface S_1 encloses the positive surface charge of the top *plate* of the capacitor except for a few stray charges on the top conductor which we hope will be a negligible amount. The charge accumulates inside S_1 at the rate of

$$i_1 - i_2 = \frac{dq}{dt} = \frac{d\psi}{dt}. \tag{2.3}$$

One could form a similar surface around the bottom plate in which an equal amount of negative charge is accumulating.

On the other hand, the surface S_2 contains essentially no surface charge, so the accumulation of charge is

$$i_1 - i_2 - i_3 = 0. \tag{2.4}$$

The growth in electric flux penetrating S_1 and creating the right-hand side of Eq. (2.3) is called *displacement current*. In circuit theory we avoid consideration of such current by making certain that any *lump* of electrical network is charge neutral, which means that the surface enclosing the lump encloses a net surface charge of zero.

In summary, then, the study of circuit theory implies the following are true to a sufficiently good approximation to closely indicate the true behavior of the system:

1. Magnetic fields are presumed to be concentrated in the neighborhoods of coils, so that all voltmeters are located well away from significant fields.

2. Surface charges are concentrated on the plates of capacitors and are negligible elsewhere, so that the algebraic sum of ammeter readings into a closed surface not intersecting circuit elements is zero.

2.3 KIRCHHOFF'S LAWS

The observations of the preceding section will now be formalized into the two circuit laws of fundamental importance in network theory.

Consider a collection of conductors entering a closed surface as shown in Fig. 2.3(a). The surface does not intersect any electric components, though there may be such things as resistors, capacitors, inductors, or sources

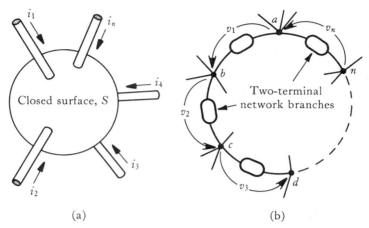

Fig. 2.3   *Illustrating Kirchhoff's laws. (a) Current law. (b) Voltage law.*

completely within it. The accumulation of charge within the surface is

$$\frac{dq}{dt} = \frac{dq_1}{dt} + \frac{dq_2}{dt} + \frac{dq_3}{dt} + \cdots + \frac{dq_n}{dt}$$

$$= i_1 + i_2 + i_3 + \cdots + i_n.$$

However, all electrical components and conductors contained within the surface are electrically neutral in gross, and there can be no accumulation of charge. Therefore, $dq/dt = 0$, or

$$i_1 + i_2 + i_3 + \cdots + i_n = 0. \tag{2.5}$$

This is a statement of *Kirchhoff's current law*, which we shall often designate simply as KCL.

When the surface S contains no circuit elements but contains just the connection, or junction, of the entering conductors, the surface may be reduced in size until it just surrounds the junction. It then becomes a *node* in the network.

Consider Fig. 2.3(b), showing a collection of nodes, a, b, c, ..., n in some electrical network. (A network is simply a collection of arbitrarily interconnected circuit elements.) The *network branches* shown may be either single elements or sources or combinations of sources and circuit elements forming subnetworks of the main network. We have chosen a collection of branches which form a closed *loop*, which threads through all n network branches.

Next, assume that all n *branch voltages* are simultaneously measured with voltmeters of high enough quality that their connection to the network will not disturb it within the accuracy of our measurements. Generally speaking, for any loop Faraday's law must apply, so that the sum of the voltage drops around the loop must be

$$v_1 + v_2 + v_3 + \cdots + v_n = \frac{d\phi}{dt},$$

where ϕ is the magnetic flux linking the closed loop. However, in most cases of practical interest all magnetic fluxes of significance may be considered to be produced by coils and concentrated in the immediate neighborhood of the coils producing them. (An exception to this might exist within a *microcircuit* module, where circuit elements and leads have similar dimensions.) Thus, the branch network boundaries shown in the figure may be presumed to totally enclose the magnetic fluxes produced by the branch, so that the net flux linking the loop is zero. Then the equation becomes

$$v_1 + v_2 + v_3 + \cdots + v_n = 0. \qquad (2.6)$$

This is called *Kirchhoff's voltage law*, which we shall often abbreviate to, simply, KVL.

The above two rules were first formulated by Gustav Robert Kirchhoff (1824–1887), a German physicist. Let us restate them, both linguistically and mathematically, in honor of their basic importance to network theory.

> *Kirchhoff's Current Law* (KCL): The algebraic sum of the current entering (or leaving) a node equals zero; that is,
>
> $$\sum i\text{'s (entering)} = 0 \qquad (2.7a)$$
> or
> $$\sum i\text{'s (leaving)} = 0. \qquad (2.7b)$$
>
> *Kirchhoff's Voltage Law* (KVL): The algebraic sum of the voltage drops around a closed loop in the clockwise (or counterclockwise) direction equals zero; that is,
>
> $$\sum v\text{'s (cw)} = 0 \qquad (2.8a)$$
> or
> $$\sum v\text{'s (ccw)} = 0. \qquad (2.8b)$$

2.4 SOURCES

In the previous chapter a two-terminal network was considered either a *source* or a *load* depending on the relative directions of positive voltages and currents. It is possible to assume source conventions when labeling a branch with its variables, even though the branch may contain only passive elements.

The term *source*, as used in this section, however, will carry the more restricted implication of a branch containing at least one active element supplying electrical energy to the network by conversion from mechanical energy, thermal energy, chemical energy, or any other form of energy. Such a source will exhibit an open-circuit terminal voltage, v_0, when no current flows from its terminals, and it will exhibit a short-circuit current, i_0, when the terminal voltage is reduced to zero by connecting the two terminals together electrically (short-circuiting the terminals). In a passive branch both v_0 and i_0 are zero.

Thévenin's Equivalent

Consider a typical source connected to a network, a case represented schematically in Fig. 2.4. When the network is disconnected, leaving the source terminals open-circuited, the open-circuit terminal voltage appears:

$$v_0 = v|_{i=0}. \tag{2.9}$$

When the network is connected, the terminal voltage usually changes by an amount dependent upon the current. We shall call this change in voltage $v_z = v_z(i)$ to emphasize its current dependence. Now the terminal voltage is

$$v = v_0 - v_z(i). \tag{2.10}$$

When the source network is *linear*, we shall find that v_z is linearly related to i as follows:

$$v_z = z_0 i. \tag{2.11}$$

Here z_0 denotes some *operation* on i to yield v_z. Examples of the forms z may take are illustrated in the following correspondences:

$$z_0 = L_0 \frac{d}{dt}(\ ) \Rightarrow v_z = L_0 \frac{di}{dt}$$

$$z_0 = \frac{1}{C_0} \int_{-\infty}^{t} (\ )\, d\tau \Rightarrow v_z = \frac{1}{C_0} \int_{-\infty}^{t} i\, d\tau$$

$$z_0 = R_0 \Rightarrow v_z = R_0 i$$

$$z_0 = R_0(\ ) + L_0 \frac{d}{dt}(\ ) + \frac{1}{C_0} \int_{-\infty}^{t} (\ )\, d\tau \Rightarrow v_z = R_0 i + L_0 \frac{di}{dt} + \frac{1}{C_0} \int_{-\infty}^{t} i\, d\tau.$$

If

$$i = i_1 + i_2 + i_3 + \cdots + i_n$$

and if it is also true that

$$z_0 i = z_0 i_1 + z_0 i_2 + z_0 i_3 + \cdots + z_0 i_n,$$

we say that z_0 is a *linear operator*. The four examples cited above are obviously linear. There are many more complicated examples which could be cited.

Substituting Eq. (2.11) into Eq. (2.10) yields

$$v = v_0 - z_0 i. \tag{2.12}$$

This equation fits the equivalent circuit shown in Fig. 2.4(b), as can be seen

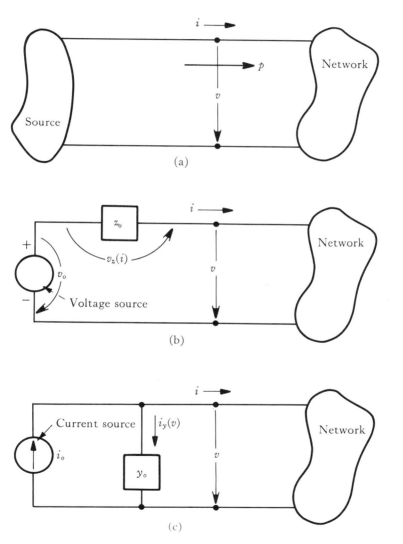

Fig. 2.4 *Representation of sources.* (a) *Actual source.* (b) *Thévenin's equivalent.* (c) *Norton's equivalent.*

by applying KVL, and we have what is called *Thévenin's equivalent circuit* for the source.

Norton's Equivalent

One can also, rather than replace the loading network by an open circuit, replace the network by a short-circuit and observe the short-circuit current

$$i_o = i|_{v=0}.$$ (2.13)

When the network is reinserted, the terminal current is reduced to

$$i = i_o - i_y(v),$$ (2.14)

where the reduction, i_y, depends on the terminal voltage, v, as indicated by the functional notation in Eq. (2.14). When the network is linear, the functional value of i_y may be replaced by some linear operation, y, on the terminal voltage, v, and we have

$$i = i_o - y_o v.$$ (2.15)

This is the *Norton's equivalent circuit* of the source, illustrated in Fig. 2.4(c).

Comparison of Equivalents

When dealing with linear operators, one can usually find an operator that "undoes" another operation. The first is said to be the *inverse* of the second, and vice-versa. An example of such a pair of inverse operations exists when y and z denote operations of the type used above, so that

$$yzi = i,$$

and

$$yz = \text{unit operator} = 1.$$

Then we say that

$$y = z^{-1} = \text{inverse of operator } z.$$

Now consider Eq. (2.12) representing Thévenin's equivalent circuit. If we operate on both sides of the inverse z_o, we have

$$z_o^{-1} v = z_o^{-1} v_o - z_o^{-1} z_o i.$$

Using the definition of the inverse operator, this becomes

$$z_o^{-1} v = z_o^{-1} v_o - i,$$

or

$$i = z_o^{-1} v_o - z_o^{-1} v.$$

When this is compared to Eq. (2.14), which must be the same equation for equivalence between the Thévenin and Norton forms, we see that the inverse of the z_0 operator is the y_0 operator, or

$$z_0^{-1} = y_0 \qquad (2.16)$$

Also, the generated current in the Norton form relates to the generated voltage in the Thévenin form as

$$i_0 = y_0 v_0, \qquad \text{or} \qquad v_0 = z_0 i_0. \qquad (2.17)$$

The Resistive Source

Although the operation denoted above can take many forms, one of the very common forms results when the decrease in voltage with increasing terminal current (or the decrease in current with increasing terminal voltage) is proportional to the current (or voltage). Then Eqs. (2.12) and (2.14) take the forms

$$v = v_0 - R_0 i, \qquad (2.18)$$

$$i = i_0 - G_0 v, \qquad (2.19)$$

where

$$G_0 = R_0^{-1} = \frac{1}{R_0}. \qquad (2.20)$$

The Thévenin's equivalent and the Norton's equivalent represented by these equations are shown in Fig. 2.5. Such source networks may be termed *resistive* for obvious reasons.

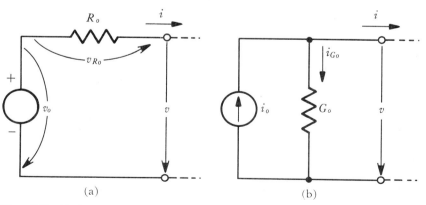

Fig. 2.5 *Equivalents to resistive source networks.* (a) *Thévenin's equivalent.* (b) *Norton's equivalent.*

Clearly, from Eqs. (2.18) and (2.19)

$$R_o = -\frac{v}{i}\bigg|_{v_o = 0}, \tag{2.21}$$

$$G_o = -\frac{i}{v}\bigg|_{i_o = 0}. \tag{2.22}$$

Since the only way v_o and i_o can be zero is for all voltage and current generators within the source network to be zero, v and i must result from the application of some external source. Then the network is passive and becomes an irreversible power absorber. This results in the minus signs on the above equations, since the directions on v and i assume that the network is a power-delivering device.

In other words:

a. The Thévenin's equivalent resistance, R_o, is the resistance looking back into the two network terminals with all internal voltage and current generators reduced to zero.

b. The Norton's equivalent conductance, G_o, is the conductance looking back into the two network terminals with all internal voltage and current generators reduced to zero.

It must be remembered that reducing a voltage generator to zero replaces it with a short circuit, whereas reducing a current generator to zero replaces it with an open circuit.

Current Source or Voltage Source?

Actually, any resistive source network for which finite nonzero R_o and G_o exist may be considered either a voltage source or a current source, depending on whether one chooses to use the Thévenin's equivalent or the Norton's equivalent in his computations.

In practice, most sources are limited either by the amount of current they can deliver without overheating or by the amount of terminal voltage that can be endured without causing insulation break-down between the terminals. Therefore, there are definite safe operating ranges of either voltage or current or both beyond which damage to equipment may occur.

It is the nature of some sources that the change in terminal voltage is relatively small over the allowable range of current. Such sources are usually designated *voltages sources*, and there is defined for them the following parameter:

$$\text{voltage regulation} = \frac{v_o - v}{v} \times 100\%, \qquad (2.23)$$

where, unless otherwise stated, v is measured at the maximum allowable, or *full-load*, or *rated*, current.

On the other hand, there are sources which show relatively small changes in current over the allowable range of voltage. Such sources are generally called *current sources*, and for them we define:

$$\text{current regulation} = \frac{i_o - i}{i} \times 100\%, \qquad (2.24)$$

where, unless otherwise stated, i is measured at full-load voltage.

Figure 2.6 shows the characteristics of typical resistive sources which lend themselves to the particular designation of *voltage source* or *current source*. It should be remembered, however, that such division is arbitrary, and all sources are in truth *energy sources*.

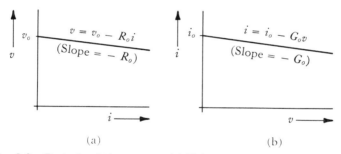

Fig. 2.6 *Typical resistive sources. (a) Voltage source. (b) Current source.*

Ideal Sources

Many times we shall be able to approximate our sources by either an *ideal voltage source* in which

$$v = v_o \qquad \text{and} \qquad R_o = 0,$$

or an *ideal current source* in which

$$i = i_o \qquad \text{and} \qquad G_o = 0.$$

Such sources have zero regulation of the quantity giving them their name. The schematic representations of ideal sources, to be used in this text, are shown in Fig. 2.7.

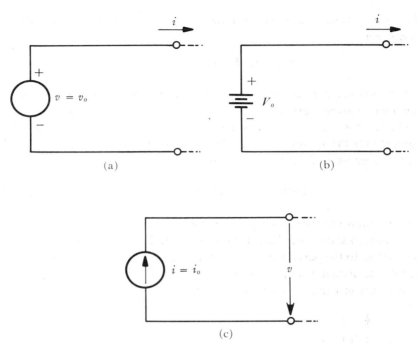

Fig. 2.7 *Schematic representation of ideal sources. (a) Voltage source, general. (b) Constant voltage source (ideal battery). (c) Current source.*

EXAMPLE 2.1. In this example the values given are representative of a 12-V lead storage battery. However, the values do not necessarily represent all typical situations because of the many variables involved. For instance, such items as battery, type and quantity of electrolyte, state of charge, temperature,

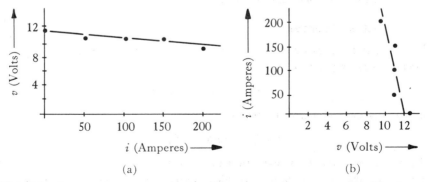

Fig. 2.8 *Storage battery test results. (a) Voltage source, v = v(i). (b) Current source, i = i(v).*

age, past history, and testing methods all influence the data given and the models obtained.

From the data shown in Fig. 2.8, determine Thévenin's and Norton's equivalents and the voltage regulation.

Solution. In order to linearize the resulting source models, a straightline is fitted to the experimental data using some minimum error criterion such as least-squared-error. Assuming that this has been done as illustrated in the figure, the parameters of the models can be determined from the ordinate intercepts and the slopes. Thus, for Thévenin's equivalent

$$v_o = \text{ordinate intercept}$$
$$= 12 \text{ V},$$

and

$$R_o = -\text{slope}$$
$$= -\Delta v/\Delta i$$
$$= -(v_1 - v_2)/(i_1 - i_2)$$
$$= -(12 - 10)/(0 - 200)$$
$$= +0.01 \ \Omega.$$

The model is shown in Fig. 2.9(a). Since it is difficult to evaluate the ordinate intercept in Fig. 2.8(b) by projection, the short-circuit current is calculated by shorting Thévenin's equivalent, or by using Eq. (2.17), to give

$$i_o = v_o/R_o$$
$$= 12/0.01$$
$$= 1200 \text{ A}.$$

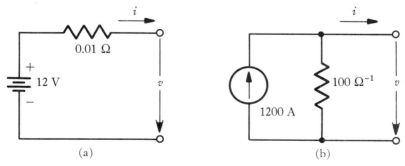

Fig. 2.9 *Storage battery models. (a) Thévenin s equivalent. (b) Norton's equivalent.*

Of course, G_o is the reciprocal of R_o or a negative of the slope in Fig. 2.8(b). Either way

$$G_o = 1/0.01 = 100 \ \Omega^{-1}.$$

If 200 amperes is assumed to be full-load current, Eq. (2.23) yields

$$\text{voltage regulation} = \frac{12 - 10}{10} \times 100\%$$

$$= 20\%. \quad \textit{Ans.}$$

For this type of source, current regulation is meaningless unless the battery is going to be used to provide large currents at low voltages for short periods of time. Even then any calculation based on the data shown in Fig. 2.8 would be inaccurate because the battery would not be operating in the region where the straight line fits the experimental data.

EXAMPLE 2.2. Shown in Fig. 2.10 is the experimental data from a power supply used for street lights connected in series, or in a *chain*, such that each street light carries the same current. Determine Norton's equivalent and the current regulation.

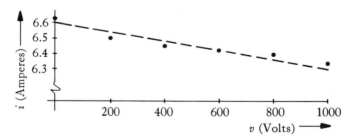

Fig. 2.10   *Power supply for series street lights.*

Solution. Since the short-circuit current is the ordinate intercept,

$$i_o = 6.6 \text{ A}.$$

The parallel conductance is obtained from the slope; that is,

$$G_o = -\text{slope}$$

$$= -(6.6 - 6.3)/(0 - 1000)$$

$$= +0.3 \times 10^{-3} \ \Omega^{-1}.$$

If the rated voltage is 1000 volts, then from Eq. (2.24),

$$\text{current regulation} = \frac{6.6 - 6.3}{6.3} \times 100\%$$

$$= 4.8\%. \quad \textit{Ans.}$$

This street-light power supply also has a Thévenin's equivalent, but it is normally considered a current source. The storage battery in Example 2.1 is normally considered a voltage source. If the student compares Fig. 2.10 to Fig. 2.8(b), he should readily understand the reason for the choices in terminology concerning the two sources.

PROBLEMS

2.1   For the system of Fig. P.2.1, write KCL at all nodes and KVL around all loops which may be formed without a loop traverse crossing itself.

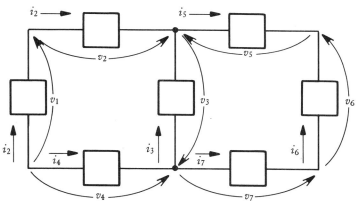

Fig. P.2.1.

2.2   Repeat Prob. 2.1 for the system of Fig. P.2.2.

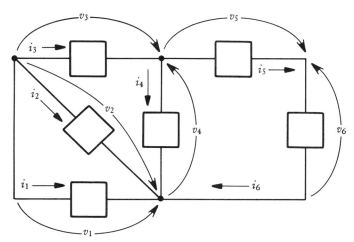

Fig. P.2.2.

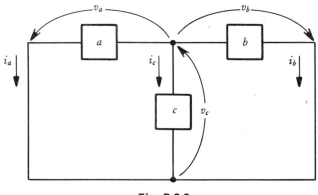

Fig. P.2.3.

2.3   At some instant of time, the values of the following variables in Fig. P.2.3 were determined:

$$v_c = 10 \text{ V} \qquad i_a = 10 \text{ A}$$
$$i_b = 5 \text{ A}.$$

Find the values of the remaining indicated circuit variables and the power *dissipated* in each circuit element. Check results by $\sum p = 0$.

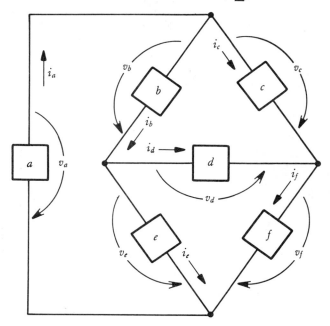

Fig. P.2.4.

2.4   At some instant of time, the values of the following variables in Fig. P.2.4 were determined:

$$v_c = 15 \text{ V} \qquad i_a = 10 \text{ A}$$
$$v_d = -10 \text{ V} \qquad i_b = 3 \text{ A}$$
$$v_e = 5 \text{ V} \qquad i_f = 6 \text{ A}.$$

Find the values of the remaining indicated circuit variables and the power *generated* by each circuit element. Check results by $\sum p = 0$.

2.5   Redraw the network of Fig. P.2.5, and show the voltage and current

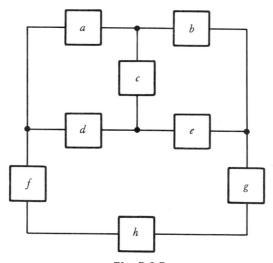

Fig. P.2.5.

for each element, making both voltage drops and currents positive to the right for horizontal elements and positive downward for vertical elements. The following voltages and currents are known:

$$v_c = 150 \text{ V} \qquad i_a = -5 \text{ A}$$
$$v_d = -50 \text{ V} \qquad i_b = 10 \text{ A}$$
$$v_e = 75 \text{ V} \qquad i_h = 5 \text{ A}.$$
$$v_f = 200 \text{ V}$$
$$v_g = 175 \text{ V}$$

Find the remaining voltages and currents. Express the power at each element as a *positive* number labelled as *watts dissipated* or as *watts generated*. Check results by comparing the dissipated and generated powers.

2.6   In Fig. P.2.1, the following quantities are known:

$$v_1 = 6 \text{ V} \qquad i_2 = -4 \text{ A}$$
$$v_3 = -20 \text{ V} \qquad i_5 = 6 \text{ A.}$$
$$v_4 = 5 \text{ V}$$
$$v_6 = 3 \text{ V}$$
$$v_7 = 4 \text{ V}$$

Find the values of the remaining circuit variables and the *generated* power at each element. Check results by $\sum p = 0$.

2.7   Repeat Prob. 2.6, except utilize Fig. P.2.2 with the following known variables:

$$v_1 = -25 \text{ V} \qquad i_2 = -4 \text{ A}$$
$$v_4 = 100 \text{ V} \qquad i_4 = -10 \text{ A}$$
$$v_5 = -50 \text{ V} \qquad i_5 = 3 \text{ A.}$$

2.8   A certain two-terminal active device is presumed to have resistive Thévenin and Norton equivalents. The following data were taken under actual operation:

| Terminal volts | 120 | 0 |
| Terminal amperes | 0 | 60 |

Find the Thévenin and Norton equivalents.

2.9   A two-terminal resistive active device yields the following operating data:

| Terminal volts | 250 | 240 |
| Terminal amperes | 0 | 100 |

The highest voltage or current given is the highest safe operating value. Determine whether this device should be considered a voltage source or a current source, then determine the proper equivalent (Thévenin or Norton) for it.

2.10   Repeat Prob. 2.9 for the following operating data:

| Terminal volts | 300 | 250 |
| Terminal amperes | 0 | 10 |

2.11   Repeat Prob. 2.9 for the following operating data:

| Terminal volts | 20 | 400 |
| Terminal amperes | 110 | 100 |

2.12 Repeat Prob. 2.9 for the following operating data:

Terminal volts	0	300
Terminal amperes	150	130

2.13 Repeat Prob. 2.9 for the following operating data:

Terminal volts	300	200
Terminal amperes	100	1000

2.14 Many (CAUTION: But by no means all!) laboratory-type power supplies are designed to be short-circuited without harm. This is done by building in current *saturation* as indicated by the typical characteristic in Fig. P.2.6. In laboratory supplies, both V_0 and I_0 are often adjustable. Perform the following for the power supply whose characteristics are given in Fig. P.2.6.

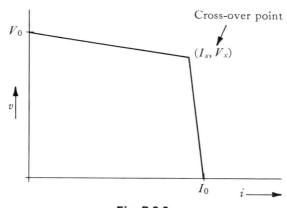

Fig. P.2.6.

a. Determine the approximate current range over which the unit acts as a voltage source, and determine the Thévenin's equivalent and the full-load voltage regulation holding over this current range.
b. Determine the approximate voltage range over which the unit acts as a current source, and determine the Norton's equivalent and the full-load current regulation holding over this range.

2.15 What are the voltage and current regulations of the ideal voltage and current sources, respectively?

2.16 A certain two-terminal device has a time-varying open-circuit voltage, $v_o(t)$, and a time-varying short-circuit current

$$i_o(t) = 10^{-6} \frac{dv_o(t)}{dt}.$$

Show the Thévenin's and Norton's equivalents in schematic forms.

2.17 A certain two-terminal device has a time-varying open-circuit voltage, $v_o(t)$, and a time-varying short-circuit current

$$i_o(t) = 0.5 \int_{-\infty}^{t} v_o(\tau)\, d\tau.$$

Show the Thévenin's and Norton's equivalents in schematic forms.

3

Single-Source Techniques in Single Element-Kind Networks

3.1 INTRODUCTION

Having established the volt-ampere characteristics of the three passive components, gained some insight into the nature of sources, and established the basic network laws, we are now ready to commence the detailed analyses of networks. In this chapter we consider the cases in which combinations of elements, all of the same kind, are excited by a single source of energy. We shall apply these techniques to multiple source cases by utilizing the *one source at a time* property of the principle of superposition.

3.2 SERIES RESISTORS

A group of resistors is said to be connected *in series* when the resistors form a *chain* so that each resistor carries the same current. This means that the resistors are connected end-to-end so that no more than two resistors connect to the same point, as shown in Fig. 3.1.

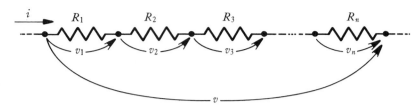

Fig. 3.1   *Series resistors.*

Applying KVL and Ohm's law, we have

$$v = v_1 + v_2 + v_3 + \cdots + v_n$$
$$= R_1 i + R_2 i + R_3 i + \cdots + R_n i. \qquad (3.1)$$

The *total resistance*, R, is the single resistor causing the same relationship between v and i as does this combination of resistors. Thus,

$$R = \frac{v}{i} = R_1 + R_2 + R_3 + \cdots + R_n, \qquad (3.2)$$

and we see that the combined resistance of series resistors is the sum of the individual resistances.

Now suppose we wish to relate the individual resistor voltages to the total applied voltage. We note from Eq. (3.2) that

$$i = \frac{v}{R} = \frac{v}{R_1 + R_2 + R_3 + \cdots + R_n}.$$

Then, using Ohm's law, we find that

$$v_1 = R_1 i = \frac{R_1}{R} v.$$

In a similar fashion, one can find the remaining resistor voltages in terms of the applied voltage. These results may be collected together in the following set of equations:

$$\frac{v_1}{v} = \frac{R_1}{R}$$

$$\frac{v_2}{v} = \frac{R_2}{R}$$

$$\vdots \qquad \vdots \qquad\qquad (3.3)$$

$$\frac{v_n}{v} = \frac{R_n}{R}.$$

These are known as the *voltage-divider equations*. When there are only two resistors, they take the form

$$\frac{v_1}{v} = \frac{R_1}{R_1 + R_2} = \frac{G_2}{G_1 + G_2}$$

$$\frac{v_2}{v} = \frac{R_2}{R_1 + R_2} = \frac{G_1}{G_1 + G_2}.$$

(3.3a)

3.3 PARALLEL RESISTORS

A group of resistors is said to be connected *in parallel* when all are connected between the same two points, so that they all have the same terminal voltage. This is illustrated in Fig. 3.2. This time the resistive elements are labeled in terms of their conductance, since the use of conductances rather than resistances is advantageous in the computations.

Applying KCL, then Ohm's law, leads to

$$i = i_1 + i_2 + i_3 + \cdots + i_n$$

$$= G_1 v + G_2 v + G_3 v + \cdots + G_n v.$$

The *total conductance* of this combination expresses the terminal volt-ampere relationship

$$G = \frac{i}{v} = G_1 + G_2 + G_3 + \cdots + G_n,$$

(3.4)

and we see that parallel conductances add to form the total conductance for parallel circuits in the same manner as resistances added in the series circuit. Of course, we can always replace a conductance by its equal, the reciprocal

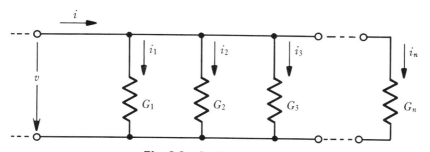

Fig. 3.2 *Parallel resistors.*

of the resistance, to obtain the alternative form for parallel circuits

$$\frac{1}{R} = \frac{1}{R_1} + \frac{1}{R_2} + \frac{1}{R_3} + \cdots + \frac{1}{R_n}.$$ (3.4a)

When only two resistors are in parallel, this may be rearranged to give

$$R = \frac{R_1 R_2}{R_1 + R_2}.$$ (3.4b)

The individual resistor currents can be related to the total current by first noting that Eq. (3.4) is equivalent to

$$v = \frac{i}{G} = \frac{i}{G_1 + G_2 + G_3 + \cdots + G_n}.$$

One can use Ohm's law to determine, for example, that

$$\frac{i_1}{i} = \frac{G_1}{G}$$

$$\frac{i_2}{i} = \frac{G_2}{G}$$

$$\vdots \qquad \vdots$$ (3.5)

$$\frac{i_n}{i} = \frac{G_n}{G}.$$

These are called the *current-divider equations*. When there are only two resistors, they take the form

$$\frac{i_1}{i} = \frac{G_1}{G_1 + G_2} = \frac{R_2}{R_1 + R_2}$$

$$\frac{i_2}{i} = \frac{G_2}{G_1 + G_2} = \frac{R_1}{R_1 + R_2}.$$ (3.5a)

3.4 SERIES-PARALLEL RESISTANCES

A seriesparallel combination of resistors is one in which all resistors or subcombinations of resistors are either in parallel or in series with other resistors or subcombinations of resistors. The solution of such networks may be accomplished by successive applications of series and parallel equivalents and of the voltage- and current-divider relationships. This can be best illustrated by examples of the type which follow.

EXAMPLE 3.1. For the network shown in Fig. 3.3(a):

a.   Calculate the total resistance connected to the practical source formed
     by the 12-V battery and R_1.
b.   Calculate all indicated voltages and currents in the network.
c.   Determine the power dissipated by each resistor and the total power
     provided by the source of energy.

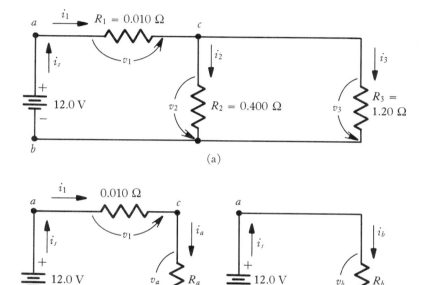

Fig. 3.3   *Reduction of a series-parallel network for Example 3.1.*

Solution.

1.   Combine the parallel 0.40-Ω and 1.20 Ω resistors, utilizing Eq. (3.4b),
     to give a single equivalent resistance of

$$R_a = \frac{R_2 R_3}{R_2 + R_3}$$

$$= \frac{0.400(1.20)}{0.400 + 1.20} = 0.300\ \Omega, \qquad Ans.$$

which is used in Fig. 3.3(b) and represents the total resistance
connected to the source.

2. Combine the series combination of the battery resistance and R_a, utilizing Eq. (3.2), to give

$$R_b = R_1 + R_a$$
$$= 0.010 + 0.300 = 0.310 \ \Omega,$$

which represents the total resistance of the network.

3. KVL, Ohm's law, and KCL applied to Fig. 3.3(c) give

$$v_b = 12.0 \ \text{V}$$

$$i_b = \frac{v_b}{R_b}$$

$$= \frac{12.0}{0.310} = 38.7 \ \text{A}$$

$$i_s = i_b = 38.7 \ \text{A}. \qquad Ans.$$

4. KCL and Ohm's law applied to Fig. 3.3(b) provide

$$i_1 = i_a = i_s = 38.7 \ \text{A} \qquad Ans.$$

$$v_1 = R_1 i_1$$
$$= 0.010(38.7) = 0.387 \ \text{V} \qquad Ans.$$

$$v_a = R_a i_a$$
$$= 0.300(38.7) = 11.6 \ \text{V}. \qquad Ans.$$

Checking by KVL,

$$12 - v_1 - v_a = 12.0 - 0.4 - 11.6$$
$$= 00.0.$$

The voltages in Fig. 3.3(b) could also be obtained from the voltage-divider equations, Eq. (3.3a); that is,

$$v_1 = \frac{R_1}{R_1 + R_a} \ 12.0$$

$$v_a = \frac{R_a}{R_1 + R_a} \ 12.0.$$

5. Applying KVL and Ohm's law to Fig. 3.3(a) yields

$$v_2 = v_3 = 12.0 - v_1 = v_a$$
$$= 11.6 \ \text{V} \qquad Ans.$$

$$i_2 = v_2/R_2$$
$$= 11.6/0.400 = 29.0 \ \text{A} \qquad Ans.$$

$$i_3 = v_3/R_3$$
$$= 11.6/1.20 = 9.66 \ \text{A}. \qquad Ans.$$

Checking by KCL,

$$i_1 - i_2 - i_3 = 38.7 - 29.0 - 9.7$$
$$= 00.0.$$

The currents i_2 and i_3 in Fig. 3.3(a) could also be obtained from the current-divider equations, Eq. (3.5a); that is,

$$i_2 = \frac{G_2}{G_2 + G_3} i_1 = \frac{R_3}{R_2 + R_3} i_1$$

$$i_3 = \frac{G_3}{G_2 + G_3} i_1 = \frac{R_2}{R_2 + R_3} i_1.$$

6.   The dissipated powers are

$$p_1 = v_1 i_1$$
$$= 0.387(38.7) = 15.0 \text{ W} \qquad Ans.$$

$$p_2 = v_2 i_2$$
$$= 11.6(29.0) = 336 \text{ W} \qquad Ans.$$

$$p_3 = v_3 i_3$$
$$= 11.6(9.66) = 112 \text{ W.} \qquad Ans.$$

The power provided by the source is

$$p_s = 12.0 \, i_s$$
$$= 12.0(38.7) = 464 \text{ W.} \qquad Ans.$$

Check by subtracting the dissipated powers from the source power

$$p_s - p_1 - p_2 - p_3 = 464 - 15 - 336 - 112$$
$$= 001.$$

Of course, the difference between the dissipated power and the source power should be zero. However, only three significant digits were used in the problem. Thus, any subtraction procedure that should actually produce a zero result might instead give a nonzero third significant-digit.

EXAMPLE 3.2. For the network shown in Fig. 3.4(a):

a.   Determine the total resistance connected to the source.
b.   Determine all indicated voltages and currents in the network.
c.   Compute the power dissipated by each resistor and the power delivered by the 12-V battery. Then check the power balance.

Note that KCL and KVL have been applied to all simple series and parallel

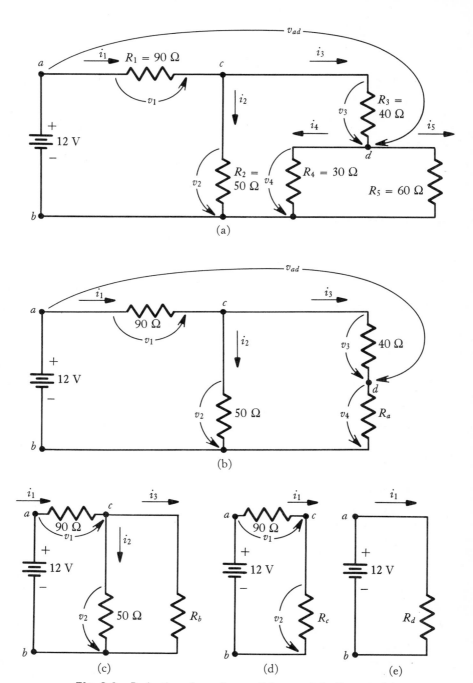

Fig. 3.4 *Reduction of a series-parallel network for Example 3.2.*

combinations in the labeling of Fig. 3.4. This process eliminates some current and voltage variables that are obviously equal to other variables already labeled in the figure. Also note that all numbers given will be assumed accurate to three significant digits.

Solution.

1. Since the reduction of the network in Fig. 3.4(a) follows the same pattern as in Example 3.1, the results are given below in the order obtained.

$$R_a = \frac{R_4 R_5}{R_4 + R_5} = \frac{30.0(60.0)}{30.0 + 60.0} = 20.0 \ \Omega$$

$$R_b = R_3 + R_a = 40.0 + 20.0 = 60.0 \ \Omega$$

$$R_c = \frac{R_2 R_b}{R_2 + R_b} = \frac{50.0(60.0)}{50.0 + 60.0} = 27.3 \ \Omega$$

$$R_d = R_1 + R_c = 90.0 + 27.3 = 117.3 \ \Omega. \qquad Ans.$$

2. KVL, Ohm's law, and KCL applied to Fig. 3.4(e) give

$$i_1 = \frac{12}{R_d} = \frac{12.0}{117.3} = 0.102 \ A. \qquad Ans.$$

3. KCL and Ohm's law applied to Fig. 3.4(d) provide

$$v_1 = R_1 i_1 = 90.0(0.102) = 9.18 \ V \qquad Ans.$$
$$v_2 = R_c i_3 = 27.3(0.102) = 2.78 \ V. \qquad Ans.$$

Checking by KVL,

$$12.0 - v_1 - v_2 = 12.0 - 9.2 - 2.8$$
$$= 00.0.$$

4. Applying KVL and Ohm's law to Fig. 3.4(c) yields

$$i_2 = \frac{v_2}{R_2} = \frac{2.78}{50.0} = 0.0556 \ A. \qquad Ans.$$

$$i_3 = \frac{v_2}{R_b} = \frac{2.78}{60.0} = 0.0463 \ A. \qquad Ans.$$

Checking by KCL,

$$i_1 - i_2 - i_3 = 0.102 - 0.056 - 0.046$$
$$= 0.000.$$

5. Application of KCL and Ohm's law to Fig. 3.4(b) gives

$$v_3 = R_3 i_3 = 40.0(0.0463) = 1.85 \ V \qquad Ans.$$
$$v_4 = R_a i_3 = 20.0(0.0463) = 0.926 \ V. \qquad Ans.$$

Checking by KVL,

$$v_2 - v_3 - v_4 = 2.78 - 1.85 - 0.93$$
$$= 0.00.$$

6. KVL and Ohm's law applied to Fig. 3.4(a) produce

$$i_4 = \frac{v_4}{R_4} = \frac{0.926}{30.0} = 0.0309 \text{ A} \qquad Ans.$$

$$i_5 = \frac{v_4}{R_5} = \frac{0.926}{60.0} = 0.0154 \text{ A}. \qquad Ans.$$

Checking by KCL,

$$i_3 - i_4 - i_5 = 0.0463 - 0.0309 - 0.0154$$
$$= 0.0000.$$

7. KVL and Fig. 3.4(a) also yield

$$v_{ad} = v_{ac} + v_{cd}.$$
$$= v_1 + v_3$$
$$= 9.18 + 1.85 = 11.03 \text{ V}. \qquad Ans.$$

Checking by using another closed path

$$v_{ad} = v_{ab} + v_{bd}$$
$$= 12.0 - v_4$$
$$= 12.0 - 0.9 = 11.1 \text{ V}.$$

This check agrees to within one unit in the third significant digit, which is close enough.

8. The dissipated powers are

$$p_1 = v_1 i_1 = 9.18(0.102) = 0.936 \text{ W} \qquad Ans.$$
$$p_2 = v_2 i_2 = 2.78(0.0556) = 0.155 \text{ W} \qquad Ans.$$
$$p_3 = v_3 i_3 = 1.85(0.0463) = 0.0857 \text{ W} \qquad Ans.$$
$$p_4 = v_4 i_4 = 0.926(0.0309) = 0.0286 \text{ W} \qquad Ans.$$
$$p_5 = v_4 i_5 = 0.926(0.0154) = 0.0143 \text{ W}. \qquad Ans.$$

The power provided by the source is

$$p_s = 12.0\, i_1 = 12.0(0.102) = 1.22 \text{ W}. \qquad Ans.$$

Check by subtracting the dissipated powers from the source power.

$$p_s - \sum_{n=1}^{5} p_n = 1.22 - 0.94 - 0.16 - 0.09 - 0.03 - 0.01$$

$$= 1.22 - 1.23$$

$$= -0.01 \text{ W.}$$

These examples have been complete. Had we been interested in only one or two of the response variables, considerably less work would have been necessary. Note, however, that results were checked whenever possible. This will usually be a good investment of time for the student, as much more time would be wasted in working the last two-thirds of either problem using wrong results from the first one-third.

The next example applies these same methods to a problem with a different objective.

EXAMPLE 3.3. For the network in Fig. 3.5(a):

a.   Find the Thévenin's equivalent circuit for that part of the network which lies to the left of points a and b.

b.   Find the Norton's equivalent for the same portion of the network.

Assume all numbers are correct to three significant digits when necessary.

Solution. The first problem is to replace that part of the network described above with its Thévenin's equivalent, as shown at the top of part (b) in Fig. 3.5.

1.   Find the Thévenin's equivalent generated voltage according to Eq. (2.9) by removing the load, R_L, to make $i = 0$, as shown at the center of Fig. 3.5(b). Since no current now flows through the 40-Ω resistor, there is no voltage across it, and v_0 is also the voltage across the 60-Ω resistor. Thus, by the voltage-divider relationship

$$\frac{v_0}{120} = \frac{60}{60 + 30},$$

and

$$v_0 = \tfrac{2}{3}(120) = 80 \text{ V.} \qquad Ans.$$

2.   Now reduce the only internal generated voltage, the 120-V ideal battery, to zero. According to Art. 2.4, the Thévenin's equivalent resistance, R_0, is the resistance looking back into the resulting dead

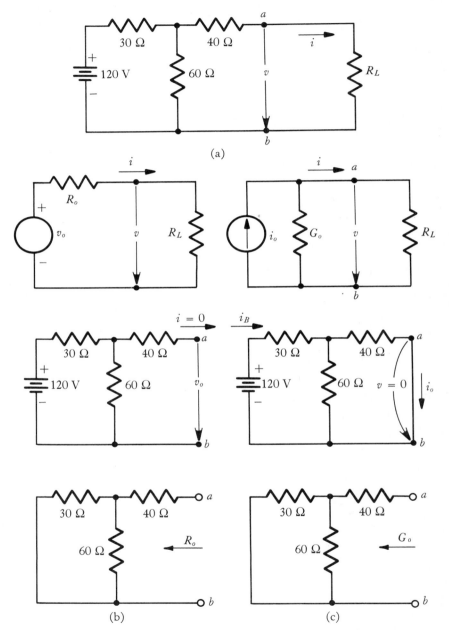

Fig. 3.5 *An example of Thévenin's and Norton's equivalents.* (*a*) *Original network.* (*b*) *Thévenin's equivalent.* (*c*) *Norton's equivalent.*

network, as shown at the bottom of part (b) of the figure. By utilizing series-parallel combinations, this resistance is

$$R_o = 40 + \frac{30(60)}{30 + 60} = 60 \ \Omega. \qquad Ans.$$

3. Now find the generated current in the Norton's equivalent at the top of part (c) of Fig. 3.5. From Art. 2.4, this is the short-circuit current, i_o, of the original network, as indicated at the center of Fig. 3.5(c). The total resistance connected to the battery in this new network is

$$R = 30 + \frac{40(60)}{40 + 60} = 54 \ \Omega.$$

The battery current (to the right through the 30-Ω resistor) is

$$i_B = \frac{120}{R} = \frac{120}{54} = \frac{20}{9} \ \text{A}.$$

Using the current-divider relationship,

$$\frac{i_o}{i_B} = \frac{60}{60 + 40} = 0.6,$$

so

$$i_o = 0.6i_B = 0.6\left(\frac{20}{9}\right) = 1.33 \ \text{A}. \qquad Ans.$$

This can be checked by a simpler method since the Thévenin's equivalent has already been calculated. From the Thévenin's equivalent, the short-circuit current is

$$i_o = \frac{v_o}{R_o} = \frac{80}{60} = 1.33 \ \text{A}.$$

4. Compute the Norton's equivalent conductance,

$$G_o = \frac{1}{R_o} = \frac{1}{60} = 0.0167 \ \Omega^{-1}. \qquad Ans.$$

3.5 THE PRINCIPLE OF SUPERPOSITION

The *principle of superposition*, which is basic to all *linear* physical systems, may be stated for spatially one-dimensional systems, in which the responses are algebraic quantities, as follows:

The system response to a group of excitations, applied at different points in the system, is the algebraic sum of the responses to the individual excitations, applied one at a time with the others zero.

Here the term *excitation* is taken to mean the voltage or current generators within the source network providing the excitation, i.e., the Thévenin's equivalent voltage or the Norton's equivalent current for each source.

It is the *one-at-a-time* property of the above principle which justifies its consideration in a chapter devoted to single-source responses. The principle will receive a brief treatment here, with the more formal treatment reserved for a later chapter on *generalized* analysis.

Suppose we have a network excited at different points by n generators, either voltage generators or current generators. Then the response current is

$$i_j = i_{j1} + i_{j2} + \cdots + i_{jk} + \cdots + i_{jn}$$

$$= \sum_{k=1}^{n} i_{jk}, \tag{3.6}$$

where

$$i_{jk} = i_j |_{\text{all except the } k\text{th generated signal zero}}. \tag{3.6a}$$

Similarly, the jth response voltage is

$$v_j = \sum_{k=1}^{n} v_{jk}, \tag{3.7}$$

where

$$v_{jk} = v_j |_{\text{all except the } k\text{th generated signal zero}}. \tag{3.7a}$$

In Fig. 3.6(a) there are three sources exciting a network. Four response variables are indicated on the diagram, but there are other response voltages not considered. The contribution of each source to a particular response variable can be seen in parts (b), (c), and (d) of the figure. Note that the direction of each contribution is taken positive in the same direction chosen as positive for the total. Though this is not necessary, it does agree with the positive signs assumed for each contribution in Eqs. (3.6) and (3.7) and lessens the chance for error.

The response currents in (a) of the figure may be written in terms of the contributions in (b), (c), and (d) as follows:

$$i_1 = i_{11} + i_{12} + i_{13}$$
$$i_2 = i_{21} + i_{22} + i_{23}$$
$$i_3 = i_{31} + i_{32} + i_{33}.$$

Similarly,

$$v_2 = v_{21} + v_{22} + v_{23}.$$

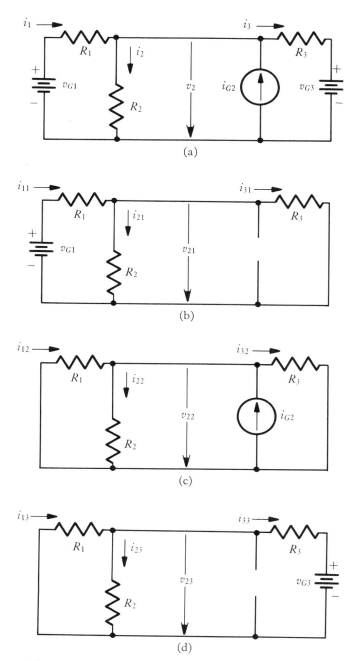

Fig. 3.6 *Solving a network by superposition.* (a) *Original network.* (b) *Responses to source No. 1.* (c) *Responses to source No. 2.* (d) *Responses to source No. 3.*

EXAMPLE 3.4. In Fig. 3.6,

$$R_1 = R_3 = 3 \ \Omega$$

$$R_2 = 6 \ \Omega$$

$$v_{G1} = 15 \text{ V}$$

$$i_{G2} = \ \ 5 \text{ A}$$

$$v_{G3} = 10 \text{ V}.$$

Find the indicated responses if the above numbers are correct to three significant digits.

Solution.

1.   From Fig. 3.6(b), using methods of previous examples,

$$i_{11} = 3.00 \text{ A}$$

$$i_{21} = 1.00 \text{ A}$$

$$i_{31} = 2.00 \text{ A}$$

$$v_{21} = 6.00 \text{ V}.$$

2.   From Fig. 3.6(c),

$$i_{12} = -2.00 \text{ A}$$

$$i_{22} = 1.00 \text{ A}$$

$$i_{32} = 2.00 \text{ A}$$

$$v_{22} = 6.00 \text{ V}.$$

3.   From Fig. 3.6(d),

$$i_{13} = -1.33 \text{ A}$$

$$i_{23} = 0.667 \text{ A}$$

$$i_{33} = -2.00 \text{ A}$$

$$v_{23} = 4.00 \text{ V}.$$

4.   Now combine components to get total responses:

$$i_1 = i_{11} + i_{12} + i_{13}$$
$$= 3.00 - 2.00 - 1.33 = -0.33 \text{ A} \qquad \textit{Ans.}$$

$$i_2 = i_{21} + i_{22} + i_{23}$$
$$= 1.00 + 1.00 + 0.67 = 2.67 \text{ A} \qquad \textit{Ans.}$$

$$i_3 = i_{31} + i_{32} + i_{33}$$
$$= 2.00 + 2.00 - 2.00 = 2.00 \text{ A} \qquad Ans.$$

$$v_2 = v_{21} + v_{22} + v_{23}$$
$$= 6.00 + 6.00 + 4.00 = 16.00 \text{ V}. \qquad Ans.$$

5. Check KCL:

$$i_1 - i_2 + i_{G2} - i_3 = -0.33 - 2.67 + 5.00 - 2.00 = 0.00.$$

6. Check KVL:

$$-v_{G1} + R_1 i_1 + v_2 = -15.0 + 3.00(-0.33) + 16.0 = 00.0$$
$$-v_{G3} - R_3 i_3 + v_2 = -10.0 - 3.00(2.00) + 16.0 = 00.0.$$

3.6 COMBINATIONS OF CAPACITORS

Capacitors, of course, can be connected in series, parallel, and series-parallel combinations, just as resistors can, and we will first consider the series combination of Fig. 3.7(a). It was shown in Art. 1.7 that the current

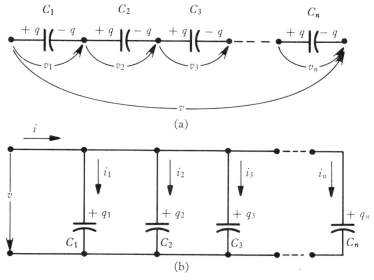

Fig. 3.7 *Combinations of capacitors. (a) Condensers in series. (b) Condensers in parallel.*

entering one terminal of a capacitor is the same as that leaving the other, so the same current flows in all conductor sections connecting series capacitors. Consequently, *when the original connections were made with uncharged capacitors,*

$$\int_{-\infty}^{t} i \, d\tau = q_1 = q_2 = q_3 = \cdots = q_n = q, \qquad (3.8)$$

and we see that *initially uncharged condensers in series all possess the same charge.* This can also be deduced by noting that the conducting material comprising condenser plates and their external interconnections must remain electrically neutral.

From the fact that capacitance is the constant of proportionality relating charge to voltage, KVL and Eq. (3.8) provide that

$$v = v_1 + v_2 + v_4 + \cdots + v_n,$$

and

$$\frac{q}{C} = \frac{q}{C_1} + \frac{q}{C_2} + \frac{q}{C_3} + \cdots + \frac{q}{C_n},$$

where C is the capacitance of the combination. Thus, for series capacitors

$$\frac{1}{C} = \frac{1}{C_1} + \frac{1}{C_2} + \frac{1}{C_3} + \cdots + \frac{1}{C_n}. \qquad (3.9)$$

When these same capacitors are connected in parallel, as in Fig. 3.7(b), they all have the same voltage across them,

$$v = v_1 = v_2 = v_3 = \cdots = v_n.$$

But, according to KCL,

$$\int_{-\infty}^{t} i \, d\tau = \int_{-\infty}^{t} (i_1 + i_2 + i_3 + \cdots + i_n) \, d\tau,$$

or, since

$$\int_{-\infty}^{t} i(\tau) \, d\tau = q(t),$$

for parallel capacitors

$$q = q_1 = q_2 + q_3 + \cdots + q_n. \qquad (3.10)$$

In terms of voltage, this is

$$Cv = C_1 v + C_2 v + C_3 v + \cdots + C_n v,$$

and, consequently, the total capacitance, C, of this group of parallel capacitors is

$$C = C_1 + C_2 + C_3 + \cdots + C_n. \qquad (3.11)$$

In summary, we have shown that:

1. The reciprocal of the total capacitance of series capacitors is the sum of the reciprocals of the individual capacitances.
2. The total capacitance of parallel capacitors is the sum of the individual capacitances.

EXAMPLE 3.5. Determine the charge on each capacitor and the voltage across each capacitor in Fig. 3.8(a), assuming that the capacitors were discharged before being connected to the ideal source.

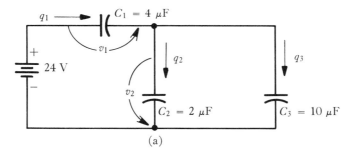

(a)

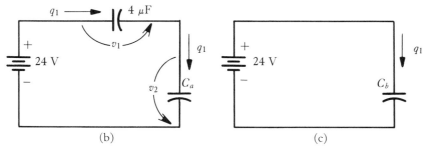

(b)   (c)

Fig. 3.8 *Reduction of a capacitive network.*

Solution.

1. Since the reduction of the capacitive network is similar to the methods used in Example 3.1, only the results are given.

$$C_a = C_2 + C_3 = 2 + 10 = 12\mu F$$

$$C_b = \frac{C_1 C_a}{C_1 + C_a} = \frac{4(12)}{4 + 12} = 3\mu F.$$

2. C_b is an equivalent capacitor that relates q_1 to the generated voltage; hence,

$$q_1 = C_b(24)$$
$$= 3 \times 10^{-6}(24) = 72 \times 10^{-6} \; C \qquad or \qquad 72 \; \mu C. \qquad Ans.$$

3.   Since the charge on C_1 and C_a is the same as that on C_b,

$$v_1 = q_1/C_1$$
$$= \frac{72 \times 10^{-6}}{4 \times 10^{-6}} = 18 \; V \qquad Ans.$$

$$v_2 = q_1/C_a$$
$$= \frac{72 \times 10^{-6}}{12 \times 10^{-6}} = 6 \; V. \qquad Ans.$$

Check KVL:

$$24 - v_1 - v_2 = 24 - 18 - 6 = 0.$$

4.   Using the value of v_2 in Fig. 3.8(a),

$$q_2 = C_2 v_2$$
$$= 2 \times 10^{-6}(6) = 12 \times 10^{-6} \; C \qquad or \qquad 12 \; \mu C. \qquad Ans.$$

$$q_3 = C_3 v_2$$
$$= 10 \times 10^{-6}(6) = 60 \times 10^{-6} \; C \qquad or \qquad 60 \; \mu C \qquad Ans.$$

Check by comparing the charge on C_1 to the charges on C_2 and C_3.

$$q_1 - (q_2 + q_3) = 72 \times 10^{-6} - 12 \times 10^{-6} - 60 \times 10^{-6} = 0.$$

3.7 COMBINATIONS OF INDUCTORS

In this section we will assume that all the flux linkages in a particular coil are entirely self-produced by the coil. This means that none of the flux linkages in the coil are the result of currents flowing in any other coil in the network. When this condition exists, we say that there is no *mutual coupling* between the coils. We will also assume that *all coil currents were zero at the time of the original interconnection* and that the coils have no resistance. In the case of n coils in series in Fig. 3.9(a), the total voltage is

$$v = v_1 + v_2 + v_3 + \cdots + v_n,$$

and, therefore,

$$\int_{-\infty}^{t} v \, d\tau = \int_{-\infty}^{t} (v_1 + v_2 + v_3 + \cdots + v_n) \, d\tau.$$

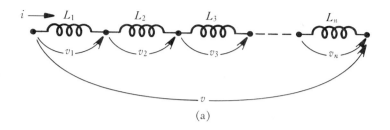

(a)

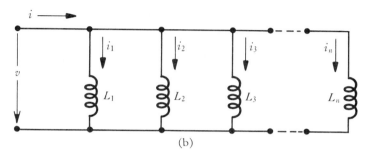

(b)

Fig. 3.9 *Combination of coils. (a) Coils in series. (b) Coils in parallel.*

According to Faraday's law, this relationship may be expressed in terms of flux linkages as

$$\lambda = \lambda_1 + \lambda_2 + \lambda_3 + \cdots + \lambda_n.$$

Since in general $\lambda = Li$, this becomes

$$Li = L_1 i + L_2 i + L_3 i + \cdots + L_n i,$$

so that for series coils, the total inductance is

$$L = L_1 + L_2 + L_3 + \cdots + L_4. \tag{3.12}$$

For the parallel coils of Fig. 3.9(b), all terminal voltages are the same, and the application of Faraday's law leads to the following for initially unexcited parallel coils:

$$\lambda = \lambda_1 = \lambda_2 = \lambda_3 = \cdots = \lambda_n. \tag{3.13}$$

According to KCL,

$$i = i_1 + i_2 + i_3 + \cdots + i_n,$$

or, in terms of flux linkages,

$$\frac{\lambda}{L} = \frac{\lambda}{L_1} + \frac{\lambda}{L_2} + \frac{\lambda}{L_3} + \cdots + \frac{\lambda}{L_n}.$$

Consequently, for parallel inductances

$$\frac{1}{L} = \frac{1}{L_1} + \frac{1}{L_2} + \frac{1}{L_3} + \cdots + \frac{1}{L_4}. \tag{3.14}$$

EXAMPLE 3.6. Determine the flux linkage of each coil and the current through each coil in Fig. 3.10(a), assuming that all coil currents were initially zero and that the coils have no resistance.

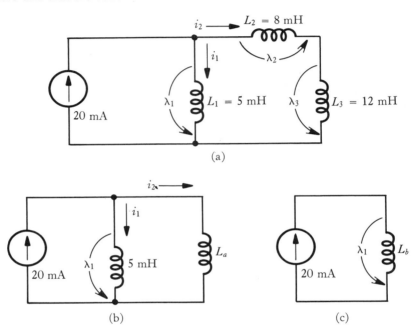

Fig. 3.10 *Reduction of an inductive network.*

Solution.

1. Since the reduction of the inductive network follows the same pattern as the previous example, only the results are listed.

$$L_a = L_2 + L_3 = 8 + 12 = 20 \text{ mH}$$

$$L_b = \frac{L_1 L_a}{L_1 + L_a} = \frac{5(20)}{5 + 20} = 4 \text{ mH}.$$

2. L_b is an equivalent inductor that relates λ_1 to the generated current; thus,

$$\lambda_1 = L_b(20 \times 10^{-3})$$
$$= (4 \times 10^{-3})(20 \times 10^{-3}) = 80 \times 10^{-6} \text{ Wb}$$

$$\text{or} \qquad 80 \text{ } \mu\text{Wb}. \qquad Ans.$$

3. The parallel inductors in Fig. 3.10(b) have the same flux linkage;

$$i_1 = \lambda_1/L_1$$

$$= \frac{80 \times 10^{-6}}{5 \times 10^{-3}} = 16 \times 10^{-3} \text{ A or 16 mA} \qquad Ans.$$

$$i_2 = \lambda_1/L_a$$

$$= \frac{80 \times 10^{-6}}{20 \times 10^{-3}} = 4 \times 10^{-3} \text{ A or 4 mA.} \qquad Ans.$$

Check KCL:

$$20 \times 10^{-3} - i_1 - i_2 = 20 \times 10^{-3} - 16 \times 10^{-3} - 4 \times 10^{-3} = 0.$$

4. Using the value for i_2 in Fig. 3.10(a),

$$\lambda_2 = L_2 i_2$$

$$= 8 \times 10^{-3}(4 \times 10^{-3}) = 32 \times 10^{-6} \text{ Wb}$$

$$\text{or} \qquad 32 \text{ } \mu\text{Wb} \qquad Ans.$$

$$\lambda_3 = L_3 i_2$$

$$= 12 \times 10^{-3}(4 \times 10^{-3}) = 48 \times 10^{-6} \text{ Wb}$$

$$\text{or} \qquad 48 \text{ } \mu\text{Wb.} \qquad Ans.$$

Check by comparing the flux linkage of L_1 to the flux linkages of L_2 and L_3.

$$\lambda_1 - (\lambda_2 + \lambda_3) = 80 \times 10^{-6} - 32 \times 10^{-6} - 48 \times 10^{-6}$$

$$= 0.$$

3.8 SUMMARY

In comparing capacitive and conductive networks and inductive and resistive networks, certain correspondences become apparent. Also, certain similarities arise concerning series and parallel components, summing quantities around closed paths, and summing quantities at nodes. A summary of these comparisons is given in Table 3.1.

TABLE 3.1 COMPARISONS BETWEEN ONE-ELEMENT-KIND NETWORKS

Network		Network	
Capacitive	Conductive	Inductive	Resistive
C	G	L	R
v	v	i	i
q	i	λ	v
$\sum_{\text{node}} q = 0$	$\sum_{\text{node}} i = 0$	$\sum_{\text{loop}} \lambda = 0$	$\sum_{\text{loop}} v = 0$
Parallel elements: Add directly		Series elements: Add directly	
Series elements: Add reciprocals		Parallel elements: Add reciprocals	

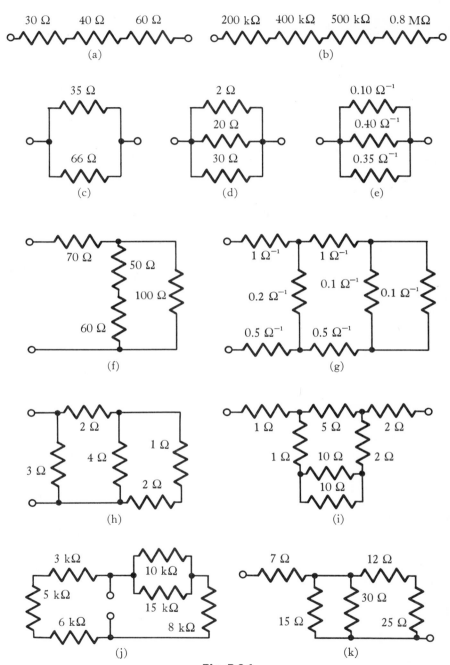

Fig. P.3.1.

PROBLEMS

3.1 Parts (a) through (k): Compute the resistance and conductance of each two-terminal passive network in Fig. P.3.1.

3.2 In Fig. P.3.2(a), $R_1 = 50\ \Omega$, $R_2 = 30\ \Omega$, $R_3 = 80\ \Omega$, and $v = 120\ V$. Compute the voltage across, the current through, and the power dissipated by each resistor. Compute the power delivered by the source and compare with the sum of the dissipated powers.

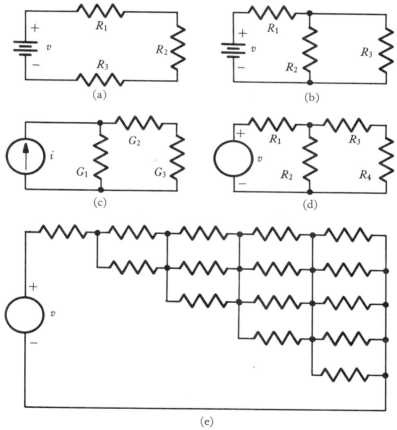

(a)

(b)

(c)

(d)

(e)

Fig. P.3.2.

3.3 In Fig. P.3.2(b), $R_1 = 50\ \Omega$, $R_2 = 30\ \Omega$, $R_3 = 80\ \Omega$, and $v = 120$ V. Repeat the calculations of Prob. 3.2 for this network.

3.4 In Fig. P.3.2(c), $G_1 = 0.1\ \Omega^{-1}$, $G_2 = 0.2\ \Omega^{-1}$, $G_3 = 0.3\ \Omega^{-1}$, and $i = 40$ A. Compute the voltage across, the current through, and the power dissipated by each conductance. Compute the power delivered by the source and compare with the sum of the dissipated powers.

3.5   In Fig. P.3.2(d), $R_1 = 500$ kΩ, $R_2 = 5$ MΩ, $R_3 = 4$ MΩ, $R_4 = 3$ MΩ, and $v = 200$ V. Find the power delivered by the source and the voltage drop from the bottom to top of R_4.

3.6   In Fig. P.3.2(e), $v = 500$ V and each resistor has a resistance of 60 Ω. Find the current and power delivered by the source.

3.7   In Fig. P.3.3(a), show that if $v_s/i_s = R_o$, then

$$R_o = \sqrt{R_1 R_2 + \frac{R_1^2}{4}},$$

and that

$$\frac{v_s}{v_L} = \frac{i_s}{i_L} = \alpha,$$

where

$$\alpha = 1 + \frac{R_1}{2R_2} + \sqrt{\frac{R_1}{R_2} + \frac{R_1^2}{4R_2^2}}.$$

(Note: When R_1 and R_2 are selected in this way, they constitute what is known as a *Tee-attenuator* or, more crudely, a *Tee-pad*.)

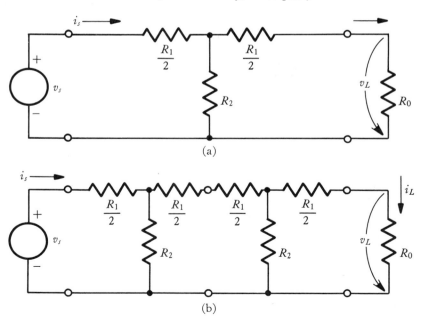

(a)

(b)

Fig. P.3.3.

3.8 Show that when, in Fig. P.3.3(b), R_o relates to R_1 and R_2 as in the previous problem, then again

$$v_s/i_s = R_o,$$

but now

$$\frac{v_s}{v_L} = \frac{i_s}{i_L} = \alpha^2.$$

3.9 Find the Thévenin's equivalent of the network of Prob. 3.3 when the two output terminals are at the ends of resistor R_3.

3.10 Find the Norton's equivalent of the network of Prob. 3.3 when the two output terminals are at the ends of resistor R_2.

3.11 Find the Thévenin's equivalent of the network of Prob. 3.4 when the output terminals are at the ends of conductance G_2.

3.12 Find the Norton's equivalent of the network of Prob. 3.4 when the output terminals are at the ends of conductance G_3.

3.13 Find the Norton's equivalent in Prob. 3.9.

3.14 Find the Thévenin's equivalent in Prob. 3.10.

3.15 Find the Norton's equivalent in Prob. 3.11.

3.16 Find the Thévenin's equivalent in Prob. 3.12.

3.17 The circuit parameters in Fig. P.3.2(b) have the values given in Prob. 3.3. Find the current through R_3 by replacing the remainder of the network with its Thévenin's equivalent. Repeat the calculation utilizing Norton's theorem rather than Thévenin's theorem.

3.18 The circuit parameters in Fig. P.3.2(c) have the values given in Prob. 3.4. Find the current in G_3 by both the methods of Prob. 3.17.

3.19 The circuit parameters in Fig. P.3.2(d) are those given in Prob. 3.5. Find the current in R_4 by both the methods of Prob. 3.17.

3.20 Find the currents in the network of Fig. P.3.4 using the principle of superposition.

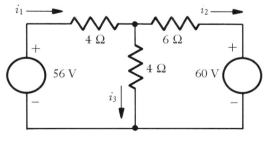

Fig. P.3.4.

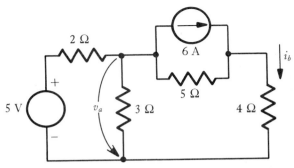

Fig. P.3.5.

3.21 Find v_a and i_b in Fig. P.3.5 using the principle of superposition.
3.22 Work Prob. 3.20 with the polarity of the 60-V source reversed.
3.23 Work Prob. 3.21 with the direction of the current source reversed.
3.24 For the network of Fig. P.3.6, find v_1, i_1, v_2, and i_2 by the principle of superposition.

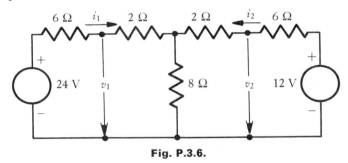

Fig. P.3.6.

3.25 Work Prob. 3.24 with the polarity of the 12-V source reversed.
3.26 Work Prob. 3.24 with the 6-Ω resistors reduced to zero ohms.
3.27 The network of Fig. P.3.7 is an example in which it is impossible to find the resistance, R, between terminals a and b utilizing series-parallel

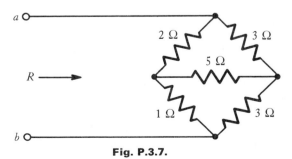

Fig. P.3.7.

reductions. Find R by assuming *any* terminal voltage (or current), then apply Thévenin's (Norton's) theorem successively in a manner strategically chosen to eventually yield the current (voltage).

3.28 In Fig. P.3.8(a), find each indicated voltage, the charge on each capacitor, the total capacitance across the voltage source, and the total stored energy.

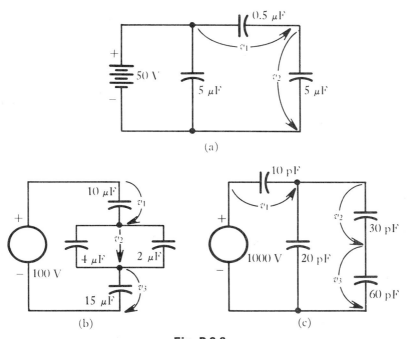

Fig. P.3.8.

3.29 Fulfill the requirements of Prob. 3.28 for Fig. P.3.8(b).

3.30 Fulfill the requirements of Prob. 3.28 for Fig. P.3.8(c).

3.31 Derive the voltage-divider relationship for two capacitors, C_1 and C_2, in series.

3.32 Derive the current-divider relationship for two capacitors, C_1 and C_2, in parallel.

3.33 The coils in Fig. P.3.9(a) have negligible resistance and are magnetically isolated from one another. Find each indicated current, the flux linkages in each coil, the total inductance in series with the current source, and the total stored energy. (Note: In the real world such resistanceless coils are hard to come by.)

3.34 Fulfill the requirements of Prob. 3.33 for Fig. P.3.9(b).

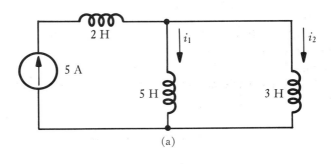

(a)

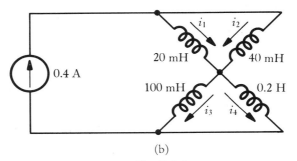

(b)

Fig. P.3.9.

3.35 In Fig. P.3.10, how much energy is dissipated as heat when the switch is opened instantly after having been closed for a long time?

3.36 Derive the voltage-divider relationship for two resistanceless coils with inductances L_1 and L_2 in series.

3.37 Derive the current-divider relationship for two resistanceless coils with inductances L_1 and L_2 in parallel.

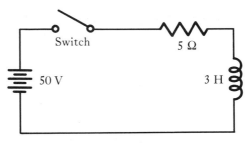

Fig. P.3.10.

4

Simple Circuits of more than One Element-Kind

4.1 INTRODUCTION

In this chapter we shall concern ourselves with circuits made up of $R\text{-}L$, $R\text{-}C$, $L\text{-}C$, or $R\text{-}L\text{-}C$ combinations. We will restrict our attention to the simple cases of all-series or all-parallel elements excited by single sources. The more complicated combinations will be covered when we reach the study of *networks* formed by many combinations of circuit elements and sources.

4.2 CONSERVATION THEOREMS (WITH FINITE SOURCES)

Whenever a system response is initiated, or takes on some new time-dependent characteristic, it is the result of a sudden change in the manner in which energy is delivered to the system. The nature of the response will depend on the nature of the system and the nature of the new excitation, but

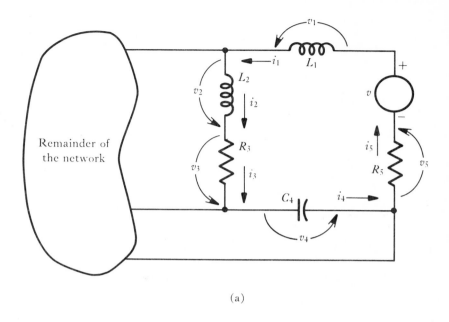

(a)

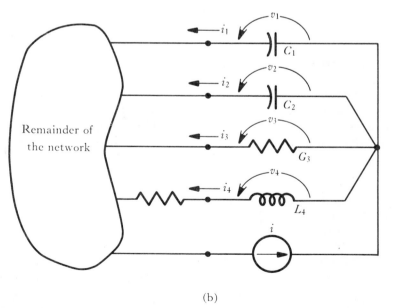

(b)

Fig. 4.1 *Illustrating conservation theorems. (a) A network loop. (b) A network node.*

the response will also be affected by energy stored in the system from sources applied prior to the suddenly imposed change. This heritage from the past is preserved by certain conservation theorems, which are the electrical counterparts of the *theorem of conservation of momentum* occurring in mechanics.

Consider one *loop* of the complicated network shown in Fig. 4.1(a) which contains a Thévenin's equivalent voltage source. Applying KVL to this loop, we find that

$$v(t) = v_1(t) + v_2(t) + v_3(t) + v_4(t) + v_5(t)$$

$$= L_1 \frac{di_1(t)}{dt} + L_2 \frac{di_2(t)}{dt} + R_3\, i_3(t)$$

$$+ \frac{1}{C_4} \int_{-\infty}^{t} i_4(\tau)\, d\tau + R_5\, i_5(t)$$

$$= \frac{d\lambda_1(t)}{dt} + \frac{d\lambda_2(t)}{dt} + R_3\, i_3(t) + \frac{1}{C_4}\, q_4(t) + R_5\, i_5(t).$$

Let us now integrate the above equation over some time interval extending from time t_1 to time t_2. Then

$$\int_{t_1}^{t_2} v(t)\, dt = \int_{t_1}^{t_2} \frac{d\lambda_1(t)}{dt}\, dt + \int_{t_1}^{t_2} \frac{d\lambda_2(t)}{dt}\, dt + R_3 \int_{t_1}^{t_2} i_3(t)\, dt$$

$$+ \frac{1}{C_4} \int_{t_1}^{t_2} q_4(t)\, dt + R_5 \int_{t_1}^{t_2} i_5(t)\, dt. \qquad (4.1)$$

There are two forms of integrals in the above equation:

(1) $\quad \displaystyle\int_{t_1}^{t_2} f(t)\, dt$

(2) $\quad \displaystyle\int_{t_1}^{t_2} \frac{d\phi_1(t)}{dt}\, dt = \int_{\phi(t_1)}^{\phi(t_2)} d\phi = \phi(t_2) - \phi(t_1).$

Now we apply the limitation that all practical sources of energy remain finite; that is, practical sources develop finite power and supply finite amounts of energy, which implies finite source currents and voltages. This means that passive elements can only dissipate or store finite amounts of energy, and from Eqs. (1.26), (1.40), and (1.59) we must conclude that resistor currents and voltages, inductor currents, and capacitor voltages must also remain finite. We can further conclude that inductor flux linkages and capacitor charges also are finite. This restriction of finiteness further implies that such functions can have at most a *step discontinuity*, which is simply a sudden change from one finite value to another.

Since the functions $v(t)$, $\lambda(t)$, $i(t)$, and $q(t)$ in Eq. (4.1) are all finite, the functions $f(t)$ and $\phi(t)$ in expressions (1) and (2) are also finite. If the time interval from t_1 to t_2 becomes arbitrarily short, we then have in the limit:

(1a) $\quad \lim\limits_{(t_2-t_1)\to 0} \displaystyle\int_{t_1}^{t_2} f(t)\, dt = 0$

(2a) $\quad \lim\limits_{(t_2-t_1)\to 0} \displaystyle\int_{t_1}^{t_2} \dfrac{d\phi(t)}{dt}\, dt = \phi(t_2) - \phi(t_1).$

Applying these results to Eq. (4.1) yields

$$[\lambda_1(t_2) + \lambda_2(t_2)] - [\lambda_1(t_1) + \lambda_2(t_1)] = 0,$$

or, in general,

$$\lim_{(t_2-t_1)\to 0} [\lambda(t_2) - \lambda(t_1)] = 0, \tag{4.2}$$

where, for an n-coil loop,

$$\lambda(t) = \sum_{k=1}^{n} \lambda_k(t) \tag{4.2a}$$

is an algebraic summation with the sign of $\lambda_k(t)$ being positive if the direction of traversing the loop is the same as the direction of $i_k(t)$, the current in the kth coil. This is the *theorem of constant flux linkages*, which states:

A.   Assuming finite sources, the algebraic sum of the flux linkages around a closed loop tends to remain constant over very small changes in time; in other words, the total loop flux linkages is a continuous function of time.

Turning to Fig. 4.1(b), we see that

$$i(t) = i_1(t) + i_2(t) + i_3(t) + i_4(t)$$

$$= C_1 \frac{dv_1(t)}{dt} + C_2 \frac{dv_2(t)}{dt} + G_3 v_3(t) + \frac{1}{L_4} \int_{-\infty}^{t} v(\tau)\, d\tau$$

$$= \frac{dq_1(t)}{dt} + \frac{dq_2(t)}{dt} + G_3 v_3(t) + \frac{1}{L_4} \lambda_4(t).$$

In a manner exactly analogous to that followed for the loop voltages above, we find that as $(t_2 - t_1) \to 0$,

$$[q_1(t_2) + q_2(t_2)] - [q_1(t_1) + q_2(t_1)] = 0.$$

In general, this shows that

$$\lim_{(t_2-t_1)\to 0} [q(t_2) - q(t_1)] = 0, \tag{4.3}$$

where, for an *n*-capacitor node,

$$q(t) = \sum_{k=1}^{n} q_k(t) \qquad (4.3a)$$

is an algebraic summation with the sign of $q_k(t)$ depending on whether $v_k(t)$, the voltage across the kth capacitor, is drawn away from or towards the node. This result is known as the *theorem of constant charge:*

B. Assuming finite sources, the algebraic sum of the capacitor charges at a node tends to remain constant over very small intervals of time; in other words, the total capacitor charge at a node is a continuous function of time.

The following two corollaries to these theorems are obvious, but the student must be alert not to confuse them with the theorems themselves:

A1. In a coil in a loop containing no other coils, the current is continuous, assuming finite sources.

B1. Across a capacitor connected to a node connecting to no other capacitors, the voltage is continuous, assuming finite sources.

4.3 EQUILIBRIUM CONDITIONS WITH CONSTANT SOURCES

In order to apply the conservation theorems of the previous section to the solution of circuit problems, one needs to know the circuit behavior just prior to the system disturbance which sets the problem in motion. In particular, he needs to know the loop flux linkage and the total capacitor charge at nodes, since it is to these quantities that the conservation theorems apply.

Often these *initial conditions* result from constant sources applied long enough ago that the equilibrium condition exists. By *equilibrium condition* we mean that condition existing after all components in the response to a particular source (or set of sources) have died out except those having the same form (or forms) of the source (or sources). In the case of constant sources, this means that all remaining responses are also constants.

If all responses are constants, then their derivatives are zero. Since the voltages across inductances are derivatives of currents and the currents through capacitors are derivatives of voltage, it follows that in the state of equilibrium due to constant sources all voltages across inductances and all currents through capacitors are zero. An element exhibiting zero voltage with nonzero current acts as a *short circuit*, and an element exhibiting zero current with nonzero voltage acts as an *open circuit*. Therefore, we may summarize this particular set of circumstances with the following statement:

> When a circuit is in equilibrium with constant sources applied, all inductances may be replaced by short circuits and all capacitances by open circuits.

Since in a coil the stored energy is $\frac{1}{2}(Li^2)$ and in a capacitor it is $\frac{1}{2}(Cv^2)$, one would expect that the current flowing in an inductance and the voltage across a capacitance just prior to a system disturbance will affect the future behavior of the circuit. We shall see that this is, indeed, the case.

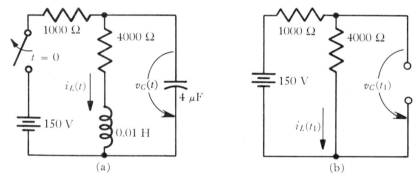

(a)   (b)

Fig. 4.2 *Equilibrium and conservation in an R-L-C network with a constant source. (a) Complete circuit. (b) Circuit in equilibrium just prior to t = 0.*

EXAMPLE 4.1. The circuit in Fig. 4.2(a) has existed in the state indicated for a long time prior to opening the switch ($t = 0$).

a.   Determine the coil current and capacitor voltage just before opening the switch. (This time will be denoted by $t_1 = 0 - \varepsilon$ where ε is an arbitrarily small number.)

b.   Determine the coil current and capacitor voltage just after opening the switch. (This time will be denoted by $t_2 = 0 + \varepsilon$.)

Solution. Since the circuit as shown has existed for a long time prior to switching, it must be in equilibrium at time t_1. Hence, the inductance may be replaced by a short circuit and the capacitance by an open circuit, as shown in (b) of Fig. 4.2. Then by simple applications of Ohm's law

$$i_L(t_1) = \frac{150}{4000 + 1000} = 30 \times 10^{-3} \text{ A} \qquad Ans.$$

$$v_C(t_1) = 4000 i_L(t_1) = 4000(30 \times 10^{-3}) = 120 \text{ V}. \qquad Ans.$$

From the two corollaries of the previous article,

$$\lim_{\varepsilon \to 0} i_L(t_2) = \lim_{\varepsilon \to 0} i_L(t_1) = i_L(0) = 30 \times 10^{-3} \text{ A} \qquad Ans.$$

$$\lim_{\varepsilon \to 0} v_C(t_2) = \lim_{\varepsilon \to 0} v_C(t_1) = v_C(0) = 120 \text{ V}. \qquad Ans.$$

Thus, the coil current and capacitor voltage are continuous in this particular network even though a sudden change occurs at $t = 0$.

4.4 NATURAL AND FORCED RESPONSES IN *R-L* CIRCUITS

When a system experiences a sudden change in excitation, one might expect the response to contain characteristics imparted by the nature of the system itself and other characteristics reflecting the nature of the new excitation. That these two sets of characteristics do exist and can, indeed, be separated is illustrated in this article by a simple example, the series *R-L* circuit.

In Fig. 4.3(a) is shown the series *R-L* circuit short circuited for $t > 0$. If the inductance has some energy stored from its previous past history ($t < 0$), then a current must exist until the stored energy is dissipated. During the

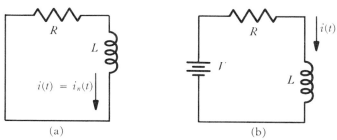

<small>(a)   (b)</small>

Fig. 4.3 *Two operating modes for the R-L series circuit. (a) Force free, t > 0. (b) Forced, t > 0.*

interval of dissipating the stored energy, KVL demands

$$Ri(t) + L\frac{di(t)}{dt} = 0, \qquad t > 0. \tag{4.4}$$

This may be rearranged to give

$$\frac{di(t)}{i(t)} = -\frac{R}{L}\,dt.$$

Integrating both sides, we have

$$\ln i(t) - \ln I_n = -\frac{R}{L}\,t,$$

where

$$\ln I_n = \text{combined constants of integration.}$$

Rewriting,

$$\ln\frac{i(t)}{I_n} = -\frac{R}{L}\,t;$$

then taking the antilogarithm of both sides yields

$$\frac{i(t)}{I_n} = e^{-(R/L)t},$$

or

$$i(t) = I_n e^{-(R/L)t}, \qquad t > 0. \tag{4.5}$$

This response resulted with no external excitation present and is, therefore, known as the *source-free*, or *natural*, response. Since exponents are dimensionless, the quantity R/L must have the units of $\sec^{-1}$, and the student should satisfy himself that this is indeed so.

Clearly, in Eq. (4.5)

$$I_n = \lim_{t \to 0} i(t) = i(0), \tag{4.6}$$

where actually $i(0)$ can mean the current just before or just after the disturbance, since by corollary (A1) of the theorem of constant flux linkages the current is continuous. Hence,

$$i(t) = i(0)e^{-(R/L)t}. \tag{4.7}$$

Now let us turn to the same series circuit, forced by a constant voltage for $t > 0$, as in Fig. 4.3(b). Now

$$V = Ri(t) + L\frac{di(t)}{dt}, \qquad t > 0. \tag{4.8}$$

This can be arranged in the form

$$\frac{di(t)}{i(t) - (V/R)} = -\frac{R}{L}dt,$$

and integrating, as before, yields

$$\ln\left[i(t) - \frac{V}{R}\right] - \ln I_n = -\frac{R}{L}t,$$

or, in the manner of the preceding case,

$$i(t) - \frac{V}{R} = I_n e^{-(R/L)t}.$$

Thus, the current in this case is

$$i(t) = \frac{V}{R} + I_n e^{-(R/L)t}, \qquad t > 0. \tag{4.9}$$

Notice that Eq. (4.9) contains one term identical in form to the *natural* response of Eq. (4.5). In other words, this term in the response is the response of the source-free network. We shall call a spade a spade and designate this component as the *natural response*,

$$i_n(t) = I_n e^{-(R/L)t}. \tag{4.10a}$$

The remaining term contains the forcing function, V, and is in fact of the same general form as the forcing voltage, i.e., a constant. Therefore, we shall designate it the *forced response*,

$$i_f(t) = \frac{V}{R}. \tag{4.10b}$$

Let us also record that

$$i(t) = i_f(t) + i_n(t). \tag{4.10c}$$

In summary, we have shown that when the applied voltage is $v(t) = V$, $t > 0$,

$$i(t) = I_f + I_n e^{mt}, \qquad t > 0, \tag{4.11}$$

where

$$I_f = \frac{V}{R} \qquad \text{(amperes)} \tag{4.12a}$$

$$m = -\frac{R}{L} \qquad \text{(sec}^{-1}) \tag{4.12b}$$

$$I_n = i(0) - \frac{V}{R} \qquad \text{(amperes)}. \tag{4.12c}$$

The last equation follows directly from Eq. (4.9).

We will now proceed on the assumption that all responses can be considered to be composed of a forced response and a natural response. If we are wrong in this assumption, the error of our ways will quickly be evident.

Suppose the same circuit is excited by the exponentially varying voltage

$$v(t) = Ve^{at}, \qquad t > 0 \qquad \text{and} \qquad a \neq m. \tag{4.13}$$

The reason for adding the constraint $a \neq m$ will appear later.

Again by KVL,

$$v(t) = Ri(t) + L\frac{di(t)}{dt}. \tag{4.14}$$

Playing our hunch that the forced response has the same form as the exciting voltage, we write

$$i_f(t) = I_f e^{at}, \qquad t > 0. \tag{4.15}$$

Let us assume a natural response of the form of Eq. (4.10a) but with the exponent left aribtrary. Thus,

$$i_n(t) = I_n e^{mt}, \qquad t > 0. \tag{4.16}$$

The total response current has now been assumed to be, as in Eq. (4.10c),

$$\begin{aligned} i(t) &= i_f(t) + i_n(t) \\ &= I_f e^{at} + I_n e^{mt}, \qquad t > 0. \end{aligned} \tag{4.17}$$

Substituting Eqs. (4.13) and (4.17) into Eq. (4.14), we have

$$Ve^{at} = (R + aL)I_f e^{at} + (R + mL)I_n e^{mt}. \tag{4.18}$$

In order for the above to hold for *all* values of t, the coefficient of each exponential on the right must be matched by an equal coefficient for the same exponential on the left. Thus,

$$V = (R + aL)I_f \tag{4.19}$$

$$0 = (R + mL)I_n, \tag{4.20}$$

and from Eq. (4.17)

$$i(0) = \lim_{t \to 0} i(t) = I_f + I_n, \tag{4.21}$$

where $i(0)$ is the current just before or just after the excitation, Ve^{at}, is applied. Equation (4.19) may be solved for I_f. In general, $I_n \neq 0$, so in Eq. (4.20),

$$R + mL = 0,$$

and m may thus be determined. Knowing I_f and $i(0)$, I_n follows from Eq. (4.21). Therefore, all the constants in Eq. (4.17) can be determined in

terms of the system parameters, the amplitude and exponential constant of
the applied voltage, and the initial current. The results are

$$I_f = \frac{V}{R + aL} \qquad \text{(amperes)} \qquad (4.22a)$$

$$m = -\frac{R}{L} \qquad \text{(sec}^{-1}\text{)} \qquad (4.22b)$$

$$I_n = i(0) - \frac{V}{R + aL} \qquad \text{(amperes)}. \qquad (4.22c)$$

Notice that in the case of $a = 0$, Eqs. (4.17) and (4.22) degenerate to the
case of constant applied voltage represented by Eqs. (4.11) and (4.12), as, of
course, they should. Also notice that, as a approaches m, I_f and I_n increase
without bound and Eq. (4.17) becomes indeterminate. This is why the constraint was added to Eq. (4.13), and since the occasion of a equaling m
arises so seldom, we will wait until later in the text to remove the constraint.

EXAMPLE 4.2. In Fig. 4.4 the switch, S, is moved from position 1 to
position 2 at $t = 0$ after having been in position 1 for a very long time. Find
$i(t)$ and $v_L(t)$ for $t > 0$.

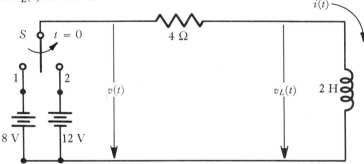

Fig. 4.4   *Switching in an R-L series circuit.*

Solution. Since the switch had been in position 1 for a very long time, the
steady-state condition had been reached so that all responses were constant
prior to $t = 0$. Then $di(t)/dt = 0$, and the inductance appears as a short-
circuit. By Ohm's law, applied just prior to $t = 0$,

$$i(0) = -\frac{8}{4} = -2 \text{ A}.$$

The applied voltage after $t = 0$ is

$$v(t) = 12 \text{ V}.$$

Equations (4.12) now yield

$$I_f = \frac{V}{R} = \frac{12}{4} = 3 \text{ A}$$

$$m = -\frac{R}{L} = -\frac{4}{2} = -2 \text{ sec}^{-1}$$

$$I_n = i(0) - \frac{V}{R} = -2 - 3 = -5 \text{ A}.$$

Therefore,

$$i(t) = I_f + I_n e^{+mt}$$
$$= 3 - 5e^{-2t} \text{ A}, \qquad t > 0. \qquad Ans.$$

The voltage across the inductance is

$$v_L(t) = L \frac{di(t)}{dt}$$

$$= 2 \frac{d}{dt} (3 - 5e^{-2t})$$

$$= 20e^{-2t} \text{ V}, \qquad t > 0. \qquad Ans.$$

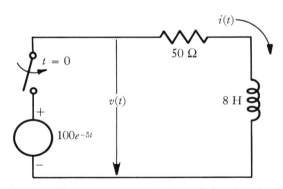

Fig. 4.5 *Exponential excitation in an R-L series circuit.*

EXAMPLE 4.3. Find $i(t)$ in Fig. 4.5.

Solution. Obviously,

$$i(0) = 0$$
$$v(t) = 100e^{-5t} \text{ V}, \qquad t > 0.$$

From Eqs. (4.22)

$$I_f = \frac{V}{R + aL} = \frac{100}{50 + (-5)(8)} = 10 \text{ A}$$

$$m = -\frac{R}{L} = -\frac{50}{8} = -6.25 \text{ sec}^{-1}$$

$$I_n = i(0) - \frac{V}{R + aL} = 0 - 10 = -10 \text{ A}.$$

Therefore,

$$i(t) = I_f e^{at} + I_n e^{mt} = 10e^{-5t} - 10e^{-6.25t}, \qquad t > 0. \qquad Ans.$$

4.5 THE *R-C* SERIES CIRCUIT

In the *R-C* series circuit of Fig. 4.6, KVL and the volt-ampere relations yield

$$v(t) = Ri(t) + \frac{1}{C} \int_{-\infty}^{t} i(\tau) \, d\tau. \tag{4.23}$$

But

$$v_C(t) = \frac{1}{C} \int_{-\infty}^{t} i(\tau) \, d\tau = \frac{1}{C} \int_{-\infty}^{0} i(\tau) \, d\tau + \frac{1}{C} \int_{0}^{t} i(\tau) \, d\tau$$

$$= \frac{1}{C} \int_{0}^{t} i(\tau) \, d\tau + \frac{q(0)}{C}$$

$$= \frac{1}{C} \int_{0}^{t} i(\tau) \, d\tau + v_C(0). \tag{4.24}$$

Therefore, an alternative form of Eq. (4.23) is

$$v(t) = Ri(t) + \frac{1}{C} \int_{0}^{t} i(\tau) \, d\tau + v_C(0). \tag{4.25}$$

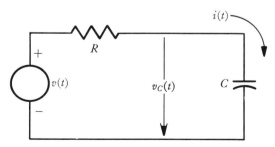

Fig. 4.6   *The R-C series circuit.*

Let us again employ the exponential forcing voltage,

$$v(t) = Ve^{at}, \qquad t > 0 \qquad \text{and} \qquad a \neq m. \qquad (4.26)$$

Furthermore, let us assume the existence of a forced and natural response as before:

$$i_f(t) = I_f e^{at} \qquad (4.27)$$
$$i_n(t) = I_n e^{mt}. \qquad (4.28)$$

The total current again is thus assumed to be

$$i(t) = i_f(t) + i_n(t)$$
$$= I_f e^{at} + I_n e^{mt}. \qquad (4.29)$$

Substituting Eqs. (4.26) and (4.29) into Eq. (4.25), we have

$$Ve^{at} = \left(R + \frac{1}{aC}\right)I_f e^{at} + \left(R + \frac{1}{mC}\right)I_n e^{mt} - \left(\frac{I_f}{aC} + \frac{I_n}{mC}\right) + v_C(0). \qquad (4.30)$$

Matching coefficients of exponents, as was done for the previous case, produces

$$V = \left(R + \frac{1}{aC}\right)I_f \qquad (4.31a)$$

$$0 = \left(R + \frac{1}{mC}\right)I_n \qquad (4.31b)$$

$$0 = -\left(\frac{I_f}{aC} + \frac{I_n}{mC}\right) + v_C(0). \qquad (4.31c)$$

From these equations we see that

$$I_f = \frac{V}{R + (1/aC)} \qquad (4.32a)$$

$$m = -\frac{1}{RC} \qquad (4.32b)$$

$$I_n = m\left[Cv_C(0) - \frac{I_f}{a}\right]$$

$$= -\frac{v_C(0)}{R} + \frac{I_f}{aRC}$$

$$= \frac{1}{R}\left[\frac{V}{1 + aRC} - v_C(0)\right]. \qquad (4.32c)$$

Notice again that the constraint $a \neq m$ applies because Eq. (4.29) becomes indeterminate.

In the special case of constant excitation, $a = 0$, Eqs. (4.32) become

$$I_f = 0 \qquad\qquad (4.33a)$$

$$m = -\frac{1}{RC} \qquad\qquad (4.33b)$$

$$I_n = \frac{1}{R}[V - v_C(0)]. \qquad\qquad (4.33c)$$

These results could also have been obtained by separating variables to find integrable combinations, as was done for the *R-L* case.

EXAMPLE 4.4. Find $i(t)$ and $v_C(t)$ in Fig. 4.7.

Solution. Since in the steady state under constant excitation no current passes through a condenser,

$$v_C(0) = 100 \text{ V}.$$

Also,

$$v(t) = 50 \text{ V}, \qquad t > 0.$$

From Eqs. (4.33)

$$I_f = 0$$

$$m = -\frac{1}{10,000(5 \times 10^{-6})} = -20 \text{ sec}^{-1}$$

$$I_n = \frac{50 - 100}{10,000} = -5 \times 10^{-3} \text{ A}.$$

Equation (4.29) now becomes

$$i(t) = -5e^{-20t} \times 10^{-3} \text{ A}, \qquad t > 0. \qquad Ans.$$

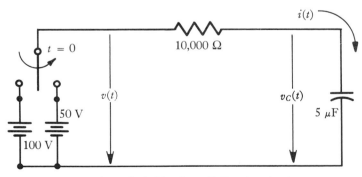

Fig. 4.7   *Switching in an R-C series circuit.*

The capacitor voltage, using Eq. (4.24), is

$$v_C(t) = \frac{1}{C} \int_0^t i(\tau)\, d\tau + v_C(0)$$

$$= \frac{-5 \times 10^{-3}}{5 \times 10^{-6}} \int_0^t e^{-20\tau}\, d\tau + 100$$

$$= 50(1 + e^{-20t})\, \text{V}, \qquad t > 0. \qquad \textit{Ans.}$$

EXAMPLE 4.5. Find $i(t)$ and $v_C(t)$ for $t > 0$ in Fig. 4.8.

Solution. The voltage across the capacitor is continuous, so it is the same just after $t = 0$ as just before $t = 0$, when 100 V was applied in the direction shown. Therefore,

$$v_C(0) = -100 \text{ V}.$$

The applied voltage is

$$v(t) = 200e^{-50t}\, \text{V}, \qquad t > 0.$$

Equations (4.32) are then

$$I_f = \frac{V}{R + \dfrac{1}{aC}} = \frac{200}{50{,}000 + \dfrac{1}{-50(0.2 \times 10^{-6})}} = -4 \times 10^{-3}\, \text{A}$$

$$m = -\frac{1}{RC} = -\frac{1}{(5 \times 10^4)(0.2 \times 10^{-6})} = -100 \text{ sec}^{-1}$$

$$I_n = \frac{1}{R}\left[\frac{V}{1 + aRC} - v_C(0)\right]$$

$$= \frac{1}{50{,}000}\left[\frac{200}{1 + (-50)(50{,}000)(0.2 \times 10^{-6})} - (-100)\right]$$

$$= +10 \times 10^{-3}\, \text{A}.$$

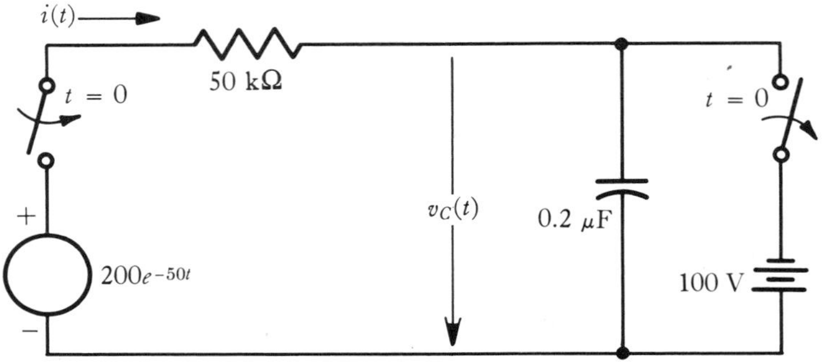

Fig. 4.8 *Exponential excitation in an R-C series circuit.*

The total current is

$$i(t) = I_f e^{at} + I_n e^{mt}$$
$$= (-4e^{-50t} + 10e^{-100t}) \times 10^{-3} \text{ A}, \qquad t > 0. \qquad Ans.$$

The capacitor voltage is

$$v_C(t) = \frac{1}{C} \int_0^t i(\tau) \, d\tau + v_C(0)$$

$$= \frac{10^{-3}}{0.2 \times 10^{-6}} \int_0^t (-4e^{-50\tau} + 10e^{-100\tau}) \, d\tau - 100$$

$$= 400e^{-50t} - 500e^{-100t} \text{ V}, \qquad t > 0. \qquad Ans.$$

4.6 THE SIMPLICITY OF CONSTANT-SOURCE EXCITATION

After a perusal of the results of the foregoing two sections, it becomes apparent that all responses to constant excitation in series R-L and R-C networks have the following in common:

1. They start from some easily determined value at $t = 0$.
2. They go to some easily determined value at $t = \infty$.
3. The change from the value in (A) to that in (B) follows an exponential variation determined by the circuit parameters.

These facts allow the determination of a standard variation applicable to all first-order responses, whether they be voltage, current, charge, or flux linkage. If $r(t)$ is such a response, then it starts at $r(0)$ and proceeds exponentially to $r(\infty)$, for a total change of $r(\infty) - r(0)$. The general form of the response then may be written

$$r(t) = r(\infty) + [r(0) - r(\infty)]e^{-(t/T)}, \qquad t > 0, \qquad (4.34)$$

where the quantity T is called the *time constant* of the circuit and is defined as

$$T = -\frac{1}{m}$$

$$= \begin{cases} RC, & R\text{-}C \text{ circuit} \\ \dfrac{L}{R}, & R\text{-}L \text{ circuit} \end{cases} \text{(seconds)}. \qquad (4.35)$$

Finding the transient response using Eq. (4.34) is very simple. One finds the initial value of the response from the conservation of current in single coils or voltage across single condensers. The final value, $r(\infty)$, is found by replacing inductances by short circuits and capacitances as open circuits.

In *R-C* or *R-L* networks with but one coil or capacitor, but more than one resistor, these same techniques apply. However, the time constant is now determined by the Thévenin's equivalent resistance as viewed by the capacitor or inductor.

EXAMPLE 4.6. Find $v_C(t)$, for $t > 0$, in Fig. 4.9, assuming switch *S* has been closed for a very long time prior to $t = 0$.

Solution. Since the system is in the steady-state prior to $t = 0$, the capacitor may be replaced by an open circuit, and

$$v_C(0) = 90 \text{ V.}$$

After the switch has been opened for a long time, the capacitor again appears as an open circuit, and the voltage-divider relationship yields

$$v_C(\infty) = \frac{6000}{6000 + 3000}(90) = 60 \text{ V.}$$

The resistance of the Thévenin's equivalent looking to the left of points *a* and *b* consists of the 2000-Ω resistance plus the 6000-Ω resistance in parallel with the 3000-Ω resistance; that is,

$$R = 2000 + \frac{3000(6000)}{3000 + 6000} = 4000 \ \Omega.$$

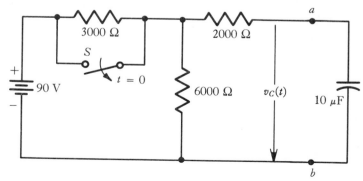

Fig. 4.9   *Circuit for Example 4.6.*

The exponential is determined by

$$m = -\frac{1}{T} = \frac{-1}{RC} = \frac{-1}{4000(10 \times 10^{-6})} = -25 \text{ sec}^{-1}.$$

Now Eq. (4.34) becomes

$$v_C(t) = v_C(\infty) + [v_C(0) - v_C(\infty)]e^{-(t/T)}$$
$$= 60 + [90 - 60]e^{-25t}$$
$$= 60 + 30e^{-25t} \text{ V}, \qquad t > 0. \qquad Ans.$$

4.7 PLOTTING EXPONENTIAL RESPONSES

Since the form of the solution is always of interest to the engineer, it is well that means of rapid plotting of the exponential functions obtained above be considered. Consider the exponential function with a real exponent and of time constant, T,

$$f(t) = Ae^{-(t/T)}$$

and its derivative

$$f'(t) = -\frac{A}{T}e^{-t/T} = -\frac{f(t)}{T}.$$

The value of the exponential one time constant later than the time t is

$$f(t + T) = Ae^{-(1/T)(t+T)}$$

$$= \frac{A}{e}e^{-(t/T)}$$

$$= \frac{1}{e}f(t).$$

This shows that in *any* interval of time one time constant in length, the function at the end of the interval has decayed to $1/e$ times the value it had at the beginning of the interval, or to approximately 37% of the value at the beginning of the interval.

A rough sketch of the exponential could be obtained by marking off the t-axis into intervals of one-time-constant duration as in Fig. 4.10, then simply dividing successively by e to obtain the values at the points. However, it should be noted that at only three time constants but 5% of the total change remains, so this method provides us with only three significant points to determine the curve, and the separation of points makes it difficult to predict the curve in between. However, knowing the slope at these points will greatly

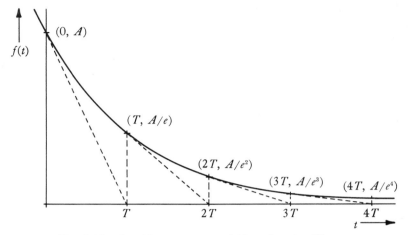

Fig. 4.10   *Graphing an exponential function, $Ae^{-t/T}$.*

enhance the accuracy of the plot by adding knowledge of the direction taken by the curve in the neighborhood of the point to knowledge of the value of the function at the point.

To this end, consider a straight line tangent to the curve at one of the interval beginnings: say that beginning at $t = t_1$. At $t = t_1$ (the point $[t_1, f(t_1)]$ in Fig. 4.11) the tangent line and the exponential curve have the same slope, and the slope of the line is

$$f'(t_1) = -\frac{f(t_1)}{T} = -\frac{f(t_1)}{\Delta t},$$

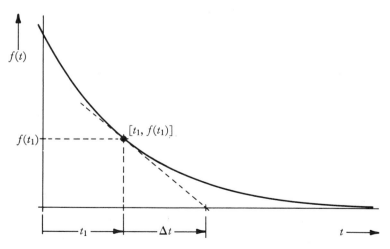

Fig. 4.11   *The tangent to an exponential function.*

where Δt is the interval of time extending from t_1 to the point at which the line intersects the t-axis. It immediately follows that

$$T = \Delta t.$$

We have now shown that the tangent to a decaying exponential always intersects the axis one time constant beyond the point of tangency. A series of such tangencies is shown in Fig. 4.10, illustrating how the above information may be applied to rapid plotting of exponentials. In the figure, the laying off of T-length intervals was started at the origin, which will usually be the most convenient starting place, but it could have started from any time at which the value of the function was known. The procedure may be summarized by listing a series of steps as follows:

1. Draw the t and $f(t)$ axes and choose scales. In choosing scales, remember that a normal plot cannot cover more than about four time constants without the function either looming unreasonably large at the origin or becoming negligibly small along the time axis.
2. Mark off successive intervals of one time constant each along the t-axis, starting at the origin or some other point where the value of the function is known.
3. At the starting point, plot the value of the function, then one time constant later 37% of that value, then another time constant later 37% of the value of the previous point, and so on, proceeding until the function becomes negligible.
4. Draw straight lines from the points plotted to the points on the t-axis one time constant beyond.
5. Draw a smooth curve through each point in step **3**, making certain that at each point the curve is tangent to the line segment drawn from that point in step **4**.

In applying this method to composite curves where the exponential is combined with a constant, it is helpful to note that the only changing part of the total function is the exponential and that in the interval from t to $t + T$, $100\% - 37\% = 63\%$ of the total change remaining at t has taken place. Stated another way, the change still to take place after $t + T$ is 37% of that which was remaining at time t.

Consider, for example, Eq. (4.34)

$$r(t) = r(\infty) + [r(0) - r(\infty)]e^{-(t/T)}$$
$$= r(\infty) + Ae^{-(t/T)},$$

where the *total* change in $r(t)$ after $t = 0$ is

$$r(0) - r(\infty) = A.$$

At the end of one time constant after $t = 0$, a *change* of 0.63 A has taken place, after two time constants an additional change of 0.63(0.63 A), and so on. The plot of such a function is shown in Fig. 4.12.

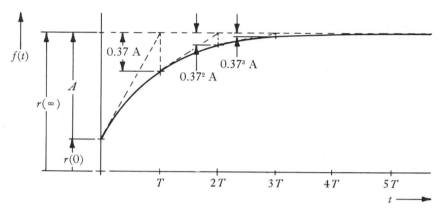

Fig. 4.12   *Plot of* $f(t) = r(\infty) - [r(\infty) - r(0)]e^{-t/T}$ *for* $t > 0$.

4.8 THE *R-L-C* SERIES CIRCUIT

The *R-L-C* series circuit of Fig. 4.13, upon application of KVL, produces

$$v(t) = v_R(t) + v_L(t) + v_C(t)$$

$$= Ri(t) + L\frac{di(t)}{dt} + \frac{1}{C}\int_{-\infty}^{t} i(\tau)\,d\tau$$

$$= Ri(t) + L\frac{di(t)}{dt} + \frac{1}{C}\int_{0}^{t} i(\tau)\,d\tau + v_C(0). \qquad (4.36)$$

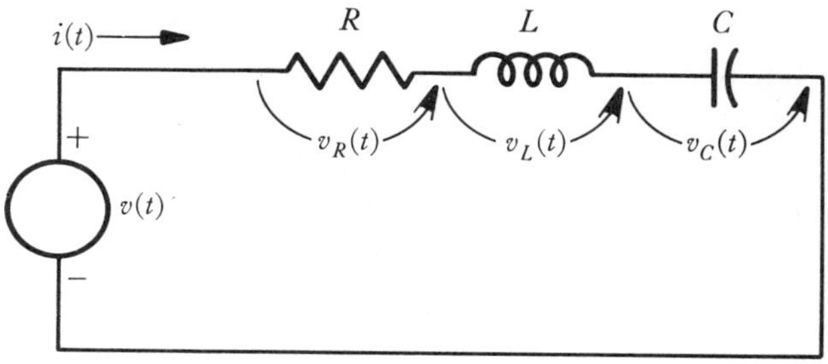

Fig. 4.13   *The R-L-C series circuit.*

The *order* of an integro-differential equation is the order of the highest derivative of any response after all integrations have been removed by: (1) successive differentiation of both sides of the equation; or (2) by the substitution of a new response variable which represents enough successive differentiations of the old to remove all integrations. The latter test may be applied to Eq. (4.36) by the substitution of capacitor charge, related to the current by

$$i(t) = \frac{dq_C(t)}{dt}.$$

Such a substitution yields

$$v(t) = R \frac{dq_C(t)}{dt} + L \frac{d^2 q_C(t)}{dq^2} + \frac{1}{C} q_C(t),$$

with the higher derivative of the response variable being the second, indicating that the system is second-order. The same result accrues when both sides of the equation are differentiated once to yield

$$\frac{dv(t)}{dt} = R \frac{di(t)}{dt} + L \frac{d^2 i(t)}{dt} + \frac{1}{C} i(t).$$

The Natural Response

We shall proceed with the solution of this second-order system for exponential forcing functions just as we did for the first-order *R-L* and *R-C* circuits. However, we first must become aware of a significant difference in the nature of the natural response. Assume first that the same form as previously found to give results will also work in this case. Then

$$i_n(t) = I_n e^{mt}.$$

Substituted into Eq. (4.36), this gives rise to

$$\left(R + Lm + \frac{1}{mC}\right) I_n = 0,$$

or that

$$m^2 + \frac{R}{L} m + \frac{1}{LC} = 0. \tag{4.37}$$

Factoring, we have

$$(m - m_1)(m - m_2) = 0, \tag{4.37a}$$

where

$$m_1 = \frac{-R}{2L} + \sqrt{\frac{R^2}{4L^2} - \frac{1}{LC}} = \frac{-R}{2L} + j\sqrt{\frac{1}{LC} - \frac{R^2}{4L^2}} \qquad (4.38a)$$

$$m_2 = \frac{-R}{2L} - \sqrt{\frac{R^2}{4L^2} - \frac{1}{LC}} = \frac{-R}{2L} - j\sqrt{\frac{1}{LC} - \frac{R^2}{4L^2}}. \qquad (4.38b)$$

The result of the original assumption is to show its insufficiency, since it is satisfied not by one value for the exponent but by two, corresponding to $m = m_1$ and $m = m_2$. This means that there are usually two exponentials, which when substituted into the second-order integro-differential equation, provide a zero or natural solution, and a complete solution must include both of them. Therefore, we back off from the original assumption and restate the natural response for all cases except that in which $m_1 = m_2$. That is, set

$$i_n(t) = I_{n1} e^{m_1 t} + I_{n2} e^{m_2 t}, \qquad t > 0, \qquad m_1 \neq m_2. \qquad (4.39)$$

In considering the nature of Eq. (4.39) at greater length, it may be helpful to simplify Eqs. (4.38) to the forms

$$m_1 = -\alpha + \sqrt{\gamma^2} \qquad (4.40a)$$

$$m_2 = -\alpha - \sqrt{\gamma^2}, \qquad (4.40b)$$

where

$$\alpha = \frac{R}{2L} \qquad (4.41a)$$

$$\gamma^2 = \frac{R^2}{4L^2} - \frac{1}{LC}$$

$$= \alpha^2 - \frac{1}{LC}. \qquad (4.41b)$$

Clearly, γ^2 may be positive, it may be negative, or it may be zero. Which of these it is has considerable effect on the nature of the response, as we shall see in the next article when we consider each possibility in turn as a special case.

The Source-Free Behavior

In the source-free case, $v(t)$ in Fig. 4.13 is zero, so that any current variations observed are those resulting from energy storage in inductors and capacitors prior to our observation. Under such conditions the behavior contains no forced response, just natural response, and Eq. (4.36) becomes

$$0 = R i_n(t) + L \frac{d i_n(t)}{dt} + \frac{1}{C} \int_0^t i_n(\tau) \, d\tau + v_C(0). \qquad (4.42)$$

Substituting Eq. (4.39) results in

$$0 = \left(R + m_1 L + \frac{1}{m_1 C}\right) I_{n1} e^{m_1 t} + \left(R + m_2 L + \frac{1}{m_2 C}\right) I_{n2} e^{m_2 t}$$

$$- \left(\frac{I_{n1}}{m_1 C} + \frac{I_{n2}}{m_2 C}\right) + v_C(0), \tag{4.43a}$$

or

$$0 = Z(m_1) I_{n1} e^{m_1 t} + Z(m_2) I_{n2} e^{m_2 t} - \left(\frac{I_{n1}}{m_1 C} + \frac{I_{n2}}{m_2 C}\right) + v_C(0), \tag{4.43b}$$

where

$$Z(m) = R + mL + \frac{1}{mC} \ \Omega \tag{4.44}$$

is called the *impedance function* characterizing this *R-L-C* series circuit.

From Eqs. (4.37), $Z(m_1)$ and $Z(m_2)$ are clearly zero by definition. Therefore, Eq. (4.43) yields

$$\frac{I_{n1}}{m_1} + \frac{I_{n2}}{m_2} = C v_C(0) = q_C(0), \tag{4.45a}$$

and evaluating Eq. (4.39) at $t = 0$ results in

$$I_{n1} + I_{n2} = \lim_{t \to 0} i(t) = i(0). \tag{4.45b}$$

Now the two constants, I_{n1} and I_{n2}, may be determined, since we have two equations in two unknowns. It may be helpful in the consideration of the three special cases to establish the result in general terms, which is done by solving Eqs. (4.45) for the two currents,

$$I_{n1} = \frac{m_1}{m_1 - m_2} \left[i(0) - m_2 q_C(0)\right] \tag{4.46a}$$

$$I_{n2} = \frac{m_2}{m_2 - m_1} \left[i(0) - m_1 q_C(0)\right]. \tag{4.46b}$$

Notice that one of these equations derives from the other by a simple interchange of m_1 with m_2.

CASE I. m_1 and m_2 are Real.
Suppose that

$$\frac{R^2}{4L^2} > \frac{1}{LC}, \tag{4.47a}$$

which, by Eq. (4.41b), is equivalent to

$$\gamma^2 > 0. \tag{4.47b}$$

Then Eqs. (4.40) may be written

$$m_1 = -\alpha + |\gamma| = -b < 0 \tag{4.48a}$$
$$m_2 = -\alpha - |\gamma| = -c < -b < 0. \tag{4.48b}$$

In this case the natural response of Eq. (4.39) takes the form

$$i(t) = i_n(t) = I_{n1}e^{-bt} + I_{n2}e^{-ct}, \qquad t > 0. \tag{4.49}$$

The condition of Eq. (4.47a) characterizes the *overdamped* second-order system having two decaying real exponentials in the natural response.

EXAMPLE 4.7. In the circuit of Fig. 4.14, the switch has been in position 1 for a long time prior to $t = 0$, at which time it is suddenly changed to position 2.

a. Find $i(t)$ for $t > 0$ and plot the result.
b. Find the total energy dissipated by the resistor between $t = 0$ and $t = \infty$ and compare with the initial energy stored in the capacitor and inductor.

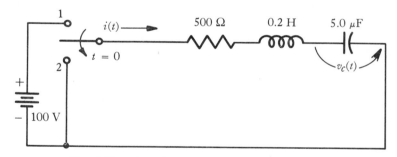

Fig. 4.14 *Natural response in an R-L-C series circuit.*

Solution.

1. Find $i(0)$ and $v_C(0)$ by the methods of Art. 4.3, then compute $q_C(0)$.

$$i(0) = 0 \qquad v_C(0) = 100 \text{ V}$$
$$q_C(0) = Cv_C(0) = 5 \times 10^{-6}(100) = 5 \times 10^{-4}C.$$

2. Find m_1 and m_2.
   Set

$$Z(m) = 500 + 0.2m + \frac{10^6}{5m} = 0,$$

from which

$$m^2 + 2500m + 10^6 = 0.$$

The roots are

$$m_1 = -500 \text{ sec}^{-1} \qquad m_2 = -2000 \text{ sec}^{-1}.$$

3.   Compute I_{n1} and I_{n2}.

$$I_{n1} = \frac{m_1}{m_1 - m_2} [i(0) - m_2 q_C(0)]$$

$$= \frac{-500}{-500 + 2000} [0 + 2000(5 \times 10^{-4})]$$

$$= -\tfrac{1}{3}$$

$$I_{n2} = \frac{m_2}{m_2 - m_1} [i(0) - m_1 q_C(0)]$$

$$= \frac{-2000}{-2000 + 500} [0 + 500(5 \times 10^{-4})]$$

$$= +\tfrac{1}{3}.$$

4.   Write the total current,

$$i(t) = i_n(t) = I_{n1} e^{m_1 t} + I_{n2} e^{m_2 t}$$
$$= \tfrac{1}{3}[e^{-2000t} - e^{-500t}]A, \qquad t > 0. \qquad Ans.$$

5.   Plot the current response as in Fig. 4.15.
6.   Compute and compare energy dissipation in the resistor with initial
       energy stored in the capacitor since the inductor has no stored energy
       initially.

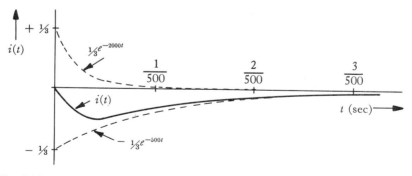

Fig. 4.15   *Current response for the overdamped R-L-C series circuit in Fig. 4.14.*

The resistor power for $t > 0$ is

$$p_R(t) = Ri^2(t) = \frac{500}{9}\left[e^{-4000t} - 2e^{-2500t} + e^{-1000t}\right].$$

The energy dissipated by the resistor is

$$w_R(\infty) = \int_0^\infty p_R(t)\, dt$$

$$= \frac{500}{9}\left[\frac{-e^{-4000t}}{4000} + \frac{2e^{-2500t}}{2500} - \frac{e^{-1000t}}{1000}\right]_0^\infty$$

$$= 0.025 \text{ J.} \qquad Ans.$$

The energy initially stored in the capacitor is

$$w_C(0) = \tfrac{1}{2}Cv_C^2(0)$$

$$= \tfrac{1}{2}(5 \times 10^{-6})(100)^2 = 0.025 \text{ J.} \qquad Ans.$$

Example 4.7 above illustrates the principle that initial stored energies in the sourceless circuit are dissipated as heat in the resistors of the circuit.

CASE II. m_1 and m_2 are Complex.
If

$$\frac{R^2}{4L^2} < \frac{1}{LC}, \tag{4.50a}$$

so that

$$\gamma^2 < 0, \tag{4.50b}$$

then Eqs. (4.40) become

$$m_1 = -\alpha + j|\gamma| = -\alpha + j\beta \tag{4.51a}$$

$$m_2 = -\alpha - j|\gamma| = -\alpha - j\beta = m_1^*, \tag{4.51b}$$

where the asterisk indicates the conjugate of a complex number.

Substituted into Eq. (4.39), the above equations produce

$$i(t) = i_n(t) = e^{-\alpha t}(I_{n1}e^{j\beta t} + I_{n2}e^{-j\beta t}). \tag{4.52}$$

In order for this to remain a real signal, I_{n1} and I_{n2} must be either equal real numbers or complex conjugates. The first possibility is a special case of the second, so we may cover both by setting

$$I_{n1} = I_{nr} + jI_{ni} = I_n e^{j\theta} \tag{4.53a}$$

$$I_{n2} = I_{nr} - jI_{ni} = I_n e^{-j\theta} = I_{n1}^*, \tag{4.53b}$$

where I_{nr} and I_{ni} are both real and where

$$I_n = \sqrt{I_{nr}^2 + I_{ni}^2} \tag{4.54a}$$

$$\theta = \tan^{-1} \frac{I_{ni}}{I_{nr}}. \tag{4.54b}$$

Now Eq. (4.52) may be rewritten

$$i_n(t) = e^{-\alpha t}[(I_{nr} + jI_{ni})e^{j\beta t} + (I_{nr} - jI_{ni})e^{-j\beta t}]$$

$$= e^{-\alpha t}\left[2I_{nr}\frac{e^{j\beta t} + e^{-j\beta t}}{2} - 2I_{ni}\frac{e^{j\beta t} - e^{j\beta t}}{2j}\right]$$

$$= e^{-\alpha t}(2I_{nr}\cos\beta t - 2I_{ni}\sin\beta t), \qquad t > 0. \tag{4.55a}$$

An alternative form, when the exponential forms of I_{n1} and I_{n2} are employed, is

$$i_n(t) = e^{-\alpha t}(I_n e^{j\theta}e^{j\beta t} + I_n e^{-j\theta}e^{-j\beta t})$$

$$= 2I_n e^{-\alpha t}\frac{e^{j(\beta t + \theta)} + e^{-j(\beta t + \theta)}}{2}$$

$$= 2I_n e^{-\alpha t}\cos(\beta t + \theta), \qquad t > 0. \tag{4.55b}$$

In the above forms we see that the arbitrary constants I_{n1} and I_{n2} have been replaced in one case by the arbitrary constants I_{nr} and I_{ni} and in the other case by the arbitrary constants I_n and θ.

The conditions of Eqs. (4.50) are those of the *underdamped* second-order system, which has a decaying sinusoid as its natural response. Such systems contain terms of the form

$$f(t) = Ae^{-(t/T)}\cos(\omega t + \theta_C) = Ae^{-(t/T)}\sin(\omega t + \theta_S).$$

This is simply a sinusoid of amplitude $Ae^{-(t/T)}$, or a sinusoidal curve of variable amplitude and constant frequency whose period is $2\pi/\omega$ seconds. The curve describing the amplitude and its reflection below the axis form the *envelope* of the decaying sinusoid as shown by the dotted curves of Fig. 4.16. Each maximum and minimum point of the sinusoid becomes a point on the envelope located at $\pi/2$ radians from a zero crossing of the sinusoid. The plotting procedure is to plot the envelope curves exactly as the exponentials in the previous examples, then to fit the sinusoid within the envelope as shown in Fig. 4.16.

EXAMPLE 4.8. Repeat Part (a) of Example 4.7 with the circuit resistance reduced to 240 Ω.

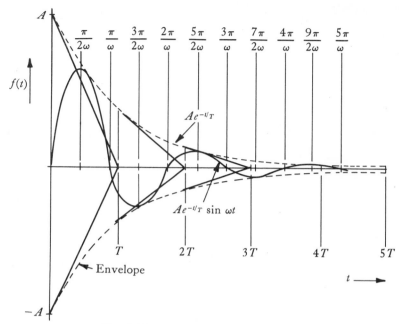

Fig. 4.16   *Plot of $Ae^{-t/T} \sin \omega t$ for $t > 0$.*

Solution.

1.   Find initial conditions as in Example 4.7.

$$i(0) = 0 \qquad v_C(0) = 100 \text{ V}$$

$$q_C(0) = 5 \times 10^{-4} \text{ C}.$$

2.   Find m_1 and m_2.
      From

$$Z(m) = 240 + 0.2m + \frac{10^6}{5m} = 0,$$

      we have

$$m^2 + 1200m + 10^6 = 0,$$

      with roots

$$m_1 = -\alpha + j\beta = -600 + j800 \text{ sec}^{-1}$$

$$m_2 = -\alpha - j\beta = -600 - j800 \text{ sec}^{-1}.$$

3.   Since the previous step yields complex roots, find $I_{n1} = I_{n2}^*$, then find I_{nr} and I_{ni} or I_n and θ as defined by Eqs. (4.53).

$$I_{n1} = I_{n2}^* = \frac{m_1}{m_1 - m_2}[i(0) - m_2 q_C(0)]$$

$$= \frac{-600 + j800}{(-600 + j800) - (-600 - j800)}$$
$$\times [0 - (-600 - j800)(5 \times 10^{-4})]$$
$$= \tfrac{5}{16} e^{j90°} = 0 + j \tfrac{5}{16}$$
$$= I_n e^{j\theta} = I_{nr} + jI_{ni}.$$

Therefore,

$$2I_{nr} = 0 \qquad 2I_{ni} = 5,$$

or

$$2I_n = \tfrac{5}{8} \qquad \theta = 90°.$$

4. Write the resultant current from Eqs. (4.55)

$$i(t) = i_n(t) = e^{-\alpha t}(2I_{nr} \cos \beta t - 2I_{ni} \sin \beta t)$$
$$= e^{-600t}(0 - \tfrac{5}{8} \sin 800t)$$
$$= -\tfrac{5}{8} e^{-600t} \sin 800t \text{ A}, \qquad t > 0, \qquad Ans.$$

or

$$i(t) = i_n(t) = 2I_n e^{-\alpha t} \cos (\beta t + \theta)$$
$$= \tfrac{5}{8} e^{-600t} \cos (800t + 90°)$$
$$= -\tfrac{5}{8} e^{-600t} \sin 800t \text{ A}, \qquad t > 0. \qquad Ans.$$

5. Plot the result as in Fig. 4.17.

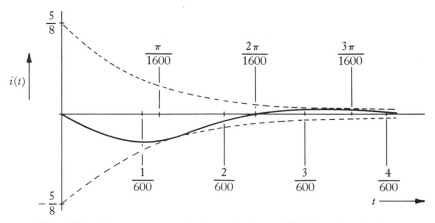

Fig. 4.17 *Current response for the underdamped R-L-C series circuit.*

EXAMPLE 4.9. Repeat Part (a) of Example 4.7 with the circuit resistance reduced to zero. Also find the instantaneous coil and capacitor voltages and the total stored energy as a function of time. Compare the instantaneous total stored energy with the initial stored energy.

Solution.

1. Find initial conditions as in Example 4.7.

$$i(0) = 0 \qquad v_C(0) = 100 \text{ V}$$

$$q_C(0) = 5 \times 10^{-4} \text{ C}.$$

2. Find m_1 and m_2.
   From

$$Z(m) = 0 + 0.2m + \frac{10^6}{5m} = 0,$$

we have

$$m^2 + 10^6 = 0$$

with roots

$$m_1 = -\alpha + j\beta = 0 + j1000 \text{ sec}^{-1}$$

$$m_2 = -\alpha - j\beta = 0 - j1000 \text{ sec}^{-1}.$$

3. Since the roots above are complex, find I_{nr} and I_{ni} or I_n and θ as in the previous example.

$$I_{n1} = I_{n2}^* = \frac{m_1}{m_1 - m_2}[i(0) - m_2 q_C(0)]$$

$$= \frac{j1000}{j1000 - (-j1000)}[0 - (-j1000)(5 \times 10^{-4})]$$

$$= 0 + j0.25 = 0.25e^{j90°}$$

$$= I_{nr} + jI_{ni} = I_n e^{j\theta}.$$

Therefore,

$$2I_{nr} = 0 \qquad 2I_{ni} = 0.5,$$

or

$$2I_n = 0.5 \qquad \theta = 90°.$$

4.   Write the resultant current,

$$i(t) = i_n(t) = e^{-\alpha t}(2I_{nr} \cos \beta t - 2I_{ni} \sin \beta t)$$
$$= e^{-0}(0 - 0.5 \sin 1000t)$$
$$= -0.5 \sin 1000t, \qquad t > 0, \qquad Ans.$$

or

$$i(t) = i_n(t) = 2I_n e^{-\alpha t} \cos (\beta t + \theta)$$
$$= 0.5e^{-0} \cos (1000t + 90°)$$
$$= -0.5 \sin 1000t \text{ A}, \qquad t > 0. \qquad Ans.$$

5.   The plot of $i(t)$ is simply a negative sine wave of zero phase angle having a maximum value of 0.5 A and a radian frequency of 1000 rad per sec.

6.   Find the coil voltage, $v_L(t)$, for $t > 0$.

$$v_L(t) = L \frac{di(t)}{dt}$$

$$= 0.2 \frac{d}{dt}(-0.5 \sin 1000t)$$

$$= -100 \cos 1000t \text{ V}, \qquad t > 0. \qquad Ans.$$

7.   Find the condenser voltage, $v_C(t)$, for $t > 0$.

$$v_C(t) = \frac{1}{C} \int_{-\infty}^{t} i(\tau) \, d\tau$$

$$= \frac{1}{C} \int_{0}^{t} i(\tau) \, d\tau + v_C(0)$$

$$= \frac{10^6}{5} \int_{0}^{t} (-0.5 \sin 1000\tau) \, d\tau + 100$$

$$= 100 \cos 1000\tau]_0^t + 100$$

$$= 100 \cos 1000t \text{ V}, \qquad t > 0. \qquad Ans.$$

8.   Compute the total stored energy.

$$w(t) = w_L(t) + w_C(t)$$
$$= \tfrac{1}{2}Li^2(t) + \tfrac{1}{2}Cv_C^2(t)$$
$$= \tfrac{1}{2}[0.2(-0.5)^2 \sin^2 1000t + (5 \times 10^{-6})(100)^2 \cos^2 1000t]$$
$$= \frac{1}{2}\left[\frac{0.05}{2}(1 - \cos 2000t) + \frac{0.05}{2}(1 + \cos 2000t)\right]$$
$$= 0.025 \text{ J}. \qquad Ans.$$

9.   Compare above stored energy with initial stored energy.

$$w(0) = w_L(0) + w_C(0)$$
$$= \tfrac{1}{2}[Li^2(0) + Cv_C^2(0)]$$
$$= \tfrac{1}{2}[0 + (5 \times 10^{-6})(100)^2] = 0.025 \text{ J.}$$

Therefore,

$$w(t) = w(0). \qquad Ans.$$

Example 4.9 above has been an example of the *undamped*, or *lossless*, circuit. The first form of description is appropriate because the exponential which normally caused the response to decay, or to be *damped*, is zero. The second is appropriate because the lack of resistance precludes the loss of energy in the form of heat. Therefore, the initially stored energy cannot be dissipated and is simply exchanged in a periodic fashion between the coil and the capacitor, as indicated by the results of the example.

Of course, there is no such thing as a truly resistanceless coil. However, there are coils with very low resistances, so that decays are slow enough to be neglected over some limited interval of time. In fact, in the field of cryogenics, dealing with materials at temperatures near absolute zero, one encounters *superconducting* coils with no measurable resistance.

CASE III. $m_1 = m_2 = m_0$.
When

$$\frac{R^2}{4L^2} = \frac{1}{LC}, \tag{4.56a}$$

so that

$$\gamma^2 = 0, \tag{4.56b}$$

setting $Z(m) = 0$ results in a perfect square. Then we have the multiple root,

$$m_1 = m_2 = m_0. \tag{4.57}$$

If we conclude that this is a simple case of $I_{n1} = I_{n2}$, and nothing more, we are immediately in trouble because Eqs. (4.45) become insoluble due to their determinant being zero. Our trouble arises because we have violated a basic rule in the theory of differential equations, the rule stating that the number of arbitrary constants to be evaluated in the complete solution is equal to the order of the equation. In this case the order is two and the assumption of a single exponential with the associated single arbitrary constant violates the rule. The only conclusion remaining is that the single exponential must be joined by a time-varying term of a different form to complete the solution.

It is for these reasons that the qualification that $m_1 \neq m_2$ was made for Eq. (4.39). To circumvent the difficulty, let us allow one of the more tractable previous cases to approach this one as a limit. As we do this, we must recognize that changing m to approach this limit involves changes in the coefficients I_{n1} and I_{n2} as well as in the exponents, so in this particular case we shall evaluate the two arbitrary constants, I_{n1} and I_{n2}, prior to taking the limits $m_1 \to m_0$ and $m_2 \to m_0$.

Suppose m_1 and m_2 are the complex pair

$$m_1 = m_0 + j\sigma$$

$$m_2 = m_0 - j\sigma.$$

Substitution into Eqs. (4.46) yields

$$I_{n1} = \frac{m_0 + j\sigma}{2j\sigma} i(0) - \frac{m_0^2 + \sigma^2}{2j\sigma} q_C(0),$$

and

$$I_{n2} = I_{n1}^*.$$

The natural response is then

$$i_n(t) = I_{n1}e^{m_1 t} + I_{n2} e^{m_2 t}$$

$$= i(0)e^{m_0 t} \frac{e^{j\sigma t} + e^{-j\sigma t}}{2}$$

$$+ [m_0 i(0) - (m_0^2 + \sigma^2)q_C(0)]e^{m_0 t} \frac{e^{j\sigma t} - e^{-j\sigma t}}{2j\sigma}$$

$$= i(0)e^{m_0 t} \cos \sigma t + [m_0 i(0) - (m_0^2 + \sigma^2)q_C(0)]t e^{m_0 t} \frac{\sin \sigma t}{\sigma t}.$$

It is shown in any calculus text that

$$\lim_{x \to 0} \frac{\sin x}{x} = 1.$$

Therefore, as we let σ approach zero the response approaches

$$i(t) = i_n(t) = i(0)e^{m_0 t} + m_0[i(0) - m_0 q_C(0)]t e^{m_0 t}. \tag{4.58}$$

The above result shows that the time-varying form referred to earlier as a necessary addition to the single exponential is of the form $t e^{m_0 t}$. The two arbitrary constants have already been conveniently evaluated using this approach. Incidentally, this result also provides the clue for removing the constraint, $a \neq m$, in Eqs. (4.13) and (4.26).

The Exponential Forcing Function

The most common type of forcing signals employed by engineers can be expressed as exponential forms, limits of exponential forms, or combinations of exponentials. For example, if in Fig. 4.13 the current is computed assuming the forcing voltage

$$v(t) = V e^{at}, \qquad t > 0, \tag{4.59}$$

the results may be used to cover many other forcing voltages.

Examples of forcing signals derivable from the exponential signal of Eq. (4.59) are

$$
\begin{aligned}
v_a(t) &= V, \qquad t > 0 \\
&= \lim_{a \to 0} v(t) \\
&= v(t)|_{a=0}.
\end{aligned}
\tag{4.59a}
$$

$$
\begin{aligned}
v_b(t) &= V_m \cos \omega t, \qquad t > 0 \\
&= \tfrac{1}{2}[V_m e^{j\omega t} + V_m e^{-j\omega t}], \qquad t > 0 \\
&= \frac{1}{2}\left[v(t)\Big|_{\substack{a=j\omega \\ V=V_m}} + v(t)\Big|_{\substack{a=-j\omega \\ V=V_m}} \right].
\end{aligned}
\tag{4.59b}
$$

$$
\begin{aligned}
v_c(t) &= V_m \cos(\omega t + \theta), \qquad t > 0 \\
&= \tfrac{1}{2}[V_m e^{j\theta} e^{j\omega t} + V_m e^{-j\theta} e^{-j\omega t}] \\
&= \frac{1}{2}\left[v(t)\Big|_{\substack{a=j\omega \\ V=V_m e^{j\theta}}} + v(t)\Big|_{\substack{a=-j\omega \\ V=V_m e^{-j\theta}}} \right].
\end{aligned}
\tag{4.59c}
$$

When the latter two cases are considered, one simply makes two calculations using the separate exponential forms, then employs the principle of superposition to effect the combined results. In this regard, if we take the symbol $\Rightarrow$ to mean *implies that* or *leads to*, then:

$$
\left.
\begin{aligned}
\text{If} \qquad\qquad\quad & v_1(t) \Rightarrow i_1(t) \\
\text{and} \qquad\qquad\quad & v_2(t) \Rightarrow i_2(t), \\
\text{then} \quad v(t) = v_1(t) + v_2(t) & \Rightarrow i(t) = i_1(t) + i_2(t).
\end{aligned}
\right\}
\tag{4.60}
$$

This is simply a restatement of the principle of superposition.

The Forced Response

For reasons which should be clear from the preceding paragraphs, the forcing function will be presumed to be the exponential form of Eq. (4.59).

When a nonzero forcing voltage is applied, the response will consist of both forced and natural components, just as it did for the two-element-kind case. However, the natural response contributes a net of nothing to the voltage balance, as indicated by Eq. (4.42), so we may, for present purposes, concentrate on the forced current, which will have the same form as the forcing voltage; that is,

$$i_f(t) = I_f e^{at}, \qquad t > 0. \tag{4.61}$$

Substituted in the voltage-balance equation, (4.36), along with the assumed form of forcing voltage, this yields

$$Ve^{at} = \left(R + aL + \frac{1}{aC} \right) I_f e^{at} + \text{other terms},$$

where none of the *other terms* contain the factor e^{at}. Since the coefficient of e^{at} on the left must match that on the right, we have

$$V = \left(R + aL + \frac{1}{aC} \right) I_f = Z(a) I_f, \tag{4.62}$$

and

$$I_f = \frac{V}{Z(a)}. \tag{4.63}$$

This result is independent from the natural response and initial conditions, which are imbedded in the *other terms* above. This result is also consistent with Eqs. (4.22a) and (4.32a) where

$$Z(a) = R + aL$$

and

$$Z(a) = R + \frac{1}{aC},$$

respectively.

EXAMPLE 4.10. In Fig. 4.13,

$$R = 500 \ \Omega \qquad v(t) = 100e^{-100t}, \qquad t > 0$$
$$L = 0.2 \ \text{H}$$
$$C = 5.0 \ \mu\text{F}.$$

Find $i_f(t)$.

Solution. Using the impedance function,

$$Z(a) = R + aL + \frac{1}{aC}$$

$$= 500 + (-100)(0.2) + \frac{1}{(-100)(5 \times 10^{-6})}$$

$$= -1520 \ \Omega,$$

we can determine the amplitude

$$I_f = \frac{V}{Z(a)} = \frac{100}{-1520} = -0.0658 \ \text{A},$$

and the forcing current

$$i_f(t) = I_f e^{at} = -0.0658 e^{-100t} \ \text{A}, \qquad t > 0. \qquad Ans.$$

EXAMPLE 4.11. Repeat Example 4.10, except change the forcing voltage to

$$v(t) = 100, \qquad t > 0.$$

Solution. By Eq. (4.59a), $a = 0$, so

$$Z(a) = Z(0) = R + (0)L + \frac{1}{(0)C} = \infty,$$

and

$$I_f = \frac{V}{Z(0)} = \frac{V}{\infty} = 0.$$

Therefore,

$$i_f(t) = I_f e^{at} = 0, \qquad t > 0. \qquad Ans.$$

The General Case

The complete solution in the general case contains the forced and natural responses and accounts for the initial energy storages in the coil and the capacitor.

Since the total current is

$$i(t) = i_f(t) + i_n(t)$$
$$= I_f e^{at} + I_{n1} e^{m_1 t} + I_{n2} e^{m_2 t}, \qquad t > 0 \qquad \text{and} \qquad a \neq m_1 \neq m_2,$$

$$(4.64)$$

the voltage balance equation becomes

$$Ve^{at} = Z(a)I_f\,e^{at} + Z(m_1)I_{n1}e^{m_1 t} + Z(m_2)I_{n2}\,e^{m_2 t}$$
$$- \left(\frac{I_f}{aC} + \frac{I_{n1}}{m_1 C} + \frac{I_{n2}}{m_2 C}\right) + v_C(0). \tag{4.65}$$

The forced current amplitude, I_f, is determined by Eq. (4.63) and Eqs. (4.64) and (4.65) yield

$$I_{n1} + I_{n2} = I_0 \tag{4.66a}$$

$$\frac{I_{n1}}{m_1} + \frac{I_{n2}}{m_2} = Q_0, \tag{4.66b}$$

where

$$I_0 = i(0) - I_f \tag{4.67a}$$

$$Q_0 = q_C(0) - \frac{I_f}{a} = Cv_C(0) - \frac{I_f}{a}. \tag{4.67b}$$

Notice that the form of Eqs. (4.66) is the same as that of the force-free case in Eqs. (4.45), except that $i(0)$ has been replaced by I_0 and $q_C(0)$ has been replaced by Q_0. Consequently, we have the following equations corresponding to Eqs. (4.45):

$$\frac{I_{n1}}{m_1} + \frac{I_{n2}}{m_2} = Q_0 \tag{4.68a}$$

$$I_{n1} + I_{n2} = I_0. \tag{4.68b}$$

Corresponding to Eqs. (4.46), we have

$$I_{n1} = \frac{m_1}{m_1 - m_2}\,(I_0 - m_2 Q_0) \tag{4.69a}$$

$$I_{n2} = \frac{m_2}{m_2 - m_1}\,(I_0 - m_1 Q_0). \tag{4.69b}$$

The current form of Eq. (4.64) suffices to complete the picture, except that special critically-damped Case III should be restated, since it involves a change in form. It follows from Eq. (4.58) that

$$i(t) = i_f(t) + i_n(t)$$
$$= I_f e^{at} + I_0 e^{m_0 t} + m_0(I_0 - m_0 Q_0)te^{m_0 t}, \tag{4.70}$$

when

$$m_0 = m_1 = m_2$$

and

$$a \neq m_0.$$

If

$$a = m_1 = m_2 = m_0,$$

then another time form results; namely, $t^2 e^{m_0 t}$.

EXAMPLE 4.12. In the circuit of Fig. 4.13,

$$R = 240 \ \Omega \qquad v(t) = 100e^{-100t} \ \text{V}, \qquad t > 0$$

$$L = 0.2 \ \text{H} \qquad i(0) = 0.1 \ \text{A}$$

$$C = 5.0 \ \mu\text{F} \qquad v_C(0) = 50 \ \text{V}.$$

Find $i(t)$ for $t > 0$.

Solution.

1. Find I_f, the amplitude of the forced current. Since $a = -100 \ \text{sec}^{-1}$ and $V = 100 \ \text{V}$,

$$Z(a) = R + aL + \frac{1}{aC}$$

$$= 240 + (-100)(0.2) + \frac{10^6}{(-100)(5)}$$

$$= -1780 \ \Omega,$$

and

$$I_f = \frac{V}{Z(a)} = \frac{100}{-1780} = -0.0562 \ \text{A}.$$

2. Find I_0 and Q_0.

$$I_0 = i(0) - I_f$$
$$= 0.1 - (-0.0562) = 0.1562 \ \text{A}$$

$$q_C(0) = C v_C(0) = 5 \times 10^{-6}(50) = 2.5 \times 10^{-4} \ \text{C}$$

$$Q_0 = q_C(0) - \frac{I_f}{a}$$

$$= 2.5 \times 10^{-4} - \frac{-0.0562}{-100} = -3.12 \times 10^{-4} \ \text{C}.$$

3.   Find m_1 and m_2.
      Set

$$Z(m) = 240 + 0.2m + \frac{10^6}{5m} = 0,$$

resulting in

$$m^2 + 1200m + 10^6 = 0,$$

which has the roots

$$m_1 = -\alpha + j\beta = -600 + j800 \text{ sec}^{-1}$$
$$m_2 = -\alpha - j\beta = -600 - j800 \text{ sec}^{-1}.$$

4.   Since the values of m_1 and m_2 are complex, find I_{nr} and I_{ni} or I_n and θ (we'll find both!):

$$2I_{n1} = 2I_{n2}^* = \frac{2m_1}{m_1 - m_2}(I_0 - m_2 Q_0)$$

$$= 2 \frac{-600 + j800}{(-600 + j800) - (-600 - j800)}$$
$$\times [0.1562 - (-600 - j800)(-3.12 \times 10^{-4}]$$
$$= 0.1562 - j0.273 = 0.315e^{-j60.2°} \text{ A}$$
$$= 2(I_{nr} + jI_{ni}) = 2I_n e^{j\theta}.$$

Therefore,

$$2I_{nr} = 0.1562 \text{ A} \qquad 2I_{ni} = -0.273 \text{ A},$$

or

$$2I_n = 0.315 \text{ A} \qquad \theta = -60.2°.$$

5.   Write the complete solution.

$$i(t) = i_f(t) + i_n(t)$$
$$= I_f e^{at} + e^{-at}(2I_{nr} \cos \beta t - 2I_{ni} \sin \beta t)$$
$$= -0.0562e^{-100t}$$
$$+ e^{-600t}(0.1562 \cos 800t + 0.273 \sin 800t) \text{ A},$$
$$t > 0, \qquad Ans.$$

or

$$i(t) = i_f(t) + i_n(t)$$
$$= I_f e^{at} + 2I_n e^{-at} \cos (\beta t + \theta)$$
$$= -0.0562e^{-100t}$$
$$+ 0.315e^{-600t} \cos (800t - 60.2°) \text{ A}, \qquad t > 0. \qquad Ans.$$

EXAMPLE 4.13. In the circuit of Fig. 4.13,

$$R = 400 \ \Omega \qquad v(t) = 100 \ \text{V}, \qquad t > 0$$

$$L = 0.2 \ \text{H} \qquad i(t) = 0.1 \ \text{A}$$

$$C = 5.0 \ \mu\text{F} \qquad v_C(0) = 50 \ \text{V}.$$

Find $i(t)$ for $t > 0$.

Solution.

1. Find I_f.
   Since

$$a = 0 \qquad \text{and} \qquad V = 100 \ \text{V},$$

$$Z(a) = Z(0) = \infty,$$

and

$$I_f = \frac{V}{Z(a)} = \frac{100}{\infty} = 0.$$

2. Find I_0 and Q_0.

$$I_0 = i(0) - I_f$$

$$= 0.1 - 0 = 0.1 \ \text{A}.$$

As in the previous example, $q_C(0) = 2.5 \times 10^{-4} C.$ However,

$$\frac{I_f}{a} = \frac{0}{0} = ?$$

which must be evaluated for $a = 0$. So let us write

$$\frac{I_f}{a} = \lim_{a \to 0} \frac{I_f}{a} = \lim_{a \to 0} \frac{V}{aZ(a)} = CV$$

$$= (5 \times 10^{-6})(100) = 5 \times 10^{-4} \ \text{C}.$$

Therefore,

$$Q_0 = Q_C(0) - \frac{I_f}{a}$$

$$= 2.5 \times 10^{-4} - 5 \times 10^{-4} = -2.5 \times 10^{-4} \ \text{C}.$$

3. Find m_1 and m_2.
   Setting $Z(m) = 0$ results in

$$m^2 + 2000m + 10^6 = 0,$$

which has the double root

$$m_0 = m_1 = m_2 = -1000 \ \text{sec}^{-1}.$$

4.   Find the complete response, using Eq. (4.70) because of the repeated roots above.

$$i(t) = i_f(t) + i_n(t)$$
$$= 0 + I_0 e^{m_0 t} + m_0(I_0 - m_0 Q_0)te^{m_0 t}$$
$$= 0 + 0.1e^{-1000t}$$
$$+ (-1000)[0.1 - (-1000)(-2.5 \times 10^{-4}]te^{-1000t}$$
$$= 0.1e^{-1000t} + 150te^{-1000t}$$
$$= 0.1e^{-1000t}(1 + 1500t) \text{ A}, \qquad t > 0. \qquad Ans.$$

4.9 THE *G-C-L* PARALLEL CIRCUIT

The *G-C-L* parallel circuit of Fig. 4.18, upon application of KCL, produces

$$i(t) = i_G(t) + i_C(t) + i_L(t)$$
$$= Gv(t) + C\frac{dv(t)}{dt} + \frac{1}{L}\int_{-\infty}^{t} v(\tau)\,d\tau$$
$$= Gv(t) + C\frac{dv(t)}{dt} + \frac{1}{L}\int_{0}^{t} v(\tau)\,d\tau + i_L(0). \qquad (4.71)$$

Now refer to Eq. (4.36) for the series *R-L-C* circuit. Observe that its mathematical form is identical with that of the equation above. In fact, Eq. (4.36) becomes Eq. (4.71) if we make the following replacements of letter symbols: *v* by *i*, *i* by *v*, *R* by *G*, *L* by *C*, and *C* by *L*. When this interchange of symbols for two networks produces identical mathematical forms in the describing equations, the two networks are said to be *duals* of one another, or the pair is said to be an example of *dual networks*. More will be said later on this subject of duality.

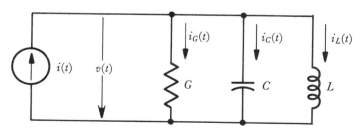

Fig. 4.18   *The G-C-L parallel circuit.*

The recognition of the property of duality allows one to very quickly deduce the responses of Eq. (4.71) based on the results which followed Eq. (4.36). Those results will be stated here, but the student is urged to verify them, and if he is truly a student, he will.

If the forcing current is of the form

$$i(t) = Ie^{at}, \qquad t > 0 \qquad \text{and} \qquad a \neq m_1 \neq m_2, \qquad (4.72)$$

then the voltage response is of the general form

$$\begin{aligned} v(t) &= v_f(t) + v_n(t) \\ &= V_f e^{at} + V_{n1} e^{m_1 t} + V_{n2} e^{m_2 t}, \qquad t > 0. \end{aligned} \qquad (4.73)$$

The forced response amplitude is

$$V_f = \frac{I}{Y(a)}, \qquad (4.74)$$

where

$$Y(a) = G + aC + \frac{1}{aL}. \qquad (4.75)$$

The constants m_1 and m_2 are determined by setting $Y(m) = 0$ just as we set $Z(m) = 0$ in the series circuit.

The arbitrary constants in the natural response are

$$V_{n1} = \frac{m_1}{m_1 - m_2}(V_0 - m_2 \Lambda_0) \qquad (4.76a)$$

$$V_{n2} = \frac{m_2}{m_2 - m_1}(V_0 - m_1 \Lambda_0), \qquad (4.76b)$$

where

$$V_0 = v(0) - V_f \qquad (4.77a)$$

and

$$\Lambda_0 = \lambda_L(0) - \frac{V_f}{a} = Li_L(0) - \frac{V_f}{a}. \qquad (4.77b)$$

The last expression contains the initial coil flux linkages,

$$\lambda_L(0) = Li_L(0). \qquad (4.78)$$

The various special cases—under-damped, over-damped, and critically-damped—should follow easily from a comparison with the series circuit expressions.

4.10 CONCLUSION

The first- and second-order series circuit has been covered in considerable detail in this chapter. When the student thinks back over the many ramifications of these simple circuits, he can well realize the complexities which will face him if he tries similar techniques with more complicated systems that have a greater number of characterizing exponents and arbitrary constants to be determined. It is rather a discouraging subject on which to ponder.

Let the student take heart, however. There are techniques available which formalize the solutions to a simple algebraic process which eliminates the mental drudgery associated with the techniques used in this chapter. This will be an *operational* technique by which considerably more complicated systems than these can be solved with considerably less work.

The method to follow will be so much simpler than those used here that the student may feel a slight resentment toward the authors for inflicting the present method upon him. However, the present method (essentially the *classical* approach) does have the advantage of continually reminding the student of the nature of the physical processes involved. It will also cause him to appreciate the forthcoming methods more than he might without having first wrestled with the classical approach.

In the next chapter we shall deal in considerable detail with the nature of a particular variety of forced response, that resulting from the application of sinusoidal forcing functions.

PROBLEMS

4.1 A 5-H coil with a resistance of 20 Ω has been connected in series with a closed switch and a 30-V battery for a long time. The switch is opened suddenly at $t = 0$. How much energy is dissipated as heat in the opening of the switch?

4.2 The switch in Fig. P.4.1 has been closed for a long time prior to $t = 0$, at which time it is opened. Find the currents $i_1(t)$ and $i_2(t)$ immediately after opening the switch and find the energy dissipated at the switch during its opening.

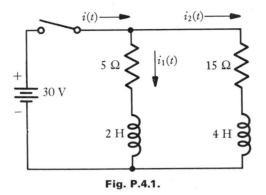

Fig. P.4.1.

4.3   In Fig. P.4.2, the switch is opened at $t = 0$ after having been closed with the circuit in equilibrium. What is $i(t)$ just after the switch is opened?

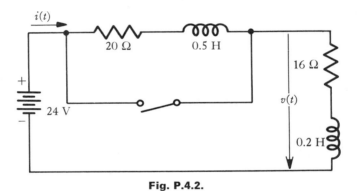

Fig. P.4.2.

4.4   The switch in Fig. P.4.3 is moved from position 1 to position 2 at $t = 0$. What are $i_1(t)$ and $i_2(t)$ just after $t = 0$?

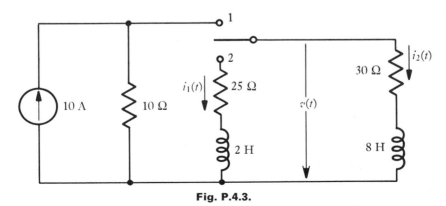

Fig. P.4.3.

4.5 In Fig. P.4.4, the switch is opened from an equilibrium condition at $t = 0$. Find $i_L(t)$, $v_{C1}(t)$, and $v_{C2}(t)$ just after $t = 0$.

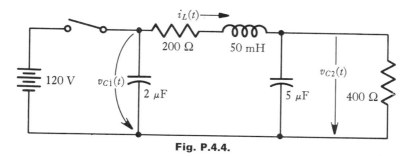

Fig. P.4.4.

4.6 The network of Fig. P.4.5 is in equilibrium when the switch is closed at $t = 0$. Find $v_1(t)$ and $v_2(t)$ just after $t = 0$. It is noted that the switch releases a snappy arc as it is closed. How much heat is dissipated?

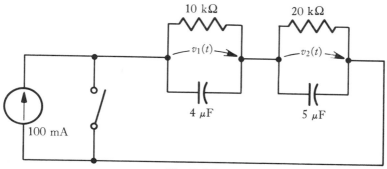

Fig. P.4.5.

4.7 Find the value of $v_2(t)$ just after $t = 0$ in Fig. P.4.6 if the switch is thrown from position 1 to position 2 at $t = 0$ after having been closed for a very long time.

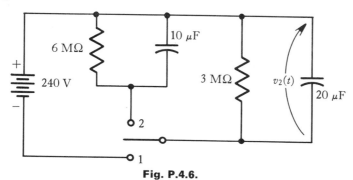

Fig. P.4.6.

4.8 A coil with an inductance, L, of 30 H and a resistance, R, of 20 Ω has a voltage of $V = 100$ V applied at $t = 0$.

    a.   What is the time constant?

    b.   Find the current and the voltage across L alone as functions of time and sketch, approximately to scale, both curves on the same graph.

    c.   List the forced and natural components of both responses in (b).

    d.   Find the stored energy as a function of time.

4.9 Repeat Prob. 4.8 when

$$L = 20 \text{ mH} \quad R = 10 \text{ k}\Omega \quad V = 50 \text{ V}.$$

4.10 Repeat Prob. 4.8 when

$$L = 25 \text{ H} \quad R = 50 \text{ }\Omega \quad V = 200 \text{ V}.$$

4.11 Repeat Prob. 4.8 when

$$L = 400 \text{ }\mu\text{H} \quad R = 10 \text{ M}\Omega \quad V = 500 \text{ V}.$$

4.12 Repeat Prob. 4.8 when

$$L = 0.5 \text{ H} \quad R = 600 \text{ }\Omega \quad V = 120 \text{ V}.$$

4.13 A 6-H coil with a resistance of 50 Ω, a constant-current source of 8 A, and an open switch are connected in parallel. The switch is closed at $t = 0$. Find the coil current for $t > 0$ and sketch as a function of time, approximately to scale.

4.14 A coil with a series ammeter of negligible resistance, a constant 20-mA current source, an infinite-resistance voltmeter, and an open switch are connected in parallel. Before $t = 0$, the voltmeter reads 40 V. The switch is closed at $t = 0$, and after 1.2 msec, the ammeter reads 5 mA. What are the resistance and inductance of the coil? What is its time constant?

4.15 A previously unexcited coil has 100 V suddenly applied to its terminals. After a lapse of 50 msec, the current is 60 mA, and after equilibrium is reached, the current is 120 mA. What are the resistance and inductance of the coil? What is its time constant?

4.16 A 10-H coil carrying 20 A has its terminals suddenly short-circuited. How much energy has been dissipated as coil heat by the time equilibrium is reached?

4.17 A 50-H coil with 1000 Ω of resistance, a voltmeter with 20,000 Ω of resistance, and a 100-V voltage source have been in parallel for a long time. At $t = 0$, the voltage source is suddenly removed. What is the voltage across the meter as a function of time for $t > 0$? Sketch the voltage curve approximately to scale.

4.18 A certain motor field coil having an inductance of 20 H and a resistance of 60 Ω carries a current of 2 amperes. Starting at $t = 0$, the current is reduced to zero in 4.0 msec. Assuming the current falls at a uniform rate, what is the voltage across the coil during this 4.0-msec interval? What is the average voltage during this time? What is the time constant of this coil?

4.19 The field coil in Prob. 4.18 is to be protected from over-voltages by permanently connecting a *field discharge resistance* across its terminals. The field current is adjusted to the same value as in Prob. 4.18. If the current to the combination of field coil in parallel with discharge resistor is assumed to go to zero instantly (as opposed to 4.0 msec in Prob. 4.18), what must be the value of the discharge resistor to limit the terminal voltage of the coil to 250 V maximum? Assuming the current is interrupted at $t = 0$, what is the terminal voltage as a function of time? Sketch the voltage curve approximately to scale.

4.20 In Fig. P.4.1, the switch is closed at $t = 0$. Find $i(t)$ for $t > 0$.

4.21 In Fig. P.4.1, the switch is opened at $t = 0$ after having been closed for a very long time. Find $i_1(t)$ and $i_2(t)$ for $t > 0$. Sketch each approximately to scale. What is the time constant of the loop formed by the two coils?

4.22 In Fig. P.4.2, the switch is opened at $t = 0$ after having been closed for a very long time. Find $i(t)$ and $v(t)$ for $t > 0$.

4.23 In Fig. P.4.3, the system has been in equilibrium until the switch is thrown from position 1 to 2 at $t = 0$. Find $i_1(t)$, $i_2(t)$, and $v(t)$ for $t > 0$. What is the time constant for $t > 0$?

4.24 An unexcited coil of 10 Ω resistance and a time constant of 2.0 msec has the voltage

$$v(t) = 1000e^{-800t}$$

applied at $t = 0$. Find the forced, natural, and total currents as functions of time.

4.25 Repeat Prob. 4.24 when

$$v(t) = 1000[e^{-800t} - e^{-100t}].$$

4.26 Find the forced current in the coil of Prob. 4.24 when

$$v(t) = 1000 \cos 1000t.$$

Express the result in the form

$$i_f(t) = I_m \cos (\omega t + \phi),$$

giving numerical values to I_m, ω, and ϕ. (Hint: Recall that $\cos x = \frac{1}{2}(e^{jx} + e^{-jx})$, where $j = \sqrt{-1}$.)

4.27 Repeat Prob. 4.26 when

$$v(t) = 1000 \sin 1000t.$$

4.28 Reverse the polarity of the 8-V battery in Example 4.2 and rework the problem.

4.29 A 2-MΩ resistor, R, and a 0.4-μF capacitor, C, are in series. A constant voltage of $V = 150$ V is suddenly applied at $t = 0$.

a. What is the time constant?

b. Find the current and the voltage across the capacitor as functions of time, and sketch, each approximately to scale, both curves on the same graph.

c. List the forced and natural components of both responses in (b).

d. Find the stored energy as a function of time.

e. Find the total energy dissipated as heat from the resistor between initial and final conditions.

4.30 Repeat Prob. 4.29 when

$$R = 10 \text{ M}\Omega \qquad C = 2 \ \mu\text{F} \qquad V = 200 \text{ V.}$$

4.31 Repeat Prob. 4.29 when

$$R = 2000 \ \Omega \qquad C = 15 \ \mu\text{F} \qquad V = 50 \text{ V.}$$

4.32 Repeat Prob. 4.29 when

$$R = 5.0 \text{ M}\Omega \qquad C = 20 \ p\text{F} \qquad V = 500 \text{ V.}$$

4.33 A 5-μF capacitor has been charged to 300 V when a 2-MΩ resistor is connected across its terminals at $t = 0$. What is the terminal voltage for $t > 0$? How much energy is dissipated as heat in the resistor during the discharging of the capacitor?

4.34 The *leakage resistance* of a capacitor is an index of the quality of the dielectric material separating the plates. It may be considered to have the effects of a resistor connected in parallel with an ideal capacitor formed by using a perfect dielectric. What is the leakage resistance of a 2-μF capacitor which on open circuit loses half its charge in 5.0 minutes?

4.35 Repeat Prob. 4.34 if the 5-μF capacitor loses half its charge in 5.0 hours.

4.36 A 100-mA current source, a closed switch, a 10-kΩ resistor, and a 4-μF capacitor are all in parallel. The switch is opened at $t = 0$. Find the capacitor voltage for $t > 0$.

4.37 In Fig. P.4.7, the switch is opened at $t = 0$ after having been closed for a long time. Find $v_C(t)$ for $t > 0$.

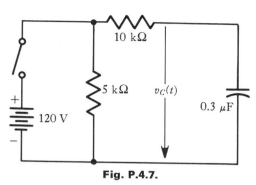

Fig. P.4.7.

4.38 In Fig. P.4.8, the switch is opened at $t = 0$ after having been closed for a long time. Find $v(t)$ for $t > 0$.

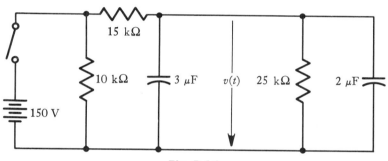

Fig. P.4.8.

4.39 In Fig. P.4.5, the switch is closed at $t = 0$ after having been opened for a long time. Find $v_1(t)$ and $v_2(t)$ for $t > 0$.

4.40 In Fig. P.4.6, the switch is thrown from position 1 to position 2 at $t = 0$. Find $v_2(t)$ for $t > 0$.

4.41 Reverse the polarity of the 50-V battery in Fig. 4.7 and rework Example 4.4.

4.42 Reverse the polarity of the 100-V battery in Fig. 4.8 and rework Example 4.5.

4.43 An initially unexcited capacitor is in series with a 20-kΩ resistor. The time constant of the combination is 200 μsec. If the voltage

$$v(t) = 500e^{-5 \times 10^4 t}$$

is applied at $t = 0$, find the forced, natural, and total currents as functions of time.

4.44 Repeat Prob. 4.43 when

$$v(t) = 500[e^{-0.05t} - e^{-0.008t}].$$

4.45 The R-C series circuit of Prob. 4.43 has the voltage

$$v(t) = 500 \cos 5000t$$

applied at $t = 0$ to the initially inert circuit. Find the current, $i(t)$, and the capacitor voltage, $v_C(t)$, taken positive in the same direction as $i(t)$, for $t > 0$. Plot on the same graph $i(t)$, $v_C(t)$, and $v(t)$.

4.46 Repeat Prob. 4.45 when

$$v(t) = 500 \sin 5000t.$$

4.47 In Fig. 4.13, the source voltage, $v(t)$, results from a battery of constant voltage V, with the polarity shown for $v(t)$, in series with a switch. The switch has been open for a long time and there is no stored energy prior to $t = 0$, at which time the switch is closed. The circuit constants are

$$V = 100 \text{ V} \qquad L = 0.2 \text{ H}$$
$$R = 1200 \ \Omega \qquad C = 5 \ \mu\text{F}.$$

Find $i(t)$, $v_C(t)$, $v_L(t)$, and $v_R(t)$ for $t > 0$. Sketch $i(t)$ approximately to scale.

4.48 Rework Prob. 4.47 with R increased to 2000 Ω.

4.49 Rework Prob. 4.47 with R decreased to 400 Ω.

4.50 Rework Prob. 4.47 with R decreased to 120 Ω.

4.51 Repeat Prob. 4.47 when the circuit constants are

$$V = 200 \text{ V} \qquad L = 5 \ \mu\text{H}$$
$$R = 10 \ \Omega \qquad C = 0.05 \ \mu\text{F}.$$

4.52 Repeat Prob. 4.51 when C is increased by a factor of 4.0.

4.53 In Fig. 4.13,

$$v(t) = \begin{cases} 100 \text{ V}, & \text{all} \quad t < 0 \\ 0, & \quad t > 0 \end{cases}$$

and the values of R, L, and C are those of Prob. 4.51. Find $i(t)$ for $t > 0$.

4.54 Repeat Prob. 4.53 when the values of R, L, and C are those of Prob. 4.47.

4.55 Repeat Prob. 4.53 when

$$v(t) = \begin{cases} 0, & \text{all} \quad t < 0 \\ 100e^{-10^6 t}, & \quad t > 0. \end{cases}$$

4.56 In Fig. 4.2, the switch is opened at $t = 0$ after having been closed for a very long time. Find $i_L(t)$ and $v_C(t)$ for $t > 0$.

4.57 Repeat Prob. 4.56 when the 4000-Ω resistor is replaced by a 400-Ω resistor.

4.58 In Fig. 4.14, the lead to point 2 is broken and a 100-V battery inserted with the positive terminal at the bottom. Rework Example 4.7 with this change.

4.59 In Fig. 4.18,

$$i(t) = \begin{cases} 0, & t < 0 \\ 10 \text{ mA}, & t > 0 \end{cases} \qquad \begin{aligned} G &= 0.1 \ \Omega^{-1} \\ C &= 0.05 \ \mu\text{F} \\ L &= 5 \ \mu\text{H}. \end{aligned}$$

Find $v(t)$, $i_G(t)$, $i_C(t)$ and $i_L(t)$ for $t > 0$.

4.60 Repeat Prob. 4.59 when G is reduced to $0.04 \ \Omega^{-1}$.

4.61 In Prob. 4.59 the current generator is replaced by a 200-V battery, with positive terminal at the top, in series with a 20-kΩ resistor and a switch. The switch is opened at $t = 0$ after having been closed for a long time. Find $v(t)$ for $t > 0$.

4.62 In Fig. 4.13,

$$v(t) = \begin{cases} 0, & t < 0 \\ 200 \cos 800t, & t > 0 \end{cases} \qquad \begin{aligned} R &= 20 \ \Omega \\ L &= 0.2 \ \text{H} \\ C &= 5 \ \mu\text{F}. \end{aligned}$$

Find the forced components of the current and the three component voltages.

4.63 Repeat Prob. 4.62 when

$$v(t) = \begin{cases} 0, & t < 0 \\ 200 \cos 1000t, & t > 0. \end{cases}$$

4.64 Repeat Prob. 4.62 when

$$v(t) = \begin{cases} 0, & t < 0 \\ 200 \cos 1200t, & t > 0. \end{cases}$$

5

The Sinusoidal Steady State

5.1 INTRODUCTION

Why do we propose to devote an entire rather lengthy chapter to the sinusoidal steady state? Why does the response to this one type of signal form appear that important when one considers the infinite variety of signal forms that exist in nature? Those students who are in the habit of posing questions may be considering such as these at this point in their course of study.

In partial answer, it might be stated that not so long ago in electrical engineering education, this topic of sinusoidal analysis may have been considered for two or more semesters—not in just one chapter. The fact that it has been now reduced to a single chapter is not an indication of any reduction in importance. Rather it is a reflection of the inroads on available time by the increased breadth of the basic background which must be provided the neophyte electrical engineer. This does not mean that the modern student learns only that part of the steady-state sinusoidal analysis his forbears learned which is proportional to the time spent on it as a particular topic.

Whatever portion of general analysis that the modern student and his predecessor have studied in common, the latter usually obtained his general analysis in a course on *alternating-current circuits*; hence the considerably greater time requirements in the area of sinusoidal analysis.

A further justification of this chapter appears when the student considers the myriad everyday tasks being performed by electricity. The vast majority are being performed in what may be considered the sinusoidal steady state. When the student looks up to the fluorescent light above his desk, he observes the results of the sinusoidal steady state. When he goes for a refreshment, he finds the refrigerator humming away in the sinusoidal steady state. He may even be one of those students who likes to study to the tune of loud music being transported over an electromagnetic carrier which may be considered to be in the sinusoidal steady state. The list of examples is essentially without end.

Finally, we shall eventually discover that *any* periodic signal may be considered to be the sum of separate sinusoids of different frequencies, usually infinite in number. Therefore, the techniques of sinusoidal analysis become invaluable aids to the study of nonsinusoidal periodic signals.

5.2 CLASSIFICATION OF SIGNALS

The signals we have had or will have occasion to consider are exponential forms, step functions, impulses, and sinusoids, besides occasional other forms of functions of time. In practice it is customary to classify these various forms, and it is time now to become acquainted with some of the classifications. You will notice that the word *current* appears as part of some classification titles. This is a result of the historical development of the terms, since they were first applied to current and then extended to other signals. In modern usage, such adjectives as *direct-current* (*dc*) and *alternating-current* (*ac*) are not considered suitable prefixes to noncurrent circuit variables. A partial list of nonrandom signal classifications follows:

1. *Constant, or Direct-current* (*dc*), *Signal*: A signal which is constant over the range of time of interest.
2. *Periodic Signal*: A signal whose values recur at equal intervals of time. This interval of recurrence is called the *period*.
3. *Alternating, or Alternating-current* (*ac*), *Signal*: A periodic signal whose average value over an integral number of periods is zero.

5.3 PROPERTIES OF PERIODIC SIGNALS

Suppose the signal $f(t)$ is periodic, with an interval of recurrence, or period, of T. Then by the definition of a periodic signal

$$f(t) = f(t + nT), \qquad n \text{ an integer.} \tag{5.1}$$

The period, T, is the time between recurrences of the function, or the time duration of one *cycle* of the periodic function. The number of cycles each second is the *frequency*, in *Hertz*, of the periodic function and certainly is the reciprocal of the number of seconds each cycle. Therefore, the frequency is

$$f = \frac{1}{T} \text{ Hertz (Hz).} \tag{5.2}$$

The *average power* flow *into* a pair of terminals with voltage drop and current in the same direction, as in Fig. 5.1, is

$$P = [p(t)]_{\text{av}}$$

$$= \frac{1}{T} \int_{t}^{t+T} p(\tau) \, d\tau$$

$$= \frac{1}{T} \int_{t}^{t+T} v(\tau) i(\tau) \, d\tau. \tag{5.3}$$

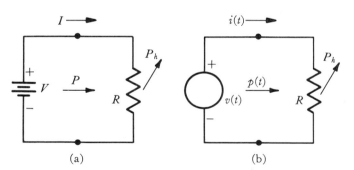

Fig. 5.1   *Illustrating effective values. (a) Direct current. (b) Periodic current.*

Assume two identical resistors in Fig. 5.1, one carrying the dc current I, due to constant voltage V, and the other carrying the periodic current $i(t)$, due to $v(t)$. Both currents are causing an average rate of dissipation of heat from each resistor which is P_h joules/sec (watts). In (a) the average dissipation is

$$P_{h_a} = P$$
$$= VI$$
$$= RI^2$$
$$= \frac{V^2}{R}, \tag{5.4}$$

and in (b) it is

$$P_{h_b} = [p(t)]_{\text{av}}$$

$$= \frac{1}{T} \int_t^{t+T} p(\tau)\, d\tau$$

$$= \frac{1}{T} \int_t^{t+T} v(\tau)i(\tau)\, d\tau$$

$$= \frac{1}{T} \int_t^{t+T} Ri^2(\tau)\, d\tau$$

$$= \frac{1}{T} \int_t^{t+T} \frac{v^2(\tau)}{R}\, d\tau. \tag{5.5}$$

If the two identical resistors dissipate the same average power, then the powers in Eqs. (5.4) and (5.5) are equal, which results in

$$I^2 = \frac{1}{T} \int_t^{t+T} i^2(\tau)\, d\tau \tag{5.6a}$$

and

$$V^2 = \frac{1}{T} \int_t^{t+T} v^2(\tau)\, d\tau. \tag{5.6b}$$

Hence, the requirement of equal average power demands that the *mean square values* of constant current and voltage equal those of the periodic current and voltage, respectively. Furthermore, the *root-mean-square* (rms) *values* of the constant current and voltage must equal the rms values of the periodic current and voltage; that is,

$$I = \sqrt{\frac{1}{T} \int_t^{t+T} i^2(\tau)\, d\tau}, \tag{5.7a}$$

and

$$V = \sqrt{\frac{1}{T} \int_t^{t+T} v^2(\tau)\, d\tau}. \tag{5.7b}$$

Thus, the rms value of a periodic current or voltage is that value of constant current or voltage which would cause the same average power dissipation in a given resistor. Consequently, the rms value is also called the *effective value*, and the names are used interchangeably.

In general, the effective value of an arbitrary signal is

$$F = \sqrt{\frac{1}{T} \int_{t}^{t+T} f^2(\tau) \, d\tau}. \tag{5.8}$$

Of course, the average square under the radical may be taken over any integral number of periods without changing the value.

Another important property of a periodic signal is its *average, or dc, value*. This is simply the average value over an integral number of periods, or

$$F_{av} = F_{dc}$$

$$= \frac{1}{T} \int_{t}^{t+T} f(\tau) \, d\tau. \tag{5.9}$$

EXAMPLE 5.1. Determine the effective and the average value of the current waveform shown in Fig. 5.2. Also calculate the average power that will be dissipated if this current flows through a 6-Ω resistor.

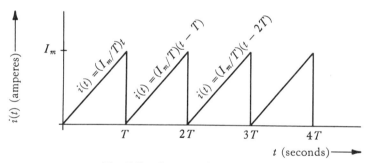

Fig. 5.2 *A sawtooth waveform.*

Solution. Using Eq. (5.7a), the effective value is

$$I = \sqrt{\frac{1}{T} \int_{0}^{T} \left(\frac{I_m}{T}\tau\right)^2 d\tau}$$

$$= \sqrt{\frac{I_m^2}{T^3} \int_{0}^{T} \tau^2 \, d\tau}$$

$$= \sqrt{\frac{I_m^2}{T^3} \left(\frac{T^3}{3}\right)}$$

$$= I_m/\sqrt{3} \text{ A.} \qquad Ans.$$

Hence, a constant current of magnitude $I_m/\sqrt{3}$ would create the same average heating effect on a given resistor as the above sawtooth current.

From Eq. (5.9) the average value is

$$I_{AV} = \frac{1}{T} \int_0^T \frac{I_m}{T} \tau d\tau$$

$$= \frac{I_m}{T^2} \left(\frac{T^2}{2}\right)$$

$$= I_m/2 \text{ A}, \qquad Ans.$$

which is less than the effective value. In fact, it can be shown that the effective value is always equal to or greater than the average value.

The average power that a 6-Ω resistor must be able to dissipate if the above current flows is, from Eq. (5.4),

$$P = 6I^2 = 6\left(\frac{I_m}{\sqrt{3}}\right)^2 = 2I_m^2 \text{ W}. \qquad Ans.$$

The periodic signal receiving special attention in this chapter is the *sinusoidal* signal, which is a sine or cosine function. Any such signal may be written in the form

$$f(t) = F_m \cos(\omega t + \phi). \tag{5.10}$$

This sinusoidal function has the *amplitude* F_m, the *radian frequency*, or *angular velocity*, ω, and the *phase angle* ϕ.

Since

$$\cos(\omega t + \phi) = \cos(\omega t + \phi + 2n\pi), \qquad n \text{ an integer,}$$

or

$$\cos\left[\omega\left(t + \frac{\phi}{\omega}\right)\right] = \cos\left[\omega\left(t + \frac{\phi}{\omega} + \frac{2n\pi}{\omega}\right)\right],$$

and from Eq. (5.1)

$$\cos\left[\omega\left(t + \frac{\phi}{\omega}\right)\right] = \cos\left[\omega\left(t + \frac{\phi}{\omega} + nT\right)\right],$$

it follows from equating the right-hand sides of these last two expressions that

$$T = \frac{2\pi}{\omega} \text{ sec} \tag{5.11}$$

and, consequently, that the radian frequency is

$$\omega = \frac{2\pi}{T} = 2\pi f \text{ rad/sec.} \tag{5.12}$$

It is left as an exercise for the student to show that the sinusoidal signal has the effective value

$$F = \frac{F_m}{\sqrt{2}}. \tag{5.13}$$

The student should also show that the average product of the two sinusoidal signals

$$f_1(t) = F_{1m} \cos (\omega t + \phi_1) = \sqrt{2}\, F_1 \cos (\omega t + \phi_1) \tag{5.14a}$$

$$f_2(t) = F_{2m} \cos (\omega t + \phi_2) = \sqrt{2}\, F_2 \cos (\omega t + \phi_2) \tag{5.14b}$$

is

$$[f_1(t)f_2(t)]_{av} = \frac{1}{T} \int_t^{t+T} f_1(\tau)f_2(\tau)\, d\tau$$

$$= F_1 F_2 \cos (\phi_1 - \phi_2), \tag{5.15}$$

where F_1 and F_2 are the effective values of the two sinusoidal signals.

5.4 SINUSOIDS AS EXPONENTIALS

It may be shown from the McLaurin expansions of $\cos \phi$ and $e^{j\phi}$ (See the Appendix.) that

$$\cos \phi = \frac{e^{j\phi} + e^{-j\phi}}{2}.$$

Consequently, the steady-state sinusoidal signal of the general form

$$f(t) = F_m \cos (\omega t + \phi)$$

$$= \sqrt{2}\, F \cos (\omega t + \phi) \tag{5.16}$$

may be written

$$f(t) = \sqrt{2}\, F \left[\frac{e^{j(\omega t + \phi)} + e^{-j(\omega t + \phi)}}{2} \right]$$

$$= \frac{1}{\sqrt{2}} [(Fe^{j\phi})e^{j\omega t} + (Fe^{-j\phi})e^{-j\omega t}]. \tag{5.17}$$

Phasors and Complex Exponential Signals

Now let us define a *phasor value* of $f(t)$ as the complex number

$$\mathbf{F} = Fe^{j\phi} = F_x + {}^jF_y. \tag{5.18}$$

Then the sinusoid, $f(t)$, may be written

$$f(t) = \frac{1}{\sqrt{2}} (\mathbf{F}e^{j\omega t} + \mathbf{F}^* e^{-j\omega t}), \tag{5.19a}$$

which is the sum of the complex exponential time variation

$$\frac{\mathbf{F}}{\sqrt{2}} e^{j\omega t}$$

and its conjugate. Since for the complex variable, Z,

$$Z + Z^* = 2 \, \text{Re} \, [Z],$$

where

$$\text{Re} \, [\quad] = \text{real part of} \, [\quad],$$

another form of the sinusoid is

$$f(t) = 2 \, \text{Re} \left[\frac{\mathbf{F}}{\sqrt{2}} e^{j\omega t} \right]$$

$$= \sqrt{2} \, \text{Re} \, [\mathbf{F} e^{j\omega t}]. \qquad (5.19b)$$

The quantity $\mathbf{F} e^{j\omega t}$ is a rotating phasor, as indicated by the term $e^{j\omega t}$, whose angle is a function of time. This rotating phasor can be represented graphically by a directed line rotating about the origin at an angular velocity of ω radians per second. The geometry of this point of view is demonstrated in Fig. 5.3(a), and the phasor value of $f(t)$, $\mathbf{F}$, is geometrically a *snapshot* of the rotating phasor taken at $t = 0$, as shown in (b) of the figure.

In effect, what we have done is to develop an alternative way of graphically representing a sinusoid. Instead of laying out a t-axis and drawing a number of cycles of a sinusoid, we have drawn a directed line segment in the complex

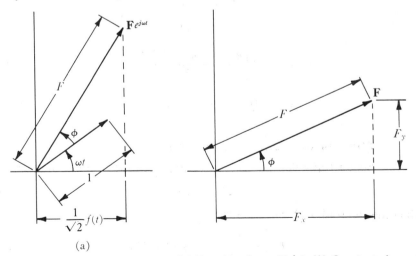

(a)

Fig. 5.3 *The geometry of phasors. (a) Rotating phasor, $\mathbf{F} e^{j\omega t}$. (b) Constant phasor, $\mathbf{F}$.*

plane that rotates about the origin at ω radians per second. As illustrated by Eq. (5.19b), the projection of this rotating line on the real axis at any instant of time multiplied by $\sqrt{2}$ gives the value of the sinusoid being represented. The important aspect of this phasor representation is that it contains just as much information as a graph of the sinusoid if ω is given.

Phasors in the Addition of Sinusoids

Assume three steady-state sinusoidal signals, all of the same form as Eq. (5.16) *and all of the same frequency,*

$$f_1(t) = \sqrt{2}\, F_1 \cos(\omega t + \phi_1) \tag{5.20a}$$

$$f_2(t) = \sqrt{2}\, F_2 \cos(\omega t + \phi_2) \tag{5.20b}$$

$$f_3(t) = \sqrt{2}\, F_3 \cos(\omega t + \phi_3) \tag{5.20c}$$

are to be added together. These functions may also be written in the form of Eq. (5.19a),

$$f_1(t) = \frac{1}{\sqrt{2}} (\mathbf{F}_1 e^{j\omega t} + \mathbf{F}_1^* e^{-j\omega t}) \tag{5.21a}$$

$$f_2(t) = \frac{1}{\sqrt{2}} (\mathbf{F}_2\, e^{j\omega t} + \mathbf{F}_2^* e^{-j\omega t}) \tag{5.21b}$$

$$f_3(t) = \frac{1}{\sqrt{2}} (\mathbf{F}_3\, e^{j\omega t} + \mathbf{F}_3^* e^{-j\omega t}). \tag{5.21c}$$

Now write the sum of these three signals as

$$f(t) = f_1(t) + f_2(t) + f_3(t), \tag{5.22}$$

or

$$f(t) = \frac{1}{\sqrt{2}} [(\mathbf{F}_1 + \mathbf{F}_2 + \mathbf{F}_3)e^{j\omega t} + (\mathbf{F}_1^* + \mathbf{F}_2^* + \mathbf{F}_3^*)e^{-j\omega t}].$$

The result is of the form

$$f(t) = \frac{1}{\sqrt{2}} (\mathbf{F}e^{j\omega t} + \mathbf{F}^* e^{-j\omega t}),$$

where

$$\mathbf{F} = \mathbf{F}_1 + \mathbf{F}_2 + \mathbf{F}_3. \tag{5.23}$$

The significance of this result lies in the identical forms of the instantaneous sum of Eq. (5.22) and the resulting phasor sum of Eq. (5.23).

The graphic display of the sum in Eq. (5.23) can be made as shown in Fig. 5.4(a), or as shown in one of its equivalents in (b) of the same figure. These phasor diagrams are a valuable adjunct to the analytical calculations of complex additions or subtractions, and the student should consistently exploit them as such. A simple sketch, only approximately to scale, will often bring to light glaring errors in the analytical calculation.

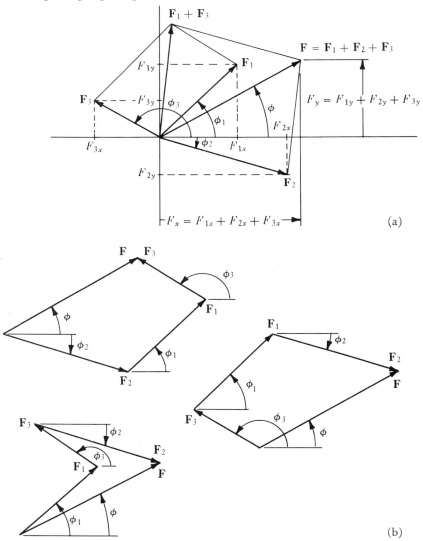

Fig. 5.4 *Graphical addition of phasors to arrive at* $\mathbf{F} = \mathbf{F}_1 + \mathbf{F}_2 + \mathbf{F}_3$. (*a*) *Conventional addition.* (*b*) *Some equivalent funicular diagrams (there are more).*

The phasor diagram in (a) also illustrates the graphical significance of the rectangular form of Eq. (5.23),

$$\mathbf{F} = F_x + jF_y$$
$$= (F_{1x} + F_{2x} + F_{3x}) + j(F_{1y} + F_{2y} + F_{3y}). \qquad (5.24)$$

EXAMPLE 5.2. If the two currents

$$i_1(t) = \sqrt{2}\, 5 \cos(377t + 36.9°) \text{ A}$$
$$i_2(t) = \sqrt{2}\, 3 \cos(377t - 30.0°) \text{ A}$$

flow respectively through two circuits connected in parallel, determine the total current supplied to the parallel combination.

Solution. The phasor values of the two given currents are

$$\mathbf{I}_1 = 5e^{j36.9°}$$
$$\mathbf{I}_2 = 3e^{-j30.0°}.$$

From Eq. (5.23) the phasor value of the total current is

$$\mathbf{I} = 5e^{j36.9°} + 3\, e^{-j30.0°}$$
$$= 4.00 + j3.00 + 2.60 - j1.50$$
$$= 6.60 + j1.50$$
$$= 6.77e^{j12.8°},$$

which is the phasor value of

$$i(t) = i_1(t) + i_2(t)$$
$$= \sqrt{2}\, 6.77 \cos(377t + 12.8°) \text{ A}. \qquad Ans.$$

It is suggested that the student check the correctness of the phasor addition by drawing a funicular diagram as illustrated in Fig. 5.4(b). The student can also check the answer by applying trigonometric identities to $i_1(t)$, $i_2(t)$, and $i(t)$.

Arbitrary Location of $t = 0$

In problems involving sinusoidal signals in the steady state, the difference in phase angles between any pair of signals is independent of the point in time chosen to be $t = 0$. This is easily illustrated by the three-element sum just considered after the translation in time represented by the substitution

$$t = \tau + T_a,$$

where τ is the new time variable and T_a is a constant. The new functions derived from Eqs. (5.20) are

$$f_{a1}(\tau) = f_1(\tau + T_a) = \sqrt{2}\, F_1 \cos(\omega\tau + \phi_1 + \phi_a)$$

$$f_{a2}(\tau) = f_2(\tau + T_a) = \sqrt{2}\, F_2 \cos(\omega\tau + \phi_2 + \phi_a)$$

$$f_{a3}(\tau) = f_3(\tau + T_a) = \sqrt{2}\, F_3 \cos(\omega\tau + \phi_3 + \phi_a),$$

where $\phi_a = \omega T_a$.

These new functions are characterized by the phasors

$$\mathbf{F}_{a1} = F_1 e^{j(\phi_1 + \phi_a)} = \mathbf{F}_1 e^{j\phi_a}$$

$$\mathbf{F}_{a2} = F_2 e^{j(\phi_2 + \phi_a)} = \mathbf{F}_2 e^{j\phi_a}$$

$$\mathbf{F}_{a3} = F_3 e^{j(\phi_3 + \phi_a)} = \mathbf{F}_3 e^{j\phi_a},$$

and their sum will be

$$\mathbf{F}_a = \mathbf{F}_{a1} + \mathbf{F}_{a2} + \mathbf{F}_{a3}$$

$$= (\mathbf{F}_1 + \mathbf{F}_2 + \mathbf{F}_3)e^{j\phi_a}.$$

What has been the result on the phasor relationships of the translation of the time origin of the sinusoidal waves? The sole effect has been to rotate all phasors in the analysis through the same angle, ϕ_a. The phasor diagrams will be identical to those in Fig. 5.4 except that in each representation the entire diagram will be rotated through the angle ϕ_a.

In many problems involving steady-state sine waves, only magnitudes and *relative* phase angles are of interest. When this is true, the time origin is chosen to suit the convenience of the one doing the computations. As a case in point, it is often convenient to have one phasor directed along the real axis, thereby saving at least one angle computation. However, this choice can be exercised but once in a given problem, because *when the phase angle on one sinusoid in a system is fixed, so are those on all other sinusoids in the system.* For example, left to a free choice of origins, we may have picked one to make $\phi_1 = 0$ in Fig. 5.4. Having done so, we would have also fixed ϕ_2 and ϕ_3, for the new diagram will exhibit a geometry identical to the old, except that the entire diagram will be rotated so that $\mathbf{F}_1$ lies along the real axis.

Phasors in Products of Sinusoids

Suppose it is desired to find the instantaneous product of the two sinusoids, $f_1(t)$ and $f_2(t)$, defined in Eqs. (5.20). Using Eqs. (5.21), we may write

$$f_1(t)f_2(t) = \left[\sqrt{2}\, \mathbf{F}_1 \frac{e^{j\omega t}}{2} + \sqrt{2}\, \mathbf{F}_1^* \frac{e^{-j\omega t}}{2}\right]$$

$$\times \left[\sqrt{2}\, \mathbf{F}_2 \frac{e^{j\omega t}}{2} + \sqrt{2}\, \mathbf{F}_2^* \frac{e^{-j\omega t}}{2}\right]$$

$$= \tfrac{1}{2}[\mathbf{F}_1\mathbf{F}_2\, e^{j2\omega t} + \mathbf{F}_1\mathbf{F}_2^* + \mathbf{F}_1^*\mathbf{F}_2 + \mathbf{F}_1^*\mathbf{F}_2^* e^{-j2\omega t}].$$

Since

$$\mathbf{F}_1^* \mathbf{F}_2^* e^{-j2\omega t} = [\mathbf{F}_1 \mathbf{F}_2\, e^{j2\omega t}]^*$$

and

$$\mathbf{F}_1^* \mathbf{F}_2 = [\mathbf{F}_1 \mathbf{F}_2^*]^*,$$

the product can be rewritten as

$$f_1(t)f_2(t) = \tfrac{1}{2}[\mathbf{F}_1 \mathbf{F}_2^* + (\mathbf{F}_1 \mathbf{F}_2^*)^* + \mathbf{F}_1 \mathbf{F}_2\, e^{j2\omega t} + (\mathbf{F}_1 \mathbf{F}_2\, e^{j2\omega t})^*].$$

Now utilizing

$$\tfrac{1}{2}(\mathbf{Z} + \mathbf{Z}^*) = \mathrm{Re}\,[\mathbf{Z}],$$

the product becomes

$$\begin{aligned}
f_1(t)f_2(t) &= \mathrm{Re}\,[\mathbf{F}_1 \mathbf{F}_2^* + \mathbf{F}_1 \mathbf{F}_2\, e^{j2\omega t}] \\
&= F_1 F_2 \cos(\phi_1 - \phi_2) + F_1 F_2 \cos(2\omega t + \phi_1 + \phi_2) \\
&= [f_1(t)f_2(t)]_{\mathrm{av}} + F_1 F_2 \cos(2\omega t + \phi_1 + \phi_2).
\end{aligned} \qquad (5.25)$$

Clearly, the product of two sinusoids consists of two terms: (1) a constant which is the average value defined earlier in Eq. (5.15) and (2) a *double-frequency* sinusoid alternating at twice the frequency of the terms $f_1(t)$ and $f_2(t)$.

The average product should now be firmly connected in the mind of the student to the phasor values of its terms in the following way:

If the two sinusoidal signals, $f_1(t)$ and $f_2(t)$, have the characterizing phasors

$$\mathbf{F}_1 = F_1 e^{j\phi_1}$$
$$\mathbf{F}_2 = F_2 e^{j\phi_2},$$

then

$$\begin{aligned}
[f_1(t)f_2(t)]_{\mathrm{av}} &= \mathrm{Re}\,[\mathbf{F}_1 \mathbf{F}_2^*] = F_1 F_2 \cos(\phi_1 - \phi_2) \\
&= \mathrm{Re}\,[\mathbf{F}_1^* \mathbf{F}_2] = F_1 F_2 \cos(\phi_2 - \phi_1).
\end{aligned} \qquad (5.26)$$

EXAMPLE 5.3. If the voltage across a two-terminal network is

$$v(t) = \sqrt{2}\, 120 \cos(377t + 30°)\ \mathrm{V}$$

and if the current through the two-terminal network, in the direction of the voltage drop, is

$$i(t) = \sqrt{2}\, 4 \cos(377t - 30°)\ \mathrm{A},$$

find the time varying form of the power delivered to the network.

Solution. The phasor values of the voltage and power are

$$\mathbf{V} = 120 e^{j30°}$$
$$\mathbf{I} = 4 e^{-j30°}$$

Eq. (5.25) then provides

$$p(t) = v(t)i(t)$$
$$= VI \cos (\phi_v - \phi_i) + VI \cos (2 \cdot 377t + \phi_v + \phi_i)$$
$$= 480 \cos 60° + 480 \cos (754t + 0°)$$
$$= 240 + 480 \cos 754t \text{ W.} \qquad Ans.$$

5.5 THE FORCED RESPONSE OF THE *R-L-C* SERIES CIRCUIT TO SINUSOIDAL EXCITATION

In linear *real* physical systems, the response will always be accompanied by some heat loss, however small, and the natural response will eventually dissipate itself. Therefore, when the sinusoidal steady state is under study, it simply means that attention is upon the forced response of the system to a sinusoidal input of constant amplitude and frequency.

Suppose that in the series *R-L-C* circuit of Fig. 5.5 the terminal voltage drop is the steady-state sinusoid

$$v(t) = V_m \cos (\omega t + \phi_v)$$
$$= \sqrt{2} \, V \cos (\omega t + \phi_v), \qquad t > 0, \qquad (5.27)$$

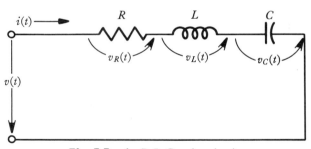

Fig. 5.5 *An R-L-C series circuit.*

where $V = V_m/\sqrt{2}$ is the effective value of the sinusoidal voltage. As for the arbitrary signal in the preceding section, we may write

$$v(t) = \frac{1}{\sqrt{2}} (\mathbf{V}e^{j\omega t} + \mathbf{V}^*e^{-j\omega t})$$
$$= \sqrt{2} \, \text{Re} \, [\mathbf{V}e^{j\omega t}], \qquad (5.28)$$

where

$$\mathbf{V} = Ve^{j\phi_v} \qquad (5.29)$$

is the *phasor value of the terminal voltage.*

The voltage, $v(t)$, may be considered to result from two sources in series, one generating the complex function of time, $(1/\sqrt{2})\mathbf{V}e^{j\omega t}$, the other generating its conjugate, as shown in Fig. 5.6(a). The resulting forced current, $i_f(t) = i(t)$, can be found using the principle of superposition, with the contribution of each component generator found as in (b) and (c) of Fig. 5.6. It must be realized that $(1/\sqrt{2})\mathbf{V}e^{j\omega t}$ and $(1/\sqrt{2})\mathbf{V}^*e^{-j\omega t}$ are mathematical concepts and

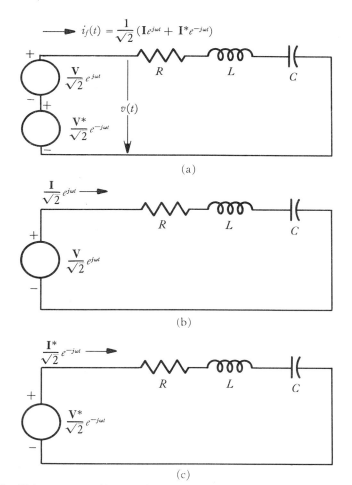

Fig. 5.6 *Using superposition to find the forced response to sinusoidal voltage.* (a) *Representing sinusoidal input voltage by two complex functions of time.* (b) *Current due to* $(\mathbf{V}/\sqrt{2})e^{j\omega t}$. (c) *Current due to* $(\mathbf{V}^*/\sqrt{2})e^{-j\omega t}$.

cannot be realized by a physical signal generator, which must always generate real-valued signals. A real off-the-shelf generator may, however, create the total voltage function represented by Eq. (5.28).

In the preceding chapter it was discovered that for exponential forcing voltages of the form

$$v(t) = Ve^{at}$$

the forced current response was of the form

$$i_f(t) = I_f e^{at},$$

where for this *R-L-C* series circuit,

$$I_f = \frac{V}{Z(a)} = \frac{V}{R + aL + \dfrac{1}{aC}}.$$

It is apparent that in the circuit of Fig. 5.6(b) the forcing voltage is again an exponential one, except this time the exponential and its coefficient are complex. Then the following correspondences between the case at hand and the previous chapter may be noted:

$$\frac{\mathbf{V}}{\sqrt{2}} e^{j\omega t} \Rightarrow v(t) = Ve^{at}$$

$$\frac{\mathbf{V}}{\sqrt{2}} \Rightarrow V$$

$$j\omega \Rightarrow a$$

$$\frac{\mathbf{I}}{\sqrt{2}} e^{j\omega t} \Rightarrow i_f(t)$$

$$\frac{\mathbf{I}}{\sqrt{2}} \Rightarrow I_f.$$

The last correspondence infers that we have considered the forced current response to be of the same form as the forcing voltage.

Being now on familiar ground, we write, corresponding to $I_f = V/Z(a)$ in the previous chapter,

$$\frac{\mathbf{I}}{\sqrt{2}} = \frac{\mathbf{V}/\sqrt{2}}{Z(j\omega)},$$

arriving at

$$\mathbf{I} = \frac{\mathbf{V}}{Z(j\omega)}. \tag{5.30}$$

If we now define
$$|Z(j\omega)| = Z,\qquad(5.31)$$
the complex number $Z(j\omega)$ may be written in the exponential form
$$Z(j\omega) = Ze^{j\phi_z}.\qquad(5.32)$$
Equation (5.30) may now be written
$$\mathbf{I} = \frac{Ve^{j\phi_v}}{Ze^{j\phi_z}} = \frac{V}{Z}e^{j(\phi_v-\phi_z)} = Ie^{j\phi_i},\qquad(5.33)$$
where
$$I = \frac{V}{Z}\qquad(5.34a)$$
$$\phi_i = \phi_v - \phi_z.\qquad(5.34b)$$

In Fig. 5.6(c) it has been presumed that the response to the conjugate of $(1/\sqrt{2})Ve^{j\omega t}$ is the conjugate of the response to $(1/\sqrt{2})Ve^{j\omega t}$. This may have indeed been presumptuous, so let us assume for the moment that the response to $(1/\sqrt{2})V^*e^{-j\omega t}$ is the complex time-varying function $(1/\sqrt{2})I_2\,e^{j\omega t}$.

As in the foregoing case,
$$\frac{I_2}{\sqrt{2}} = \frac{V^*/\sqrt{2}}{Z(-j\omega)},$$
or
$$I_2 = \frac{V^*}{Z(-j\omega)} = \frac{V^*}{Z^*(j\omega)} = I^*.$$
Therefore, the presumption on the diagram is correct.

The total forced response is, by superposition and using Eq. (5.33),
$$i_f(t) = \frac{1}{\sqrt{2}}[Ie^{j\omega t} + I^*e^{-j\omega t}]$$
$$= \frac{1}{\sqrt{2}}\left[\frac{V}{Z}e^{j(\omega t+\phi_v-\phi_z)} + \frac{V}{Z}e^{-j(\omega t+\phi_v-\phi_z)}\right]$$
$$= \sqrt{2}\,\frac{V}{Z}\frac{e^{j(\omega t+\phi_v-\phi_z)} + e^{-j(\omega t+\phi_v-\phi_z)}}{2}.$$
Therefore, the forced response is simply
$$i_f(t) = \sqrt{2}\,\frac{V}{Z}\cos(\omega t + \phi_v - \phi_z)$$
$$= \sqrt{2}\,I\cos(\omega t + \phi_i).\qquad(5.35)$$

The forced, or sinusoidal steady-state, response has now been shown to be very simply related to the sinusoidal forcing voltage. It is a sinusoid whose amplitude is that of the voltage divided by the magnitude of the impedance parameter, $Z(j\omega)$, and whose phase angle is the phase angle of the voltage minus the angle of the impedance parameter.

Let us now summarize the significant results for the R-L-C series circuit. First, it is noted that if the terminal voltage is considered to be the result of a voltage source generating

$$v(t) = \sqrt{2}\, V \cos{(\omega t + \phi_v)}, \qquad t > 0, \tag{5.36a}$$

then the steady-state voltage is

$$v_{ss}(t) = v(t)|_{t \gg 0}$$

$$= \sqrt{2}\, V \cos{(\omega t + \phi_v)} \tag{5.36b}$$

and is characterized by the phasor

$$\mathbf{V} = V e^{j\phi_v}. \tag{5.36c}$$

The resulting steady-state current is

$$i_{ss}(t) = i_f(t)$$

$$= \sqrt{2}\, I \cos{(\omega t + \phi_i)}, \tag{5.36d}$$

characterized by the phasor

$$\mathbf{I} = \frac{\mathbf{V}}{\mathbf{Z}} = I e^{j\phi_i} = \frac{V}{Z} e^{j(\phi_v - \phi_z)}, \tag{5.36e}$$

where

$$\mathbf{Z} = Z(j\omega) = Z e^{j\phi_z} \tag{5.36f}$$

is the *complex impedance* based on the previously defined impedance function

$$Z(a) = R + aL + \frac{1}{aC}. \tag{5.36g}$$

The reciprocal of the complex impedance is the *complex admittance*

$$Y(j\omega) = \mathbf{Y} = \frac{1}{Z(j\omega)} = \frac{1}{Z} e^{-j\phi_z} = Y e^{j\phi_Y}. \tag{5.36h}$$

EXAMPLE 5.4. If the component values in Fig. 5.5 are

$$R = 30\ \Omega, \qquad L = 40\ \text{mH}, \qquad \text{and } C = 25\ \mu F$$

and if the steady-state terminal voltage is

$$v_{ss}(t) = \sqrt{2}\ 100 \cos{500t}\ \text{V},$$

determine the resulting steady-state current.

Solution. Following the procedure given in Eqs. (5.36), the complex impedance at 500 rad/sec is

$$\mathbf{Z} = Z(j500) = R + j500\,L + \frac{1}{j500\,C}$$
$$= 30 + j20 - j80$$
$$= 30 - j60$$
$$= 67.1e^{-j63.4°}.$$

The resulting phasor current is then

$$\mathbf{I} = \frac{\mathbf{V}}{\mathbf{Z}} = \frac{100e^{j0°}}{67.1e^{-j63.4°}}$$
$$= 1.49e^{j63.4°},$$

from which we can write the steady-state answer as

$$i_{ss}(t) = \sqrt{2}\ 1.49\cos(500t + 63.4°)\ \text{A}.\qquad Ans.$$

The voltage responses, $v_R(t)$, $v_L(t)$, and $v_C(t)$, may be found easily by recognizing that they relate to the current as special cases of the general R-L-C series circuit. This is indicated in Fig. 5.7, where each of the three elements in

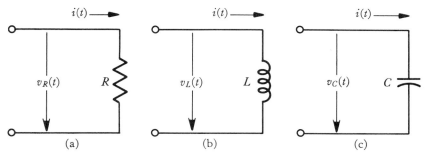

Fig. 5.7 *Simple R, L, and C circuits.*

the circuit of Fig. 5.5 are shown separately. The impedance function associated with each is a special case of the total *R-L-C* series impedance, as illustrated below:

$$Z_R(a) = Z(a)]_{\substack{L=0\\C=\infty}} = R,\qquad (5.37a)$$

$$Z_L(a) = Z(a)]_{\substack{R=0\\C=\infty}} = aL,\qquad (5.37b)$$

$$Z_C(a) = Z(a)]_{\substack{R=0\\L=0}} = \frac{1}{aC}.\qquad (5.37c)$$

Obviously,

$$Z(a) = Z_R(a) + Z_L(a) + Z_C(a).\qquad (5.38)$$

To find the forced voltage responses, now that we know the current response, we first observe that, corresponding to Eq. (5.32) for the total circuit, we have

$$\mathbf{Z}_R = Z_R(j\omega) = R = Re^{j0},$$ (5.39a)

$$\mathbf{Z}_L = Z_L(j\omega) = j\omega L = \omega L e^{j90°},$$ (5.39b)

$$\mathbf{Z}_C = Z_C(j\omega) = \frac{1}{j\omega C} = \frac{1}{\omega C} e^{-j90°}.$$ (5.39c)

The phasor values of each of the steady-state component voltages, $v_{R_{ss}}(t)$, $v_{L_{ss}}(t)$, and $v_{C_{ss}}(t)$, will relate to the total current just as the total voltage does in Eq. (5.36e). Therefore,

$$\mathbf{V}_R = \mathbf{Z}_R \mathbf{I} = RIe^{j\phi_i},$$ (5.40a)

$$\mathbf{V}_L = \mathbf{Z}_L \mathbf{I} = \omega LIe^{j(\phi_i+90°)},$$ (5.40b)

$$\mathbf{V}_C = \mathbf{Z}_C \mathbf{I} = \frac{1}{\omega C} Ie^{j(\phi_i-90°)}.$$ (5.40c)

The steady-state sinusoids associated with these phasors are

$$V_{R_{ss}}(t) = \sqrt{2} RI \cos(\omega t + \phi_i),$$ (5.41a)

$$V_{L_{ss}}(t) = \sqrt{2} \omega LI \cos(\omega t + \phi_i + 90°),$$
$$= -\sqrt{2} \omega LI \sin(\omega t + \phi_i),$$ (5.41b)

$$V_{C_{ss}}(t) = \sqrt{2} \frac{I}{\omega C} \cos(\omega t + \phi_i - 90°),$$
$$= \sqrt{2} \frac{I}{\omega C} \sin(\omega t + \phi_i).$$ (5.41c)

Equations (5.41) lead immediately to the following conclusions concerning the sinusoidal steady state:

1. The voltage across a resistor is in phase with the current through it.
2. The voltage across an inductance leads the current through it by 90°.
3. The voltage across a capacitor lags the current through it by 90°.

The term *voltage* above refers to the voltage drop taken positive in the direction of current through the element. The individual voltages are plotted, along with current, in Fig. 5.8, where they are shown as generated by their associated rotating phasors. Note that this is simply a graphic representation of Eq. (5.19b), which states that

$$f(t) = \text{Re } \sqrt{2} \, \mathbf{F}e^{j\omega t}.$$

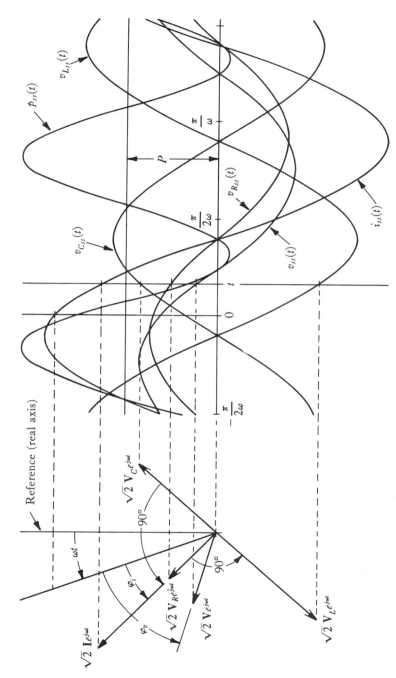

Fig. 5.8 *The steady-state sinusoidal variables in the R-L-C series circuit and the complex time function generating them.*

A form of the total applied voltage showing its relation to the current may now be written using Eqs. (5.41):

$$v_{ss}(t) = v_{R_{ss}}(t) + v_{L_{ss}}(t) + v_{C_{ss}}(t)$$

$$= \sqrt{2}\, I \left[R \cos(\omega t + \phi_i) - \omega L \sin(\omega t + \phi_i) + \frac{1}{\omega C} \sin(\omega t + \phi_i) \right].$$

$$(5.42)$$

The sinusoidal sum indicated in the above equation has the corresponding phasor sum

$$\mathbf{V} = \mathbf{V}_R + \mathbf{V}_L + \mathbf{V}_C$$

$$= \mathbf{I}\left(R + j\omega L + \frac{1}{j\omega C} \right)$$

$$= \mathbf{I}\left[R + j\left(\omega L - \frac{1}{\omega C} \right) \right]$$

$$= \mathbf{IZ}$$

$$= IZe^{j(\phi_i + \phi_z)}$$

$$= Ve^{j\phi_v}.$$

$$(5.43)$$

In the expressions for the *total R-L-C series impedance,*

$$\mathbf{Z} = Ze^{j\phi_z} = R + j(X_L + X_C).$$

$$(5.44)$$

The magnitude and angle are

$$Z = \sqrt{R^2 + \left(\omega L - \frac{1}{\omega C} \right)^2} = \sqrt{R^2 + (X_L + X_C)^2}$$

$$(5.45a)$$

$$\phi_z = \tan^{-1} \frac{\omega L - \dfrac{1}{\omega C}}{R} = \tan^{-1} \frac{X_L + X_C}{R},$$

$$(5.45b)$$

and the *inductive reactance* and *capacitive reactance* are respectively

$$X_L = \omega L \ (\Omega)$$

$$(5.46a)$$

$$X_C = -\frac{1}{\omega C} \ (\Omega).$$

$$(5.46b)$$

Corresponding to Eq. (5.43), the total instantaneous steady-state voltage has the alternative form

$$v_{ss}(t) = \sqrt{2}\, V \cos(\omega t + \phi_v)$$

$$= \sqrt{2}\, ZI \cos(\omega t + \phi_i + \phi_z).$$

$$(5.47)$$

This voltage is also shown on Fig. 5.8, along with its generating rotating phasor, which is the phasor sum of the three rotating phasors generating the component voltages. This result is exactly that which would have come about from a point-by-point addition of the three sinusoidal component voltages.

EXAMPLE 5.5. Determine the steady-state voltage across each component in Example 5.4.

Solution. The impedances of the three components at 500 rad/sec are

$$\mathbf{Z}_R = 30 = 30e^{j0°}$$
$$\mathbf{Z}_L = j20 = 20e^{j90°}$$
$$\mathbf{Z}_C = -j80 = 80e^{-j90°}.$$

Using the phasor value of the current from the previous example and Eqs. (5.40), the phasor voltages are

$$\mathbf{V}_R = 44.7e^{j63.4°}$$
$$\mathbf{V}_L = 29.8e^{j153.4°}$$
$$\mathbf{V}_C = 119e^{-j26.6°}.$$

The steady-state sinusoids associated with these phasors are

$$v_{R_{ss}}(t) = \sqrt{2}\ 44.7 \cos{(500t + 63.4°)}\ V \qquad Ans.$$
$$v_{L_{ss}}(t) = \sqrt{2}\ 29.8 \cos{(500t + 153.4°)}\ V \qquad Ans.$$
$$v_{C_{ss}}(t) = \sqrt{2}\ 119 \cos{(500t - 26.6°)}\ V. \qquad Ans.$$

5.6 POWER AND VECTOR VOLT-AMPERES

Let us consider the total voltage and current of the previous section:

$$v(t) = v_{ss}(t) = \sqrt{2}\ V \cos{(\omega t + \phi_v)}$$
$$i(t) = i_{ss}(t) = \sqrt{2}\ I \cos{(\omega t + \phi_i)}.$$

It follows immediately from Eqs. (5.25) and (5.26) that the instantaneous power is, in the steady state,

$$p = p_{ss}(t) = v(t)i(t)$$
$$= P + VI \cos{(2\omega t + \phi_i + \phi_v)}. \qquad (5.48)$$

This power variation, consisting of a double-frequency sinusoid plus a constant, is shown in Fig. 5.8 along with the voltage and current variations for the *R-L-C* series circuit. Such a variation is very easily sketched by noting the following:

1. The power is zero whenever either the associated voltage or current is zero.
2. The power is positive whenever the voltage and current are both positive *or* both negative.
3. The power is negative whenever either the voltage or current, but not both, is negative.

During that portion of time when the power is negative, the circuit is actually delivering energy back to the source exciting it. Obviously, for a pure inductance or a pure capacitance, in which the current and voltage are ninety degrees out of phase with one another, the power is negative for an amount of time equal to that during which it is positive. The constant *P* is then zero. In this case, the inductance or capacitance receives a given amount of electrical energy from the source one-half the period of the power variation (one-quarter of the period of the voltage and current variation). During the next equal amount of time, an equal amount of energy is returned to the source. Consequently, the average power, or average rate of energy transfer, is zero. It is of basic importance, however, that the average power absorbed by a passive network is always non-negative. That is, for passive networks, $P \geqslant 0$.

In Eq. (5.48) the average power is

$$
\begin{aligned}
P &= [v(t)i(t)]_{\text{av}} \\
&= [p(t)]_{\text{av}} \\
&= \text{Re } [\mathbf{VI}^*] \\
&= VI \cos (\phi_v - \phi_i) \\
&= VI \cos \theta \\
&= VI(pf).
\end{aligned}
\tag{5.49}
$$

Here we have defined the *power factor angle* as

$$
\theta = \phi_v - \phi_i = \phi_Z = -\phi_Y
\tag{5.50}
$$

and the *power factor* as

$$
pf = \cos \theta.
\tag{5.51}
$$

Equation (5.49) shows that the average power, P, is the real part of a complex quantity which may be designated

$$\mathbf{S} = \mathbf{VI}^*$$
$$= VIe^{j(\phi_v - \phi_i)}$$
$$= VIe^{j\theta}$$
$$= VI\cos\theta + jVI\sin\theta$$
$$= P + jQ \text{ (VA)}. \tag{5.52}$$

The imaginary part of $\mathbf{S}$, called the reactive volt-amperes, is

$$Q = \text{Im } [\mathbf{S}]$$
$$= VI\sin\theta \text{ (vars)}. \tag{5.53}$$

Obviously, the *var* is a unit introduced to indicate those volt-amperes which are imaginary, just as the *watt* may be considered an indicator of those volt-amperes which are real.

For the series *R-L-C* case just studied, it is worthwhile to note that

$$\mathbf{S} = \mathbf{VI}^*$$
$$= \mathbf{ZII}^*$$
$$= I^2\mathbf{Z}$$
$$= I^2R + jI^2(X_L + X_C). \tag{5.54}$$

This shows that

$$P = I^2R \tag{5.55}$$
$$Q = I^2(X_L + X_C) = Q_L + Q_C. \tag{5.56}$$

EXAMPLE 5.6. For Example 5.4 determine the quantities θ, pf, $\mathbf{S}$, P, Q, Q_L, and Q_C.

Solution. The power factor angle is

$$\theta = \phi_Z = -63.4°, \qquad Ans.$$

and the power factor is

$$pf = \cos(-63.4°) = 0.447. \qquad Ans.$$

Equation (5.52) gives the vector volt-amperes as

$$\mathbf{S} = 100(1.49)e^{-j63.4°}$$
$$= 149e^{-j63.4°}$$
$$= 66.6 - j133 \text{ VA}, \qquad Ans.$$

from which we can obtain the average power,

$$P = 66.6 \text{ W}, \quad Ans.$$

and the reactive volt-amperes,

$$Q = -133 \text{ vars.} \quad Ans.$$

Equation (5.56) provides the means for obtaining the inductive vars,

$$Q_L = 1.49^2(20) = 44.4 \text{ vars}, \quad Ans.$$

and the capacitive vars,

$$Q_C = 1.49^2(-80) = -178 \text{ vars.} \quad Ans.$$

EXAMPLE 5.7. After the network shown in Fig. 5.9 reached steady-state operation, the following meter readings were recorded:

RMS Ammeter Reading $= 8.50$ A

RMS Voltmeter Reading $= 120$ V

Wattmeter Reading $\quad = 816$ W.

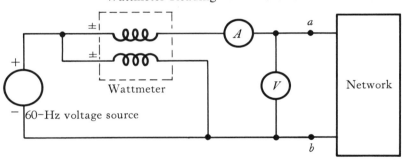

Fig. 5.9   *An instrumented network.*

The network is passive and is known to contain no capacitors. Determine *pf*, θ, **Z**, **S**, and *Q*.

Solution. The meter readings provide

$$I = 8.50, \quad V = 120, \quad \text{and} \quad P = 816.$$

Substituting these values into Eq. (5.49) yields

$$pf = \frac{816}{120(8.50)} = 0.800, \quad Ans.$$

from which we get

$$\theta = \cos^{-1}(0.800) = \pm 36.9°, \quad Ans.$$

which is the angle of the impedance parameter. Since the network is known to contain no capacitors, the impedance can have only a positive reactance component and, therefore, a positive angle. Thus, we can write

$$\mathbf{Z} = \frac{120}{8.50} e^{j36.9°}$$

$$= 14.1 e^{j36.9°} \ \Omega. \qquad Ans.$$

Finally, using Eq. (5.52), we obtain

$$\mathbf{S} = 120(8.50) e^{j36.9°}$$

$$= 1020 e^{j36.9°} = 816 + j611 \ \text{VA}, \qquad Ans.$$

and

$$Q = 611 \ \text{vars}. \qquad Ans.$$

5.7 THE *G-C-L* PARALLEL CIRCUIT

The parallel *G-C-L* circuit of Fig. 5.10 is presumed to be excited by a current source in the sinusoidal steady state. Following a procedure analogous to that for the voltage-excited *R-L-C* series circuit of Art. 5.5, one arrives at a set of conclusions analogous to those of Eqs. (5.36).

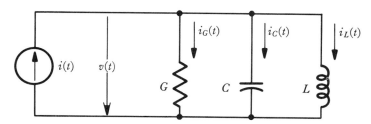

Fig. 5.10 *The G-C-L parallel circuit.*

These conclusions start with the presumption of a current source generating

$$i(t) = \sqrt{2} \, I \cos (\omega t + \phi_i), \qquad t > 0, \qquad (5.57a)$$

so that the steady-state current is

$$i_{ss}(t) = i(t)|_{t \gg 0}$$

$$= \sqrt{2} \, I \cos (\omega t + \phi_i). \qquad (5.57b)$$

The steady-state current source is characterized by the phasor

$$\mathbf{I} = I e^{j\phi_i}. \qquad (5.57c)$$

The resulting steady-state voltage is

$$v_{ss}(t) = v_f(t)$$

$$= \sqrt{2}\, V \cos{(\omega t + \phi_v)}, \qquad (5.57d)$$

characterized by the phasor

$$\mathbf{V} = \frac{\mathbf{I}}{\mathbf{Y}} = V e^{j\phi_v} = \frac{I}{Y}\, e^{j(\phi_i - \phi_Y)}, \qquad (5.57e)$$

where

$$\mathbf{Y} = Y(j\omega) = Y e^{j\phi_Y} \qquad (5.57f)$$

is the *complex admittance* based on the *admittance function*

$$Y(a) = G(a) + aC + \frac{1}{aL}$$

$$= Y_G(a) + Y_C(a) + Y_L(a). \qquad (5.57g)$$

The components of the admittance function are, specifically,

$$Y_G(a) = Y(a)]_{\substack{C=0 \\ L=\infty}} = G \qquad (5.58a)$$

$$Y_C(a) = Y(a)]_{\substack{G=0 \\ L=\infty}} = aC \qquad (5.58b)$$

$$Y_L(a) = Y(a)]_{\substack{G=0 \\ C=0}} = \frac{1}{aL}. \qquad (5.58c)$$

The corresponding complex admittances are

$$\mathbf{Y}_G = Y_G(j\omega) = G = G e^{j0}, \qquad (5.59a)$$

$$\mathbf{Y}_C = Y_C(j\omega) = j\omega C = \omega C e^{j90°}, \qquad (5.59b)$$

$$\mathbf{Y}_L = Y_L(j\omega) = \frac{1}{j\omega L} = \frac{1}{\omega L}\, e^{-j90°}. \qquad (5.59c)$$

The total steady-state current is the sum

$$i_{ss}(t) = i_{G_{ss}}(t) + i_{C_{ss}}(t) + i_{L_{ss}}(t)$$

$$= \sqrt{2}\, V \left[G \cos{(\omega t + \phi_v)} - \omega C \sin{(\omega t + \phi_v)} + \frac{1}{\omega L} \sin{(\omega t + \phi_v)} \right].$$

$$(5.60)$$

The corresponding phasor sum is

$$\mathbf{I} = \mathbf{I}_G + \mathbf{I}_L + \mathbf{I}_C$$

$$= \mathbf{V}\left(G + j\omega C + \frac{1}{j\omega L}\right)$$

$$= \mathbf{V}\left[G + j\left(\omega C - \frac{1}{\omega L}\right)\right]$$

$$= \mathbf{V}\mathbf{Y}$$

$$= V Y e^{j(\phi_v + \phi_Y)}$$

$$= I e^{j\phi_i}. \tag{5.61}$$

In this expression the *total G-C-L parallel admittance*

$$\mathbf{Y} = Y e^{j\phi_Y} = G + j(B_C + B_L) \tag{5.62}$$

has the magnitude and angle

$$Y = \sqrt{G^2 + \left(\omega C - \frac{1}{\omega L}\right)^2} = \sqrt{G^2 + (B_C + B_L)^2} \tag{5.63a}$$

$$\phi_Y = \tan^{-1}\frac{\omega C - \dfrac{1}{\omega L}}{G} = \tan^{-1}\frac{B_C + B_L}{G}, \tag{5.63b}$$

and the *capacitive susceptance* and *inductive susceptance* are respectively

$$B_C = \omega C \; (\Omega^{-1}) \tag{5.64a}$$

$$B_L = -\frac{1}{\omega L} \; (\Omega^{-1}). \tag{5.64b}$$

Corresponding to Eq. (5.61) is the time-varying form of the total steady-state current,

$$i_{ss}(t) = \sqrt{2} \, I \cos (\omega t + \phi_i)$$

$$= \sqrt{2} \, YV \cos (\omega t + \phi_v + \phi_Y). \tag{5.65}$$

Finally, let us make note of another expression for the vector volt-amperes:

$$\mathbf{S} = \mathbf{V}\mathbf{I}^*$$

$$= \mathbf{V}\mathbf{Y}^*\mathbf{V}^*$$

$$= V^2\mathbf{Y}^*$$

$$= V^2 G - jV^2(B_C + B_L)$$

$$= P + jQ. \tag{5.66}$$

Consequently,

$$P = V^2 G \tag{5.67}$$

$$Q = -V^2(B_C + B_L) = Q_C + Q_L. \tag{5.68}$$

EXAMPLE 5.8. Determine a *G-L* parallel combination that could be used to represent the network in Example 5.7 at the source frequency, 60 Hz.

Solution. From the results of Example 5.7

$$\mathbf{Y} = \frac{1}{\mathbf{Z}} = \frac{1}{14.1 e^{j36.9°}}$$

$$= 0.0709 e^{-j36.9°} = 0.0566 - j0.0425.$$

Comparing this to the admittance form of Eq. (5.62), we see that

$$G = 0.0566 \ \Omega^{-1} \qquad Ans.$$

and

$$B_L = -0.0425 \ \Omega^{-1}.$$

Equation (5.64b) then provides

$$L = -\frac{1}{\omega B_L}$$

$$= -\frac{1}{(2\pi 60)(-0.0425)} = 0.0625 \ \text{H.} \qquad Ans.$$

It is left for the student to verify that 120 V across *G* gives 816 W of power dissipation. Also verify that 120 V across *L* yields 611 vars.

EXAMPLE 5.9. Assuming that the voltage source remains unchanged, determine what capacitance added in parallel with the network of Example 5.7, or with the *G-L* model of Example 5.8, will give a total *Q* of zero.

Solution. To make the reactive volt-amperes zero, a capacitor is needed that will provide a negative 611 vars at an effective voltage of 120 V and at a frequency of 60 Hz. Using Eq. (5.68), we get

$$B_C = -\frac{Q_C}{V^2}$$

$$= -\frac{-611}{120^2} = 0.0425,$$

and Eq. (5.64a) then yields

$$C = \frac{B_C}{\omega}$$

$$= \frac{0.0425}{377} = 113 \times 10^{-6} \text{ F.} \qquad Ans.$$

5.8 THE SEVERAL COMPLEX PLANES

When complex quantities are plotted, both the real axis and the imaginary axis must be scaled with the dimensions of the quantity in question. For example, whatever units associate with the complex quantity $\mathbf{w} = u + jv$ must be the units measured along both axes. It is customary to label the complex plane with the general name of the variable plotted, i.e., the plot of $\mathbf{w}$ is generally on a set of coordinates constituting what is known as the $\mathbf{w}$-*plane*, having u as the abscissa and v as the ordinate, both plotted to the same scale.

In steady-state sinusoidal circuit analysis, complex variables of several dimensions occur. Each will be noted and discussed briefly here.

The Planes of Rotating Phasors

These are complex planes on which are plotted the complex time-varying current and voltage functions of the form $\mathbf{F}e^{j\omega t}$. These, you will recall, are the component functions which, along with their conjugates, make up the real sinusoidal functions. *Their projections on the real axis, multiplied by* $\sqrt{2}$, *yield the equations of the real sinusoids in the circuit.*

Generally, the current and voltage phasors are superposed so that voltage and current phase relationships are apparent. The quantities associated with each are made apparent through the convention of solid arrowheads for currents and open arrowheads for voltages.

For the R-L-C series circuit, these plots are nothing more than the rotating phasors of Fig. 5.8 after division of each variable by $\sqrt{2}$, as shown in Fig. 5.11(a). A similar plot for the G-C-L parallel circuit is shown in Fig. 5.12(a).

THE I- and V-Planes

If one sets $\omega t = 0$ in the above plots, the result is the *circuit phasor diagram* of the **I**-plane, **V**-plane plots. These are shown, with both forms of phasor addition, in (b) of Figs. 5.11 and 5.12. These diagrams are used practically to the exclusion of the time-varying diagrams, since they are simpler

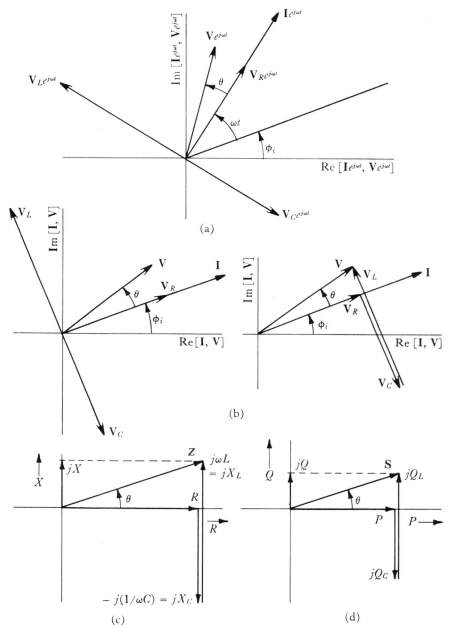

Fig. 5.11 *Complex planes associated with the R-L-C series circuit. (a) The rotating phasor. (b) Equivalent forms in the* **I***- and* **V***-planes. (c) The* **Z***-plane. (d) The* **S***-plane.*

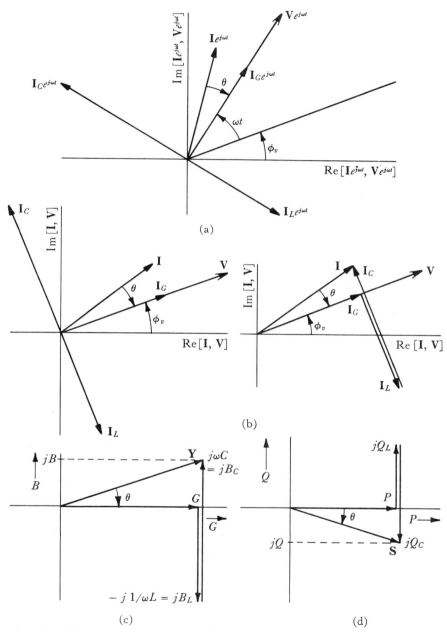

Fig. 5.12 *Complex planes associated with the G-C-L parallel circuit. (a) The rotating phasors. (b) Equivalent forms in the* **I**- *and* **V**-*planes. (c) The* **Y**-*plane. (d) The* **S**-*plane.*

yet carry all the information contained in the rotating phasor configurations.

The student should note that the power factor angle, θ, is taken positive from current to voltage, regardless of the circuit configuration.

The Y- and Z-Planes

These are the complex plane plots of $\mathbf{Z} = Z(j\omega)$ and $\mathbf{Y} = Y(j\omega)$ for any network. They are shown in (c) of Figs. 5.11 and 5.12 for the series and parallel three-element-kind networks we have studied so far.

It should be carefully noted that, except for their rotational position in space, similar geometrics exist between the V-plane and Z-plane plots and for the I-plane and Y-plane plots. The relation between the power factor angle, θ, and the angles ϕ_Z and ϕ_Y should also be observed.

The S-Plane Plot

The plot of vector volt-amperes on the S-plane is shown for the series *R-L-C* circuit in Fig. 5.11(d) and for the parallel *G-C-L* circuit in Fig. 5.12(d).

Notice that the S-plane plot is similar in all respects to the Z-plane plot. For the S-plane plot to be similar to the Y-plane plot, however, it would be necessary to take the conjugate of either $\mathbf{S}$ or $\mathbf{Y}$. This is because both positive X's and Q's are inductive in nature, but positive B's are capacitive in nature. Therefore, the imaginary parts of $\mathbf{Z}$ and $\mathbf{S}$ are of the same sign, while those of $\mathbf{Y}$ and $\mathbf{S}$ are of opposite sign.

The student should study these sets of diagrams until he understands each thoroughly and until he has complete understanding of the relationship of any one to any other.

5.9 PHASORS AND THE CIRCUIT LAWS

In reality, all of circuit theory is based on Kirchhoff's laws and the volt-ampere characteristics of the circuit elements. The beauty of the use of phasors in the sinusoidal steady state lies in the fact that they obey Kirchhoff's laws and reduce the volt-ampere relationships for all linear circuit elements to a simple statement of *Ohm's law* utilizing complex quantities in place of real numbers. These properties are the subject of this section.

Kirchhoff's Laws

It was shown in Sec. 5.3 that if there exists the sinusoidal sum of sinusoidal functions

$$f(t) = f_1(t) + f_2(t) + f_3(t),$$

then the phasor values of the functions are related as follows:

$$\mathbf{F} = \mathbf{F}_1 + \mathbf{F}_2 + \mathbf{F}_3.$$

This shows that the same additive laws apply to phasor values under complex addition as applied to their corresponding real-valued signals under real addition. To emphasize the significance of these properties to Kirchhoff's laws, let us restate the two laws, adding their phasor-value counterparts, in the table below.

Law	Real Functions	Phasors	
KCL	$\Sigma i(t) = 0$	$\Sigma \mathbf{I} = 0$	(5.69)
KVL	$\Sigma v(t) = 0$	$\Sigma \mathbf{V} = 0.$	(5.70)

In performing the above additions, the student should exploit both the analytical procedures possible with complex numbers and the graphical procedures embodied in phasor diagrams. The phasor diagrams are a valuable adjunct to the analytical calculations of complex additions or subtractions, and the student should consistently exploit them as such.

Since phasors do obey Kirchhoff's laws, it is quite proper to label circuit diagrams of systems in the sinusoidal steady state with the phasor values of the variables, as is done in Fig. 5.13.

Ohm's Law

The *boxes* labeled as $\mathbf{Z}$'s or $\mathbf{Y}$'s in Fig. 5.13 may contain any combination of passive elements. The series and parallel combinations just studied are but two possibilities.

When the variables result from steady-state sinusoidal excitation, they will in turn be steady-state sinusoids characterized by the phasors shown on the diagrams. In fact, branches within the network can always be selected which will be no more complicated than the series and parallel configurations which have already had our attention to detail. The complex impedance and admittance operators are defined to relate phasor voltage and current in general in the same way that they did in the special case of the R-L-C series circuit. That is, with positive directions as shown in Fig. 5.13(a),

$$\mathbf{V} = \mathbf{ZI} = \mathbf{Z}(j\omega)\mathbf{I}, \qquad (5.71a)$$

or

$$\mathbf{I} = \mathbf{YV} = Y(j\omega)\mathbf{V}, \qquad (5.71b)$$

where

$$\left(\mathbf{Y} = \frac{1}{\mathbf{Z}}\right) = \left(Y(j\omega) = \frac{1}{Z(j\omega)}\right). \qquad (5.71c)$$

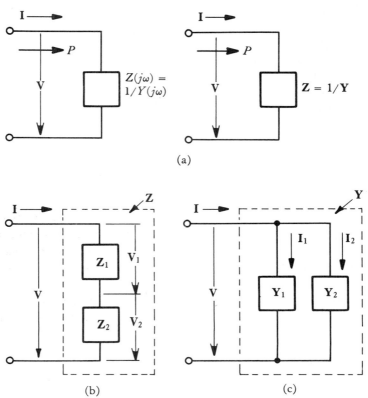

Fig. 5.13 *Symbolic representation of networks in the sinusoidal steady state. (a) Alternative representations of a two-terminal device or network. (b) Impedances (or admittances) in series. (c) Admittances (or impedances) in parallel.*

Network Reductions

Since phasor relationships satisfy Kirchhoff's and Ohm's laws in the manner specified above, all the calculations made for resistor networks in Chapter 3 have a counterpart in phasor analysis. The conceptual difference in the two cases is slight. In the case of the resistor networks, one dealt with real-valued forcing and response functions connected by conventional algebraic additions and multiplications by constants. In the case of phasor analysis, one deals with forcing and response functions whose values are complex numbers connected by phasor additions and multiplications by complex constants.

Having established these correspondences, there is no point in repeating the developments of Chapter 3 regarding network reductions. Of course, the term *single-element* has acquired a new breadth. It may now mean the impedance (or admittance) associated with the three basic circuit parameters, either singly or in the series or parallel combinations heretofore studied. Since the only new conceptual item is the replacement of real-valued quantities with complex quantities, the establishment of network reduction techniques for resistances (or conductances) in Chapter 3 has also established the techniques for phasor analysis. We may simply list them.

1.   The total impedance and admittance of series impedances, as in Fig. 5.13(b), are

$$\mathbf{Z} = \mathbf{Z}_1 + \mathbf{Z}_2 \qquad\qquad\qquad (5.72a)$$

$$\mathbf{Y} = \frac{1}{\mathbf{Z}} = \frac{\mathbf{Y}_1 \mathbf{Y}_2}{\mathbf{Y}_1 + \mathbf{Y}_2}. \qquad\qquad (5.72b)$$

2.   The total admittance and impedance of parallel admittances, as in Fig. 5.13(c), are

$$\mathbf{Y} = \mathbf{Y}_1 + \mathbf{Y}_2 \qquad\qquad\qquad (5.73a)$$

$$\mathbf{Z} = \frac{1}{\mathbf{Y}} = \frac{\mathbf{Z}_1 \mathbf{Z}_2}{\mathbf{Z}_1 + \mathbf{Z}_2}. \qquad\qquad (5.73b)$$

3.   The voltage-divider equation, applicable to Fig. 5.13(b), is

$$\frac{\mathbf{V}_1}{\mathbf{V}} = \frac{\mathbf{Z}_1}{\mathbf{Z}_1 + \mathbf{Z}_2} = \frac{\mathbf{Y}_2}{\mathbf{Y}_1 + \mathbf{Y}_2}. \qquad (5.74)$$

4.   The current-divider equation, applicable to Fig. 5.13(c), is

$$\frac{\mathbf{I}_1}{\mathbf{I}} = \frac{\mathbf{Y}_1}{\mathbf{Y}_1 + \mathbf{Y}_2} = \frac{\mathbf{Z}_2}{\mathbf{Z}_1 + \mathbf{Z}_2}. \qquad (5.75)$$

EXAMPLE 5.10. The following values apply to Fig. 5.14(a):

$$v_G(t) = \sqrt{2}\, 100 \cos 10{,}000t \text{ V}$$

$$Z_1(j10{,}000) = 20.0 + j100 \ \Omega$$

$$Z_2(j10{,}000) = -j100 \ \Omega$$

$$Z_3(j10{,}000) = 200 \ \Omega.$$

Determine the steady-state time functions for all of the unknown variables shown in the figure.

Solution.

1.   Since the reduction of the network in Fig. 5.14(a) follows the same

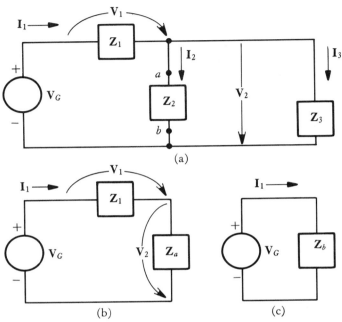

Fig. 5.14   *Reduction of a series-parallel network for Example 5.10.*

pattern as in Examples 3.1 and 3.2, the results are given below in the order obtained.

$$\mathbf{Z}_a = \frac{\mathbf{Z}_2 \mathbf{Z}_3}{\mathbf{Z}_2 + \mathbf{Z}_3} = \frac{100 e^{-j90.0°}(200)}{-j100 + 200} = \frac{20{,}000 e^{-j90.0°}}{224 e^{-j26.6°}}$$

$$= 89.5 e^{-j63.4°} = 40.0 - j80.0$$

$$\mathbf{Z}_b = \mathbf{Z}_1 + \mathbf{Z}_a$$
$$= 60.0 + j20.0 = 63.2 e^{j18.4°}.$$

2.   KVL, Ohm's law, and KCL applied to Fig. 5.14(c) give

$$\mathbf{I}_. = \frac{\mathbf{V}_G}{\mathbf{Z}_b} = \frac{100 e^{j0°}}{63.2 e^{j18.4°}} = 1.58 e^{-j18.4°}.$$

3. The voltage-divider equation applied to Fig. 5.14(b) yields

$$\mathbf{V}_1 = \mathbf{V}_G \frac{\mathbf{Z}_1}{\mathbf{Z}_1 + \mathbf{Z}_a} = \frac{100e^{j0°}(20.0 + j100)}{63.2e^{j18.4°}}$$

$$= 1.58e^{-j18.4°}(102e^{j78.7°})$$

$$= 161e^{j60.3°}$$

$$\mathbf{V}_2 = \mathbf{V}_G \frac{\mathbf{Z}_a}{\mathbf{Z}_1 + \mathbf{Z}_a} = \frac{100e^{j0°}(89.5e^{-j63.4°})}{63.2e^{j18.4°}}$$

$$= 141e^{-j81.8°}$$

Checking by KVL,

$$\mathbf{V}_G - \mathbf{V}_1 - \mathbf{V}_2 = 100e^{j0°} - 161e^{j60.3°} - 141e^{-j81.8°}$$

$$= 100 - (79.9 + j140) - (20.1 - j140)$$

$$= 000 + j000.$$

4. Applying the current-divider equation to Fig. 5.14(a) produces

$$\mathbf{I}_2 = \mathbf{I}_1 \frac{\mathbf{Z}_3}{\mathbf{Z}_2 + \mathbf{Z}_3} = \frac{1.58e^{-j18.4°}(200)}{224e^{-j26.6°}}$$

$$= 1.41e^{j8.2°}$$

$$\mathbf{I}_3 = \mathbf{I}_1 \frac{\mathbf{Z}_2}{\mathbf{Z}_2 + \mathbf{Z}_3} = \frac{1.58e^{-j18.4°}(100\ e^{-j90°})}{224e^{-j26.6°}}$$

$$= 0.707e^{-j81.8°}.$$

Checking by KCL,

$$\mathbf{I}_1 - \mathbf{I}_2 - \mathbf{I}_3 = 1.58e^{-j18.4°} - 1.41e^{j8.2°}$$

$$-0.707e^{-j81.8°}$$

$$= (1.50 - j0.499) - (1.40 + j0.201)$$

$$-(0.101 - j0.700)$$

$$= 0.00 + j0.000.$$

5. We are now ready to list the steady-state variables, which we do in the following table alongside their phasor values.

$\mathbf{V}_G = 100 e^{j0°}$

$$v_{Gss}(t) = \sqrt{2}\, 100 \cos 10{,}000t \text{ V}$$

$\mathbf{I}_1 = 1.58 e^{-j18.4°}$

$$i_{1ss}(t) = \sqrt{2}\, 1.58 \cos (10{,}000 - 18.4°) \text{ A} \qquad Ans.$$

$\mathbf{V}_1 = 161 e^{j60.3°}$

$$v_{1ss}(t) = \sqrt{2}\, 161 \cos (10{,}000t + 60.3°) \text{ V} \qquad Ans.$$

$\mathbf{V}_2 = 141 e^{-j81.8°}$

$$v_{2ss}(t) = \sqrt{2}\, 141 \cos (10{,}000t - 81.8°) \text{ V} \qquad Ans.$$

$\mathbf{I}_2 = 1.41 e^{j8.2°}$

$$i_{2ss}(t) = \sqrt{2}\, 1.41 \cos (10{,}000t + 8.2°) \text{ A} \qquad Ans.$$

$\mathbf{I}_3 = 0.707 e^{-j81.8°}$

$$i_{3ss}(t) = \sqrt{2}\, 0.707 \cos (10{,}000t - 81.8°) \text{ A.} \qquad Ans.$$

The Principle of Superposition

Since the principle of superposition is an additive property in the real-valued case and since addition in the real-valued case implies addition in the corresponding phasor analysis, the principle of superposition holds for the complex-valued computations of phasor analysis.

Thévenin's and Norton's Theorems

For phasor analysis the Thévenin and Norton forms indicated by Eqs. (2.12) and (2.15) become respectively

$$\mathbf{V} = \mathbf{V}_o - \mathbf{Z}_o \mathbf{I} \qquad (5.76)$$

and

$$\mathbf{I} = \mathbf{I}_o - \mathbf{Y}_o \mathbf{V}. \qquad (5.77)$$

These results are illustrated in Fig. 5.15.

Corresponding to Eq. (2.16), we have

$$\mathbf{Z}_o = \frac{1}{\mathbf{Y}_o}. \qquad (5.78)$$

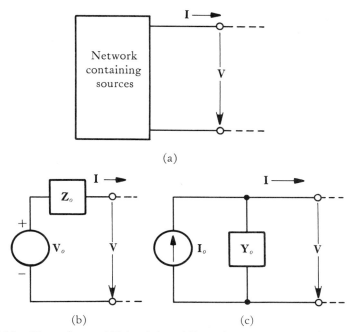

Fig. 5.15 *Phasor forms of Thévenin's and Norton's equivalents. (a) Original network.*
(b) Thévenin's equivalent. (c) Norton's equivalent.

EXAMPLE 5.11. The following values apply to Fig. 5.16(a):

$$v_{G1}(t) = \sqrt{2}\ 100 \cos 10{,}000t \text{ V}$$

$$i_{G2}(t) = \sqrt{2}\ 2.00 \cos (10{,}000t - 45.0°) \text{ A}$$

$$Y_1(j10{,}000) = \frac{1}{20.0 + j100} = (1.92 - j9.61)\ 10^{-3}\ \Omega^{-1}$$

$$Y_2(j10{,}000) = \frac{1}{-j100} = j10.0 \times 10^{-3}\ \Omega^{-1}$$

$$Y_3(j10{,}000) = \frac{1}{200} = 5.00 \times 10^{-3}\ \Omega^{-1}.$$

Determine the steady-state time function for $i_2(t)$ using superposition.

Solution. Since the network in Fig. 5.16 becomes the network in Fig. 5.14 when the ideal current source is opened, the phasor value of $i_{2ss}(t)$ contributed by the voltage source, $v_{G1}(t)$, is the result given in Example 5.10; namely,

$$\mathbf{I}_{21} = 1.41e^{j8.2°}.$$

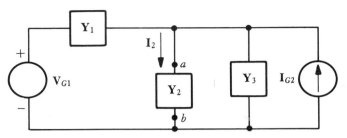

Fig. 5.16 *A two-source network.*

The phasor value of $i_{2ss}(t)$ contributed by the current source is obtained by shorting the ideal voltage source. Using the current-divider equation, the result is

$$\mathbf{I}_{22} = \mathbf{I}_{G2} \frac{\mathbf{Y}_2}{\mathbf{Y}_2 + (\mathbf{Y}_1 + \mathbf{Y}_3)}$$

$$= \frac{2.00e^{-j45.0°}(10.0e^{j90°})10^{-3}}{(j10.0 + 1.92 - j9.61 + 5.00)10^{-3}}$$

$$= \frac{2.00e^{-j45.0°}(10.0e^{j90°})}{6.92 + j0.4}$$

$$= \frac{20.0e^{j45.0°}}{6.39e^{j3.3°}}$$

$$= 2.89e^{j41.7°}.$$

The total phasor current is

$$\mathbf{I}_2 = 1.41e^{j8.2°} + 2.89e^{j41.7°}$$

$$= (1.40 + j0.201) + (2.16 + j1.92)$$

$$= 3.56 + j2.12 = 4.14e^{j30.8°},$$

and the steady-state answer is

$$i_{2ss}(t) = \sqrt{2}\, 4.14 \cos (10{,}000t + 30.8°) \text{ A.} \qquad \textit{Ans.}$$

EXAMPLE 5.12. Repeat Example 5.11 by obtaining a Norton's equivalent as seen from terminals a and b.

Solution. The short-circuit current, using superposition, is

$$\mathbf{I}_o = \mathbf{I}_{o1} + \mathbf{I}_{o2}$$

$$= \mathbf{V}_{G1}\mathbf{Y}_1 + \mathbf{I}_{G2}$$

$$= 100e^{j0°}(9.80e^{-j78.7°})\,10^{-3} + 2.00e^{-j45°}$$

$$= 0.980e^{-j78.7°} + 2.00e^{-j45°}$$

$$= (0.192 - j0.961) + (1.41 - j1.41)$$

$$= 1.60 - j2.37 = 2.86e^{-j56.0°}.$$

Norton's equivalent admittance is the parallel combination

$$\mathbf{Y}_o = \mathbf{Y}_1 + \mathbf{Y}_3$$
$$= (1.92 - j9.61)\,10^{-3} + 5.00 \times 10^{-3}$$
$$= (6.92 - j9.61)\,10^{-3}.$$

The network in Fig. 5.16 has now been reduced to the form shown in Fig. 5.15(c) with $\mathbf{Y}_2$ connected to the output terminals, and the current–divider equation yields

$$\mathbf{I}_2 = \mathbf{I}_o \frac{\mathbf{Y}_2}{\mathbf{Y}_o + \mathbf{Y}_2}$$

$$= \frac{2.86e^{-j56.0°}(10.0e^{j90.0°})\,10^{-3}}{(6.92 - j9.61 + j10.0)\,10^{-3}}$$

$$= \frac{2.86e^{-j56.0°}(10.0e^{j90.0°})}{6.93e^{j3.3°}}$$

$$= 4.13e^{j30.7°},$$

which agrees to within one unit in the third significant figure with the answer obtained in the previous example. The steady-state answer is

$$i_{2ss}(t) = \sqrt{2}\,4.13 \cos{(10{,}000t + 30.7°)}\text{ A}. \qquad Ans.$$

5.10 GENERAL IMPEDANCE AND ADMITTANCE FUNCTIONS

The more complicated impedance or admittance functions, such as those which may result from the reduction to a single impedance of some series-parallel combination, generally will have their magnitude and angle, or their real and imaginary parts, functions of the radian frequency, ω. That is, the exponential form will be

$$\mathbf{Z} = Z(j\omega) = |Z(j\omega)|\,e^{j\phi_Z(\omega)} \tag{5.79}$$

and

$$\mathbf{Y} = Y(j\omega) = |Y(j\omega)|\,e^{j\phi_Y(\omega)}. \tag{5.80}$$

Now that the complex impedance and admittance functions have been defined, it is time to become familiar with the standard nomenclature regarding their real and imaginary parts.

You will recall that for purely resistive elements the impedance consisted of only a real part, the *resistance*. Similarly, the admittance consisted of only a real part, the *conductance*. We will continue to use these terms for the real parts of two-terminal impedances and admittances, recognizing, however, the important fact that these components may now be functions of frequency. These components may alternatively be referred to as *resistive* or *conductive components.*

The imaginary part of an impedance will, in general, be a function of frequency which will be called the *reactance* or the *reactive component.* The imaginary part of an admittance is a function of frequency called the *susceptance* or *susceptive component.*

In general, then

$$Z(j\omega) = R(\omega) + jX(\omega) \tag{5.81}$$

$$Y(j\omega) = G(\omega) + jB(\omega), \tag{5.82}$$

where

$R(\omega) = $ resistive component of $Z(j\omega)$ in ohms $\quad = R$

$X(\omega) = $ reactive component of $Z(j\omega)$ in ohms $\quad = X$

$G(\omega) = $ conductive component of $Y(j\omega)$ in mhos $= G$

$B(\omega) = $ susceptive component of $Y(j\omega)$ in mhos $= B$.

Whenever the functional notation is not important to computation, as in computing with ω equal to a constant, it is often dropped for conciseness, as at the right of the above definitions of impedance and admittance components.

In the special case of the series *R-L-C* circuit,

$$Z(j\omega) = R + j\omega L + \frac{1}{j\omega C}$$

$$= R + j\left(\omega L - \frac{1}{\omega C}\right)$$

$$= R + j(X_L + X_C)$$

$$= R(\omega) + jX(\omega). \tag{5.83}$$

In this case $R(\omega) = R$ and $X(\omega) = X_L + X_C = \omega L - \dfrac{1}{\omega C}$.

The *dual* of this special case is the parallel *G-C-L* circuit, where

$$Y(j\omega) = G + j\omega C + \frac{1}{j\omega L}$$

$$= G + j\left(\omega C - \frac{1}{\omega L}\right)$$

$$= G + j(B_C + B_L)$$

$$= G(\omega) + jB(\omega). \tag{5.84}$$

Here $G(\omega) = G$ and $B(\omega) = B_C + B_L = \omega C - \dfrac{1}{\omega L}$.

In each of the above special cases, the resistive, or dissipative, components were constants and therefore independent of ω. An example of frequency-dependent resistance is readily supplied by expressing the parallel case of Eq. (5.84) as an impedance:

$$Z(j\omega) = \frac{1}{Y(j\omega)}$$

$$= \frac{1}{G + j[\omega C - (1/\omega L)]}$$

$$= \frac{G}{G^2 + [\omega C - (1/\omega L)]^2} - j\frac{\omega C - (1/\omega L)}{G^2 + [\omega C - (1/\omega L)]^2}$$

$$= R(\omega) + jX(\omega).$$

Here both the resistive and reactive components are obviously functions of ω and, therefore, of frequency.

One more item of terminology remains. In the series R-L circuit, which is a special case of Eq. (5.83),

$$Z(j\omega) = R + j\omega L$$

$$= R + jX_L,$$

whereas for the series R-C circuit

$$Z(j\omega) = R + \frac{1}{j\omega C}$$

$$= R - j\frac{1}{\omega C}$$

$$= R + jX_C.$$

By analogy to these two situations, *when $X(\omega)$ is positive, the network is said to be inductive*, and *when $X(\omega)$ is negative, the network is said to be capacitive.* Conversely, *positive $B(\omega)$ infers a capacitive network while negative $B(\omega)$ infers an inductive network.* In other words, a network which could be replaced, at some particular frequency, by an R-L series circuit (or G-L parallel circuit) is inductive at that frequency, while one which may be replaced at a particular frequency by an R-C series circuit (or G-C parallel circuit) is capacitive at that frequency.

Let us now look at the concepts of *in-phase* and *quadrature* components of voltage or current. The phasor current and voltage are related through the impedance operating on the current, or conversely, through the admittance operating on the voltage. In the first case

$$\mathbf{V} = \mathbf{ZI}$$
$$= R\mathbf{I} + jX\mathbf{I}$$
$$= \mathbf{V}_R + \mathbf{V}_X$$
$$= (V\cos\theta + jV\sin\theta)\,e^{j\phi_i}$$
$$= (V_R + jV_X)e^{j\phi_i}, \tag{5.85}$$

where

$$\mathbf{V}_R = R\mathbf{I} = (V\cos\theta)e^{j\phi_i} = \text{resistive, or in-phase, component of voltage} \tag{5.86a}$$

$$\mathbf{V}_X = jX\mathbf{I} = (V\sin\theta)je^{j\phi_i} = \text{reactive, or quadrature, component of voltage.} \tag{5.86b}$$

The resolution of the voltage into such perpendicular components is illustrated in the first phasor diagram of Fig. 5.17(a).

The alternative resolution of components results when $\mathbf{Y} = 1/\mathbf{Z}$ operates on the voltage:

$$\mathbf{I} = \mathbf{YV}$$
$$= G\mathbf{V} + jB\mathbf{V}$$
$$= \mathbf{I}_G + \mathbf{I}_B$$
$$= [I\cos(-\theta) + jI\sin(-\theta)]e^{j\phi_v}$$
$$= (I\cos\theta - jI\sin\theta)e^{j\phi_v}$$
$$= (I_G + jI_B)e^{j\phi_v}, \tag{5.87}$$

where

$$\mathbf{I}_G = G\mathbf{V} = (I\cos\theta)e^{j\phi_v} = I_G\,e^{j\phi_v}$$
$$= \text{conductive, or in-phase, component of current} \tag{5.88a}$$

$$\mathbf{I}_B = jB\mathbf{V} = -j(I\sin\theta)e^{j\phi_v} = jI_B\,e^{j\phi_v}$$
$$= \text{reactive, or quadrature, component of current.} \tag{5.88b}$$

This resolution of the current into in-phase and quadrature components is illustrated in the second phasor diagram of Fig. 5.17(a).

The impedance and admittance diagrams for the same two-terminal network or device are shown in (b) and (c) of Fig. 5.17. The similarities between the voltage and impedance diagrams and between the current and admittance diagrams should be carefully noted.

Finally, let us observe the nature of the vector volt-amperes as related to voltage and current in this general two-terminal case. Equivalent forms are

$$\mathbf{S} = \mathbf{V}\mathbf{I}^* = P + jQ \tag{5.89}$$

$$\mathbf{S} = (\mathbf{V}_R + \mathbf{V}_X)\mathbf{I}^* = V_R I + jV_X I \tag{5.89a}$$

$$\mathbf{S} = \mathbf{V}(\mathbf{I}_G^* + \mathbf{I}_B^*) = VI_G - jVI_B \tag{5.89b}$$

$$\mathbf{S} = I^2\mathbf{Z} = RI^2 + jXI^2 \tag{5.89c}$$

$$\mathbf{S} = V^2\mathbf{Y}^* = GV^2 - jBV^2. \tag{5.89d}$$

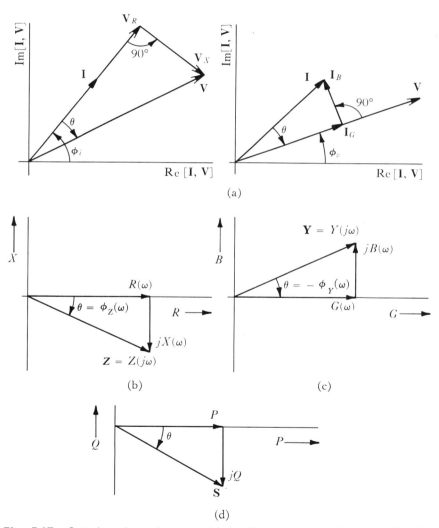

Fig. 5.17 *Complex plane plots associated with the terminal characteristics of a passive two-terminal network or device. (a) Alternative forms of the circuit phasor diagram. (b) The* **Z**-plane plot. *(c) The* **Y**-plane plot. *(d) The* **S**-plane plot.*

The student should satisfy himself that these forms are indeed equivalent. The S-plane plot appears in (d) of Fig. 5.17, and its similarities with the other four diagrams of that figure should be noted.

One can now list quite an array of expressions for the average power and reactive volt-amperes into a passive two-terminal network with voltage **V** across it and current **I** through it in the same direction as **V**. The power expressions are

$$P = \text{Re } [\mathbf{S}] = S \cos \theta$$
$$= VI \cos \theta$$
$$= RI^2$$
$$= V_R I$$
$$= GV^2$$
$$= VI_G. \tag{5.90}$$

Expressions for the reactive volt-amperes are

$$Q = \text{Im } [\mathbf{S}] = S \sin \theta$$
$$= VI \sin \theta$$
$$= XI^2$$
$$= V_X I$$
$$= -BV^2$$
$$= -VI_B. \tag{5.91}$$

Finally, let us observe that, in general,

$$G(\omega) \neq \frac{1}{R(\omega)} \tag{5.92a}$$

and

$$jB(\omega) \neq \frac{1}{jX(\omega)}. \tag{5.92b}$$

In other words, the parallel conductive component, G, is not generally equal to the reciprocal of the series resistive component, $1/R$. Likewise, the parallel susceptance component is not generally equal to the reciprocal of the series reactive component.

EXAMPLE 5.13. The voltage across a certain two-terminal network is

$$\mathbf{V} = 120e^{j70°} = 41.0 + j113 \text{ V},$$

and the current through the network in the direction of voltage drop is

$$\mathbf{I} = 5e^{j40°} = 3.83 + j3.22 \text{ A}.$$

a.   Calculate $\mathbf{V}_R$, $\mathbf{V}_X$, P, and Q.

b.   Calculate $\mathbf{I}_G$, $\mathbf{I}_B$, P, and Q.

Solution. From Eq. (5.85)

$$\begin{aligned}
\mathbf{V} &= (V_R + jV_X)e^{j\phi_i} \\
&= (120e^{j30°})e^{j40°} \\
&= (104 + j60)e^{j40°}.
\end{aligned}$$

Consequently,

$$\mathbf{V}_R = 104e^{j40°} \text{ V} \qquad Ans.$$
$$\mathbf{V}_X = 60e^{j130°} \text{ V}, \qquad Ans.$$

and, using Eqs. (5.90) and (5.91),

$$P = V_R I = 520 \text{ W} \qquad Ans.$$
$$Q = V_X I = 300 \text{ vars}. \qquad Ans.$$

From Eq. (5.87)

$$\begin{aligned}
\mathbf{I} &= (I_G + jI_B)e^{j\phi_v} \\
&= (5e^{-j30°})e^{j70°} \\
&= (4.33 - j2.50)e^{j70°}.
\end{aligned}$$

Consequently,

$$\mathbf{I}_G = 4.33e^{j70°} \text{ A} \qquad Ans.$$
$$\mathbf{I}_B = 2.50e^{-j20°} \text{ A}, \qquad Ans.$$

and, using Eqs. (5.90) and (5.91),

$$P = VI_G = 520 \text{ W} \qquad Ans.$$
$$Q = -VI_B = 300 \text{ vars}. \qquad Ans.$$

5.11 RESONANCE

We will speak briefly of resonance here but will leave the detailed discussion of the phenomenon until we can undertake it with more sophistication than at present.

The magnitude of an impedance or admittance containing both inductive and capacitive elements will usually show a maximum or minimum value at some frequency of operation. At or near the same frequency, the phase angle will go to zero. Circuits possessing such impedance or admittance functions are said to be *resonant circuits*.

There are a number of definitions of the *resonant frequency*, and these will be discussed later in some detail. Rather than attempt to pin down a strict definition of resonant frequency at this point, let us list three well-defined frequencies:

ω_m = radian frequency at which a fixed-parameter $|Z(j\omega)|$
or $|Y(j\omega)|$ is a maximum, Z_m or Y_m,   (5.93a)

ω_u = radian frequency at which the angle on a fixed-parameter $Z(j\omega)$ or $Y(j\omega)$ is zero (unity power factor),   (5.93b)

$\omega_n = 1/\sqrt{LC}$ in any circuit containing one inductor and one
capacitor.   (5.93c)

At this moment, ω_n is simply chosen to be a convenient constant having the units rad/sec = sec^{-1}. You will recall that

$$\text{the units on } L = \frac{V \cdot \sec}{A} = \Omega \cdot \sec$$

and

$$\text{the units on } C = \frac{A \cdot \sec}{V} = \Omega^{-1} \cdot \sec$$

so that

$$\text{the units on } \frac{1}{\sqrt{LC}} = \sec^{-1}.$$

In a word, ω_n is defined as it has been simply as a convenience to the matter at hand. In a later chapter, however, we shall take note of the important physical significance of this convenient constant.

The *R-L-C* Series Circuit

Consider the series *R-L-C* circuit, where

$$Y(j\omega) = \frac{1}{R + j\left(\omega L - \dfrac{1}{\omega C}\right)}.$$

Obviously, this admittance function is maximum when the denominator is least, which occurs when

$$\omega L - \frac{1}{\omega C} = 0.$$

The solution is

$$\omega = \omega_m = \frac{1}{\sqrt{LC}}.$$

This is also clearly the frequency at which the phase angle is zero, so for the R-L-C series circuit,

$$\omega_m = \omega_u = \omega_n = \frac{1}{\sqrt{LC}}. \tag{5.94}$$

It is obvious that

$$Y(j\omega_m) = Y_m = \frac{1}{R}, \qquad \text{(series } R\text{-}L\text{-}C \text{ circuit)}. \tag{5.95}$$

In the special case of $R = 0$,

$$\frac{1}{Y(j\omega)} = j\left(\omega L - \frac{1}{\omega C}\right) = j(X_L + X_C) = jX(\omega),$$

and

$$\frac{1}{Y_m} = \frac{1}{Y(j\omega_n)} = 0.$$

The variation of this admittance with radian frequency is plotted as the algebraic sum of the inductive and capacitive reactance variations in Fig. 5.18(a). The case of $R = 0$ is a special case in which the student may write the usually verboten $|X| = 1/|B|$, or $jX = -1/jB$, which leads to Fig. 5.18(b).

The results of these plots can be translated into the solid-line plots in Fig. 5.19. From these results, it is apparent that in the case of zero resistance (the lossless case) the admittance is zero at zero frequency. As the frequency increases admittance becomes a higher and higher value of purely capacitive susceptance, its magnitude increasing without limit at radian frequencies approaching ω_n. As ω_n is passed we find that the susceptance has switched from purely capacitive to purely inductive and decreases as the frequency increases.

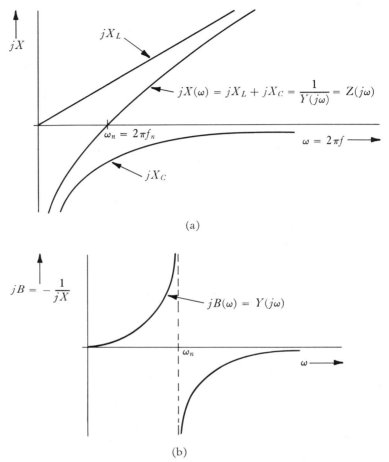

(a)

(b)

Fig. 5.18 *Reactance and susceptance variations with frequency in the L-C series circuit. (a) Reactance variation. (b) Susceptance variation.*

When the series circuit is not lossless the impedance variation becomes just the variation of the imaginary part of the impedance. In addition, there is the real part, R. Since for finite X,

$$\frac{1}{|R + jX|} < \frac{1}{|jX|}$$

the admittance frequency variation for the lossy case will lie below that of the lossless case for any nonzero frequency. Furthermore, in the lossy case the magnitude does not increase without limit as ω approaches ω_n; rather it increases to a maximum of $1/R$ at ω_n, as indicated by Eq. (5.95). The admittance is *purely* reactive only at $\omega = 0$ and $\omega = \infty$, but it is capacitive with phase angles between $90°$ and zero for $\omega < \omega_n$ and inductive with phase angles between zero and $-90°$ for $\omega > \omega_n$. These results are indicated by the dotted curve in Fig. 5.19.

Obviously, the *R-L-C* series circuit can be made to have the admittance in the neighborhood of $\omega = \omega_n$ much greater than that at frequencies outside this neighborhood, and the narrowness of the neighborhood is enhanced as R is decreased. Therefore, this circuit can be made quite *frequency-selective*, passing large currents in the neighborhood of $\omega = \omega_n$ and negligibly small currents outside the neighborhood.

The region of frequency passing large currents is called the *pass-band*, and it is usually taken as the range of frequencies over which the average power absorbed by the circuit exceeds one-half the maximum power absorbed, with

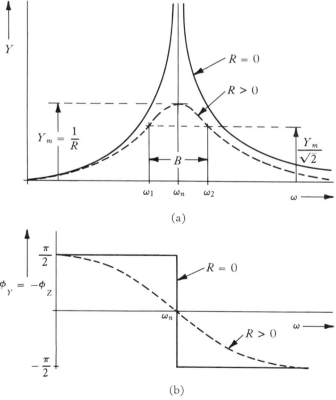

(a)

(b)

Fig. 5.19 *R-L-C series admittance variation with frequency. (a) Magnitude variation. (b) Angle variation.*

the effective value of the applied voltage remaining constant. The boundaries of this region are called the *cut-off frequencies* or the *half-power points*.

Since

$$Y(j\omega) = \frac{1}{R + j\left(\omega L - \dfrac{1}{\omega C}\right)}$$

$$= \left[R - j\left(\omega L - \frac{1}{\omega C}\right)\right] |Y(j\omega)|^2$$

$$= G(\omega) + jB(\omega),$$

it is clear that

$$G(\omega) = R |Y(j\omega)|^2.$$

With an applied voltage of constant rms value, V, regardless of frequency, the average power is

$$P = V^2 G(\omega) = V^2 R |Y(j\omega)|^2. \tag{5.96}$$

This power is maximum whenever $G(\omega)$ is maximum, which in turn occurs at maximum $|Y(j\omega)|$. The maximum admittance is $Y_m = Y(j\omega_n) = 1/R$, so

$$P_{\text{max}} = V^2 G(\omega_n) = V^2 R Y_m^2 = \frac{V^2}{R}, \tag{5.97}$$

which is the same power that results when the input voltage is applied to the resistor alone, as indeed it is at resonance.

If the cut-off, or half-power, frequency is called ω_c, then

$$\tfrac{1}{2} P_{\text{max}} = V^2 G(\omega_c) = V^2 R |Y(j\omega_c)|^2. \tag{5.98}$$

Combining Eqs. (5.97) and (5.98) results in

$$\frac{1}{2} \frac{V^2}{R} = V^2 R |Y(j\omega_c)|^2$$

$$= \frac{V^2 R}{R^2 + \left(\omega_c L - \dfrac{1}{\omega_c C}\right)^2},$$

an equation wherein ω_c is the only unknown. Rearranging the resulting equation yields

$$\omega_c L - \frac{1}{\omega_c C} = \pm R. \tag{5.99}$$

From the definition of ω_n,

$$\frac{1}{C} = \omega_n^2 L,$$

so C may be eliminated in Eq. (5.99) to yield

$$\omega_c L \mp R - \frac{\omega_n^2 L}{\omega_c} = 0.$$

Multiplication by ω_c / ω_n^2 and division by L then produces

$$\left(\frac{\omega_c}{\omega_n}\right)^2 \mp \frac{1}{Q}\left(\frac{\omega_c}{\omega_n}\right) - 1 = 0, \tag{5.100}$$

where

$$Q = \frac{\omega_n L}{R}. \tag{5.101}$$

In these quadratics ω_c / ω_n has the four solutions

$$\frac{\omega_c}{\omega_n} = \pm\frac{1}{2Q} \pm \sqrt{\frac{1}{4Q^2} + 1}.$$

Now real frequencies are always positive, and, therefore, only those solutions which result in positive frequencies are of interest to us. Since Q is positive, only two of the solutions are positive. If we call the smallest of these ω_1 / ω_n and the largest ω_2 / ω_n, they are

$$\frac{\omega_1}{\omega_n} = \sqrt{\left(\frac{1}{2Q}\right)^2 + 1} - \frac{1}{2Q} \tag{5.102a}$$

$$\frac{\omega_2}{\omega_n} = \sqrt{\left(\frac{1}{2Q}\right)^2 + 1} + \frac{1}{2Q}. \tag{5.102b}$$

The radian frequencies ω_1 and ω_2 are called the *lower half-power* and the *upper half-power* points, respectively.

The *bandwidth* is the span of frequencies covered by the pass band, or, utilizing Eqs. (5.102),

$$B = \omega_2 - \omega_1$$

$$= \frac{\omega_n}{Q}. \tag{5.103}$$

Notice that for a given L and C, and, therefore, a fixed ω_n, the higher the value of Q the smaller will be the bandwidth and the more frequency-selective the circuit will be. Therefore, the largeness of Q is an indicator of the quality of the circuit as far as frequency selectivity is concerned. This is the historical reason for calling Q the *quality factor* of the circuit. High-Q circuits designed to pass a narrow band of frequencies are called *tuned circuits*.

Before leaving the series tuned circuit, we should note from Eqs. (5.97) and (5.98) that

$$|Y(j\omega_c)| = |Y(\omega_1)| = |Y(j\omega_2)| = \frac{Y_m}{\sqrt{2}}. \tag{5.104}$$

At cut-off frequencies, then, the magnitude of the admittance is the peak value divided by $\sqrt{2}$. The interrelations between cut-off frequencies, bandwidth, and peak admittance magnitude are shown graphically on Fig. 5.19(a).

EXAMPLE 5.14. Determine ω_n, Q, ω_1, ω_2, and B for the circuit in Example 5.4.

Solution. Using Eq. (5.93c),

$$\omega_n = \frac{1}{\sqrt{(40 \times 10^{-3})(25 \times 10^{-6})}} = 1000 \text{ sec}^{-1}. \quad Ans.$$

Equation (5.101) gives the quality factor

$$Q = \frac{1000(40 \times 10^{-3})}{30} = 1.33, \quad Ans.$$

indicating that this particular circuit has a relatively low frequency selectivity or large pass band. The lower and upper half-power frequencies are, according to Eqs. (5.102),

$$\omega_1 = \left[\sqrt{\left(\frac{1}{2 \times 1.33}\right)^2 + 1} - \frac{1}{2 \times 1.33}\right] 1000$$
$$= (1.060 - 0.375)1000$$
$$= 685 \text{ rad/sec} \quad Ans.$$
$$\omega_2 = (1.060 + 0.375)1000 = 1435 \text{ rad/sec}. \quad Ans.$$

The corresponding bandwidth is

$$B = \frac{1000}{1.33} = 750 \text{ rad/sec}. \quad Ans.$$

The *G-C-L* Parallel Circuit

In the *G-C-L* parallel circuit,

$$Z(j\omega) = \frac{1}{G + j\left(\omega C - \frac{1}{\omega L}\right)}.$$

Since the mathematical form is identical with that of the R-L-C series circuit admittance, the results are identical providing that Z replaces Y, G replaces R, B replaces X, C replaces L, and L replaces C. Therefore, the reactance, susceptance, and admittance curves of Figs. 5.18 and 5.19 for the series circuit are identical in form to the susceptance, reactance, and impedance curves for the parallel circuit.

The quality factor for the parallel circuit becomes, by the above interchange of symbols,

$$Q = \frac{\omega_n C}{G}. \qquad (5.105a)$$

Substitution of

$$\omega_n^2 L = \frac{1}{C}$$

and

$$R = \frac{1}{G}$$

results in the form

$$Q = \frac{R}{\omega_n L}, \qquad (5.105b)$$

which appears to be the reciprocal of the Q obtained in Eq. (5.101). The student is thereby cautioned to observe that the R in Eq. (5.105b) is a parallel resistance.

EXAMPLE 5.15. Evaluate ω_u for the parallel G-C-L circuit obtained in Example 5.9.

Solution. The unity power factor radian frequency, according to Eq. (5.94), is

$$\omega_u = \omega_n = \frac{1}{\sqrt{CL}} = \frac{1}{\sqrt{(113 \times 10^{-6})(62.5 \times 10^{-3})}}$$

$$= 376 \text{ rad/sec.} \quad Ans.$$

The significance of this result is that in reducing Q (reactive volt-amperes) to zero by adding a parallel capacitor to the network of Fig. 5.9, the original system was tuned to 60 Hz.

The R-L-C **Series-Parallel Circuit**

The series-parallel arrangement of Fig. 5.20 is of considerable practical importance. It usually is constructed from a coil of inductance, L, and resistance, R, in parallel with a capacitance, C. It is used to form a large

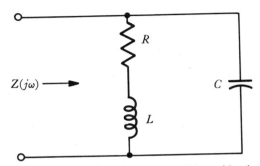

Fig. 5.20 *An important series-parallel combination.*

impedance in the neighborhood of the tuned frequency, at or near ω_n, and a small impedance at frequencies outside the neighborhood.

The impedance is

$$Z(j\omega) = \frac{(R + j\omega L)\dfrac{1}{j\omega C}}{R + j\left(\omega L - \dfrac{1}{\omega C}\right)}$$

$$= \frac{R + j\omega L}{j\omega C}\, Y_s(j\omega), \tag{5.106}$$

where

$$Y_s(j\omega) = \frac{1}{R + j\left(\omega L - \dfrac{1}{\omega C}\right)}. \tag{5.106a}$$

Let us now note some approximations. First, we observe that

$$Z(0) = R, \tag{5.107}$$

and we see that at the very low frequencies the capacitance acts as an open circuit, leaving just the R-L branch active with, of course, $\omega L \cong 0$. Actually, she above result is obvious from an inspection of the circuit. A more important approximation results when R is small enough that the following holds for some range of frequency containing ω_n:

$$\frac{R}{L} \ll \omega. \tag{5.108}$$

Under this condition $R + j\omega L \simeq j\omega L$, and

$$Z(j\omega) \simeq \frac{L}{C} Y_s(j\omega), \qquad \omega \gg \frac{R}{L}. \tag{5.109}$$

Furthermore, $Y_s(j\omega)$ is exactly the same, for a given R, L, and C, as the $Y(j\omega)$ plotted in Fig. 5.19; and $Z(j\omega)$ is of the same form. Therefore, $Z(j\omega)$ has a peak at approximately $\omega = \omega_n$, well within the frequency range for which Eq. (5.108) is valid.

The end points of inequality (5.108) are equivalent to

$$\frac{R}{\omega_n L} \ll 1 \qquad \text{or} \qquad \frac{\omega_n L}{R} \gg 1.$$

The left side of the second form defines Q, so we are dealing with the situation wherein $Q \gg 1$. Thus we can make the following statement: "*As the Q of the R-L-C series-parallel tuned circuit becomes higher, its impedance-frequency characteristic more nearly approaches in form that of the admittance-frequency characteristic of the R-L-C series circuit of the same Q.*" This is illustrated in Fig. 5.21, which shows that the curve for $Q = \infty$ is exactly of the same form

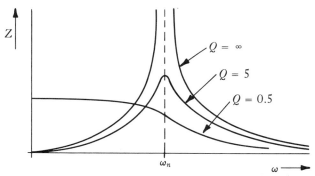

Fig. 5.21   *Impedance magnitude variation with frequency in the R-L-C series-parallel circuit.*

as that for the series circuit, but that similarity in form decreases for decreasing Q.

It is left as a student exercise to show that unity power factor resonance occurs at

$$\omega_u = \omega_n \sqrt{1 - \frac{1}{Q^2}}, \tag{5.110}$$

rather than at $\omega_u = \omega_n$ as for the series R-L-C admittance. Here again, though, the two cases become more the same as Q increases. It should also be noted that ω_m does not equal ω_n but approaches ω_n in the limit as Q approaches infinity.

More to Follow

In this chapter we have just touched on the nature of electric circuits capable of resonance. In a later chapter they will be met again and dealt with in greater detail and with more generality.

PROBLEMS

5.1   Find average and effective values of the periodic function in Fig. P.5.1(a).

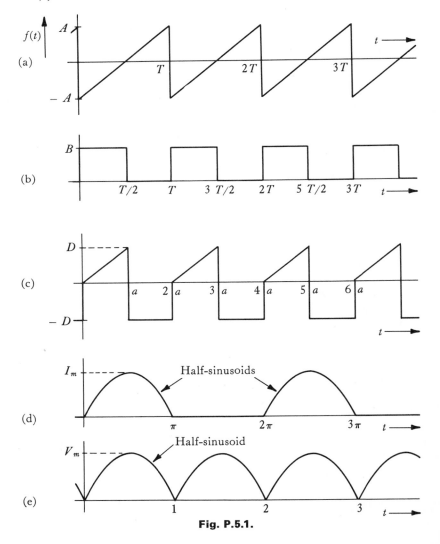

Fig. P.5.1.

5.2. Repeat Prob. 1 for Fig. P.5.1(b).
5.3 Repeat Prob. 1 for Fig. P.5.1(c).
5.4 Repeat Prob. 1 for Fig. P.5.1(d).
5.5 Repeat Prob. 1 for Fig. P.5.1(e).
5.6 Plot on one graph the following functions of time:

a. $f_1(t) = 100 \cos 200t$,
b. $f_2(t) = 150 \sin 200t$,
c. $f_3(t) = 75 \cos (200t + \pi/6)$,
d. $q(t) = 100 \cos 400t$.

5.7 Express each of the sinusoids in Fig. P.5.2 as cosines with a phase angle, giving numerical values throughout.

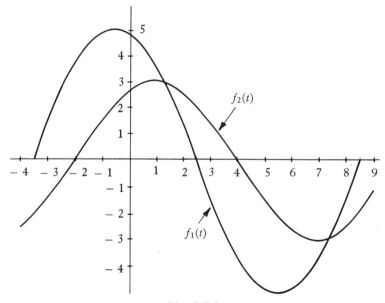

Fig. P.5.2.

5.8 Give the frequency, period, amplitude, and phase angle of each sinusoid in Prob. 5.6.
5.9 Give the frequency, period, amplitude, and phase angle of each sinusoid in Fig. P.5.2.
5.10 Prove that Eq. (5.13) is a valid expression relating the effective value of a sinusoid to its amplitude.
5.11 Prove that Eq. (5.15) follows from Eqs. (5.14).
5.12 Give **F** corresponding to each sinusoidal variation in Prob. 5.6.
5.13 Give **F** for each sinusoidal variation in Fig. P.5.2.

5.14 Find the sum of $f_1(t)$ and $f_2(t)$ in Fig. P.5.2 by phasor methods.

5.15 Find the following sums, using phasor methods:

a. $120 \cos 10^6 t + 400 \cos (10^6 t - 40°)$,
b. $16.2 \cos 1000t + 20.0 \sin 1000t$,
c. $18.5 \cos (25t + 30°) + 15.0 \sin (25t - 125°)$,
d. $2 \cos t + 5 \sin t + 3 \cos (t - 3)$.

5.16 Find the product of $f_1(t)$ and $f_2(t)$ in Fig. P.5.2 by application of Eqs. (5.25) and check the result using trigonometric identities.

5.17 The voltage and current at the terminals of a certain two-terminal device are the steady-state sinusoids

$$v_{ss}(t) = 10 \cos (300t + 30°) \text{ V}$$

$$i_{ss}(t) = 15 \cos (300t - 30°) \text{ A}.$$

Current through the device is taken positive in the same direction as the voltage drop. Plot on one graph $v_{ss}(t)$, $i_{ss}(t)$, and the instantaneous power, $p(t)$. Indicate on the graph the average power, P, into the device.

5.18 Repeat Prob. 5.17 when

$$v_{ss}(t) = -250 \cos (500t - 30°)$$

$$i_{ss}(t) = 20 \sin (500t - 60°).$$

5.19 Repeat Prob. 5.17 when

$$v_{ss}(t) = 250 \cos 500t$$

$$i_{ss}(t) = 20 \sin 500t.$$

5.20 Repeat Prob. 5.17 when

$$v_{ss}(t) = 250 \cos 500t$$

$$i_{ss}(t) = 20 \cos (500t + 120°).$$

5.21 In Fig. 5.5, $R = 500\ \Omega$, $L = 0.2$ H, and $C = 0.8\ \mu$F. The terminal voltage is the steady-state sinusoid

$$v_{ss}(t) = 250 \cos \omega t.$$

When $\omega = 400$ rad per sec, find **Z** in the rectangular and exponential forms; find the phasor values of applied voltage, current, resistor voltage, inductor voltage, and capacitor voltage; and find the average power.

5.22 Repeat Prob. 5.21 when $\omega = 2000$ rad per sec.
5.23 Repeat Prob. 5.21 when $\omega = 2500$ rad per sec.
5.24 Repeat Prob. 5.21 when $\omega = 3000$ rad per sec.
5.25 Repeat Prob. 5.21 when $\omega = 10,000$ rad per sec.

5.26 In Fig. P.5.3(a), the forcing voltage is the steady-state value of $v(t)$:

$$v_{ss}(t) = 141.4 \cos \omega t.$$

For $\omega = 500$, $\omega = 1000$, and $\omega = 2000$, determine the steady-state sinusoidal component of the indicated current response using phasor methods.

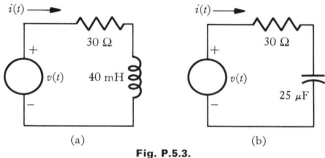

Fig. P.5.3.

5.27 Repeat Prob. 5.26 for the circuit of Fig. P.5.3(b).
5.28 In Fig. P.5.4(a), the forcing voltage is the steady-state value of $v(t)$:

$$v_{ss}(t) = 141.4 \cos\left(\omega t - \frac{\pi}{6}\right).$$

For $\omega = 500$, $\omega = 1000$, and $\omega = 2000$, find the steady-state value of $v_C(t)$, $v_{Css}(t)$, using phasor methods.

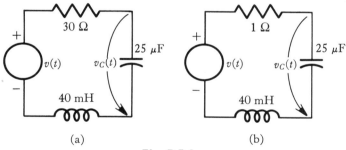

Fig. P.5.4.

5.29 Repeat Prob. 5.28 for the circuit of Fig. P.5.4(b).
5.30 For Prob. 5.26, find **V**, **I**, and **S** for each frequency. In each case, find the average power by three methods: $P = \text{Re}[S]$, $P = VI \cos \theta$, and $P = I^2 R$. Also find Q by three similar methods.
5.31 Repeat the requirements of Prob. 5.30 as applied to Prob. 5.27.
5.32 Repeat the requirements of Prob. 5.30 as applied to Prob. 5.28.

5.33 Repeat the requirements of Prob. 5.30 as applied to Prob. 5.29.

5.34 Show that for the admittance of the *G-C-L* parallel circuit of Fig. 5.10 to be equal to that of the *R-L-C* series circuit of Fig. 5.5, the following must be true:

$$G = \frac{R}{Z} \qquad B = \frac{1}{Z^2}\left(\omega L - \frac{1}{\omega C}\right),$$

where Z is the magnitude of the *R-L-C* series circuit impedance.

5.35 Suppose the resistance, capacitance, and inductance of Prob. 5.21 are reconnected for the *G-C-L* parallel combination of Fig. 5.10 and the forcing voltage is the steady-state sinusoid

$$v(t) = v_{ss}(t) = 250 \cos \omega t.$$

When $\omega = 400$ rad/sec, find the complex admittance, **Y**, in the rectangular and exponential forms; find the phasor values of applied voltage, total current, conductance current, inductor current, and capacitor current; and find the average power.

5.36 Repeat Prob. 5.35 when $\omega = 2000$ rad/sec.

5.37 Repeat Prob. 5.35 when $\omega = 2500$ rad/sec.

5.38 Repeat Prob. 5.35 when $\omega = 3000$ rad/sec.

5.39 Repeat Prob. 5.35 when $\omega = 10{,}000$ rad/sec.

5.40 In Fig. P.5.5, the network is known to be inductive and the following meter readings are obtained:

wattmeter	2200 W
voltmeter	240 V
ammeter	15 A.

a. Find the vector volt-amperes, the average power, the reactive volt-amperes, and the power factor.

b. Find the complex impedance, the resistance, and the reactance.

c. Find the complex admittance, the conductance, and the susceptance.

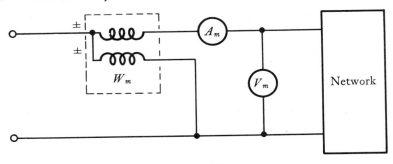

Fig. P.5.5.

5.41 Repeat Prob. 5.40 for the following meter readings:

wattmeter	800 W
voltmeter	120 V
ammeter	9.5 A.

5.42 In Prob. 5.41, the frequency is 60 Hz. What value of capacitance in parallel with the given network will cause the power factor to be unity?

5.43 In Fig. P.5.5, the impedance consists of 8.28 Ω of resistance in series with 16.45 Ω of capacitive reactance and the applied voltage is 240 V. What are the remaining two meter readings and the power factor?

5.44 In Fig. P.5.5, the meter readings are

wattmeter	500 W
voltmeter	80 V
ammeter	15 A.

The frequency is 60 Hz.

a. What are the two possible combinations of just two circuit elements (*R-L*, *R-C*, or *L-C*) in series?

b. What are the two possible combinations of just two circuit elements in parallel?

5.45 A certain 2400-V industrial load is 100 kVA at a lagging power factor of 0.7. In order to cut transmission costs for transmitting the usable power, it has been decided to place a capacitor bank in parallel with the load to raise the power factor to unity. What must be the kVA rating of the capacitor bank?

5.46 In Probs. 5.21 through 5.25, check KVL using phasor diagrams drawn to scale.

5.47 In Probs. 5.35 through 5.39, check KCL using phasor diagrams drawn to scale.

5.48 For Prob. 5.40:

a. Draw the S-plane diagram.

b. Draw to scale from one origin the circuit phasor diagram, assuming that the network consists of a resistance in series with a reactance.

c. Follow the instructions of (b), except assume the network consists of a conductance in parallel with a susceptance.

5.49 Draw to scale from one origin the circuit phasor diagram for Prob. 5.42.

5.50 Draw to scale the S-plane diagram for Prob. 5.45.

5.51 Using phasors drawn to scale, check KVL and KCL in Example 5.10.

5.52 In Fig. P.5.6, find $i_{ss}(t)$ if

$$v_{1ss}(t) = 10 \sin 10{,}000t.$$

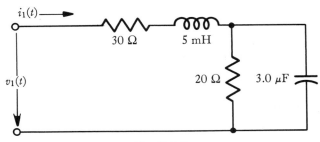

Fig. P.5.6.

5.53 If, in Fig. P.5.7,

$$v_{ss}(t) = 100 \cos 1000t,$$

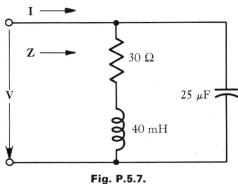

Fig. P.5.7.

find:

a. **I**   b. **Z**
c. $X(\omega)$ d. $R(\omega)$
e. S   f. P
g. Q
h. Sketch the complete circuit phasor diagram showing all voltages and currents.

5.54 If, in Fig. P.5.8,

$$\mathbf{V}_2 = 100 + j0,$$

find $\mathbf{V}_1$, $\mathbf{I}_1$, $\mathbf{I}_2$, and $\mathbf{I}$.

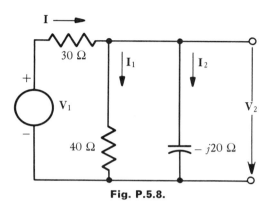

Fig. P.5.8.

5.55 In Fig. P.5.9,

$$R_1 = 20\ \Omega \qquad R_2 = 30\ \Omega$$
$$C = 2\ \mu F \qquad \omega = 250{,}000\ \text{rad/sec}$$
$$\mathbf{V} = 120e^{j30°}\ \text{V}.$$

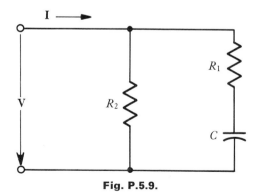

Fig. P.5.9.

a. Sketch the complete circuit phasor diagrams, showing all voltages and currents.
b. Find $\mathbf{I}$, the average power, and the power factor.

5.56 In Fig. P.5.10, $I_C = 20e^{j0}$A.

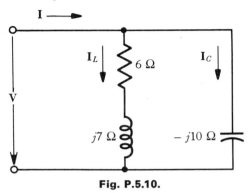

Fig. P.5.10.

a.   Sketch the circuit phasor diagram, showing $\mathbf{V}$, $\mathbf{I}$, $\mathbf{I}_L$, and $\mathbf{I}_C$.
b.   Compute analytically $\mathbf{I}_L$ and $\mathbf{V}$.

5.57 Find the Thévenin and Norton equivalents to the network in Fig. P.5.11 if the frequency is 159 Hz.

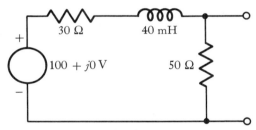

Fig. P.5.11.

5.58 In Fig. P.5.12, $\omega = 1000$ rad/sec. Find:

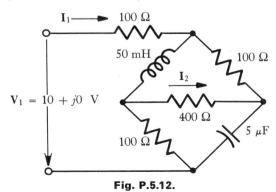

Fig. P.5.12.

a. I_1 and I_2.
b. The average power supplied to the network and to the 400-Ω resistor.
c. The complex input impedance at this frequency.
Hint. First apply Thévenin's or Norton's theorem to find I_2.

5.59 For the circuit of Fig. P.5.13:

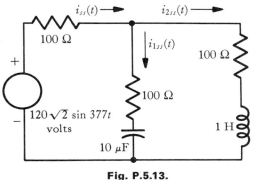

Fig. P.5.13.

a. Sketch the complete circuit phasor diagram.
b. Find the indicated three steady-state currents.
c. Compute the average power in each resistor, then compare the sum of the resistor powers with that computed by $P = \text{Re}\,[\mathbf{I}*\mathbf{V}]$.

5.60 In the "phase-shifting network" of Fig. P.5.14, $R_1 \ll |1/\omega C|$. Show

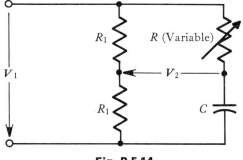

Fig. P.5.14.

that

$$\frac{\mathbf{V}_2}{\mathbf{V}_1} = \tfrac{1}{2}e^{-j2\theta}, \qquad \text{where } \tan\theta = R\omega C.$$

Thus, for a constant $\mathbf{V}_1$, changing R changes the angle of $\mathbf{V}_2$ without changing its magnitude.

5.61 In Fig. P.5.15, ammeter Am_2 reads 10.0 A. Assume negligible resistance in ammeters and wattmeter current coils and infinite resistance in voltmeters and wattmeter potential coils. What are the readings of the remaining meters?

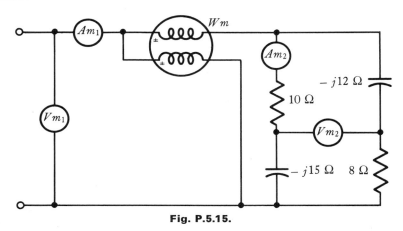

Fig. P.5.15.

5.62 Plot as functions of radian frequency $G(\omega)$, $B(\omega)$, $|Y(j\omega)|$, and $\phi_Y(\omega)$ for the circuit of Fig. P.5.4(a).

5.63 Repeat Prob. 5.62 for the circuit of Fig. P.5.4(b).

5.64 Plot as functions of radian frequency $R(\omega)$, $X(\omega)$, $|Z(j\omega)|$, and $\phi_Z(\omega)$ for the circuit of Fig. P.5.7.

5.65 Find V_R, V_X, I_G, and I_B associated with the impedance $\mathbf{Z} = 40 + j75\,\Omega$ when the applied voltage is 150 V rms.

5.66 Find V_R, V_X, I_G, and I_B associated with the admittance $\mathbf{Y} = 0.7 + j0.2\ \Omega^{-1}$ when the applied voltage is 72 V rms.

5.67 Find V_R, V_X, I_G, and I_B in Prob. 5.40.

5.68 Find V_R, V_X, I_G, and I_B in Prob. 5.41.

5.69 Find V_R, V_X, I_G, and I_B in Prob. 5.44.

5.70 Find I_G and I_B in Prob. 5.45 both with and without the capacitor bank.

5.71 A 5.0-mH coil has a resistance of 50 Ω.

a. What capacitance in series with the coil will cause resonance at 100 kHz?

b. What will be the maximum value of the admittance?

c. What will be the quality factor, Q?

d. What will be the bandwidth and the half-power frequencies?

5.72 Repeat Prob. 5.71 when the resistance is 500 Ω.

5.73 Repeat Prob. 5.71 when the total series resistance is 5000 Ω.

5.74 Repeat Prob. 5.71 when the resonant frequency is to be 1.0 MHz.

5.75 Repeat Prob. 5.74 when the resistance is increased to 500 Ω.

5.76 Repeat Prob. 5.74 when the resistance is 5000 Ω.

5.77 When the voltage applied is 20.0 V rms at the resonant frequency, find the voltage across the capacitor in Probs. 5.71, 5.72, and 5.73.

5.78 When the voltage applied is 20.0 V rms at the resonant frequency, find the voltage across the capacitor in Probs. 5.74, 5.75, and 5.76.

5.79 Design a series *R-L-C* circuit that has maximum admittance at 10 kHz and $Q = 50$. What is the maximum admittance?

5.80 Design a series *R-L-C* circuit that has maximum admittance at 100 kHz with $Q = 300$. What is the maximum admittance?

5.81 A 0.5-H inductance having a resistance of 500 Ω is to be used to design a "tank" circuit of the type in Fig. 5.20 to obtain a network offering a high impedance at one frequency.

    a.   What is the lowest design value of ω_n if $Q \geqslant 100$?

    b.   What range of capacitance will cause $Q \geqslant 100$?

5.82 Repeat Prob. 5.81 for $Q \geqslant 50$.

5.83 Repeat Prob. 5.81 for $Q \geqslant 200$.

5.84 Prove Eq. (5.110).

5.85 For what value of Q does $\omega_1 = 0$ in Fig. 5.20?

5.86 A 200-mH coil has a resistance of 50 Ω. When a 0.03-μF condenser is placed in parallel with the coil, find:

    a. ω_n **b.** ω_u

    c. ω_1 and ω_2 (if both exist)

    d. Q **e.**   bandwidth.

5.87 Repeat Prob. 5.86 when the coil resistance is 500 Ω.

5.88 Repeat Prob. 5.86 using a 200-pF condenser.

5.89 Repeat Prob. 5.88 when the coil resistance is 500 Ω.

5.90 Find the current to the right in the 6-Ω resistor in Fig. P.5.16 by superposition.

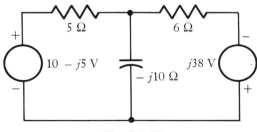

Fig. P.5.16.

5.91 Find the current to the right in the 6-Ω resistor in Fig. P.5.16 by use of Thévenin's theorem.

5.92 Find the phasor current $\mathbf{I}_a$ in Fig. P.5.17 using superposition.

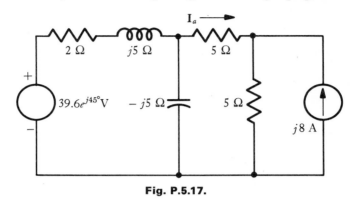

Fig. P.5.17.

5.93 Find the phasor current $\mathbf{I}_a$ in Fig. P.5.17 by application of Thévenin's and/or Norton's theorem.

5.94 Prove that the locus of the admittance of the series combination of R and jX as X is varied is the circle of Fig. P.5.18, along which

$$\mathbf{Y} = \frac{1}{2R}(1 + e^{-j2\alpha}),$$

where $\alpha = \tan^{-1} X/R$.

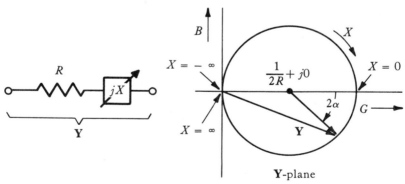

Fig. P.5.18.

5.95 Prove that the locus of the admittance of the *R-L-C* series circuit as frequency is varied is the circle of Fig. P.5.19, along which

$$Y(j\omega) = \frac{1}{2R}[1 + e^{-j2\alpha(\omega)}],$$

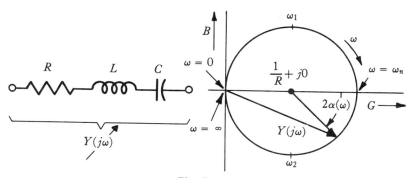

Fig. P.5.19.

where

$$\alpha(\omega) = \tan^{-1} Q\left(\frac{\omega}{\omega_n} - \frac{\omega_n}{\omega}\right),$$

and that the points $\omega = 0$, ω_1, ω_n, ω_2, ∞ divide the locus into quadrants as shown. (*Note*: ω_1 and ω_2 are, as usual, the half-power frequencies.)

5.96 Show that the locus of the admittance of a series combination of R and jX as R is varied is the semicircle of Fig. P.5.20 (when X is positive), along which

$$\mathbf{Y} = -j\frac{1}{2X}(1 + e^{j2\beta}),$$

where

$$\beta = \tan^{-1}\frac{R}{X}.$$

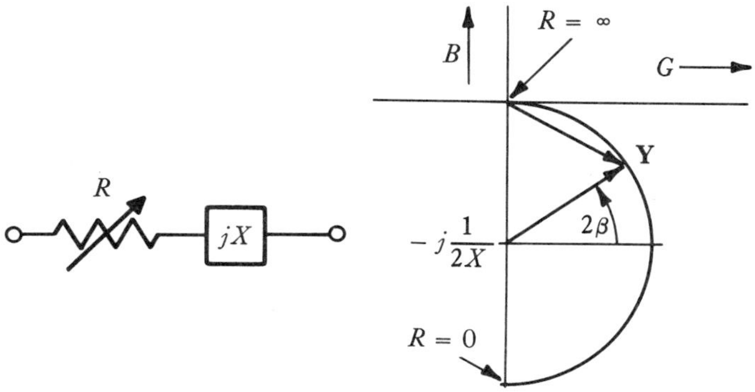

Fig. P.5.20.

5.97 Show that the combination of a low-resistance coil in parallel with a capacitance may be approximated by a *G-C-L* parallel circuit in the neighborhood of $\omega = \omega_n$, provided that $Q \gg 1$, as indicated in Fig. P.5.21. In the

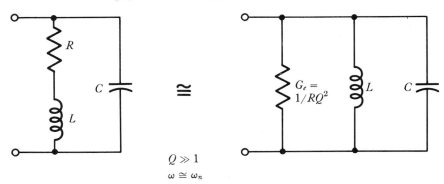

$$Q \gg 1$$
$$\omega \cong \omega_n$$

Fig. P.5.21.

figure, the *G-C-L* parallel circuit has the same capacitance and approximately the same inductance as the original circuit, and the equivalent conductance is

$$G_e \simeq \frac{1}{RQ^2}.$$

Express the impedance in terms of G_e, L, and C, and compare the result with the expression for the admittance of the series *R-L-C* circuit.

6

Network Analysis

6.1 INTRODUCTION

We have dealt with networks, some of them rather complicated, in the preceding chapters. However, in each case considered, there has either been but one source or the principle of superposition utilizing single-source techniques has been employed. The latter method will serve to solve the most complicated of linear systems, but it is probably evident to the student that the solution of a network with several sources can become quite tedious, particularly if a *complete* solution for *all* variables is attempted.

In this chapter we shall investigate formal techniques for simplifying and ordering the procedures for obtaining complete solutions to networks. Acceptance of the principle of superposition is implied in these methods, but the principle will not be applied directly to the obtaining of a solution. The techniques to be developed will be based entirely on Kirchhoff's laws and the volt-ampere characteristics of the passive circuit elements. The final results will, in some cases, be simple ordering routines which will reduce the writing of system equations to mere rituals. It is to be hoped that by now the student has acquired that maturity which will allow him to take advantage of such formalisms while maintaining his perspective with regard to the basics supporting them.

6.2 INDEPENDENT VARIABLES AND EQUATIONS

Suppose all the measurable currents in a network are i_1, i_2, i_3, i_4, and i_5, and they all depend on the values of the voltage and current sources exciting the system. Suppose also that, *regardless of source magnitude*,

$$i_4 = i_1 - i_2 + i_3$$
$$i_5 = i_1 + i_3.$$

This means that if any three of the currents are known, then all five are known from simple linear combinations* of the three known currents. In other words, two of the currents depend on the other three, and there are three *independent* current variables in the system. Which of the five currents form the independent set is an arbitrary choice, but the *number* of currents in the set is fixed at three. In a similar way, for a given network there will be a given number of voltages in each of the independent sets of voltages which form subsets of the set of all voltages.

The following statement summarizes the concept of variable independence in a manner suited to the purposes of this chapter:

> The number of independent variables of like dimension in a system is the least number of variables which must be known in order that all variables can be determined by linear combinations.

In our work the nature of the linear combination will be determined by Kirchhoff's laws.

In order to solve for *n* unknown variables, they must appear in *n independent equations*. We will adopt the following definition of a set of independent equations:

> A set of independent equations is one in which no one of the equations in the set may be derived from the remaining members of the set.

---

* The form $a_{11} x_1 + a_{12} x_2 + a_{13} x_3$ is called a *linear combination* of x_1, x_2, and x_3.

For example, the set of *linear equations*

$$5 = 3x_1 - 2x_2 - x_3$$
$$6 = -2x_1 + 4x_2 - 3x_3$$
$$16 = 4x_1 + 0x_2 - 5x_3$$

is not an independent set, because the third equation may be formed by adding twice the first to the second. Notice that the determinant of this set of equations is zero, so that a nontrivial solution for the x's cannot be found.

The major task of this chapter will be to establish routine methods for determining values of independent variables and for writing a proper set of independent equations for their solution.

6.3 THE REDUNDANCY PROBLEM

Consider the example of Fig. 6.1, illustrating a network of six passive elements, a voltage source, and a current source. Assuming the sources are known, there are fourteen unknown voltage and current response variables. On the other hand, the number of equations which may be written is illustrated

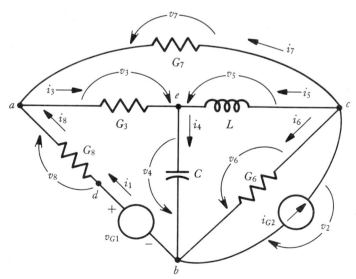

Fig. 6.1 *The circuit model of a network which has seven unknown currents and seven unknown potential differences.*

in the following tabulation:

> Equations from KCL, using only nodes   5
> Equations from KVL, using only simple loops   12
> Volt-ampere equations   6
>
>   Total   23 .

In this example we are now faced with twenty-three equations in only fourteen unknowns, which cannot constitute an independent set. The question is which subset, or subsets, of fourteen of the twenty-three equations do constitute an independent set, or sets. We shall turn to *topological* considerations for an escape from this dilemma. Before doing so, however, we should perhaps satisfy the student who claims that there are only twelve unknown variables. Such a claim is based on the fact that the currents i_1 and i_8 must obviously be equal, and of course the voltages v_2 and v_6 are also equal, as can be demonstrated mathematically by applying KCL and KVL to the simple series and parallel combinations respectively. Thus, two unknown variables can be eliminated in Fig. 6.1, but this does not change the basic dilemma. There would still be twenty-one equations in twelve unknowns.

6.4 GENERALIZED VOLT-AMPERE EQUATIONS

Let us recall the various ways in which voltage has related to current in the simple *R-L* series circuit by listing them as follows:

1.   The complete behavior in the time domain is described by

$$v(t) = Ri(t) + L\frac{di(t)}{dt}$$

$$= \left(R + L\frac{d}{dt}\right)i(t).$$

2.   The forced current related to a constant (dc) applied voltage is given by

$$V = RI.$$

3.   The forced current related to the applied exponential voltage, $v(t) = V_o e^{at}$, is provided by

$$V_o = (R + aL)I_f.$$

4.   The phasor relationship is

$$\mathbf{V} = (R + j\omega L)\mathbf{I}.$$

In each of the above four cases a voltage-dimensioned variable is formed by

**TABLE 6.1 TYPICAL OPERATIONS REPRESENTABLE BY THE GENERAL-
IZED IMPEDANCE OPERATOR**

$v = zi$	v	i	z
$v(t) = Ri(t) + \dfrac{1}{C}\displaystyle\int_{-\infty}^{t} i(\tau)\,d\tau$	$v(t)$	$i(t)$	$\left[R + \dfrac{1}{C}\displaystyle\int_{-\infty}^{t} (\ )\,d\tau \right]$
$V = (\mathbf{Z}_1 + \mathbf{Z}_2)\mathbf{I}$	$\mathbf{V}$	$\mathbf{I}$	$\mathbf{Z}_1 + \mathbf{Z}_2$
$V = \dfrac{R_1 R_2}{R_1 + R_2}\, I$	V	I	$\dfrac{R_1 R_2}{R_1 + R_2}$
$V_o e^{at} = \left(R + aL + \dfrac{1}{aC} \right) I_f e^{at}$	$V_o e^{at}$	$I_f e^{at}$	$R + aL + \dfrac{1}{aC}$

some operation on a current-dimensioned variable. Although the forms are different, the last three are implicitly tied to the first, and a unity pervades the entire set. This unity can be exploited by letting one equation represent all four of the above forms; that is, in general, we will write

$$v = zi,$$

where

$$v = v(t),\ V,\ V_o,\ \text{or } \mathbf{V}$$

$$i = i(t),\ I,\ I_f,\ \text{or } \mathbf{I}$$

$$z = R + L\frac{d}{dt},\ R,\ R + aL,\ \text{or } R + j\omega L.$$

In a similar way, we may represent the *G-C-L* parallel combination by the single equation

$$i = yv.$$

Table 6.1 illustrates some typical situations covered by the volt-ampere relationship where a generalized *impedance operator*, z, is used. A similar illustration of the use of a generalized admittance operator is shown in Table 6.2.

**TABLE 6.2 TYPICAL OPERATIONS REPRESENTABLE BY THE GENERAL-
IZED ADMITTANCE OPERATOR**

$i = yv$	i	v	y
$i(t) = Gv(t) + C\dfrac{dv(t)}{dt}$	$i(t)$	$v(t)$	$G + C\dfrac{d}{dt}$
$I = GV$	I	V	G
$I = \dfrac{\mathbf{Y}_1 \mathbf{Y}_2}{\mathbf{Y}_1 + \mathbf{Y}_2}\, V$	$\mathbf{I}$	V	$\dfrac{\mathbf{Y}_1 \mathbf{Y}_2}{\mathbf{Y}_1 + \mathbf{Y}_2}$
$I = \dfrac{1}{R + j\omega L + \dfrac{1}{j\omega C}}\, V$	$\mathbf{I}$	V	$\dfrac{1}{R + j\omega L + \dfrac{1}{j\omega C}}$

The operators z and y are used here in exactly the same sense as the operators z_0 and y_0 in Chapter 3. As for those operators, the inverse operator, z^{-1}, is defined so that

$$z^{-1}z = 1, \tag{6.1}$$

and y^{-1} is similarly defined.

It should be carefully noted that, *in general*, $z^{-1} \neq 1/z$, though this is sometimes the case. For example, if

$$z = \text{the operation } R + L\frac{d}{dt},$$

$$\text{then } z^{-1} \text{ is not } \cfrac{1}{R + L\dfrac{d}{dt}},$$

because the latter is not a defined operation. It has no meaning. On the other hand, if

$$z = \text{the operation } \mathbf{Z} = R + j\omega L,$$

then the inverse operation is

$$z^{-1} = \text{the operation } \frac{1}{\mathbf{Z}} = \frac{1}{R + j\omega L}.$$

Hence, we can only say that, in general,

$$z^{-1} \neq \frac{1}{z} \quad \text{and} \quad y^{-1} \neq \frac{1}{y}.$$

The generalized schematic representation of a passive two-terminal device or network will be either of the two forms appearing in Fig. 6.2. In the first form

$$v = zi. \tag{6.2}$$

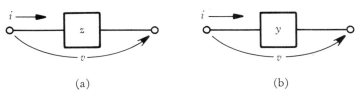

(a)   (b)

Fig. 6.2 *Equivalent schematic representations of generalized passive impedance or admittance and associated variables. (a) Generalized impedance. (b) Generalized admittance.*

Operating on both sides by z^{-1} yields

$$z^{-1}v = z^{-1}zi = i,$$

or

$$i = z^{-1}v. \tag{6.3}$$

The second form has the volt-ampere relation

$$i = yv. \tag{6.4}$$

If the two representations are to be equivalent, then comparison of Eqs. (6.3) and (6.4) produces

$$y = z^{-1}, \tag{6.5a}$$

or, conversely, that

$$z = y^{-1}. \tag{6.5b}$$

A final word of caution: *Before considering power and energy, one must return to the specific forms,* as there is no specific meaning attached to the products of generalized current and/or voltage variables.

6.5 MODELS

The work in this chapter involves a number of abstractions based on the realities of circuit analysis. To be in the proper spirit for such abstractions, we should take note of the philosophical difference between actual things and our representations of them. For example, the equation

$$v(t) = Ri(t) + L\frac{di(t)}{dt}$$

is a *mathematical model* of the R-L series circuit, not the circuit itself. On the other hand, the equation

$$f(t) = Bv(t) + M\frac{dv(t)}{dt}$$

is a mathematical model of the system consisting of a body of mass M and friction B acted on by force f to create a velocity v. But it is a model of precisely the same structure as that for the R-L series circuit. Anyone who has seen an actual R-L series circuit can readily distinguish it from a mass with friction, but he will be hard put to point out differences in the mathematical models of the two.

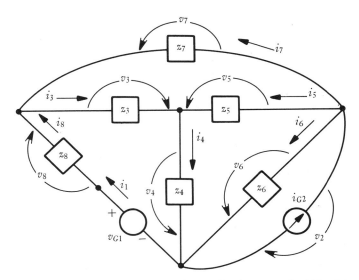

Fig. 6.3 *A generalized circuit diagram for the network of Fig. 6.1.*

Another model of the electrical system is the schematic diagram, or *circuit model*, of the system. Fig. 6.1, for example, shows such a model. The actual passive elements are indicated on the figure, though the circuit variables are indicated in the general form. This is a simple acknowledgement of the fact that the study of the circuit may be based on the instantaneous values of the variables or phasor methods may be employed. With the general forms, we are uncommitted.

This same network of Fig. 6.1 is shown in Fig. 6.3 with generalized impedances representing the actual circuit elements. The circuit elements could have been labelled as y's with the same generality.

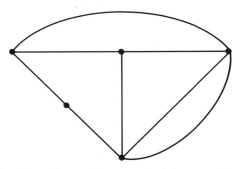

Fig. 6.4 *The undirected linear graph of the network of Fig. 6.1.*

Another model of the circuit of Fig. 6.1 is its *linear graph*, which is simply the circuit diagram with each element and source replaced by a simple line segment. The graph may be *directed* with each line segment assigned a positive direction corresponding with that of the admittance (or impedance) currents and voltage drops. On the other hand, the graph may be *undirected*, yielding a linear "skeleton" of the network. There is a place for both models, but for the present our work will make use of just the undirected graph, shown in Fig. 6.4 for the network of Fig. 6.1.

6.6 TOPOLOGICAL TERMINOLOGY

The study of graphs such as that of Fig. 6.4 is the subject of an area of mathematics known as *topology*. Some of the techniques of this mathematical discipline may be borrowed by the electrical engineer to show him systematic ways around the aforementioned redundancy problem. However, this is a simple matter of "chickens coming home to roost," since the existence of electrical networks has provided a significant stimulus to the study of topology.

Let us now define some terms which are useful in the study of networks and their graphs.

> Branch: Every network element or source will be called a *branch*, or *network branch*.
>
> Node: Every junction where two or more branches come together will be called a *node*.
>
> Tree: A *tree* will be any combination of branches which connects to all nodes but forms no closed paths.
>
> Tree Branch: Any network branch contained in the chosen tree is called a *tree branch*.
>
> Link: Any network branch not contained in the chosen tree is called a *link*.

The following symbols will designate the number of the various graph components:

$$n_B = \text{number of branches} \qquad (6.6a)$$

$$n_N = \text{number of nodes} \qquad (6.6b)$$

$$n_T = \text{number of tree branches} \qquad (6.6c)$$

$$n_L = \text{number of links.} \qquad (6.6d)$$

When it is necessary, on a graph, to differentiate between tree branches and links, tree branches will be indicated by heavy solid lines, links by dotted lines.

To draw a subdivided graph for a circuit model, all nodes should be drawn first; then one branch should be added at a time without creating any closed paths. The first tree branch drawn will connect two nodes together, and each additional branch will connect one additional node to the tree. Therefore, we can conclude that

$$n_T = n_N - 1 \tag{6.7}$$

and, therefore, that

$$n_L = n_B - (n_N - 1). \tag{6.8}$$

EXAMPLE 6.1. Find five separate trees for the network of Fig. 6.1 and draw the links associated with each tree. Give the value for each of the n's in Eqs. (6.6).

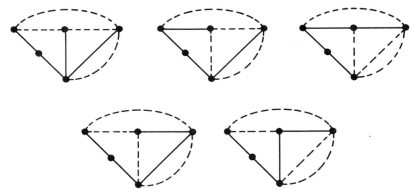

Fig. 6.5 *Some of the trees, and associated links, for the network of Fig. 6.1.*

Solution. Five possible tree-link combinations are shown in Fig. 6.5. There are more, and the student should find them. For this network

$$n_B = 8 \qquad n_T = 4$$

$$n_N = 5 \qquad n_L = 4. \qquad \textit{Ans.}$$

6.7 SELECTING SETS OF INDEPENDENT VARIABLES

Consider any one of the trees for the network of Fig. 6.1, or, for that matter, any other network. The following observations are easily extrapolated to the general case by the definitions of trees and links:

1. If the tree-branch voltages are all reduced to zero (i.e., if all tree branches are short-circuited), then every branch voltage in the network is reduced to zero.
2. If the link currents are reduced to zero (i.e., if all links are open-circuited), then every branch current in the network is reduced to zero.

These observations show that the branch voltages are completely determined by the tree-branch voltages, and the branch currents are completely determined by the link currents. Thus, no link voltages can exist independently from the tree-branch voltages. In other words, the link voltages are dependent on the independent set of tree-branch voltages. Similarly, the tree-branch currents are dependent on the independent set of link currents.

These results may be summarized in the form of equations:

$$\{\text{Number of independent voltages}\} = n_T$$
$$= n_N - 1, \tag{6.9}$$
$$\{\text{Number of independent currents}\} = n_L$$
$$= n_B - (n_N - 1). \tag{6.10}$$

We now have established a routine way of selecting independent sets of variables. As many different sets can be established by this method as there are trees for the network. This does not mean that all possible sets are selected by this procedure; it simply means that the sets so selected will assuredly be proper sets.

The current from an ideal source cannot be a dependent current, because its nature is in no way dependent on the network to which it is connected. Therefore, if the set of link currents is to truly contain independent currents only, all *ideal current sources must be links*. Similarly, if a set of tree branches is to contain independent voltages only, all *ideal voltage sources must be included as tree branches*. Consequently,

1. The number of unknown independent currents is the number of links minus the number of ideal current sources.
2. The number of unknown independent voltages is the number of tree branches minus the number of ideal voltage sources.

6.8 SELECTING INDEPENDENT EQUATIONS

It is now to our advantage to define two new topological terms, applicable to the network graph after the selection of a tree.

Cut: A *cut* is a closed surface that divides the network into two parts, with one portion inside the surface and the other outside. A cut which is penetrated by just one tree branch will be called a *basic cut*.

Loop: A *loop* is a closed path formed by transversing network branches. A loop traversing just one link will be called a *basic loop*.

A *complete set of cuts* (often called a *cut set*) is the set of basic cuts which causes every tree branch in the network to be cut. A *complete set of loops* (often called a *tie set*) is the set of basic loops causing every link in the network to be traversed.

The network of Fig. 6.1, with the fifth tree of Fig. 6.5 selected, provides an example for illustrating cuts and loops. The subdivided network is shown twice in Fig. 6.6, once with a complete set of cuts with branch currents indicated, once with a complete set of loops with branch voltages indicated. Basic cuts will be identified with the single tree branch they cut and basic loops by the single link they traverse.

Kirchhoff's current law is basically the summation of currents entering (or leaving) a closed surface, though in most of our considerations the closed surface has shrunk to the dimensions of a node. Let us restate Kirchhoff's laws as applied to cuts and loops:

$$\text{KCL:} \qquad \sum i\text{'s}\Big|_{\text{entering a cut}} = 0 \qquad\qquad (6.11a)$$

$$\text{KVL:} \qquad \sum v\text{'s}\Big|_{\text{around a loop}} = 0. \qquad\qquad (6.11b)$$

Applying KCL to the cuts in (a) in the figure:

$$\text{At cut 1:} \qquad i_1 - i_3 + i_7 = 0 \qquad\qquad (6.12a)$$

$$\text{At cut 4:} \qquad -i_{G2} - i_3 + i_4 + i_6 + i_7 = 0 \qquad\qquad (6.12b)$$

$$\text{At cut 5:} \qquad i_{G2} - i_5 - i_6 - i_7 = 0 \qquad\qquad (6.12c)$$

$$\text{At cut 8:} \qquad -i_3 + i_7 + i_8 = 0. \qquad\qquad (6.12d)$$

These equations are independent, because there is one current in each that does not appear in any other. It is clear that in general the number of independent current equations is equal to the number of tree branches, or

$$\{\text{Number of independent current equations}\} = n_T$$
$$= n_N - 1. \qquad (6.13)$$

This is the same as the number of independent voltage variables.

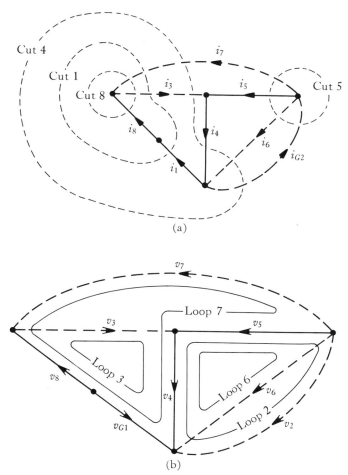

Fig. 6.6 *Illustrating cuts and loops associated with the network of Fig. 6.1. (a) A complete set of basic cuts. (b) A complete set of basic loops.*

Applying KVL to the loops in (b) of the figure:

Loop 2:	$v_2 - v_4 - v_5 = 0$	(6.14a)
Loop 3:	$-v_{G1} + v_3 + v_4 + v_8 = 0$	(6.14b)
Loop 6:	$-v_4 - v_5 + v_6 = 0$	(6.14c)
Loop 7:	$v_{G1} - v_4 - v_5 + v_7 - v_8 = 0.$	(6.14d)

These are also independent equations, and in general

{Number of independent voltage equations} $= n_L = n_B - (n_N - 1)$.   (6.15)

This is the same as the number of independent current variables.

6.9 SOLUTION BY TREE-BRANCH VOLTAGES

The material in the preceding articles has shown that one can choose n_T independent current equations and n_T independent voltages. If the unknown currents in the set of independent current equations are all admittance currents, they can be expressed in terms of the n_T independent voltages through the volt-ampere relationships. We then have n_T equations in terms of n_T unknowns, and we may solve for the n_T independent voltages.

If the set of n_T voltages contains some which are known (i.e., ideal source voltages), then there exists an apparent redundancy of equations over unknown tree-branch voltages. This is not a true redundancy, however, because associated with each ideal voltage source is an unknown current through it that cannot be expressed in terms of tree-branch voltages by volt-ampere relations. An advantage of using the method of cuts for applying KCL is that these unknown currents each occur in only one equation. Therefore, one always has available in the complete set of equations a subset equal in number to the unknown voltages and containing only the voltage unknowns after application of the volt-ampere relations.

A solution for the unknown tree-branch voltages may be organized as follows, once the circuit has been drawn and all known variables (ideal sources) labeled:

1. Select a tree, making sure that all ideal voltage sources are included in its branches and that all ideal current sources appear as links.
2. Use KVL around basic loops to express link voltages in terms of tree-branch voltages.
3. Apply KCL at basic cuts to obtain n_T current equations.
4. Employ the volt-ampere relationships at each passive branch to express the admittance currents in Step 3 in terms of tree-branch voltages.
5. Substitute the results of Step 4 into the results of Step 3 and solve for the unknown tree-branch voltages.
6. If all or part of the remaining unknown voltages and the unknown currents are desired, substitute the results of Step 5 into those of Step 2 to find remaining voltages and into Step 4 to find the unknown currents.

EXAMPLE 6.2. Set up the equations leading to a solution for a set of tree-branch voltages for the circuit of Fig. 6.1.

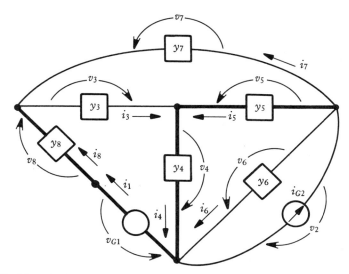

Fig. 6.7 *The circuit model of Fig. 6.1 redrawn in the general form applicable to solution for tree-branch voltages.*

Solution. Let us redraw the circuit in a general form with the leads in tree branches shown as heavy lines. This is done in Fig. 6.7, using the tree selected for Fig. 6.6, so that the same cuts and loops apply. Label all branch voltages and all branch currents. Now proceed through the first five steps enumerated above.

1. The chosen tree is indicated by the heavy leads in the figure.
2. This step has been essentially accomplished in Eqs. (6.14) which yield the link voltages

$$v_2 = v_4 + v_5$$

$$v_3 = v_{G1} - v_4 - v_8$$

$$v_6 = v_4 + v_5$$

$$v_7 = -v_{G1} + v_4 + v_5 + v_8.$$

3. This has been done in Eqs. (6.12) which may be rearranged to give

$$0 = i_1 - i_3 + i_7$$

$$i_{G2} = -i_3 + i_4 + i_6 + i_7$$

$$i_{G2} = i_5 + i_6 + i_7$$

$$0 = -i_3 + i_7 + i_8$$

4.
$$i_3 = y_3 v_3 = y_3(v_{G1} - v_4 - v_8)$$
$$i_4 = y_4 v_4$$
$$i_5 = y_5 v_5$$
$$i_6 = y_6 v_6 = y_6(v_4 + v_5)$$
$$i_7 = y_7 v_7 = y_7(-v_{G1} + v_4 + v_5 + v_8)$$
$$i_8 = y_8 v_8 .$$

5.
$$0 = i_1 - y_3(v_{G1} - v_4 - v_8) + y_7(-v_{G1} + v_4 + v_5 + v_8)$$
$$i_{G2} = -y_3(v_{G1} - v_4 - v_8) + y_4 v_4 + y_6(v_4 + v_5)$$
$$+ y_7(-v_{G1} + v_4 + v_5 + v_8)$$
$$i_{G2} = y_5 v_5 + y_6(v_4 + v_5) + y_7(-v_{G1} + v_4 + v_5 + v_8)$$
$$0 = -y_3(v_{G1} - v_4 - v_8) + y_7(-v_{G1} + v_4 + v_5 + v_8) + y_8 v_8 .$$

Rearranging:

$$(y_3 + y_7)v_{G1} = \qquad i_1 + (y_3 + y_7)v_4 + \qquad\qquad y_7 v_5$$
$$+ (y_3 + y_7)v_8$$

$$i_{G2} + (y_3 + y_7)v_{G1} = (y_3 + y_4 + y_6 + y_7)v_4 + \qquad (y_6 + y_7)v_5$$
$$+ (y_3 + y_7)v_8$$

$$i_{G2} + \qquad y_7 v_{G1} = \qquad (y_6 + y_7)v_4 + (y_5 + y_6 + y_7)v_5$$
$$+ y_7 v_8$$

$$(y_3 + y_7)v_{G1} = \qquad\qquad (y_3 + y_7)v_4 + \qquad\qquad y_7 v_5$$
$$+ (y_3 + y_7 + y_8)v_8.$$

The last three equations form the subset which may be solved for the three unknown voltages v_4, v_5, and v_8.

The tedium of the above procedure may be relieved, after a little practice, by combining some of the steps. For instance, to solve for the unknown tree-branch voltages only, one might condense the procedure to the following steps, after the circuit has been drawn with known variables labeled:

1. Select a tree, making sure that all ideal voltage sources but no ideal current sources are included, and label all unknown tree-branch voltages.

2. Using KVL around basic loops, label all link voltages in terms of tree-branch voltages.

3. Apply KCL at the basic cuts associated with unknown tree-branch voltages, writing admittance currents in terms of tree-branch voltages by using the volt-ampere relations.

4. Solve the resulting equations for the unknown tree-branch voltages.

6.10 NODAL ANALYSIS

Suppose a network has n unknown tree-branch voltages. Suppose we then choose another set of n voltages in such a way that the new set may be expressed as linear combinations of the tree-branch voltages and, inversely, that the tree-branch voltages may be expressed as linear combinations of the new voltages. Then the new set of voltages leads to just as complete a description of the system as does the set of unknown tree-branch voltages, once they are determined. This is basically a fundamental rule of algebra that states that any new set of variables which are formed by linear combinations of an original set of independent variables is also independent, provided that the original set of variables can be inversely expressed as linear combinations of the new set.

Although there are, for a given network, many possible linear combinations of tree-branch voltages which constitute a solution, we shall confine our attention now to those of a single type. This is the type of combination yielding a set of voltages called *node voltages*, or the *common datum node set*. Analysis utilizing these voltage variables is called *nodal analysis*.

Figure 6.8 contains a tree arbitrarily chosen from some network. Every node in the network is, of course, connected to the tree somewhere. One of the nodes has been designated, quite arbitrarily, a *datum node*, or *reference node*, and the remaining n nodes have each been identified with a letter. The node voltage is always associated with a lettered (or otherwise tagged) node

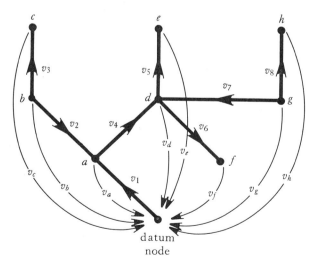

Fig. 6.8 *A network tree and one associated common datum node set of voltages.*

and is the voltage drop measured from the lettered node to the datum node. We take note of the following relations between node voltages and tree-branch voltages:

1. The node voltages are equal in number to tree-branch voltages.
2. Each node voltage may be expressed as a linear combination of tree-branch voltages by applying KVL to a closed path consisting of one node voltage arrow and the tree branches spanning it.
3. Each tree-branch voltage may be expressed as a linear combination of node voltages by applying KVL to a closed path consisting of one tree branch and the node-voltage arrows spanning it.

Thus, the node voltages form an independent set of voltages derived from tree-branch voltages.

It is easy to show that the number of unknown node voltages reduces to the number of unknown tree-branch voltages. Suppose, for example, that v_3 is an ideal voltage source and, therefore, a known tree-branch voltage. This tree-branch voltage enters into the formation of only two node voltages, v_b and v_c. These two node voltages are

$$v_b = v_2 - v_1$$
$$v_c = -v_3 + v_2 - v_1 = -v_3 + v_b.$$

Therefore, v_c can be expressed in terms of the one node voltage v_b, reducing the number of unknown node voltages by one.

When it is possible to choose an ideal voltage source as a node voltage, the reduction in order is immediately obvious. For example, had branch 1 been an ideal voltage source, then node voltage v_a would have become a known voltage.

The node-voltage arrows may be considered to form a "non-physical" tree with all its branches connecting to the datum node. A cut penetrated by just one such non-physical tree branch may be closed so that just the lettered node connected to the "tree branch" is enclosed, with all other nodes outside the cut. KCL applied to such a cut is nothing more than KCL applied to the associated node.

We may now organize a procedure, similar to that used for tree-branch voltages, leading to a solution in terms of node voltages, once the circuit has been drawn and all known variables labeled:

1. Select a datum node and assign a tag letter or number to all remaining nodes. Label each node voltage with the node tag attached, except label only one of the node voltages adjacent to an ideal voltage

source, preferably that associated with the node having the most connecting branches. Label the voltage of the remaining node connected to the ideal voltage source in terms of the source voltage and the first connecting node voltage.

2. Use KVL around loops containing just one network branch and node-voltage arrows to express passive branch voltages in terms of node voltages.

3. Apply KCL at tagged nodes to obtain n_T current equations.

4. Employ the volt-ampere relations at each passive branch to express the admittance currents in terms of node voltages.

5. Substitute the results of Step 4 into the results of Step 3 and solve for the unknown node voltages.

6. If all voltage and current variables are required, substitute the results of Step 5 into Step 2 to find the branch voltages and into Step 4 to find the unknown currents.

EXAMPLE 6.3. Set up the nodal equations leading to a solution of the network of Fig. 6.1.

Solution. Draw the circuit with all known sources identified, as in Fig. 6.9. Label all branch currents and voltages, then proceed through the first five steps enumerated above.

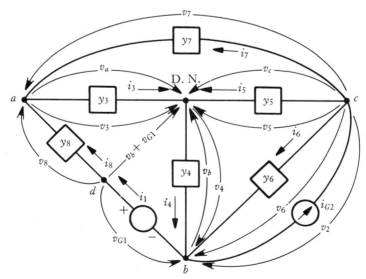

Fig. 6.9 *The generalized form of the network of Fig. 6.1 set up for nodal analysis.*

1. In Fig. 6.9 the datum node is identified by $D \cdot N$, and the remaining nodes tagged a, b, c, and d. The node voltage v_d has been expressed in terms of node voltage v_b and the known voltage v_{G1}.

2.
$$v_3 = v_a$$
$$v_4 = -v_b$$
$$v_5 = v_c$$
$$v_6 = -v_b + v_c$$
$$v_7 = -v_a + v_c$$
$$v_8 = -v_a + v_b + v_{G1}.$$

3. Writing admittance currents positive leaving nodes:

Node a: $0 = i_3 - i_7 - i_8$

Node b: $-i_{G2} = i_1 - i_4 - i_6$

Node c: $i_{G2} = i_5 + i_6 + i_7$

Node d: $0 = -i_1 + i_8$.

4.
$$i_3 = y_3 v_3 = y_3 v_a$$
$$i_4 = y_4 v_4 = -y_4 v_b$$
$$i_5 = y_5 v_5 = y_5 v_c$$
$$i_6 = y_6 v_6 = y_6(-v_b + v_c)$$
$$i_7 = y_7 v_7 = y_7(-v_a + v_c)$$
$$i_8 = y_8 v_8 = y_8(-v_a + v_b + v_{G1}).$$

5.
$$0 = y_3 v_a - y_7(-v_a + v_c) - y_8(-v_a + v_b + v_{G1})$$
$$-i_{G2} = i_1 - (-y_4 v_b) - y_6(-v_b + v_c)$$
$$i_{G2} = y_5 v_c + y_6(-v_b + v_c) + y_7(-v_a + v_c)$$
$$0 = -i_1 + y_8(-v_a + v_b + v_{G1}).$$

Combining terms and rearranging:

$$y_8 v_{G1} = (y_3 + y_7 + y_8)v_a \quad -y_8 v_b \quad\quad\quad -y_7 v_c$$
$$-i_1 - i_{G2} = \quad\quad\quad (y_4 + y_6)v_b \quad\quad -y_6 v_c$$
$$i_{G2} = \quad -y_7 v_a \quad -y_6 v_b + (y_5 + y_6 + y_7)v_c$$
$$i_1 - y_8 v_{G1} = \quad -y_8 v_a \quad +y_8 v_b.$$

Adding the second and third equations eliminates i_1, yielding the following set of equations to be solved for the node voltages v_a, v_b, and v_c:

$$y_8 v_{G1} \quad = (y_3 + y_7 + y_8)v_a \qquad\qquad -y_8 v_b$$
$$-y_7 v_c$$

$$-i_{G2} - y_8 v_{G1} = \qquad -y_8 v_a + (y_4 + y_6 + y_8)v_b$$
$$-y_6 v_c$$

$$i_{G2} \qquad = \qquad -y_7 v_a \qquad\qquad -y_6 v_b$$
$$+ (y_5 + y_6 + y_7)v_c. \qquad\qquad\qquad Ans.$$

The final form of the system equations in the above example are illuminating if one recognizes that $y_8 v_{G1}$ is the value of the current source in the Norton's equivalent of the combination of v_{G1} and y_8 in series. Such a combination absorbs node d leaving a circuit with but three unknown node voltages, as illustrated in Fig. 6.10. Following the procedures of Example 6.3 with this equivalent network leads directly to the set of three equations given as the end result without the intervening step of eliminating i_1.

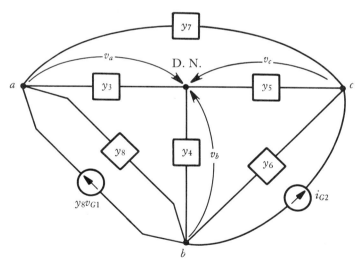

Fig. 6.10 *The circuit model of Fig. 6.8 with two-terminal active networks in Norton form.*

The left-hand side of each of the three equations is seen to be the sum of the *generated* currents *entering* the associated node from ideal current sources, while the right-hand side is the sum of the *dissipative* currents leaving through admittances. The results of these observations may be formalized as follows:

In a network of $n + 1$ nodes containing a datum node and nodes $1, 2, 3, \ldots, n$ and with all active devices in the Norton form, the current equation associated with the jth node takes the form

$$i_j = \sum_{k=1}^{n} y_{jk} v_k, \qquad (6.16)$$

where

$$i_j = \begin{Bmatrix} \text{the algebraic sum of the currents} \\ \text{entering the node directly from} \\ \text{ideal current sources} \end{Bmatrix} \qquad (6.16a)$$

$$y_{jj} = \begin{Bmatrix} \text{the sum of all admittance opera-} \\ \text{tors directly connected to node } j \end{Bmatrix} \qquad (6.16b)$$

$$y_{jk} = \begin{Bmatrix} \text{the negative of the sum of all ad-} \\ \text{mittance operators connected to} \\ \text{both node } j \text{ and node } k \end{Bmatrix} \qquad (6.16c)$$

$$v_k = \begin{Bmatrix} \text{the voltage drop from node } k \text{ to} \\ \text{the datum node} \end{Bmatrix} \qquad (6.16d)$$

The following nomenclature associated with the nodal admittances is in common use:

$$y_{jk} = \begin{Bmatrix} \text{self admittance of node } j, j = k \\ \\ \text{mutual admittance between nodes} \\ j \text{ and } k, j \neq k \end{Bmatrix}. \qquad (6.16e)$$

There is an inherent danger in the use of formalized proceedings of the type just discussed. The danger is that the student may learn a routine at the expense of the basic applications of Kirchhoff's laws and volt-ampere relationships supporting them. However, the student who does is building himself a house of cards that will not stand. At this stage of the game it is extremely important that he check the simple ordering routines with step-by-step application of the basic circuit laws for enough examples that he becomes quite convinced of the identity of results. Only then is he justified in availing himself of the great economies of time and effort afforded by the formalized techniques.

6.11 SOLUTION BY LINK CURRENTS

We have shown in Arts. 6.7 and 6.8 that one can choose n_L independent voltage equations and n_L independent currents for any network. When the unknown voltages in the set of independent voltage equations are all voltages across impedances, they can be expressed in terms of the n_L independent currents through the volt-ampere relationships. The result will be n_L

equations in terms of n_L unknowns which may be solved for the n_L independent currents.

If the set of n_L currents contains some which are known (i.e., ideal source currents), then there is associated with each such known current an unknown voltage that cannot be expressed in terms of link currents by volt-ampere relations. The advantage of using basic loops for applying KVL is that these unknown voltages each occur in only one equation. Therefore, there is always available in the complete set of equations a ready-made subset equal in number to the unknown currents and containing only the current unknowns after application of the volt-ampere relations.

A solution for the unknown link currents may be organized, once the schematic has been drawn and all known variables (ideal sources) labeled, as follows:

1. Select a tree, making sure that all ideal current sources appear as links and that all ideal voltage sources are included as tree branches.

2. Apply KCL at basic cuts to express tree-branch currents in terms of link currents.

3. Use KVL around basic loops to obtain n_L voltage equations.

4. Employ the volt-ampere relations at each passive branch to express the impedance voltages in Step 3 in terms of link currents.

5. Substitute the results of Step 4 into the results of Step 3 and solve for the unknown link currents.

6. If all or part of the remaining unknown currents and the unknown voltages are desired, substitute the results of Step 5 into those of Step 2 to find the remaining currents and into Step 4 to find the unknown voltages.

EXAMPLE 6.4. Set up the equations leading to a solution for a set of link currents for the circuit of Fig. 6.1.

Solution. Draw the schematic in a general form with the leads in tree branches shown as heavy lines, as in Fig. 6.7. Label all branch voltages and branch currents, and proceed through the first five steps enumerated above.

1. The chosen tree is indicated by the heavy leads in the figure.

2. This step was essentially accomplished in Eqs. (6.12) which may be rearranged to give the tree-branch currents.

$$i_1 = i_3 - i_7$$
$$i_4 = i_{G2} + i_3 - i_6 - i_7$$
$$i_5 = i_{G2} - i_6 - i_7$$
$$i_8 = i_3 - i_7 .$$

3.   This has been done in Eqs. (6.14) which may be rearranged into

$$0 = v_2 - v_4 - v_5$$
$$v_{G1} = v_3 + v_4 + v_8$$
$$0 = -v_4 - v_5 + v_6$$
$$-v_{G1} = -v_4 - v_5 + v_7 - v_8 .$$

4.
$$v_3 = z_3 i_3$$
$$v_4 = z_4 i_4 = z_4(i_{G2} + i_3 - i_6 - i_7)$$
$$v_5 = z_5 i_5 = z_5(i_{G2} - i_6 - i_7)$$
$$v_6 = z_6 i_6$$
$$v_7 = z_7 i_7$$
$$v_8 = z_8 i_8 = z_8(i_3 - i_7).$$

5.
$$0 = v_2 - z_4(i_{G2} + i_3 - i_6 - i_7) - z_5(i_{G2} - i_6 - i_7)$$
$$v_{G1} = z_3 i_3 + z_4(i_{G2} + i_3 - i_6 - i_7) + z_8(i_3 - i_7)$$
$$0 = -z_4(i_{G2} + i_3 - i_6 - i_7) - z_5(i_{G2} - i_6 - i_7) + z_6 i_6$$
$$-v_{G1} = -z_4(i_{G2} + i_3 - i_6 - i_7) - z_5(i_{G2} - i_6 - i_7) + z_7 i_7$$
$$- z_8(i_3 - i_7).$$

Combining terms and rearranging:

$$(z_4 + z_5)i_{G2} = v_2 \qquad\qquad -z_4 i_3 \qquad\qquad +(z_4 + z_5)i_6$$
$$+ (z_4 + z_5)i_7$$

$$v_{G1} - z_6 i_{G2} = \quad (z_3 + z_4 + z_8)i_3 \qquad\qquad -z_4 i_6$$
$$- (z_4 + z_8)i_7$$

$$(z_4 + z_5)i_{G2} = \qquad\qquad -z_4 i_3 +(z_4 + z_5 + z_6)i_6$$
$$+ (z_4 + z_5)i_7$$

$$-v_{G1} + (z_4 + z_5)i_{G2} = \qquad -(z_4 + z_8)i_3 \qquad +(z_4 + z_5)i_6$$
$$+(z_4 + z_5 + z_7 + z_8)i_7 .$$

The last three equations form the subset which may be solved for the three unknown currents i_3, i_6, and i_7.

The procedure above may be condensed in a manner similar to that followed for solution by tree-branch voltages:

1.   Select a tree, making sure that the associated links include all ideal current sources but no ideal voltage sources, and label all unknown link currents.

2.   Using KCL at basic cuts, label all tree-branch currents in terms of link currents.

3.   Apply KVL around basic loops associated with unknown link currents, writing impedance voltages in terms of link currents by using the volt-ampere relations.

4.   Solve the resulting equations for the unknown link currents.

6.12 MESH CURRENT ANALYSIS

Now we shall consider a method which is to link-current solutions what nodal analysis was to tree-branch solutions. Here our task will be to replace the set of m unknown link currents with a newly defined set of m unknown currents in such a way that each set may be expressed in terms of the other.

A couple of definitions are required to get us started:

A.   A *network mesh*, or, simply, a *mesh*, is a "hole" completely through the network which is not penetrated by any branches.

B.   A *mesh current* is the total current circulating, in the network, around the associated mesh.

A mesh current is easily determined by using a *semicut*, which is a surface extending from an edge within the mesh to the exterior of the network. Two meshes and associated semicuts are illustrated in Fig. 6.11. Also shown in the

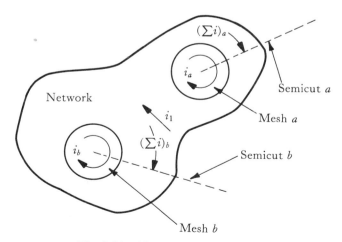

Fig. 6.11   *Illustrating mesh currents.*

figure are the symbolic representations of mesh currents i_a and i_b. Both are shown with positive circulation clockwise, which will generally be the case for mesh currents in this text.

The total current circulating around mesh a is simply the algebraic summation of branch currents penetrating the semicut between the interior of mesh a and the exterior of the network, with the positive direction of penetration corresponding to the positive circulating direction for the symbolic mesh currents. If the summation of currents penetrating semicut a are $(\sum i)_a$, then

$$i_a = (\sum i)_a. \qquad (6.17a)$$

Similarly,

$$i_b = (\sum i)_b. \qquad (6.17b)$$

It should also be apparent that the total circulating current for mesh a is the sum of the circulating current for mesh b and the *separating current*, i_1, flowing through that portion of the network separating mesh a and b. Thus,

$$(\sum i)_a = (\sum i)_b + i_1,$$

so that

$$i_1 = i_a - i_b. \qquad (6.18)$$

The separating current is clearly the algebraic sum of the adjacent mesh currents, with positive direction in the direction of the separating current.

The utility of meshes in network analysis comes when each simple "window," or loop not crossed by branches, is designated a mesh. This creates the maximum possible number of meshes. Then the separating currents simply become branch currents which may be expressed in terms of mesh currents by Eq. (6.18). Since a semicut may always be drawn so that all network branches it intersects are links, it is easy to make the right-hand sides of Eqs. (6.17) be summations of link currents, thereby expressing mesh currents in terms of link currents.

Figure 6.12 contains the subdivided graph of a particular network. The tree has been chosen quite arbitrarily. The maximum possible number of meshes has been chosen and each mesh current and each branch current has been tagged. Semicuts intersecting links only have been drawn for meshes a and e, leaving undrawn seven other such semicuts. In general, semicuts can be drawn in such an order that each new semicut intersects a new link, so that the number of semicuts will equal the number of links. Consequently, the number of meshes and the number of links are the same; that is, the number of meshes equals n_L.

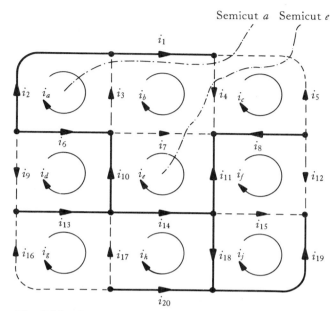

Fig. 6.12 *A network and its maximum set of mesh currents.*

Semicuts *a* and *e* provide examples of Eqs. (6.17) applied to an actual network:

$$i_a = -i_3 + i_4 - i_5$$
$$i_e = + i_4 - i_5 + i_7.$$

Examples of the form of Eq. (6.18) are also clearly in evidence:

$$i_1 = i_b$$
$$i_2 = i_a$$
$$i_3 = -i_a + i_b$$
$$i_4 = i_b - i_c$$
$$\vdots \qquad \vdots$$

The above considerations lead to the following general observations:

1. The mesh currents are equal in number to the link currents.

2. Each mesh current may be expressed as a linear combination of link currents by summing currents penetrating properly chosen semicuts.

3.   Each link current may be expressed as a combination of mesh currents, since link currents form the separating currents between meshes.

Thus, we are assured that the mesh currents form an independent set of currents derived from the link currents.

Suppose that link current i_7 is a known current (an ideal current source). Then adjacent mesh currents are

$$i_b = i_4 - i_5$$

$$i_e = i_4 - i_5 + i_7 = i_b + i_7.$$

Therefore, i_e can be expressed in terms of the one mesh current, i_b, reducing the number of unknown mesh currents by one. Clearly, then, the number of unknown mesh currents reduces to the number of unknown link currents. When it is possible to choose an ideal current source as a mesh current, as would be possible in the case of a known i_{16}, the reduction in order is immediately obvious.

We may now organize a procedure similar to that followed for link currents, leading to a solution in terms of mesh currents, once the circuit has been drawn and all known variables labeled:

1.   Draw the maximum set of clockwise mesh currents and label each with the tag identifying the mesh attached, except label only one of the mesh currents adjacent to an ideal current source, preferably that for the mesh with the most adjacent branches. Label the remaining mesh adjacent to the ideal current source in terms of the source current and the first adjacent mesh.

2.   Using the concept of a separating current, as in Eq. (6.18), express passive branch currents in terms of mesh currents.

3.   Apply KVL around meshes to obtain n_L voltage equations.

4.   Employ the volt-ampere relations of each passive branch to express the impedance voltages in terms of mesh currents.

5.   Substitute the results of Step 4 into the results of Step 3 and solve for the unknown mesh currents.

6.   If all current and voltage variables are required, substitute the results of Step 5 into Step 2 to find the branch currents and into Step 4 to find the unknown voltages.

EXAMPLE 6.5. Set up the mesh-current equations leading to a solution for the network of Fig. 6.1.

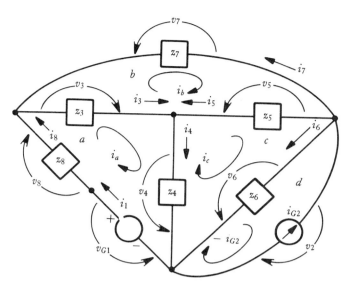

Fig. 6.13   *General form of the network of Fig. 6.1 set up for mesh current analysis.*

Solution. Draw the circuit with all known sources identified, as in Fig. 6.13. Label all branch voltages and currents, then proceed through the first five steps enumerated above.

1. In Fig. 6.13 the maximum number of four meshes are tagged a, b, c, and d, except that mesh current d has been labeled in terms of the known current i_{G2}.

2.
$$i_3 = i_a - i_b$$
$$i_4 = i_a - i_c$$
$$i_5 = i_b - i_c$$
$$i_6 = i_c - (-i_{G2}) = i_c + i_{G2}$$
$$i_7 = -i_b$$
$$i_8 = i_a.$$

3. Writing impedance voltages positive in the direction of mesh circulation:

mesh a: $v_{G1} = v_3 + v_4 + v_8$

mesh b: $0 = -v_3 + v_5 - v_7$

mesh c: $0 = -v_4 - v_5 + v_6$

mesh d: $0 = v_2 - v_6.$

4.
$$v_3 = z_3 i_3 = z_3(i_a - i_b)$$
$$v_4 = z_4 i_4 = z_4(i_a - i_c)$$
$$v_5 = z_5 i_5 = z_5(i_b - i_c)$$
$$v_6 = z_6 i_6 = z_6(i_c + i_{G2})$$
$$v_7 = z_7 i_7 = -z_7 i_b$$
$$v_8 = z_8 i_8 = z_8 i_a .$$

5.
$$v_{G1} = z_3(i_a - i_b) + z_4(i_a - i_c) + z_8 i_a$$
$$0 = -z_3(i_a - i_b) + z_5(i_b - i_c) + z_7 i_b$$
$$0 = -z_4(i_a - i_c) - z_5(i_b - i_c) + z_6(i_c + i_{G2})$$
$$0 = v_2 - z_6(i_c + i_{G2}).$$

Combining terms and rearranging the first three equations results in

$$v_{G1} = (z_3 + z_4 + z_8)i_a \qquad\qquad -z_3 i_b \qquad\qquad -z_4 i_c$$
$$0 = \qquad\qquad -z_3 i_a + (z_3 + z_5 + z_7)i_b \qquad\qquad -z_5 i_c$$
$$-z_6 i_{G2} = \qquad\qquad -z_4 i_a \qquad\qquad -z_5 i_b + (z_4 + z_5 + z_6)i_c .$$

Ans.

These three equations may be solved for the three unknown mesh currents i_a, i_b, and i_c. They appear before us without the preliminary necessity of eliminating the unknown voltage v_2, because mesh current i_d was expressible in terms of known source currents only. Had the generated current been a mesh separating current, two equations would have needed to be combined to eliminate v_2 in a manner similar to the way in which the unknown current i_1 was eliminated in the nodal solution of Example 6.3. In the present case, after the mesh currents are determined, v_2 may be computed using the fourth equation (that for mesh d),

$$v_2 = z_6(i_c + i_{G2}). \qquad \textit{Ans.}$$

The formalization of mesh analysis depends on the recognition, in the example above, that the voltage $z_6 i_{G2}$ in the fourth equation is the value of the ideal voltage source in the Thévenin equivalent of the combination of z_6 and i_{G2} in parallel. Such a combination absorbs mesh d, leaving a circuit with but three unknown mesh currents, as illustrated in Fig. 6.14. Following the procedures of Example 6.5 for this equivalent network leads directly to the set of three equations given as the first part of the answer.

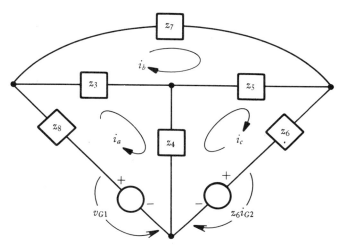

Fig. 6.14 *The circuit model of Fig. 6.8 with two-terminal active networks in the Thévenin form.*

The left-hand side of each of the three equations is clearly the algebraic sum of the *generated* voltage drops opposite the direction of mesh circulation. The right-hand side is the sum of the *dissipative* voltage across impedances in the direction of mesh circulation. The results may be formalized as follows:

In a network with a maximum of m meshes tagged $1, 2, \ldots, m$ and with all active devices in the Thévenin form, the voltage equation associated with the jth mesh is

$$v_j = \sum_{k=1}^{m} z_{jk} i_k, \qquad (6.19)$$

where

$$v_j = \begin{cases} \text{the algebraic sum of the voltage drops of} \\ \text{ideal sources around the mesh in the} \\ \text{direction opposite mesh circulation} \end{cases} \quad (6.19a)$$

$$z_{jj} = \begin{cases} \text{the sum of all impedance operators adja-} \\ \text{cent to mesh } j \end{cases} \quad (6.19b)$$

$$z_{jk} = \begin{cases} \text{the negative of the sum of all impedance} \\ \text{operators adjacent to both mesh } j \text{ and} \\ \text{mesh } k \end{cases} \quad (6.19c)$$

$$i_k = \begin{cases} \text{the clockwise current circulating around} \\ \text{mesh } k \end{cases}. \quad (6.19d)$$

The following is standard nomenclature associated with mesh impedances:

$$z_{jk} = \begin{cases} \text{self impedance of mesh } j, j = k \\ \\ \text{mutual impedance between meshes } j \text{ and} \\ k, j \neq k \end{cases}. \quad (6.19e)$$

EXAMPLE 6.6. Set up the integro-differential equations leading to a solution for the time-varying forms of the variables in Fig. 6.15(a), using the method of mesh currents.

Solution. To use the formalized approach, the parallel combination of current source and capacitor must be changed to the Thévenin form. The open-circuit voltage of this combination is

$$v_o(t) = \frac{1}{C} \int_{-\infty}^{t} i_G(\tau) \, d\tau,$$

and the impedance looking into the two terminals with the current source reduced to zero is that represented by the capacitor, C. Therefore, the Thévenin form is that shown in Fig. 6.15(b).

Having chosen mesh currents $i_1(t)$ and $i_2(t)$ as shown in Fig. 6.15(b), we list the mesh forcing voltages:

$$v_1(t) = \frac{1}{C} \int_{-\infty}^{t} i_G(\tau) \, d\tau$$

$$v_2(t) = -v_G(t) - \frac{1}{C} \int_{-\infty}^{t} i_G(\tau) \, d\tau.$$

The mesh impedances are

$$z_{11} = R_a + L \frac{d}{dt} + \frac{1}{C} \int_{-\infty}^{t} (\ ) \, d\tau$$

$$z_{22} = R_b + R_c + \frac{1}{C} \int_{-\infty}^{t} (\ ) \, d\tau$$

$$z_{12} = z_{21} = -\frac{1}{C} \int_{-\infty}^{t} (\ ) \, d\tau.$$

Therefore, Eqs. (6.19) take the form

$$\frac{1}{C} \int_{-\infty}^{t} i_G(\tau) \, d\tau = \left[R_a + L \frac{d}{dt} + \frac{1}{C} \int_{-\infty}^{t} (\ ) \, d\tau \right] i_1(t) - \frac{1}{C} \int_{-\infty}^{t} i_2(\tau) \, d\tau$$

$$-v_G(t) - \frac{1}{C} \int_{-\infty}^{t} i_G(\tau) \, d\tau = -\frac{1}{C} \int_{-\infty}^{t} i_1(\tau) \, d\tau + \left[R_b + R_c + \frac{1}{C} \int_{-\infty}^{t} (\ ) \, d\tau \right] i_2(\tau).$$

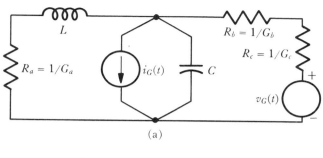

(a)

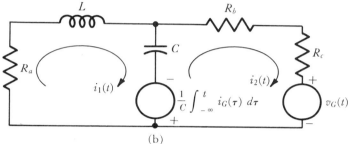

(b)

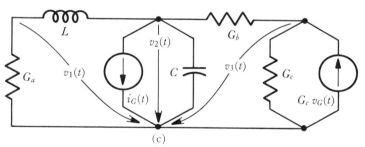

(c)

Fig. 6.15 *Network forms for mesh and nodal analysis in the time domain. (a) Given network. (b) Set-up for mesh currents. (c) Set-up for nodal analysis.*

These combine into the two integro-differential equations

$$\frac{1}{C}\int_{-\infty}^{t} i_G(\tau)\, d\tau = R_a i_1(t) + L\frac{di_1(t)}{dt} + \frac{1}{C}\int_{-\infty}^{t} i_1(\tau)\, d\tau - \frac{1}{C}\int_{-\infty}^{t} i_2(\tau)\, d\tau$$

$$-v_G(t) - \frac{1}{C}\int_{-\infty}^{t} i_G(\tau)\, d\tau = -\frac{1}{C}\int_{-\infty}^{t} i_1(\tau)\, d\tau + (R_b + R_c)i_2(t)$$

$$+ \frac{1}{C}\int_{-\infty}^{t} i_2(\tau)\, d\tau. \qquad Ans.$$

The left-hand side of each equation is known. The next chapter will present methods leading to the complete solution for $i_1(t)$ and $i_2(t)$.

EXAMPLE 6.7. Repeat Example 6.6, except use nodal analysis.

Solution. First, the series combination of $v_G'(t)$ and G_c is replaced by its Norton's equivalent, as shown in Fig. 6.15(c). Having chosen the bottom node as a datum node and labeled node voltages as shown, the node forcing currents may be listed.

$$i_1(t) = 0 \qquad i_2(t) = -i_G(t) \qquad i_3(t) = G_c v_G(t).$$

The node admittances are

$$y_{11} = G_a + \frac{1}{L} \int_{-\infty}^{t} (\ ) \, d\tau$$

$$y_{22} = \frac{1}{L} \int_{-\infty}^{t} (\ ) \, d\tau + C \frac{d}{dt} + G_b$$

$$y_{33} = G_b + G_c$$

$$y_{12} = y_{21} = -\frac{1}{L} \int_{-\infty}^{t} (\ ) \, d\tau$$

$$y_{13} = y_{31} = 0$$

$$y_{23} = y_{32} = -G_b.$$

Substituting the above voltages and admittances into Eq. (6.16) yields the three equations

$$0 = G_a v_1(t) + \frac{1}{L} \int_{-\infty}^{t} v_1(\tau) \, d\tau - \frac{1}{L} \int_{-\infty}^{t} v_2(\tau) \, d\tau$$

$$-i_G(t) = -\frac{1}{L} \int_{-\infty}^{t} v_1(\tau) \, d\tau + \frac{1}{L} \int_{-\infty}^{t} v_2(\tau) \, d\tau + C \frac{dv_2(t)}{dt}$$

$$+ G_b v_2(t) - G_b v_3(t)$$

$$G_c v_G(t) = -G_b v_2(t) + (G_b + G_c) v_3(t). \qquad \textit{Ans.}$$

This time there are three equations in three unknowns to be solved.

6.13 CHOOSING A METHOD

The criterion for choosing one of the foregoing methods for a given problem is simple: choose the method which gives the desired results in the quickest and most straight-forward manner.

Which method satisfies this criterion depends on a number of factors, i.e., the number and type of variables for which values are sought, the number of simultaneous equations to be solved, whether admittance forms or impedance forms apply most easily, etc.

One factor which is often a prime consideration is the number of equations which must be solved simultaneously to obtain a solution. In the case of the network of Fig. 6.15, for example, the solution by mesh currents required only two equations to be so solved, but the solution by nodal analysis required three equations. In this case a solution by mesh currents is more direct than by node voltages. In another case the reverse situation may be true. This aspect of choosing a method has the assistance of the following truths about networks:

A. The number of independent unknown link currents or mesh currents to be determined is the number of links minus the number of ideal current sources.

B. The number of independent unknown tree-branch voltages or node voltages is the number of tree branches minus the number of ideal voltage sources.

6.14 POWER IN NETWORKS

Suppose meshes 1 and 2 are separated by the impedance z_a in series with the ideal voltage source v_{Ga}. Then the power supplied to the network by this series combination is

$$p_a(t) = v_{Ga}(t)i_a(t) = v_{Ga}(t)[i_1(t) - i_2(t)]$$
$$= p_{a1}(t) + p_{a2}(t).$$

The power

$$p_{a1}(t) = v_{Ga}(t)i_1(t)$$

is the power generated in source-impedance combination a by mesh current 1. If similar series combinations b, c, and d complete the list of sources adjacent to mesh 1, then the total power contributed to the network by mesh 1 is

$$p_1(t) = p_{a1}(t) + p_{b1}(t) + p_{c1}(t) + p_{d1}(t)$$
$$= [v_{Ga}(t) + v_{Gb}(t) + v_{Gc}(t) + v_{Gd}(t)]i_1(t).$$

But the voltage in brackets is the forcing voltage for mesh 1, v_1, so

$$p_1(t) = v_1(t)i_1(t).$$

Similarly, the power supplied by mesh j is

$$p_j(t) = v_j(t)i_j(t),$$

and the total power supplied to the network of m meshes is

$$p(t) = \sum_{j=1}^{m} p_j(t) = \sum_{j=1}^{m} v_j(t)i_j(t). \tag{6.20}$$

For another point of view, suppose combination a above is replaced by its Norton's equivalent consisting of an ideal current source i_{Ga} in parallel with admittance y_a. Suppose that the combination connects between nodes j and k. Then

$$p_a(t) = i_{Ga}(t)[v_j(t) - v_k(t)] = p_{aj}(t) - p_{ak}(t),$$

where p_{aj} is the contribution due to node voltage j. The total contribution of node voltage j to all such combinations is

$$p_j(t) = p_{aj}(t) + p_{bj}(t) + p_{cj}(t) + \cdots$$
$$= [i_{Ga}(t) + i_{Gb}(t) + i_{Gc}(t) + \cdots]v_j(t).$$

The bracketed current is the forcing current for node j, so

$$p_j(t) = i_j(t)v_j(t),$$

and the total power supplied to an $(n + 1)$-node network is

$$p(t) = \sum_{j=1}^{n} p_j(t) = \sum_{j=1}^{n} i_j(t)v_j(t). \tag{6.21}$$

PROBLEMS

In Probs. 6.1 through 6.8, write the general form corresponding to the specific form given and identify each general quantity by the specific quantity it represents. The following sample illustrates the task at hand.

Given:

$$v_2(t) = v_1(t) + R_2\,i_2(t) + L\frac{di_2(t)}{dt} + \frac{1}{C}\int_{-\infty}^{t} i_1(\tau)\,d\tau.$$

Solution:

$$v_2 = v_1 + z_2\,i_2 + z_1\,i_1,$$

where

$$v_2 \to v_2(t), \qquad i_1 \to i_1(t), \qquad i_2 \to i_2(t)$$

$$z_1 \to \frac{1}{C} \int_{-\infty}^{t} (\ ) \, d\tau$$

$$z_2 \to R_2 + L\frac{d}{dt}.$$

6.1 $V_1 = R_{11}I_1 + R_{12}I_2 + R_{13}I_3$.

6.2 $V = (R_a + jX_a)I_a + V_b$.

6.3 $C_1 \dfrac{dv_1(t)}{dt} + G_1 v_1(t) + i_a(t) + \dfrac{1}{L}\displaystyle\int_{-\infty}^{t} v_2(\tau)\, d\tau = 0$.

6.4 $I_1 = (G_{11} + jB_{11})V_1 + (G_{12} + jB_{12})V_2 + (G_{13} + jB_{13})V_3$.

6.5 $v_j(t) = \displaystyle\sum_{k=1}^{m}\left[R_{jk}\, i_k(t) + L_{jk}\dfrac{di_k(t)}{dt} + \dfrac{1}{C_{jk}}\int_{-\infty}^{t} i_k(\tau)\, d\tau\right]$.

6.6 $V_j = \displaystyle\sum_{k=1}^{m} Z_{jk}(j\omega)I_k$.

6.7 $i_j(t) = \displaystyle\sum_{k=1}^{n}\left[G_{jk}\, v_k(t) + C_{jk}\dfrac{dv_k(t)}{dt} + \dfrac{1}{L_{jk}}\int_{-\infty}^{t} v_k(\tau)\, d\tau\right]$.

6.8 $I_j = \displaystyle\sum_{k=1}^{n} Y_{jk} V_k$.

6.9 To the network of Fig. 6.1 assign the voltage and current variables as shown in Fig. 6.6. Utilizing the first tree in Fig. 6.5, establish sets of independent voltage and current equations similar to those in Eqs. (6.12) and (6.14).

6.10 Repeat Prob. 6.9 using the third tree of Fig. 6.5.

6.11 Solve for all currents in Fig. P.6.1 by first solving for tree-branch voltages, then applying Ohm's law.

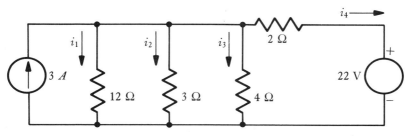

Fig. P.6.1.

6.12 Solve the network of Fig. P.6.2 by tree-branch voltages.

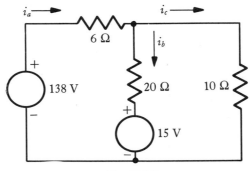

Fig. P.6.2.

6.13 Solve the network of Fig. P.6.3 by tree-branch voltages.

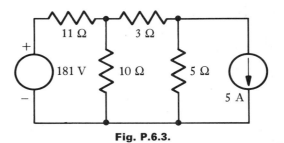

Fig. P.6.3.

6.14 Solve the network of Fig. P.6.4 by tree-branch voltages.

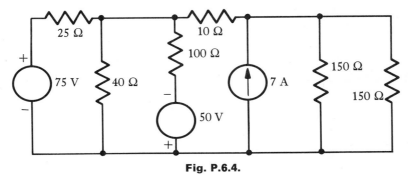

Fig. P.6.4.

6.15 Solve illustrative Example 3.4 by tree-branch voltages.

6.16 Find the indicated voltages in Fig. P.6.5 by solving first for tree-branch voltages.

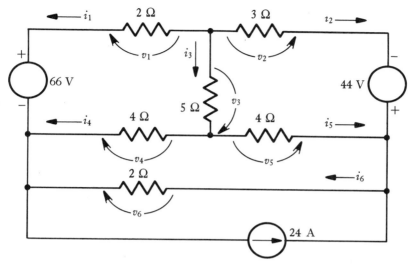

Fig. P.6.5.

6.17 Solve the circuit of Fig. P.5.16, in Chapter 5, for the phasor voltages by the method of tree-branch voltages.

6.18 Solve Prob. 5.93 by tree-branch voltages.

6.19 Verify the results of illustrative Example 5.11 by solution for tree-branch voltages.

6.20 In Fig. P.6.6, find v_a, v_b, and i_c, using solution for tree-branch voltages.

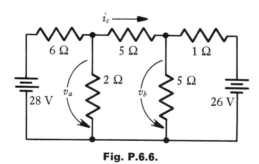

Fig. P.6.6.

6.21 Repeat Prob. 6.11, except solve by nodal analysis.
6.22 Solve the network of Fig. P.6.3 by nodal analysis.
6.23 Solve the network of Fig. P.6.4 by nodal analysis.
6.24 Solve the network of Fig. P.6.5 by nodal analysis.
6.25 Solve the network of Fig. P.6.6 by nodal analysis.

6.26 Solve the network of Fig. P.6.2 by first solving for link currents.

6.27 Solve the network of Fig. P.6.3 through a solution for link currents.

6.28 Solve the network of Fig. P.6.4 using a solution for link currents. Compare with Prob. 6.14 insofar as the compactness of the solution for the initial set of variables is concerned.

6.29 Solve the network of Fig. P.6.5 by the method of link currents.

6.30 Utilize the method of link currents to solve Prob. 6.20.

6.31 Specify for each of the networks in Figs. P.6.1 through P.6.6 whether a solution from tree-branch voltage or a solution for link currents, if either, will result in fewer equations to be solved simultaneously.

6.32 Solve the network in Fig. P.6.2 by the mesh-current method.

6.33 Solve the network of Fig. P.6.3 by the mesh-current method.

6.34 Use mesh currents to obtain a solution for the network of Fig. P.6.5.

6.35 Solve Prob. 6.20 by mesh currents.

6.36 Use mesh currents to solve Prob. 5.58.

6.37 Solve Prob. 5.90 using mesh currents.

6.38 Solve Prob. 5.92 by mesh currents.

6.39 Solve Prob. 5.92 by nodal analysis.

6.40 Find the indicated voltages in Fig. P.6.7 by first solving for the mesh currents.

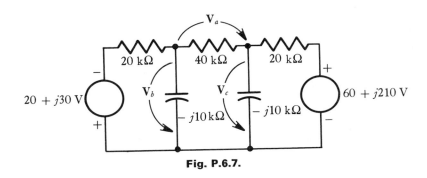

Fig. P.6.7.

6.41 Repeat Prob. 6.40 using nodal analysis.

6.42 Solve for the mesh currents in Fig. P.6.8, then compute the total power supplied to the network using the adaptation of Eq. (6.20) to phasor methods.

6.43 If in Fig. P.6.9, $\omega = 10{,}000$ rad/sec, what are I_1 and I_2?

6.44 Set up the integro-differential equations leading to a solution for the indicated three mesh currents in Fig. P.6.10 in terms of the generated quantities.

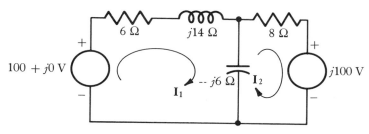

Fig. P.6.8.

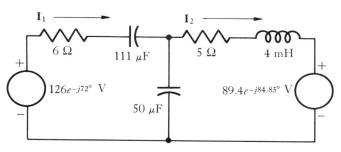

Fig. P.6.9.

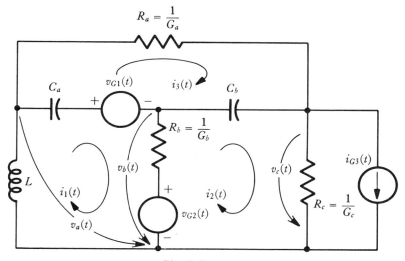

Fig. P.6.10.

6.45 Set up the integro-differential equations leading to a solution for the indicated three node voltages in Fig. P.6.10 in terms of the generated quantities.

6.46 Write the integro-differential equations comprising a complete set of mesh-current equations for Fig. P.6.11.

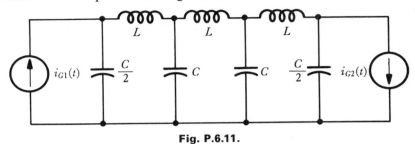

Fig. P.6.11.

6.47 Write the integro-differential equations comprising a complete set of mesh-current equations for Fig. P.6.12.

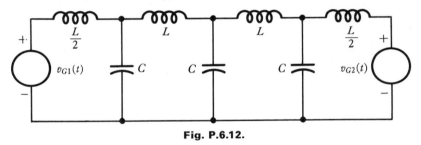

Fig. P.6.12.

6.48 Show that for a system in the sinusoidal steady state, the total average power is

$$P = \text{Re}\left[\sum_{j=1}^{m} \mathbf{V}_j \mathbf{I}_j^*\right],$$

where $\mathbf{V}_j$ is the phasor forcing voltage for mesh j and $\mathbf{I}_j$ is the jth phasor mesh current.

6.49 Show that for a system in the sinusoidal steady state, the total average power transferred is

$$P = \text{Re}\left[\sum_{k=1}^{m} \mathbf{I}_k^* \mathbf{V}_k\right],$$

where $\mathbf{I}_k$ is phasor forcing current for node k and $\mathbf{V}_k$ is the kth node voltage.

6.50 Use the results of Probs. 6.40 and 6.48 to find the total average power and compare with the power computed by adding resistor powers computed by $P_a = I_a^2 R_a$.

6.51 Use the results of Probs. 6.41 and 6.49 to find the total average power and compare with the result of adding resistor powers computed by $P_a = V_a^2 G_a$.

7

Operational
Representations of Signals

7.1 INTRODUCTION

In Chapter 6 procedures were developed for establishing, in a routine manner, the set of n equations in n unknowns required for a determination of system variables. Systems containing inductance and capacitance to be solved in their time-varying forms gave rise to equations containing derivatives and integrals of variables, such equations having the name of integro-differential equations. The equations involved were linear; that is, all operations on the variables were linear operations not functions of the variables themselves.

In this chapter an operational method of solving the integro-differential equations of Chapter 6 is developed. The method is reminiscent of the technique first introduced by the great English electrical engineer, Oliver Heaviside, just prior to the turn of the century. However, the conceptual approach is more along the lines established in the 1920's by a countryman of Heaviside, H. Jeffreys.

7.2 DISCONTINUOUS SIGNALS IN PHYSICAL PROCESSES

In Chapter 4 it was pointed out that a transient was observed over that interval of time during which a signal was undergoing transition from one steady-state value to another. In order for such a transition to prevail in a response function, there must have been a nonperiodic change in the mathematical description of the forcing function. In fact, we can never achieve a nonzero steady state unless somewhere in the past such a change has taken place.

Usually our mathematical description of these changes will involve functions, or signals, which are discontinuous or have a discontinuity in a finite-ordered derivative. It is important that we recognize, however, that physical processes are never truly discontinuous, because the inherent inertia of nature forces the requirement of a finite time for a finite change. But it is equally important to recognize that when our scale of observation is such as to allow us to observe an entire transient, the changes in forcing functions—and in some instances in response signals—are achieved over such short periods of time compared to the transient duration that they appear to us to be discontinuities. If such they appear to be, it is only proper that our mathematical description should so describe them.

Since the initiation of a system transient invariably involves discontinuities in at least those variables which are forcing functions, the introduction of techniques which facilitate the description of functions at discontinuities seems to have much to recommend it. Of course, natural processes are series of ordered events which always require time to evolve, but if our *scale of observation* is such that we are observing behavior over a range of time of practical interest to us, the time required for a change in a variable from one value to another value different from the first by a finite amount often appears to be zero. Or the variable may appear to behave in a wild fashion over an interval of time which appears to be zero. The first example is one of a *step* discontinuity, the second of an *impulsive* discontinuity.

Examples of discontinuities are shown in Fig. 7.1. They are shown in (a) at the normal time scale for observing the signal and in (b) with the time scale greatly expanded to make it possible to observe the actual process of change at the discontinuity. It has been assumed that signals $f_1(t)$ and $f_2(t)$ arise from successive differentiations with respect to time of $f(t)$. This sort of thing often happens to signals in physical systems, as you no doubt recall from earlier chapters. The original function on normal time has a step discontinuity but

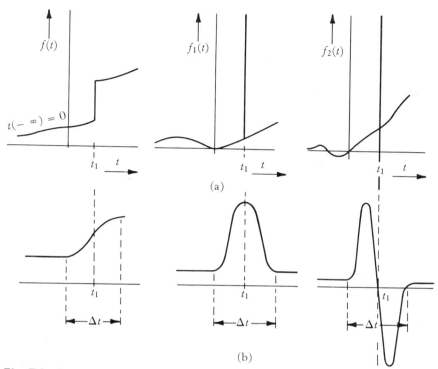

Fig. 7.1 *Step and impulsive discontinuities of physical signals. (a) Normal time scale. (b) Expanded time scale.*

on expanded time proves to be continuous over the interval Δt, which is long enough to be visible only on the greatly expanded time scale. The first differentiation takes us to the continuous function with a *pulse* of width Δt, represented by $f_1(t)$ on the expanded scale, which appears as a widthless spike, or *impulse*, on the normal time scale. The second differentiation results in $f_2(t)$, which is a continuous function with a pair of pulses of opposite signs contained in the time Δt. On the normal time scale, these appear as a pair of widthless spikes of opposite signs. This is often called a doublet.

Obviously, one can "undifferentiate" by integrating $f_2(t)$ to return to $f_1(t)$ and integrating $f_1(t)$ to return to $f(t)$. That is,

$$\int_{-\infty}^{t} f_2(\tau) \, d\tau = f_1(t),$$

$$\int_{-\infty}^{t} f_1(\tau) \, d\tau = f(t).$$

It should be clear that carrying this process one step further will result in a continuous function, since the contribution to the integral by passing over the interval Δt at t_1 becomes zero. Thus the following result in continuous functions: one integration of $f(t)$, two integrations of $f_1(t)$, and three integrations of $f_2(t)$. By a sufficient number of integrations, then, the discontinuity in each function is removed. As a matter of fact, the scope of the methods involved here are such that:

> "The techniques developed in this chapter apply to signals which are continuous or have discontinuities which may be removed by a finite sequence of successive integrations."

7.3 THE UNIT IMPULSE (DIRAC DELTA) AND THE UNIT STEP FUNCTION

We shall now define two discontinuous functions which are going to be of great use to us in the description of any discontinuous signal in the class defined in the previous article and in the determination of responses of systems to such signals. They will provide for us the mathematical description of signals which on a normal scale of observation appear to be discontinuous.

First, let us define the pulse in expanded time, which will be called $\delta_T(t)$, having the following properties:

$$\delta_T(-t) = \delta_T(t) \tag{7.1a}$$

$$\int_{-\infty}^{\infty} \delta_T(t)\,dt = 1 \tag{7.1b}$$

$$\delta_T(t) = 0, \qquad t \leqslant -T, \qquad t \geqslant T. \tag{7.1c}$$

This defines *any* pulse which is centered at $t = 0$, is symmetric about the y-axis, is of maximum width $2T$, and has an area of 1 between it and the t-axis.

The second of the two functions is defined in terms of the first as

$$u_T(t) = \int_{-\infty}^{t} \delta_T(\tau)\,d\tau. \tag{7.2}$$

This is sufficient definition of the function, but let us tabulate some of its properties which follow from the properties of $\delta_T(t)$.

Condition (7.1c) shows that

$$u_T(t) = \int_{-\infty}^{t} 0\,d\tau = 0, \qquad t \leqslant -T, \tag{7.3}$$

and that

$$u_T(t) = \int_{-\infty}^{t} \delta_T(\tau)\, d\tau$$

$$= \int_{-\infty}^{T} \delta_T(\tau)\, d\tau, \qquad t \geqslant T$$

$$= \int_{-\infty}^{\infty} \delta_T(\tau)\, d\tau = 1, \qquad t \geqslant T. \tag{7.4}$$

The last form of Eq. (7.4) may be written

$$\int_{-\infty}^{0} \delta_T(\tau)\, d\tau + \int_{0}^{\infty} \delta_T(\tau)\, d\tau = 1. \tag{7.5}$$

However, Eq. (7.1a) leads to

$$\int_{0}^{\infty} \delta_T(\tau)\, d\tau = \int_{0}^{\infty} \delta_T(-\tau)\, d\tau,$$

and if we replace $-\tau$ by x, we obtain

$$\int_{0}^{\infty} \delta_T(\tau)\, d\tau = -\int_{0}^{-\infty} \delta_T(x)\, dx$$

$$= \int_{-\infty}^{0} \delta_T(x)\, dx.$$

Since both x and τ are dummy variables of integration, Eq. (7.5) becomes

$$2 \int_{-\infty}^{0} \delta_T(\tau)\, d\tau = 1.$$

From the definition of $u_T(t)$ in Eq. (7.2), the integral in this expression is $u_T(0)$, and the expression is the equivalent of

$$u_T(0) = \tfrac{1}{2}. \tag{7.6}$$

The results of Eqs. (7.3), (7.4), and (7.6) may be collected into the single statement below

$$u_T(t) = \begin{cases} 0, & t \leqslant -T \\ \tfrac{1}{2}, & t = 0 \\ 1, & t \geqslant T. \end{cases} \tag{7.7}$$

If

$$u_T'(t) = \frac{du_T(t)}{dt},$$

one may write

$$\int_{-\infty}^{t} u_T'(\tau) \, d\tau = u_T(\tau) \Big]_{-\infty}^{t}$$

$$= u_T(t) - u_T(-\infty)$$

$$= u_T(t).$$

Therefore,

$$\int_{-\infty}^{t} u_T'(\tau) \, d\tau = \int_{-\infty}^{t} \delta_T(\tau) \, d\tau,$$

and $u_T'(t) = \delta_T(t)$ or

$$\delta_T(t) = \frac{du_T(t)}{dt}. \tag{7.8}$$

As a final note on these two functions, we observe that

$$u_T(-t) = \begin{cases} 1, & t \leqslant -T \\ \frac{1}{2}, & t = 0 \\ 0, & t \geqslant T \end{cases} \tag{7.9a}$$

and it follows that

$$u_T(t) + u_T(-t) = 1. \tag{7.9b}$$

From the properties (7.1) of the function $\delta_T(t)$, it is clear that a large group of functions fit its specifications. To list a few possibilities:

(1) $$\delta_T(t) = \begin{cases} 0, & t \leqslant -T \\ \dfrac{1}{2T}, & -T < t < T \qquad \text{(a rectangular pulse)} \\ 0, & t \geqslant T \end{cases}$$

(2) $$\delta_T(t) = \begin{cases} 0, & t \leqslant -T \\ \dfrac{1}{T}\left(1 + \dfrac{t}{T}\right), & -T < t < 0 \qquad \text{(a triangular pulse)} \\ \dfrac{1}{T}\left(1 - \dfrac{t}{T}\right), & 0 < t < T \\ 0, & t \geqslant T \end{cases}$$

(3) $$\delta_T(t) = \begin{cases} 0, & t \leqslant -T \\ \dfrac{\pi}{4T} \cos \dfrac{\pi t}{2T}, & -T < t < T \qquad \text{(a sinusoidal pulse)} \\ 0, & t \geqslant T \end{cases}$$

(4) $$\delta_T(t) = \begin{cases} 0, & t \leqslant -T \\ \dfrac{1}{T} \cos^2 \dfrac{\pi t}{2T}, & -T < t < T \\ 0, & t \geqslant T. \end{cases}$$

One of these, (3), and the associated function $u_T(t)$ are shown in Fig. 7.2.

The two *singularity functions* which will be important to us are the functions approached by $\delta_T(t)$ and $u_T(t)$ as the width $2T$ of $\delta_T(t)$ approaches zero symmetrically while all the defining properties of $\delta_T(t)$ and $u_T(t)$ are maintained.

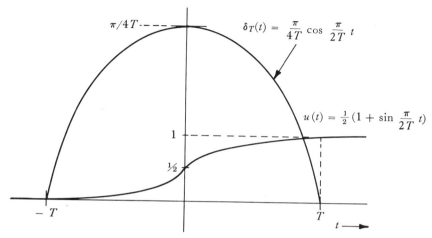

$$\pi/4T \quad\quad\quad \delta_T(t) = \frac{\pi}{4T} \cos \frac{\pi}{2T} t$$

$$u(t) = \frac{1}{2}\left(1 + \sin \frac{\pi}{2T} t\right)$$

Fig. 7.2   *One of many possible pairs of forms for $\delta_T(t)$ and $u_T(t)$.*

By $2T$ "approaching zero symmetrically," we are making a statement recognizing that if the symmetry property of Eq. (7.1a) is to be maintained, then $2T$ must shrink symmetrically about $t = 0$. This means that $-T$ approaches zero from the left and T approaches zero from the right. As this is a limiting process and we only get arbitrarily close to zero, we need to differentiate between zero approached from the left and zero approached from the right, since in truth they each are an arbitrarily small number (smaller than any number we care to state) different from exact zero. This is done by letting $2T$ approach true zero with true zero always centered in the interval $2T$, indicating this special way of taking the limit by the following correspondence:

$$2T \to 0 \Rightarrow \begin{matrix} -T \to 0^- \\ +T \to 0^+. \end{matrix} \tag{7.10}$$

Here $\Rightarrow$ indicates "corresponds to," and 0^- is zero approached from the left while 0^+ is zero approached from the right.

The *unit impulse*, or *Dirac Delta*, is

$$\delta(t) = \lim_{\substack{-T \to 0^- \\ +T \to 0^+}} \delta_T(t), \tag{7.11}$$

and the *unit step function* is

$$u(t) = \lim_{\substack{-T \to 0^- \\ +T \to 0^+}} u_T(t). \tag{7.12}$$

Let us note that if t is less than or equal to 0^-, $u(t)$ is certainly less than zero and that if t is greater than or equal to 0^+, it is certainly greater than zero. Thus the following correspondences

$$\begin{aligned} t \leqslant 0^- &\Rightarrow t < 0 \\ t \geqslant 0^+ &\Rightarrow t > 0. \end{aligned} \tag{7.13}$$

Equations (7.1), (7.2), (7.7), (7.8), and (7.9) then lead to the following properties and relationships:

1.   Properties of the unit impulse

$$\delta(t) = \delta(-t) \tag{7.14a}$$

$$\int_{-\infty}^{\infty} \delta(\tau)\, d\tau = 1 \tag{7.14b}$$

$$\delta(t) = 0, \qquad t \neq 0. \tag{7.14c}$$

2.   Definition of the unit step function

$$u(t) = \int_{-\infty}^{t} \delta(\tau)\, d\tau. \tag{7.15}$$

3.   Properties of the unit step function

$$u(t) = \begin{cases} 0, & t < 0 \\ \frac{1}{2}, & t = 0 \\ 1, & t > 0 \end{cases} \tag{7.16a}$$

$$u(-t) = \begin{cases} 1, & t < 0 \\ \frac{1}{2}, & t = 0 \\ 0, & t > 0 \end{cases} \tag{7.16b}$$

$$u(-t) + u(t) = 1. \tag{7.16c}$$

4.   Derivative of the unit step function

$$\frac{du(t)}{dt} = \delta(t). \tag{7.17}$$

The step function will often be associated with discontinuities in functions at the origin. For example, if $f(t)$ is a continuous function at the origin,

$$f(t)u(t) = \begin{cases} 0, & t < 0 \\ \tfrac{1}{2}f(0), & t = 0 \\ f(t), & t > 0, \end{cases} \tag{7.18}$$

or

$$f(t) + au(t) = \begin{cases} f(t), & t < 0 \\ f(0) + \dfrac{a}{2}, & t = 0 \\ f(t) + a, & t > 0. \end{cases} \tag{7.19}$$

Examples of such discontinuous functions as well as the two forms taken by the unit step function are shown in Fig. 7.3.

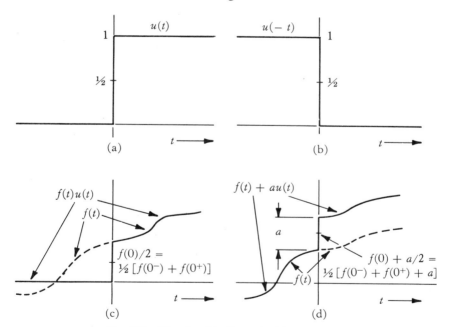

Fig. 7.3 *Signals with discontinuities at the origin.*

The use of the unit impulse and the unit step function will involve formal manipulations based on their defining properties. This is done with the realization that nature herself will yield signals which only approach these idealized forms in the neighborhood of $t = 0$. Nevertheless the differences between the physical and mathematical results exist only at the exact location of the origin;

and since we are concerned about this for but an instant briefer than any of practical interest, the mathematical behavior to all practical purposes will be an accurate description of actual behavior.

7.4 THE OPERATOR CONCEPT AGAIN

If we observe condition B and are able to establish that it exists because of, or is somehow connected to, condition A, then we may say that

$$B = \mathcal{O}A \tag{7.20}$$

where $\mathcal{O}$ is the description of how condition A yields condition B, and it is called an *operator*. Obviously,

$$\mathcal{O}A \neq A\mathcal{O} \tag{7.21}$$

as, although we can operate on condition A, we cannot, in general, condition A the operation, no more than the fact that (my aunt = my father's sister) infers that (my aunt = my sister's father). Therefore, the operator symbol always precedes the symbol representing the condition operated upon. So operators generally are not commutative.

For our purposes, the operator will indicate how one variable, or function, is derived from another, so Eq. (7.20) takes the form

$$y(t) = \mathcal{O}x(t). \tag{7.22}$$

Some examples of such operators are:

$$\mathcal{O} = \sin(\quad) \qquad \mathcal{O} = \sqrt{(\quad)}$$

$$\mathcal{O} = \frac{d}{dt}(\quad) \qquad \mathcal{O} = \int (\quad)\, dt.$$

Now suppose that

$$x(t) = x_1(t) + x_2(t) + x_3(t) + \cdots + x_n(t) \tag{7.23}$$

$$= \sum_{k=1}^{n} x_k(t).$$

Then if

$$\mathcal{O}x(t) = \mathcal{O} \sum_{k=1}^{n} x_k(t)$$

$$= \mathcal{O}x_1(t) + \mathcal{O}x_2(t) + \mathcal{O}x_3(t) + \cdots + \mathcal{O}x_n(t)$$

$$= \sum_{k=1}^{n} \mathcal{O}x_k(t), \tag{7.24}$$

the operator $\mathcal{O}$ is said to be *linear*. Thus a linear operator is one which is distributive. Operators which are not linear are, oddly enough, called *non-linear*.

If

$$\mathcal{O}x(t) = x(t), \qquad (7.25a)$$

then $\mathcal{O}$ is said to be the *unit operator*, since it has the properties of the scalar " 1." The inverse of $\mathcal{O}$, designated $\mathcal{O}^{-1}$, " undoes " the operation of $\mathcal{O}$, so that

$$\mathcal{O}^{-1}\mathcal{O}x(t) = x(t). \qquad (7.25b)$$

7.5 INTEGRAL OPERATOR

We are now in a position to develop a method whereby integro-differential equations can be rewritten in an equivalent form and essentially solved algebraically. Our method will use the symbol $1/p$ which will represent the following mathematical operation:

$$\frac{1}{p}\,[x(t)] = \int_{0^-}^{t} [x(\tau)]\, d\tau. \qquad (7.26)$$

This operation can be performed on any function that can be integrated over the indicated interval, and the function itself may be defined over negative as well as positive time.

Basically, the operator $1/p$ simply changes one function of time into another function of time in the specified manner of Eq. (7.26). To illustrate, let

$$x(t) = \frac{dy(t)}{dt}. \qquad (7.27)$$

Then

$$\frac{1}{p}\,[x(t)] = \int_{0^-}^{t} \left[\frac{dy(\tau)}{d\tau}\right] d\tau$$

$$= y(\tau)\big|_{0^-}^{t}$$

$$= y(t) - y(0^-). \qquad (7.28)$$

Let us now examine the effects of successive applications of the operator to the unit impulse function:

1. $\dfrac{1}{p}\,[\delta(t)] = \displaystyle\int_{0^-}^{t} \left[\dfrac{du(\tau)}{d\tau}\right] d\tau$

$= u(\tau)\big|_{0^-}^{t}$

$= u(t) - u(0^-)$

$= u(t);$

2. $\dfrac{1}{p}\left[\dfrac{1}{p}\delta(t)\right] = \dfrac{1}{p}[u(t)]$

$$= \int_{0-}^{t} u(\tau)\,d\tau$$

$$= \int_{0-}^{t} \frac{d[\tau u(\tau)]}{d\tau}\,d\tau$$

$$= \tau u(\tau)\,|_{0-}^{t}$$

$$= tu(t);$$

3. $\dfrac{1}{p}\left[\dfrac{1}{p^2}\delta(t)\right] = \dfrac{1}{p}[tu(t)]$

$$= \int_{0-}^{t} \tau u(\tau)\,d\tau$$

$$= \int_{0-}^{t} \frac{d[\frac{1}{2}\tau^2 u(\tau)]}{\cdot\, d\tau}\,d\tau$$

$$= \tfrac{1}{2}\tau^2 u(\tau)\,|_{0-}^{t}$$

$$= \tfrac{1}{2}t^2 u(t).$$

The foregoing illustrates how the integral operator changes the unit impulse function into other equivalent functions of time of one form of Eq. (7.18). If the results of the previous example are rewritten as

$$\frac{1}{p}\delta(t) = \frac{t^0}{0!}u(t) \qquad\qquad (7.29a)$$

$$\frac{1}{p^2}\delta(t) = \frac{t^1}{1!}u(t) \qquad\qquad (7.29b)$$

$$\frac{1}{p^3}\delta(t) = \frac{t^2}{2!}u(t), \qquad\qquad (7.29c)$$

we can see that, in general, the sequence of operations leads to

$$\frac{1}{p^n}\delta(t) = \frac{t^{n-1}}{(n-1)!}u(t). \qquad\qquad (7.30)$$

Thus, there is a family of functions that can be written in terms of the integral operator operating upon the unit impulse. In other words, the notation on either side of the equal sign in Eq. (7.30) can be used depending upon which notation is more convenient for solving a problem.

7.6 LINEARITY OF THE INTEGRAL OPERATOR

Before proceeding with another example, let us apply the integral operator to Eq. (7.23) and check for linearity; that is,

$$\frac{1}{p}\sum_{k=1}^{n} x_k(t) = \int_{0^-}^{t} \sum_{k=1}^{n} x_k(\tau)\, d\tau$$

$$= \sum_{k=1}^{n} \int_{0^-}^{t} x_k(\tau)\, d\tau$$

$$= \sum_{k=1}^{n} \frac{1}{p} x_k(t). \qquad (7.31)$$

This last equation illustrates that the operator $1/p$ can operate on each portion of a series separately, thus the integral operator is distributive, and therefore, a *linear operator*.

7.7 OPERATOR FORMS OF TIME FUNCTIONS

Let us now investigate those functions which can be expressed as a McLaurin's series; that is, suppose that

$$x(t) = x(0)\frac{t^0}{0!} + x'(0)\frac{t^1}{1!} + x''(0)\frac{t^2}{2!} + x'''(0)\frac{t^3}{3!} + \cdots. \qquad (7.32)$$

Multiplication of both sides by $u(t)$ gives

$$x(t)u(t) = x(0)\frac{t^0}{0!}u(t) + x'(0)\frac{t^1}{1!}u(t) + x''(0)\frac{t^2}{2!}u(t)$$

$$+ x'''(0)\frac{t^3}{3!}u(t) + \cdots. \qquad (7.33)$$

Use of Eq. (7.30) provides an alternative way to write Eq. (7.33) which is

$$x(t)u(t) = x(0)\frac{1}{p}\delta(t) + x'(0)\frac{1}{p^2}\delta(t) + x''(0)\frac{1}{p^3}\delta(t) + x'''(0)\frac{1}{p^4}\delta(t) + \cdots$$

$$= \left[\frac{x(0)}{p} + \frac{x'(0)}{p^2} + \frac{x''(0)}{p^3} + \frac{x'''(0)}{p^4} + \cdots\right]\delta(t)$$

$$= X(p)\delta(t). \qquad (7.34)$$

Here $X(p)$ is a function of p (often expressible as the ratio of two polynomials in p) which operates upon the unit impulse to give $x(t)u(t)$, a function of the form of Eq. (7.18). The units on $\delta(t)$ are $\sec^{-1}$, so *the units on $X(p)$ are* $(x$-*units$) \cdot \sec$.

Let us now observe that

$$e^{-at}u(t) = \left[1 - at + a^2 \frac{t^2}{2!} - a^3 \frac{t^3}{3!} + \cdots\right]u(t)$$

$$= \left[\frac{1}{p} - \frac{a}{p^2} + \frac{a^2}{p^3} - \frac{a^3}{p^4} + \cdots\right]\delta(t)$$

$$= \frac{1}{p+a}\delta(t),$$

and

$$te^{-at}u(t) = \left[t - at^2 - a^2\frac{t^3}{2!} - a^3\frac{t^4}{3!} + \cdots\right]u(t)$$

$$= \left[t - 2a\frac{t^2}{2!} + 3a^2\frac{t^3}{3!} - 4a^3\frac{t^4}{4!} + \cdots\right]u(t)$$

$$= \left[\frac{1}{p^2} - \frac{2a}{p^3} + \frac{3a^2}{p^4} - \frac{4a^3}{p^5} + \cdots\right]\delta(t)$$

$$= \frac{1}{(p+a)^2}\delta(t).$$

Continuing this sequence leads to the generalization

$$\frac{1}{(p+a)^n}\delta(t) = e^{-at}\frac{t^{n-1}}{(n-1)!}u(t), \tag{7.35}$$

where n is any positive integer. Thus, there is a second family of functions that can be written in terms of the integral operator operating upon the unit impulse.

An extension of Eq. (7.34) can be obtained by multiplying both sides of Eq. (7.33) by e^{-at} to produce

$$e^{-at}x(t)u(t) = x(0)e^{-at}\frac{t^0}{0!}u(t) + x'(0)e^{-at}\frac{t^1}{1!}u(t) + x''(0)e^{-at}\frac{t^2}{2!}u(t) + \cdots.$$

$$\tag{7.36}$$

Application of Eq. (7.35) yields

$$e^{-at}x(t)u(t) = \left[\frac{x(0)}{(p+a)} + \frac{x'(0)}{(p+a)^2} + \frac{x''(0)}{(p+a)^3} + \cdots\right]\delta(t)$$

$$= X(p+a)\delta(t), \tag{7.37}$$

where $X(p+a)$ is the $X(p)$ of Eq. (7.34) with every p replaced by $p+a$.

EXAMPLE 7.1. Determine the operator form of $e^{-10t}tu(t)$.

Solution. From Eq. (7.29)

$$tu(t) = \frac{1}{p^2}\,\delta(t).$$

Then, by Eq. (7.37),

$$e^{-10t}tu(t) = \frac{1}{(p + 10)^2}\,\delta(t).$$

It should be noted that any combination of the integral operator operating on the unit impulse always produces a function that is zero for all negative time. In other words, the integral operator cannot create any portion of a function from a unit impulse *until* the unit impulse occurs; therefore, Eqs. (7.30), (7.34), (7.35), and (7.37) and the example resulted in functions in which the unit step function was necessary as in Eq. (7.18), illustrated in Fig. 7.3(c). This means that a function such as $u(-t)$ cannot be written in the form of $X(p)\delta(t)$.

7.8 THE INVERSE INTEGRAL OPERATOR

As the integral operator converts one function of time into another function of time, it seems logical to assume that some other operator should exist which will convert the second function back into the first function. If this operator is some operation $\mathcal{O}$, then it must be that

$$\mathcal{O}\,\frac{1}{p}\,x(t) = x(t),$$

and, according to Eq. (7.25),

$$\mathcal{O}\,\frac{1}{p} = \text{unit operator} = 1.$$

Thus it seems logical to designate

$$\mathcal{O} = p,$$

so that

$$p\,\frac{1}{p} = \text{unit operator} = 1. \tag{7.38}$$

Let us apply the second operator, p, to both sides of Eq. (7.28) in an effort to find out just what this operation accomplishes. Thus,

$$p\left[\frac{1}{p}\,x(t)\right] = p[y(t) - y(0^-)], \tag{7.39}$$

and from Eq. (7.38)

$$x(t) = p[y(t) - y(0^-)].$$ (7.40)

Substitution of Eq. (7.27) now gives

$$\frac{dy(t)}{dt} = p[y(t) - y(0^-)].$$ (7.41)

Equation (7.41) gives us an alternative way to write a derivative in integro-differential equations. Of course, one must be careful to replace any derivative with p operating on the original function *minus* its value at $t = 0^-$.

We may now complete the operational connection between $\delta(t)$ and $u(t)$ by rewriting Eq. (7.17)

$$\delta(t) = \frac{du(t)}{dt},$$

then applying Eq. (7.41) to get

$$\delta(t) = p[u(t) - u(0^-)]$$
$$= pu(t).$$ (7.42)

We have shown that p $1/p$ is equivalent to the unit operator. Now let us operate on both sides of Eq. (7.41) with the integral operator to obtain

$$\frac{1}{p}\frac{dy(t)}{dt} = \frac{1}{p}p[y(t) - y(0^-)],$$

which is equivalent, by the definition of $1/p$, to

$$\int_{0^-}^{t} \frac{dy(\tau)}{d\tau}\,d\tau = \frac{1}{p}p[y(t) - y(0^-)],$$

or

$$y(t) - y(0^-) = \frac{1}{p}p[y(t) - y(0^-)].$$

Thus, by Eqs. (7.25) and (7.38),

$$\frac{1}{p}p = p\frac{1}{p} = \text{unit operator} = 1,$$ (7.43)

and the operator and its inverse are commutative. The symbol p now is seen to take on the algebraic properties of a scalar, except that multiplication with functions of time does not commute. One evidence of this algebraic property is the fact that Eq. (7.42) is equivalent to an algebraic manipulation of Eq. (7.29a).

The inverse operator can be extended to include p^n and nth derivatives just as the integral operator was extended, but such an approach is not necessary at the present time. Eq. (7.41) is an important result and will be used extensively in following developments.

7.9 *TEMPUS FUGIT*, BUT FROM WHERE?

In actual practice a function of time, such as a source voltage, is seldom just one simple mathematical expression. For example, during one interval of time, perhaps for all negative time, the function might have been constant; but during another interval of time, perhaps for all positive time, the function might be sinusoidal. Or perhaps some other pair of different kinds of functions were involved in some way.

We may write any function of the class defined in Art. 7.2 in the form

$$f(t) = f_-(t)u(-t) + f_R(t), \tag{7.44}$$

where

$$f_R(t) = f_+(t)u(t) + \text{any impulsive discontinuities at the origin.} \tag{7.45a}$$

By an *impulsive discontinuity* we mean either an impulse function or a function resulting from a finite sequence of differentiations of an impulse. Such functions must be allowed in order to fill the class of signals we are considering. The other functions to be defined are

$$f_-(t) = f(t) \qquad \text{for } t < 0$$
$$\text{and is continuous through } t = 0 \tag{7.45b}$$

$$f_+(t) = f(t) \qquad \text{for } t > 0$$
$$\text{and is continuous through } t = 0. \tag{7.45c}$$

Although $f_-(0^-) = f_-(0^+)$ and $f_+(0^-) = f_+(0^+)$, it is not necessarily true that $f(0^-) = f(0^+)$. Thus Eq. (7.44) may be a description of *any* function in the class we are considering.

Some examples of functions in this class are

1. $f(t) = 4e^{3t}u(-t) + 4e^{-5t}u(t),$
      where

$$f_-(t) = 4e^{3t}$$
$$f_+(t) = 4e^{-5t}$$
$$f_R(t) = 4e^{-5t}u(t).$$

2. $f(t) = -5u(-t) + (30 \sin 377t)u(t),$
where

$$f_-(t) = -5$$
$$f_+(t) = 30 \sin 377t$$
$$f_R(t) = (30 \sin 377t)u(t).$$

3. $f(t) = (3 \cos 377t)u(-t) + 3\delta(t) - 2e^{-t}u(t),$
where

$$f_-(t) = 3 \cos 377t$$
$$f_+(t) = -2e^{-t}$$
$$f_R(t) = 3\delta(t) - 2e^{-t}u(t).$$

Because $f_R(t)$, by definition, is zero for all negative time, there is an alternative way to write Eq. (7.44) using the integral operator and the unit impulse. Hence,

$$f(t) = f_-(t)u(-t) + F(p)\delta(t), \qquad (7.46)$$

where

$$F(p)\delta(t) = f_R(t). \qquad (7.47)$$

Some examples are

1. $$f(t) = 5$$
$$= 5u(-t) + 5u(t)$$
$$= 5u(-t) + \frac{5}{p}\delta(t).$$

2. $$f(t) = 2(\sin 377t)u(-t) + 3e^{-10t}u(t)$$
$$= 2(\sin 377t)u(-t) + \frac{3}{p + 10}\delta(t).$$

3. $$f(t) = 10u(-t) + 5\delta(t) - 7u(t)$$
$$= 10u(-t) + 5\delta(t) - \frac{7}{p}\delta(t)$$
$$= 10u(-t) + \frac{5p - 7}{p}\delta(t).$$

Perhaps the reader is wondering why only one-half of $f(t)$ was written in operator notation, but he will soon discover that the only part of $f(t)$ that needs to be determined after $t = 0$ is $f_R(t)$. Furthermore, the past is seldom known to such a degree of accuracy that an explicit equation can be written. As a matter of fact, we will generally be willing to let bygones be bygones, once we have received our inheritance from what has gone before, and turn, starry-eyed and eager, toward the future.

The examples used in this article merely show what $f_-(t)u(-t)$ might have been like. Let us not forget, however, that whether our history of events past is accurately compiled or compiled at all, we are faced with its consequences *right now*!

7.10 OPERATIONAL EQUIVALENT OF INTEGRATION

Whenever one or more integrals appears in a network equation, the equation becomes more difficult to solve than if only first order derivatives and constants occurred; so we will attempt to determine an equivalent representation which can be used to replace the integral of a function. First, we will start by using the equivalent notation of Eq. (7.46); and we will break the integration into two parts to give

$$\int_{-\infty}^{t} f(\tau)\, d\tau = \int_{-\infty}^{t} [f_-(\tau)u(-\tau) + F(p)\delta(\tau)]\, d\tau$$

$$= \int_{-\infty}^{0^-} [f_-(\tau)u(-\tau) + F(p)\delta(\tau)]\, d\tau$$

$$+ \int_{0^-}^{t} [f_-(\tau)u(-\tau) + F(p)\delta(\tau)]\, d\tau. \qquad (7.48)$$

As $F(p)\delta(\tau)$ is zero and $u(-\tau)$ is unity for all negative values of τ and τ only has negative values in the one integral; therefore, we can write that

$$\int_{-\infty}^{t} f(\tau)\, d\tau = \int_{-\infty}^{0^-} f_-(\tau)1\, d\tau + \int_{0^-}^{t} f_-(\tau)u(-\tau)\, d\tau$$

$$+ \int_{0^-}^{t} F(p)\delta(\tau)\, d\tau. \qquad (7.49)$$

Furthermore, if t is negative, the second integral in Eq. (7.49) becomes

$$\int_{0^-}^{t} f_-(\tau)u(-\tau)\, d\tau = \int_{0^-}^{t} f_-(\tau)1\, d\tau, \qquad t < 0$$

$$= \left[\int_{0^-}^{t} f_-(\tau)\, d\tau \right] 1, \qquad t < 0, \qquad (7.50)$$

and if t is positive, we have

$$\int_{0-}^{t} f_-(\tau)u(-\tau)\,d\tau = \int_{0-}^{t} f_-(\tau)0\,d\tau, \qquad t > 0$$

$$= \left[\int_{0-}^{t} f_-(\tau)\,d\tau\right]0, \qquad t > 0. \qquad (7.51)$$

Equations (7.50) and (7.51) can be written as one equation; that is,

$$\int_{0-}^{t} f_-(\tau)u(-\tau)\,d\tau = \left[\int_{0-}^{t} f_-(\tau)\,d\tau\right]u(-t). \qquad (7.52)$$

If we use Eq. (7.52) and if we apply the definition of the integral operator, we obtain from Eq. (7.49) the form

$$\int_{-\infty}^{t} f(\tau)\,d\tau = \int_{-\infty}^{0-} f_-(\tau)\,d\tau + \left[\int_{0-}^{t} f_-(\tau)\,d\tau\right]u(-t) + \frac{F(p)}{p}\delta(t). \qquad (7.53)$$

At this point it will be convenient to introduce the notation for the antiderivative of a function, which can be written as

$$g(t) = \frac{dg^{(-1)}(t)}{dt}, \qquad (7.54)$$

where $g^{(-1)}(t)$ represents the antiderivative of $g(t)$ and is chosen so that $g^{(-1)}(-\infty)$ is zero. [Remember that there are an infinite number of functions whose derivative equals $g(t)$.]

An alternative way to represent the antiderivative is to integrate $g(t)$ as shown below.

$$\int_{-\infty}^{t} g(\tau)\,d\tau = \int_{-\infty}^{t} \frac{dg^{(-1)}(\tau)}{d\tau}\,d\tau$$

$$= g^{(-1)}(\tau)\,|_{-\infty}^{t}$$

$$= g^{(-1)}(t) - g^{(-1)}(-\infty)$$

$$= g^{(-1)}(t). \qquad (7.55)$$

This result illustrates that the antiderivative is an equation which describes the net area under a curve from $-\infty$ to t. Furthermore, we can write that

$$\int_{t_1}^{t_2} g(\tau)\,d\tau = \int_{t_1}^{t_2} \frac{dg^{(-1)}(\tau)}{d\tau}\,d\tau$$

$$= g^{(-1)}(\tau)\,|_{t_1}^{t_2}$$

$$= g^{(-1)}(t_2) - g^{(-1)}(t_1). \qquad (7.56)$$

Thus, the net area under $g(t)$ between t_2 and t_1 is a difference between $g^{(-1)}(t)$ evaluated at t_2 and t_1.

If we apply the antiderivative notation to Eq. (7.53), we can write that

$$\int_{-\infty}^{t} f(\tau)\, d\tau = f_{-}^{(-1)}(0^-) + [f_{-}^{(-1)}(t) - f_{-}^{(-1)}(0^-)]u(-t) + \frac{F(p)}{p}\,\delta(t)$$

$$= f_{-}^{(-1)}(t)u(-t) + f_{-}^{(-1)}(0^-)[1 - u(-t)] + \frac{F(p)}{p}\,\delta(t)$$

$$= f_{-}^{(-1)}(t)u(-t) + f_{-}^{(-1)}(0^-)u(t) + \frac{F(p)}{p}\,\delta(t)$$

$$= f_{-}^{(-1)}(t)u(-t) + \frac{1}{p}[F(p) + f_{-}^{(-1)}(0^-)]\,\delta(t), \qquad (7.57)$$

where $f_{-}^{(-1)}(0^-)$ can be interpreted as the *net* area under the $f(t)$ function from $-\infty$ to 0^- and written as $f^{(-1)}(0^-)$, because

$$f_{-}^{(-1)}(0^-) = \int_{-\infty}^{0^-} f_{-}(\tau)\, d\tau$$

$$= \int_{-\infty}^{0^-} f(\tau)\, d\tau$$

$$= f^{(-1)}(0^-).$$

Hence,

$$\int_{-\infty}^{t} f(\tau)\, d\tau = f_{-}^{(-1)}(t)u(-t) + \frac{1}{p}[F(p) + f^{(-1)}(0^-)]\,\delta(t), \qquad (7.58)$$

a very important result.

7.11 OPERATIONAL EQUIVALENT OF THE DERIVATIVE

We already have one equivalent representation for a derivative, Eq. (7.41), whenever a function can be written with one equation holding for all time. Let us try to find an equivalent representation for Eq. (7.46) where the given function is assumed to have two distinct parts. First, we can write that

$$\frac{df(t)}{dt} = \frac{d[f_{-}(t)u(-t) + F(p)\delta(t)]}{dt}$$

$$= \frac{df_{-}(t)}{dt}u(-t) + f_{-}(t)\frac{du(-t)}{dt} + F(p)\frac{d\delta(t)}{dt}. \qquad (7.59)$$

Then we can apply Eq. (7.41) to the last part of Eq. (7.59) to obtain

$$\frac{d\delta(t)}{dt} = p[\delta(t) - \delta(0^-)]$$

$$= p\delta(t), \tag{7.60}$$

and we can use Eqs. (7.16c) and (7.17) to produce

$$\frac{du(-t)}{dt} = \frac{d[1 - u(t)]}{dt}$$

$$= 0 - \frac{du(t)}{dt}$$

$$= -\delta(t). \tag{7.61}$$

Substitution of these two relationships into Eq. (7.59) gives

$$\frac{df(t)}{dt} = \frac{df_-(t)}{dt} u(-t) - f_-(t)\delta(t) + pF(p)\delta(t), \tag{7.62}$$

and since the unit impulse is zero everywhere but at the origin, there is really only one value of $f(t)$ in the center term of Eq. (7.62) that contributes to the term, the one at the origin. This means that

$$f_-(t)\delta(t) = f_-(0)\delta(t), \tag{7.63}$$

where $f_-(0)$ simply indicates the magnitude of the impulse function (amount of area under the impulse curve). Equation (7.63) now becomes

$$\frac{df(t)}{dt} = \frac{df_-(t)}{dt} u(-t) + [pF(p) - f_-(0)]\delta(t). \tag{7.64}$$

It is convenient to determine just how $f_-(0)$ is related to the function $f(t)$. Figure 7.4 contains an example illustrating that the condition of continuity on $f_-(t)$ requires that

$$f_-(0) = f(0^-). \tag{7.65}$$

Equation (7.65) provides the final form for Eq. (7.64); that is,

$$\frac{df(t)}{dt} = \frac{df_-(t)}{dt} u(-t) + [pF(p) - f(0^-)] \delta(t), \tag{7.66}$$

another very important result.

EXAMPLE 7.2. For the function shown in Fig. 7.5(a), use ordinary methods of calculus to obtain the derivative and the integral. Then use operator methods to obtain the derivative and the integral, and show that the answers agree with the calculus approach.

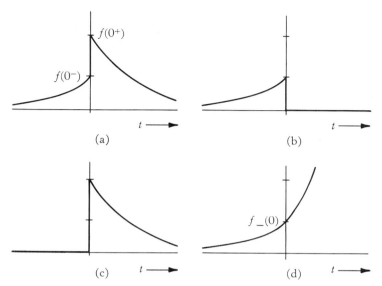

Fig. 7.4 *Illustration of Eq. (7.65). (a) $f(t)$. (b) $f_-(t)u(-t)$. (c) $f_+(t)u(t) = F(p)\delta(t)$. (d) $f_-(t)$.*

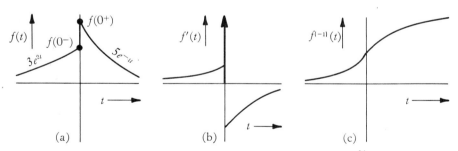

Fig. 7.5 *Function for Example 7.2. (a) $f(t)$. (b) $df(t)/dt$. (c) $\int_{-\infty}^{t} f(\tau)\,d\tau$.*

Solution. An explicit equation for $f(t)$ is

$$f(t) = 3e^{2t}u(-t) + 5e^{-4t}u(t),$$

and the differentiation operation yields

$$\frac{df(t)}{dt} = 3e^{2t}\frac{du(-t)}{dt} + \frac{d(3e^{2t})}{dt}u(-t) + 5e^{-4t}\frac{du(t)}{dt} + \frac{d(5e^{-4t})}{dt}u(t)$$

$$= 3e^{2t}[-\delta(t)] + 6e^{2t}u(-t) + 5e^{-4t}\delta(t) - 20e^{-4t}u(t)$$

$$= 6e^{2t}u(-t) + [5e^{-4(0)} - 3e^{2(0)}]\delta(t) - 20e^{-4t}u(t)$$

$$= 6e^{2t}u(-t) + 2\delta(t) - 20e^{-4t}u(t). \qquad Ans.$$

The process of integration gives

$$\int_{-\infty}^{t} f(\tau)\, d\tau = \int_{-\infty}^{t} [3e^{2\tau}u(-\tau) + 5e^{-4\tau}u(\tau)]\, d\tau,$$

which can be evaluated in three steps as follows:

1. For $t < 0$:

$$\int_{-\infty}^{t} f(\tau)\, d\tau = \int_{-\infty}^{t} (3e^{2\tau} + 0)\, d\tau$$

$$= \tfrac{3}{2}e^{2\tau} \big|_{-\infty}^{t}$$

$$= \tfrac{3}{2}e^{2t}.$$

2. For $t = 0$:

$$\int_{-\infty}^{0} f(\tau)\, d\tau = \tfrac{3}{2}e^{2\tau} \big|_{-\infty}^{0}$$

$$= \tfrac{3}{2}.$$

3. For $t > 0$:

$$\int_{-\infty}^{t} f(\tau)\, d\tau = \int_{-\infty}^{0} 3e^{2\tau}\, d\tau + \int_{0}^{t} 5e^{-4\tau}\, d\tau$$

$$= \tfrac{3}{2} + \frac{5}{-4} e^{-4\tau} \bigg|_{0}^{t}$$

$$= \tfrac{3}{2} + \tfrac{5}{4} - \tfrac{5}{4}e^{-4t}.$$

Combining the three results into one equation produces

$$\int_{-\infty}^{t} f(\tau)\, d\tau = \tfrac{3}{2}e^{2t}u(-t) + (\tfrac{11}{4} - \tfrac{5}{4}e^{-4t})u(t). \qquad Ans.$$

For the operator approach we use

$$f(t) = 3e^{2t}u(-t) + \frac{5}{p+4}\, \delta(t),$$

and the derivative, according to Eq. (7.66), is

$$\frac{df(t)}{dt} = \frac{d(3e^{2t})}{dt} u(-t) + \left[p\,\frac{5}{p+4} - 3 \right] \delta(t). \qquad Ans.$$

While this easily obtained form will prove to be sufficient in many problems to follow, it can be rewritten to show that it is indeed identical to the previous result. Thus

$$\frac{df(t)}{dt} = 6e^{2t}u(-t) + \left[\frac{5(p+4) - 20}{p+4} - 3 \right] \delta(t)$$

$$= 6e^{2t}u(-t) + \left[2 - \frac{20}{p+4} \right] \delta(t)$$

$$= 6e^{2t}u(-t) + 2\delta(t) - 20e^{-4t}u(t). \qquad Ans.$$

Equation (7.58) provides a relatively easy way to obtain the integral; accordingly

$$\int_{-\infty}^{t} f(\tau)\, d\tau = \left[\int_{-\infty}^{t} 3e^{2\tau}\, d\tau \right] u(-t) + \frac{1}{p}\left[\frac{5}{p+4} + \int_{-\infty}^{0^-} 3e^{2\tau}\, d\tau \right]\delta(t)$$

$$= \tfrac{3}{2}e^{2t}u(-t) + \frac{1}{p}\left[\frac{5}{p+4} + \tfrac{3}{2} \right]\delta(t), \qquad Ans.$$

which, while sufficient for many problems, can be written as

$$\int_{-\infty}^{t} f(\tau)\, d\tau = \tfrac{3}{2}e^{2t}u(-t) + \frac{5}{p(p+4)}\,\delta(t) + \tfrac{3}{2}\,u(t)$$

$$= \tfrac{3}{2}e^{2t}u(-t) + \left[\frac{5/4}{p} + \frac{-5/4}{p+4} \right]\delta(t) + \tfrac{3}{2}\,u(t)$$

$$= \tfrac{3}{2}e^{2t}u(-t) + \tfrac{5}{4}\,u(t) - \tfrac{5}{4}e^{-4t}u(t)$$
$$\quad + \tfrac{3}{2}u(t)$$

$$= \tfrac{3}{2}e^{2t}u(-t) + (\tfrac{11}{4} - \tfrac{5}{4}e^{-4t})u(t), \qquad Ans.$$

which is identical to the previous answer.

7.12 A CIRCUIT APPLICATION

In order to illustrate application of the foregoing material, a simple example will be solved in *detail*.

EXAMPLE 7.3. Determine the current which flows in the circuit model shown in Fig. 7.6 after the switch is closed. The capacitor is known to have been charged to 5 V by the past current and never discharged. (We will call the instant when the switch closes $t = 0$.)

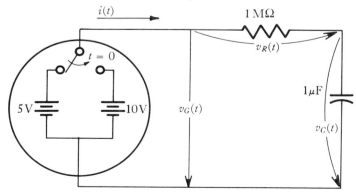

Fig. 7.6 *Series R-C circuit.*

Solution. Applying KVL and the volt-ampere relationships, we may write

$$v_G(t) = v_R(t) + v_C(t)$$

$$= 10^6 i(t) + 10^6 \int_{-\infty}^{t} i(\tau) \, d\tau.$$

We now use Eqs. (7.46) and (7.58) to write an equivalent form for the above equation.

$$v_-(t)u(-t) + \frac{10}{p} \delta(t) = 10^6[i_-(t)u(-t) + I(p)\delta(t)]$$

$$+ 10^6 \Big\{ i_-^{(-1)}(t)u(-t)$$

$$+ \frac{1}{p}[I(p) + i^{(-1)}(0^-)]\delta(t) \Big\}.$$

This equation has two distinct parts on each side of the equal sign. We might call these parts the past [all $u(-t)$-terms] and the future [all $\delta(t)$-terms] and equate these parts to each other to make two separate equations. Such a process would be similar to equating the real and the imaginary parts of complex numbers separately. As we do not know much about the past (except that it left the capacitor charge to 5 V), we will concentrate on the future terms to obtain

$$\frac{10}{p} \delta(t) = 10^6 I(p)\delta(t) + \frac{10^6}{p}[I(p) + i^{(-1)}(0^-)]\delta(t).$$

We have seen that

$$i(t) = \frac{dq(t)}{dt},$$

which means that $q(t)$ is the antiderivative of $i(t)$ or that

$$i^{(-1)}(0^-) = q(0^-).$$

Therefore,

$$\frac{10}{p} \delta(t) = \Big\{ 10^6 I(p) + \frac{10^6}{p}[I(p) + q(0^-)] \Big\}\delta(t),$$

and if two operators operate on $\delta(t)$ to give the same function, we can assume that they are equivalent operations, or

$$\frac{10}{p} = 10^6 I(p) + \frac{10^6}{p}[I(p) + q(0^-)],$$

which can be solved for $I(p)$ to give

$$I(p) = \left[\frac{10}{p} - \frac{10^6 q(0^-)}{p} \right] \frac{1}{10^6 + 10^6/p}$$

$$= [10 - 10^6 q(0^-)] \frac{1}{10^6} \frac{1}{p+1}.$$

Since $q(t) = Cv(t)$,

$$q(0^-) = Cv(0^-)$$
$$= 10^{-6}(5),$$

which can be used to give

$$I(p) = (10 - 5)10^{-6} \frac{1}{p+1}$$

$$= 5 \times 10^{-6} \frac{1}{p+1}.$$

Finally, we know that

$$i(t) = I(p)\delta(t)$$

$$= 5 \times 10^{-6} \frac{1}{p+1} \delta(t)$$

$$= 5 \times 10^{-6} e^{-t} u(t) \text{ A}, \qquad Ans.$$

which is the solution that was sought.

In case the student is about to throw in the towel, it might be of some assurance to know that the problems generally need not be tackled with the foregoing detail. The past history of a model is needed only to the extent that we know the condition the model is in at zero minus; that is, at the very beginning of the problem at hand. The reasons for and results of this aspect of the problem are discussed in the following articles.

7.13 EFFECTS OF ENERGY LIMITS ON PHYSICAL SIGNALS

It is of fundamental importance in the study of physical systems, whether they be electrical or otherwise, that the amount of energy available from sources is finite, a fact that was exploited in developing the conservation theorems of Chapter 4. Consequently, we can exclude any behavior of the system that infers otherwise. Thus, the energy stored in electric and magnetic fields at every instant of time must be finite, as must be the total energy dissipated as heat or the total energy converted from one form to another during any finite interval of time.

An immediate result of this concept of limited energy is that there can be no voltage impulses across condensers or current impulses through inductances, since either infers an infinite stored energy at $t = 0$. More accurately, any impulse of either type considered would necessarily be hypothetical, introduced mathematically, and could not be presumed to exist as a measurable effect in a physical system. Thus, currents through inductances or voltages across condensers can be expected to have at most finite discontinuities; and the measurable variables existing throughout the system may have impulses as a result of differentiation at a discontinuity. However, the possibility of a physical differentiation of an impulse does not need to be considered.

Although we have defined the value of a function at a discontinuity as the mean of the values at either side of the discontinuity, this value is of small concern to us in physical problems, where we are interested in the value with which the function approachês the discontinuity from one side or the other. However, impulses resulting at the point of discontinuity are of interest, because they may often indicate an exceeding of rated peak values for components in the system. Such would be the case if the current was discontinuous in an inductance, because the voltage is directly proportional to the derivative of the current. Keep in mind that it is the voltage and not the stored energy that tends toward infinity when the current is discontinuous. The stored energy is simply changing from some finite value, $Li_1^2/2$, to another finite value, $Li_2^2/2$, in a time interval tending toward zero.

Let us agree, then, to concern ourselves only with impulses exactly at points of discontinuity, and to give our attention to other types of functions at the nearest point off the discontinuity, either to the right or to the left. Here we mean a *system discontinuity*, which exists if there is a discontinuity in *any* variable in the system. Some variables may be continuous through a system discontinuity.

7.14 A SYSTEM DISCONTINUITY AT $t = 0$

In a system which is not in some steady-state condition, interest is generally in its response to some disturbance, like closing a switch, short-circuiting a portion of the network, or otherwise introducing a sudden change in the state of the network. Normally we commence marking time at this point, so the disturbance occurs at $t = 0$, resulting in a discontinuity at the origin. The question of most concern to us is: *What happens from now on?*

Suppose we consider an integro-differential equation containing all forms which could possibly result from substituting volt-ampere relationships in either a KCL equation or a KVL equation. Such an equation is

$$f(t) = a_1 \frac{dx(t)}{dt} + a_2 x(t) + a_3 \int_{-\infty}^{t} x(\tau)\,d\tau, \tag{7.67}$$

where we assume only one unknown variable, $x(t)$, while realizing that in a system having several loops and nodes there may be several variables, each treated as this one will be treated.

If it is assumed that all variables take the form of $f(t)$ in Eq. (7.46), and if Eqs. (7.57) and (7.66) are applied, then Eq. (7.1) becomes

$$f_-(t)u(-t) + F(p)\delta(t)$$

$$= a_1 \left\{ \frac{dx_-(t)}{dt} u(-t) + [pX(p) - x(0^-)]\delta(t) \right\} + a_2\{x_-(t)u(-t) + X(p)\delta(t)\}$$

$$+ a_3 \left\{ \left[\int_{-\infty}^{t} x_-(\tau)\,d\tau \right] u(-t) + \frac{1}{p}[X(p) + x^{(-1)}(0^-)]\delta(t) \right\},$$

which, on collecting coefficients of $u(t)$ and $\delta(t)$, becomes

$$f_-(t)u(-t) + F(p)\delta(t)$$

$$= \left[a_1 \frac{dx_-(t)}{dt} + a_2 x_-(t) + a_3 \int_{-\infty}^{t} x_-(\tau)\,d\tau \right] u(-t)$$

$$+ \left[\left(a_1 p + a_2 + \frac{a_3}{p} \right) X(p) - a_1 x(0^-) + a_3 \frac{x^{(-1)}(0^-)}{p} \right] \delta(t). \tag{7.68}$$

In this equation, those terms of each side containing $u(-t)$ are *assuredly* zero for times greater than 0, while those containing $\delta(t)$ are *assuredly* zero for times less than 0. It can be said without qualification, then, that

$$f(t) = \left[a_1 \frac{dx_-(t)}{dt} + a_2 x_-(t) + a_3 \int_{-\infty}^{t} x_-(\tau)\,d\tau \right], \qquad t < 0, \tag{7.69a}$$

and

$$f(t) = \left[\left(a_1 p + a_2 + \frac{a_3}{p} \right) X(p) - a_1 x(0^-) + a_3 \frac{x^{(-1)}(0^-)}{p} \right] \delta(t), \qquad t > 0.$$

$$\tag{7.69b}$$

Exactly at the origin, however, both variables have the following values:

$$f(0) = \tfrac{1}{2}f(0^-) + \tfrac{1}{2}f(0^+) + [\text{any impulse in } F(p)\delta(t)] \qquad (7.70\text{a})$$

$$x(0) = \tfrac{1}{2}x(0^-) + \tfrac{1}{2}x(0^+) + [\text{any impulse in } X(p)\delta(t)]. \qquad (7.70\text{b})$$

If we stick to our agreement to concern ourselves only with impulses at the discontinuity, then only the impulsive parts of Eqs. (7.70) will be of concern to us; and they are contributed entirely in Eq. (7.69b). Therefore, as far as *useful* information is concerned, the time interval in Eq. (7.69b) may be ex-tended to the left to include the origin, and

$$f(t) = F(p)\delta(t)$$

$$= \left[\left(a_1 p + a_2 + \frac{a_3}{p}\right)X(p) - a_1 x(0^-) + a_3 \frac{x^{(-1)}(0^-)}{p}\right]\delta(t), \qquad t \geqslant 0.$$

$$(7.71)$$

TABLE 7.1   EQUIVALENTS HOLDING FOR NONNEGATIVE TIME

Entry Number	Time function = Equivalent representation	Complete Equation Number
1.	$\displaystyle\int_{0-}^{t} f(\tau)\,d\tau = \frac{1}{p}[f(t)]$	(7.26)
2.	$\dfrac{t^{n-1} u(t)}{(n-1)!} = \dfrac{1}{p^n}\delta(t), \qquad n = 1, 2, 3, 4, \ldots$	(7.30)
3.	If $\qquad\qquad x(t)u(t) = X(p)\delta(t)$	(7.34)
4.	then $\qquad\quad e^{-at}x(t)u(t) = X(p+a)\delta(t)$	(7.37)
5.	or, alternately, $\quad e^{-at}X(p)\delta(t) = X(p+a)\delta(t)$	
6.	If for $t \geqslant 0$ $\qquad\qquad f(t) = F(p)\delta(t)$	(7.46)
7.	then for $t \geqslant 0$ $\displaystyle\int_{-\infty}^{t} f(\tau)\,d\tau = \frac{1}{p}\left[F(p) + \int_{-\infty}^{0-} f(\tau)\,d\tau\right]\delta(t)$	
	$\qquad\qquad\qquad = \dfrac{1}{p}\left[F(p) + f^{(-1)}(0^-)\right]\delta(t)$	(7.58)
8.	and for $t \geqslant 0$ $\dfrac{df(t)}{dt} = [pF(p) - f(0^-)]\delta(t)$	(7.66)

Although Eq. (7.71) contains all *useful* information on the variable *after* imposition of a system discontinuity, it is important to remember that Eq. (7.68) contains the complete information for *all* time. Extracting this information for all negative time, however, entails solution of the integro-differential equation which is the coefficient of $u(-t)$ in Eq. (7.69a), and this equation is no less complex than the original complete one. In those cases where the system is in equilibrium (steady state) when the discontinuity is imposed, the forms of the variables extending into the past for a finite interval to the left of the origin will usually be evident.

Because primary interest will generally be in what happens for positive times, it may be convenient to tabulate the important results of this chapter to the extent that they apply to nonnegative time. This is done in Table 7.1, which also includes entries which are unchanged by the restriction on the time interval.

7.15 OPERATIONAL FORMS

In the expression $f(t) = F(p)\delta(t)$, the function of p, $F(p)$, is called the *operational form* of the time-varying function, $f(t)$. For example, Eq. (7.30) indicates that the operational form of

$$f(t) = \frac{t^{n-1}}{(n-1)!}\, u(t)$$

is

$$F(p) = \frac{1}{p^n}.$$

A short listing of such pairs for the most commonly used time-varying signals appears in Table 7.2. Table 7.1 contains all of the information required for establishing the validity of the entries in Table 7.2, with the exception of entries 7 and 8, which will be established in Art. 7.17. Entries in the latter table not proved in the text are left as student exercises.

7.16 OPERATIONAL METHOD AND THE LAPLACE TRANSFORM

Consider the integral

$$\int e^{-at} f(t)\, dt = \int u\, dv,$$

TABLE 7.2   OPERATIONAL FORMS OF SOME COMMON SIGNALS

Entry number	Time-varying form	Operational form
1.	$f(t)$	$F(p)$
2.	$Af(t)$	$AF(p)$
3.	$f_1(t) + f_2(t)$	$F_1(p) + F_2(p)$
4.	$\dfrac{df(t)}{dt}$	$pF(p) - f(0^-)$
5.	$\displaystyle\int_{-\infty}^{t} f(\tau)\,d\tau = f^{(-1)}(t)$	$\dfrac{F(p)}{p} + \dfrac{f^{(-1)}(0^-)}{p}$
6.	$e^{-at}f(t)$	$F(p + a)$
7.	$f(t - T)$	$e^{-pT}F(p)$
8.	$tf(t)$	$-\dfrac{d}{dp}F(p)$
9.	$\delta(t)$	1
10.	$u(t)$	$\dfrac{1}{p}$
11.	$\dfrac{t^{n-1}}{(n-1)!}u(t)$	$\dfrac{1}{p^n}$
12.	$(\cos \omega t)u(t)$	$\dfrac{p}{p^2 + \omega^2}$
13.	$(\sin \omega t)u(t)$	$\dfrac{\omega}{p^2 + \omega^2}$

which we can integrate by parts by setting

$$dv = e^{-at}dt \quad \text{and} \quad u = f(t)$$

to get

$$\int e^{-at}f(t)\,dt = -\frac{1}{a}\,e^{-at}f(t) + \frac{1}{a}\int e^{-at}f'(t)\,dt, \qquad (7.72)$$

where

$$f'(t) = \frac{df(t)}{dt}. \qquad (7.72a)$$

Suppose that for some σ, $e^{-\sigma t}f(t)$ is zero for $t \to \infty$. Then application of Eq. (7.72) leads to

$$\int_0^\infty e^{-pt}f(t)\,dt = -\frac{1}{p}e^{-pt}f(t)\bigg|_0^\infty + \frac{1}{p}\int_0^\infty e^{-pt}f'(t)\,dt$$

$$= \frac{f(0)}{p} + \frac{1}{p}\int_0^\infty e^{-pt}f'(t)\,dt.$$

The integral on the right side of the equation also lends itself to application of Eq. (7.72), and repeated application yields

$$\int_0^\infty e^{-pt}f(t)\,dt = \frac{f(0)}{p} + \frac{f'(0)}{p^2} + \frac{1}{p^2}\int_0^\infty e^{-pt}f''(t)\,dt$$

$$= \frac{f(0)}{p} + \frac{f'(0)}{p^2} + \frac{f''(0)}{p^3} + \frac{1}{p^3}\int_0^\infty e^{-pt}f'''(t)\,dt$$

$$= \frac{f(0)}{p} + \frac{f'(0)}{p^2} + \frac{f''(0)}{p^3} + \frac{f'''(0)}{p^4} + \cdots. \qquad (7.73)$$

Upon comparison of Eqs. (7.34) and (7.73), we see that

$$\int_0^\infty e^{-pt}f(t)\,dt = F(p). \qquad (7.74)$$

Equation (7.74) does not define the operational form, $F(p)$; rather it is derived from our definition of the operator, $1/p$. However, accepting Eq. (7.74) as the original definition would have led to the same formalisms we have tabulated in Table 7.2, except that 0^- would have been replaced by 0^+. When this approach is used (and it is a common one), it is customary to replace p by s and to call the resulting $F(s)$ the *Laplace transform* of $f(t)$. As we shall see in Chapter 14, there is an important conceptual difference between the " operator " we have defined here and the Laplace " transform " defined there, even though the formalisms involved in their use in solving linear systems are identical (except at exactly $t = 0$).

This important difference lies in the fact that our definition allows us to write, when it suits us,

$$f(t) = F(p)\delta(t). \qquad (7.75a)$$

This cannot be done with Laplace transforms, where we must write

$$f(t) = \mathscr{L}^{-1}[F(s)]$$
$$= [\text{inverse Laplace transform of } F(s)]. \qquad (7.75b)$$

This is true even though $F(s)$ is nothing more than $F(p)$ with p replaced by s. To maintain the distinctions between the two, the language we shall use is this:

$$F(p) = [\text{operational form of } f(t)] \tag{7.76a}$$

$$F(s) = \mathscr{L}[f(t)] = [\text{Laplace transform of } f(t)]. \tag{7.76b}$$

The latter of them we shall not meet again until Chapter 14. However, the student should take note of the fact that tables of Laplace transforms will contain pairs identical with those occurring in Table 7.2, except that 0^+ (or sometimes simply 0) will occur in place of 0^-. The extensive tables of Laplace transforms that are available are thus applicable to the techniques we are using here.

7.17 SOME USEFUL THEOREMS

Establishing Eq. (7.74) provides easy access to the following theorems.

Initial Value Theorem

Equations (7.73) and (7.74) lead immediately to the *initial value theorem*:

$$f(0) = \lim_{p \to \infty} pF(p). \tag{7.77}$$

When there exists a discontinuity in $f(t)$ at the origin, then in Eq. (7.77)

$$f(0) = [\lim_{t \to 0} f(t), \quad t > 0] = f(0^+). \tag{7.77a}$$

That is, $f(t)$ is evaluated just to the right of the discontinuity.

Final Value Theorem

Suppose $f(t)$ is continuous through the origin, so that $f(0^-) = f(0)$. Then Eq. (7.74) and entry 4 in Table 7.2 yield

$$\lim_{p \to 0} \int_0^\infty e^{-pt} \frac{df(t)}{dt}\, dt = \lim_{p \to 0} [pF(p) - f(0)],$$

or

$$\int_0^\infty \frac{df(t)}{dt}\, dt = \lim_{p \to 0} [pF(p) - f(0)].$$

Evaluating the integral on the left-hand side, we have

$$f(\infty) - f(0) = \lim_{p \to 0} [pF(p) - f(0)],$$

so that

$$\lim_{p \to 0} pF(p) = f(\infty). \qquad (7.78)$$

This constitutes the *final value theorem*.

The student should be aware that the limit in Eq. (7.78) is meaningless except for those functions which approach some constant value for large t. An example for which there is no such value is

$$f(t) = \sin \omega t \, u(t),$$

which, by entry 13 in Table 7.2, is associated with

$$F(p) = \frac{\omega}{p^2 + \omega^2}.$$

For this function,

$$\lim_{p \to 0} pF(p) = 0.$$

However, we know that

$$f(t) = \sin \omega t, \qquad \text{for large } t,$$

so the final value theorem does not apply. On the other hand, the zero value for the limit is valid in the case of

$$f(t) = Ae^{-at}u(t),$$

generated by

$$F(p) = \frac{A}{p + a}.$$

Real Translation Theorem

If

$$f(t) = F(p)\delta(t), \qquad (7.79a)$$

and

$$f_1(t) = f(t - T), \qquad (7.79b)$$

then by Eq. (7.74)

$$F_1(p) = \int_0^\infty e^{-pt} f(t - T) \, dt.$$

Let us substitute

$$\tau = t - T,$$

or its equivalent,

$$t = \tau + T.$$

Now

$$F_1(p) = e^{-pT} \int_{-T}^{\infty} e^{-p\tau} f(\tau) \, d\tau.$$

But Eq. (7.79a) implies that

$$f(t) = 0, \qquad -T < t < 0,$$

and we can write

$$F_1(p) = e^{-pT} \int_{0}^{\infty} e^{-p\tau} f(\tau) \, d\tau.$$

Again applying Eq. (7.74) causes this to become

$$F_1(p) = e^{-pT} F(p).$$

In summary, if

$$f(t) = F(p)\delta(t), \tag{7.80a}$$

then

$$f(t - T) = e^{-pT} F(p)\delta(t). \tag{7.80b}$$

This *real translation theorem* is codified as entry 7 in Table 7.2.

EXAMPLE 7.4 If $f(t)$ is the pulse in Fig. 7.7, find $F(p)$.

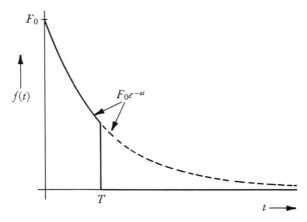

Fig. 7.7 *Pulse for Example 7.4.*

Solution. The pulse description is

$$f(t) = \begin{cases} 0, & t < 0 \\ F_0 e^{-at}, & 0 < t < T \\ 0, & T < t < \infty \end{cases}$$

$$= F_0 e^{-at}[u(t) - u(t - T)]$$

$$= F_0 [e^{-at}u(t) - e^{-aT}e^{-a(t - T)}u(t - T)].$$

Applying entries 6 and 7,

$$F(p) = F_0 \left[\frac{1}{p + a} - e^{-aT} \frac{e^{-pT}}{p + a} \right]$$

$$= F_0 \frac{1 - e^{-(p+a)T}}{p + a}. \qquad Ans.$$

Notice that the real translation theorem could not be applied until the mixture of t's and $(t - T)$'s were manipulated to give a term with $(t - T)$'s only, other than constants.

Multiplication by t

Differentiation of both sides of Eq. (7.74) results in

$$\frac{d}{dp} F(p) = \frac{d}{dp} \int_0^\infty e^{-pt}f(t)\, dt$$

$$= \int_0^\infty \frac{d}{dp} e^{-pt}f(t)\, dt$$

$$= - \int_0^\infty e^{-pt}tf(t)\, dt.$$

The integral on the right is of the form of the integral in Eq. (7.74) with $f(t)$ replaced by $tf(t)$. Therefore, if

$$f(t) = F(p)\delta(t), \qquad (7.81a)$$

then

$$tf(t) = \left[-\frac{d}{dp} F(p) \right]\delta(t). \qquad (7.81b)$$

This result is listed as entry 8 in Table 7.2.

PROBLEMS

7.1 Determine the expression for $u_T(t)$ corresponding with each $\delta_T(t)$ on page 272.

7.2   Four examples of mathematical operators are given on page 276. List at least ten other such operators you are acquainted with, giving each a name and a commonly-used symbol.

7.3   Which of the operators on page 276 are nonlinear?

7.4   Verify that

$$\frac{1}{p^4}\delta(t) = \frac{t^3}{3!}u(t).$$

In the next four problems, one can completely describe the given function in the form

$$f(t) = F(p)\delta(t).$$

In each case, express $F(p)$ as a rational fraction whose numerator and denominator are polynomials in p.

7.5 $f(t) = (10 - 5e^{-3t})u(t).$

7.6 $f(t) = 5\delta(t) + 4e^{-7t}u(t).$

7.7 $f(t) = 8(e^{-2000t} - e^{-500t})u(t).$

7.8 $f(t) = 5e^{-8t}(e^{6t} - e^{-6t})u(t).$

7.9   Given that

$$f(t) = 5e^{-10t}u(t),$$

show that Eqs. (7.58) and (7.66) lead to the same result as does direct integration and differentiation.

7.10   Repeat Prob. 7.9 when

$$f(t) = -6e^{4t}u(-t) + 5e^{-3t}u(t).$$

7.11   Reverse the switching in Example 7.3 and determine $i(t)$.

7.12   Prove entry 12 in Table 7.2 utilizing previous entries in the table.

7.13   Prove entry 13 in Table 7.2 utilizing previous entries in the table.

7.14   If

$$f(t) = (\cosh 6t)u(t),$$

what is $F(p)$?

7.15   If

$$f(t) = (\sinh 6t)u(t),$$

what is $F(p)$?

7.16   If

$$f(t) = e^{-at}(\cos \omega t)u(t),$$

what is $F(p)$?

7.17 If

$$f(t) = t(\sin \omega t)u(t),$$

what is $F(p)$?

7.18 If

$$F(p) = \frac{100(p + 5)(p + 12)}{p(p^2 + 20p + 200)},$$

what are $f(0)$ and $f(\infty)$, provided that each exists?

7.19 Repeat Prob. 7.18 when

$$F(p) = \frac{200p}{(p + 5)(p + 10)}.$$

7.20 Repeat Prob. 7.18 when

$$F(p) = \frac{50(p + 6)}{(p + 2)(p + 12)}.$$

7.21 Find $F(p)$ when

$$f(t) = 20[u(t) - u(t - 0.3)].$$

7.22 Find $V(p)$ when

$$v(t) = \begin{cases} 0, & t < 0 \\ 200 \sin 4t, & 0 < t < \dfrac{\pi}{4} \\ 0, & t > \dfrac{\pi}{4}. \end{cases}$$

7.23 Find $I(p)$ when

$$i(t) = \begin{cases} 0, & t < 0 \\ 5(1 - e^{-25t}), & 0 < t < 0.1 \\ 5[e^{-25(t-0.1)} - e^{-25t}], & t > 0.1. \end{cases}$$

Reduce the result to its simplest form.

7.24 Consider the periodic (after $t = 0$) function

$$f(t) = \sum_{n=1}^{\infty} f_1(t - nT),$$

where $f_1(t)$ is the equation of the first cycle of the function and is zero *except* in the interval $0 < t < T$. Show that the operational form of $f(t)$ is

$$F(p) = \frac{F_1(p)}{1 - e^{-Tp}},$$

where $F_1(p)$ is the operational form of $f_1(t)$. (*Hint.* Recall the sum of a geometric progression and assume that p takes on values such that $|e^{-Tp}| < 1$.)

7.25 Find $F(p)$ for the periodic function of Prob. 7.24 when

$$f_1(t) = \begin{cases} 0, & t < 0 \\ A, & 0 < t < \dfrac{T}{2} \\ -A, & \dfrac{T}{2} < t < T \\ 0, & t > T. \end{cases}$$

7.26 Repeat Prob. 7.25 when

$$f_1(t) = \begin{cases} 0, & t < 0 \\ F_m \sin \omega t, & 0 < t < \dfrac{\pi}{\omega} \\ 0, & t > \dfrac{\pi}{\omega}. \end{cases}$$

7.27 Repeat Prob. 7.25 when

$$f_1(t) = \begin{cases} 0, & t < 0 \\ 2t, & 0 < t < 5 \\ 0, & t > 5. \end{cases}$$

Utilizing only entries 6 through 13 in Table 7.2, and specifying which entry is used in each step, find the operational forms of the functions in Probs. 7.28 through 7.35, using as few steps as possible.

7.28 $te^{-at}u(t)$.

7.29 $t^2 e^{-at}u(t)$.

7.30 $(t \cos 100t)u(t)$.

7.31 $(te^{-5t} \cos 100t)u(t)$.

7.32 $t^3 \sin 25t$.

7.33 $e^{-(t-2)}u(t)$.

7.34 $e^{-t}u(t-2)$.

7.35 $t[u(t) - u(t-2)]$.

8

Operational Methods
of
Network Analysis

8.1 INTRODUCTION

In Chapter 6 techniques for setting up the integro-differential equations for a system, or network, were established. In the last chapter the basic operations involved in these equations were studied from the standpoint of operations on the unit impulse by an operator defining integration over a time interval with a specified beginning. We turn now to putting the results of these two chapters to work in the complete solution of a network containing any combination of the three linear elements we have studied. So far, you will recall, complete solutions have been obtained only for resistance networks and for the simplest R-L-C combinations.

8.2 RESPONSES OF SIMPLE SYSTEMS FOR $t \geqslant 0$ BY OPERATIONAL METHODS

In the systems which were studied in Chapter 6, the sets of equations which were established to describe the systems contained two types of variables. One type was the known variables resulting from voltage or current sources, called the *excitation variables* or *forcing functions*. As a result of impressing these variables on a system, there existed the variables which were the unknowns in the equations, called the *response variables* or *response functions*.

Generally, forcing functions may be expressed directly in one of the operational forms in Table 7.2. Operational forms of the response functions will then be expressed in one of the forms of entries 1, 4, or 5, with known initial conditions included as indicated in entries 4 and 5. Solution of the system then involves the finding of $F(p)$ for each variable by algebraic methods, after which the explicit form of the variable is determined by a reverse application of entry 1 in the table.

Some simple examples will serve to illustrate the method.

EXAMPLE 8.1. In Fig. 8.1, V is a constant voltage and the switch is closed at $t = 0$. Determine $i(t)$ for $t \geqslant 0$.

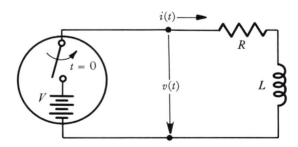

Fig. 8.1 *Series R-L model.*

Solution. Since no current flows prior to closing the switch,

$$i(0^-) = 0,$$

and since

$$v(t) = \begin{cases} 0, & t < 0 \\ V, & t > 0, \end{cases}$$

it is adequately described by

$$v(t) = Vu(t).$$

Applying KVL and substituting volt-ampere relationships results in

$$Vu(t) = Ri(t) + L\frac{di(t)}{dt},$$

which from entries 1, 2, 3, 4, and 10 in Table 7.2 has the operational form

$$\frac{V}{p} = RI(p) + L[pI(p) - i(0^-)].$$

But $i(0^-) = 0$, so

$$\frac{V}{p} = (R + Lp)I(p),$$

and the operational form of the current is

$$I(p) = \frac{V}{p(R + Lp)}$$

$$= \frac{V}{L}\frac{1}{p\left(p + \dfrac{R}{L}\right)}.$$

Now let

$$\frac{1}{p\left(p + \dfrac{R}{L}\right)} = \frac{A}{p} + \frac{B}{p + \dfrac{R}{L}}.$$

This, you may recall, is the start of the partial fraction expansion of the rational fraction on the left. Multiplying through by the common denominator results in

$$1 = (A + B)p + A\frac{R}{L}.$$

In order for this equality to hold, we must have the coefficients of like powers of p on the two sides equal, so

$$A\frac{R}{L} = 1, \qquad A + B = 0,$$

and these two equations in A and B have the solution

$$A = -B = \frac{L}{R}.$$

Hence

$$I(p) = \frac{V}{L} \frac{1}{p\left(p + \frac{R}{L}\right)}$$

$$= \frac{V}{R} \left[\frac{1}{p} - \frac{1}{p + \frac{R}{L}}\right].$$

Utilizing entries 2, 3, 10, and 6 in Table 7.2,

$$i(t) = I(p)\delta(t) = \frac{V}{R}(1 - e^{-Rt/L})u(t), \qquad t \geqslant 0. \qquad Ans.$$

The above method is indicative of the general method which will be employed for more complicated systems, but there is an alternative method which once again illustrates that $1/p$ is an integral operator. We can write that

$$I(p)\delta(t) = \frac{V}{L}\frac{1}{p}\left[\frac{1}{p + \frac{R}{L}}\delta(t)\right]$$

$$= \frac{V}{L}\frac{1}{p}[e^{-Rt/L}u(t)]$$

$$= \frac{V}{L}\int_{0-}^{t} e^{-R\tau/L}u(\tau)\,d\tau$$

$$= \frac{V}{L}\left[\int_{0-}^{t} e^{-R\tau/L}\,d\tau\right]u(t)$$

$$= \frac{V}{R}(1 - e^{-Rt/L})u(t)$$

$$= i(t), \qquad t \geqslant 0. \qquad Ans.$$

EXAMPLE 8.2. In Fig. 8.2, determine the operational form of $i(t)$ for $t \geqslant 0$ if the system was in equilibrium prior to $t = 0$.

Solution. The forcing voltage is $v(t) = Vu(-t)$. Applying KVL and substituting volt-ampere relations

$$v(t) = Ri(t) + L\frac{di(t)}{dt} + \frac{1}{C}\int_{-\infty}^{t} i(\tau)\,d\tau.$$

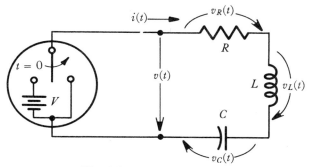
Fig. 8.2   *Series R-L-C model.*

As $v(t) = 0$, $t \geqslant 0$, this has the operational form

$$0 = RI(p) + L[pI(p) - i(0^-)] + \frac{1}{Cp}[I(p) + i^{(-1)}(0^-)].$$

In equilibrium, those terms depending on derivatives vanish, so $i(0^-) = 0$ (since $dv_C/dt = 0$) and $v_L(0^-) = 0$ (since $di/dt = 0$). As a result, $v_R(0^-) = 0$ and $v_C(0^-) = V$. Furthermore,

$$\frac{1}{C} i^{(-1)}(0^-) = \frac{1}{C} \int_{-\infty}^{0^-} i(\tau) \, d\tau = v_C(0^-) = V.$$

So the above equation becomes

$$0 = \left(R + Lp + \frac{1}{Cp}\right)I(p) + \frac{V}{p},$$

and

$$I(p) = \frac{-V}{p\left(R + Lp + \dfrac{1}{Cp}\right)}$$

$$= \frac{-V/L}{p^2 + \dfrac{R}{L}p + \dfrac{1}{LC}}. \qquad Ans.$$

EXAMPLE 8.3. Suppose the system parameters in Example 8.2 have the following numerical values:

$$V = 1000 \text{ V} \qquad L = 25 \text{ H}$$
$$R = 1250 \ \Omega \qquad C = 100 \ \mu\text{F}.$$

Find $i(t)$ for $t \geqslant 0$.

Solution. With the above values substituted in the results of the previous example the current becomes

$$I(p) = \frac{-40}{p^2 + 50p + 400}$$

$$= \frac{-40}{(p + 10)(p + 40)}$$

$$= \frac{-\frac{4}{3}}{p + 10} + \frac{+\frac{4}{3}}{p + 40}$$

or for $t \geqslant 0$

$$i(t) = I(p)\delta(t) = \tfrac{4}{3}[e^{-40t} - e^{-10t}]u(t)\,\text{A}. \qquad Ans.$$

EXAMPLE 8.4. Repeat Example 8.3 with R reduced to 250 Ω.

Solution.

$$I(p) = \frac{-40}{p^2 + 10p + 400}.$$

Now we could proceed by factoring the denominator, as in the previous example, but in this case we would get complex roots. The results would be correct, but let's try a different procedure, first completing the square in the denominator by adding and subtracting the quantity necessary for making a perfect square from the first two terms.

$$I(p) = \frac{-40}{p^2 + 10p + 25 + 400 - 25}$$

$$= \frac{-40}{(p + 5)^2 + 375} = -2.06\,\frac{19.4}{(p + 5)^2 + 19.4^2}.$$

Applying entries 6 and 13 in Table 7.2,

$$i(t) = -2.06e^{-5t}(\sin 19.4t)u(t)\,\text{A}, \qquad t \geqslant 0. \qquad Ans.$$

8.3 HEAVISIDE'S EXPANSION THEOREM

As should be apparent from the preceding examples, the changing of operational forms to explicit forms of time-varying functions usually involves a partial fraction expansion of the operational form to obtain simple and easily recognized time functions.

Suppose that

$$f(t) = F(p)\delta(t). \tag{8.1}$$

The operational form may be expressed as the rational fraction

$$F(p) = \frac{P(p)}{Q(p)}, \tag{8.2}$$

where $P(p)$ and $Q(p)$ are each polynomials in p which may be factored. If we recall that energy and continuity considerations admit impulses as the least continuous response of a physical system, then terms which require differentiation of impulses cannot exist. This precludes terms in $f(t)$ of the form $Kp^n \delta(t)$ with $n > 0$. Such terms would exist if the order of $P(p)$ were greater than that of $Q(p)$. For physical signals, then, we may restrict ourselves to the cases where *the degree of the numerator of the operational form is at most equal to that of the denominator.* If the degree of $P(p)$ is m and that of $Q(p)$ is n, all possible combinations of m and n are included in the following:

$$\lim_{p \to \infty} F(p) = \text{a finite value, possibly zero.} \tag{8.3}$$

Suppose that $Q(p)$ has a simple root at $p = -a$ and a second-order root at $p = -b$. Then the partially factored form will be

$$Q(p) = (p + a)(p + b)^2 Q_1(p), \tag{8.4}$$

where $Q_1(p)$ may have any number of first or higher ordered roots, but none at either $p = -a$ or $p = -b$. Then if we admit the possibility of impulses, a partially executed partial fraction expansion of $F(p)$ in Eq. (8.2) will become

$$F(p) = \frac{P(p)}{(p + a)(p + b)^2 Q_1(p)}$$

$$= K_o + \frac{K_a}{p + a} + \frac{K_{b1}}{p + b} + \frac{K_{b2}}{(p + b)^2} + \frac{P_1(p)}{Q_1(p)}. \tag{8.5}$$

The order of $P_1(p)$ will be less than that of $Q_1(p)$. Therefore

$$\lim_{p \to \infty} \frac{P_1(p)}{Q_1(p)} = 0. \tag{8.6}$$

It follows immediately from Eqs. (8.5) and (8.6) that

$$K_o = \lim_{p \to \infty} F(p) = F(\infty). \tag{8.7}$$

If both sides of Eq. (8.5) are multiplied by $(p + a)$, we have

$$(p + a)F(p) = K_o(p + a) + K_a + \frac{K_{b1}(p + a)}{p + b} + \frac{K_{b2}(p + a)}{(p + b)^2} + \frac{(p + a)P_1(p)}{Q_1(p)}.$$

The left of this expression does not contain the factor $(p + a)$ in numerator or denominator. since the $(p + a)$ multiplier is cancelled by the like factor in $Q(p)$. However, $Q_1(p)$ in the last term on the right does not contain such a factor to be cancelled by the multiplier. Therefore, it is clear that letting p approach $-a$ on both sides results in

$$K_a = \lim_{p \to -a} [(p + a)F(p)]$$

$$= [(p + a)F(p)]_{p=-a}. \tag{8.8}$$

Multiplying both sides of Eq. (8.5) by $(p + b)^2$ results in

$$(p + b)^2 F(p) = K_o(p + b)^2 + \frac{K_a(p + b)^2}{p + a} + K_{b1}(p + b)$$

$$+ K_{b2} + \frac{(p + b)^2 P_1(p)}{Q_1(p)}. \tag{8.9}$$

In a manner similar to that leading to Eq. (8.8), it is readily shown that this leads to

$$K_{b2} = \lim_{p \to -b} [(p + b)^2 F(p)]$$

$$= [(p + b)^2 F(p)]_{p=-b}. \tag{8.10}$$

Now differentiate both sides of Eq. (8.9) with respect to p:

$$\frac{d}{dp} [(p + b)^2 F(p)] = 2K_o(p + b) + \frac{2K_a(p + b)}{p + a} - \frac{K_a(p + b)^2}{(p + a)^2}$$

$$+ K_{b1} + 0 + \frac{2(p + b)P_1(p)}{Q_1(p)}$$

$$+ \frac{(p + b)^2}{Q_1(p)} \frac{d}{dp} [P_1(p)] + (p + b)^2 P_1(p) \frac{d}{dp} \left[\frac{1}{Q_1(p)}\right].$$

Letting p approach $-b$ results in

$$K_{b1} = \lim_{p \to -b} \frac{d}{dp} [(p + b)^2 F(p)]$$

$$= \left[\frac{d}{dp} (p + b)^2 F(p)\right]_{p=-b}. \tag{8.11}$$

Although in this course it will seldom be necessary to consider roots of higher order than the second, the student should realize that the procedure leading to Eqs. (8.10) and (8.11) easily extends to the coefficients associated with higher ordered roots. For example, a third-order root would require multiplication through by the cubic factor followed by two differentiations to determine the three constants associated with the root.

Equations (8.6), (8.8), (8.10), and (8.11) demonstrate one form of *Heaviside's expansion theorem.*

Since most roots are simple ones, it may be convenient to "mechanize" the procedure indicated by Eq. (8.8) to the so-called "hiding" method:

> To find a coefficient corresponding to a simple root in the partial fraction expansion of $F(p)$, cover the factor in the denominator corresponding to the coefficient, then substitute in the uncovered portion of $F(p)$ whatever value of p causes the covered factor to be zero.

EXAMPLE 8.5. Find the time function corresponding to the operational form

$$I(p) = \frac{40}{p^3 + 9p^2 + 20p}.$$

Solution. Here K_o is zero since $I(\infty) = 0$, and with the polynomial, $Q(p)$, factored,

$$I(p) = \frac{40}{p(p + 4)(p + 5)}.$$

Observe that the roots of $Q(p)$ are 0, -4, and -5 corresponding to the factors p, $(p + 4)$, and $(p + 5)$. Apply the hiding method to get

$$I(p) = \frac{\dfrac{40}{\cancel{p}(0 + 4)(0 + 5)}}{p} + \frac{\dfrac{40}{-4(\cancel{p+4})(-4 + 5)}}{p + 4}$$

$$+ \frac{\dfrac{40}{-5(-5 + 4)(\cancel{p+5})}}{p + 5}$$

$$= \frac{2}{p} - \frac{10}{p + 4} + \frac{8}{p + 5}$$

and

$$i(t) = I(p)\delta(t)$$

$$= \left[\frac{2}{p} - \frac{10}{p + 4} + \frac{8}{p + 5}\right]\delta(t)$$

$$= (2 - 10e^{-4t} + 8e^{-5t})u(t).   Ans.$$

EXAMPLE 8.6. Find the time function corresponding to

$$V(p) = \frac{40}{(p+5)(p+4)^2}.$$

Solution. Again K_o is zero and $V(p)$ can be expanded by partial fractions. Since $V(p)$ has two different roots, we can determine two of the constants quite readily.

$$V(p) = \frac{\dfrac{40}{\cancel{(p+5)}(-5+4)^2}}{p+5} + \frac{K_{b1}}{p+4} + \frac{\dfrac{40}{(-4+5)(p+4)^2}}{(p+4)^2}$$

$$= \frac{40}{p+5} + \frac{K_{b1}}{p+4} + \frac{40}{(p+4)^2}.$$

To obtain the third constant, Eq. (8.11) is used to give

$$K_{b1} = \left[\frac{d}{dp}\frac{40}{p+5}\right]_{p=-4}$$

$$= \left[\frac{(-1)(40)}{(p+5)^2}\right]_{p=-4}$$

$$= -40.$$

Finally

$$v(t) = \left[\frac{40}{p+5} - \frac{40}{p+4} + \frac{40}{(p+4)^2}\right]\delta(t)$$

$$= 40[e^{-5t} - e^{-4t} + te^{-4t}]u(t). \qquad Ans.$$

EXAMPLE 8.7. Determine the time function for

$$I(p) = \frac{2p^2 + 4}{p^2 + 4p}.$$

Solution. This is one of those not-very-common cases, where the degree of the numerator is the same as that of the denominator ($n = m$). Thus

$$K_o = \lim_{p \to \infty} \frac{2p^2 + 4}{p^2 + 4p} = 2,$$

and

$$I(p) = 2 + \frac{\dfrac{2(0)^2 + 4}{\cancel{p}(0+4)}}{p} + \frac{\dfrac{2(-4)^2 + 4}{-4\cancel{(p+4)}}}{p+4}$$

$$= 2 + \frac{1}{p} - \frac{9}{p+4}$$

and

$$i(t) = \left(2 + \frac{1}{p} - \frac{9}{p+4}\right)\delta(t)$$

$$= 2\delta(t) + (1 - 9e^{-4t})u(t). \qquad Ans.$$

EXAMPLE 8.8. Use Heaviside's expansion theorem to verify the results of Example 8.4.

Solution.

$$I(p) = \frac{-40}{(p+5)^2 + 19.4^2}$$

$$= \frac{-40}{(p+5-j19.4)(p+5+j19.4)}$$

$$= \frac{\dfrac{-40}{(\cancel{p+5-j19.4})(-5+j19.4+5+j19.4)}}{p+5-j19.4}$$

$$+ \frac{\dfrac{-40}{(-5-j19.4+5-j19.4)(\cancel{p+5+j19.4})}}{p+5+j19.4}$$

$$= \frac{\dfrac{-40}{j2(19.4)}}{p+5-j19.4} + \frac{\dfrac{-40}{-j2(19.4)}}{p+5+j19.4}$$

$$= -\frac{2.06}{j}\left[\frac{\frac{1}{2}}{p+5-j19.4} - \frac{\frac{1}{2}}{p+5+j19.4}\right].$$

Utilizing entries 6 and 10 in Table 7.2,

$$i(t) = I(p)\,\delta(t)$$

$$= -\frac{2.06}{j}\left[\tfrac{1}{2}e^{-(5-j19.4)t} - \tfrac{1}{2}e^{-(5+j19.4)t}\right]u(t)$$

$$= -2.06e^{-5t}\frac{e^{j19.4t} - e^{-j19.4t}}{2j}\,u(t)$$

$$= -2.06e^{-5t}(\sin 19.4t)u(t)\,\text{A}, \qquad t \geqslant 0. \qquad Ans.$$

8.4 COMPLEX PAIRS OF ROOTS

Any quadratic factor in the denominator of $F(p)$ presents one of three possibilities:

A.   It factors into two simple roots.

B.   It is a perfect square yielding a second-order root on the real axis.

C.   It factors into a complex pair of simple roots which are conjugates of one another. (The roots are conjugates because the coefficients in the denominator polynomial, $Q(p)$, are all real.)

All three of the above possibilities can be handled by a direct application of Heaviside's expansion theorem. However, in case C there are three equivalent forms the time-varying form may take:

1.   A damped cosine curve of zero phase angle plus a damped sine curve of zero phase angle.

2.   A damped cosine with a phase angle.

3.   A damped sine with a phase angle.

Direct application of Heaviside's expansion theorem yields a pair of complex exponentials which may be combined into either form 2 or form 3. On the other hand, a partial fraction technique treating the quadratic factor intact, as in Example 8.4, will yield form 1. Depending on the problem, it may be more convenient to use the conventional partial fraction expansion for quadratic factors than to treat the simple complex roots by Heaviside's method; or it may be the other way round. However, the results of one are very easily inverted to those of the other.

For example, suppose $Q(p)$ has the only one of the quadratic factors, $p^2 + ap + b$, with complex roots. Then we may write

$$F(p) = \frac{P(p)}{Q(p)} = \frac{P(p)}{(p^2 + ap + b)Q_1(p)}, \qquad (8.12a)$$

and completing the square on the quadratic factor yields

$$F(p) = \frac{P(p)}{[(p + \alpha)^2 + \omega^2]Q_1(p)}. \qquad (8.12b)$$

Conventional partial fraction expansion may take the form

$$F(p) = \frac{Cp + D}{(p + \alpha)^2 + \omega^2} + \frac{P_1(p)}{Q_1(p)},$$

but it will in general be more convenient to assume the equivalent form

$$F(p) = A \frac{p + \alpha}{(p + \alpha)^2 + \omega^2} + B \frac{\omega}{(p + \alpha)^2 + \omega^2} + \frac{P_1(p)}{Q_1(p)}, \qquad (8.13)$$

which simply replaces C by A and D by $A\alpha + B\omega$. The constants A and B can be determined by the conventional technique of multiplying through by the denominator of $F(p)$, then matching coefficients of like powers of p on the two sides of the resulting equation. This method will yield very quick results if $Q_1(p)$ contains simple real roots whose corresponding coefficients have already been determined by Heaviside's method.

The time function directly resulting from Eq. (8.13) is

$$\begin{aligned}
f(t) = F(p)\delta(t) &= Ae^{-\alpha t}(\cos \omega t)u(t) \\
&\quad + Be^{-\alpha t}(\sin \omega t)u(t) + f_1(t) \\
&= e^{-\alpha t}(A \cos \omega t + B \sin \omega t)u(t) + f_1(t). \qquad (8.14)
\end{aligned}$$

On the other hand, Eq. (8.12) might have been written

$$\begin{aligned}
F(p) &= \frac{P(p)}{(p + \alpha - j\omega)(p + \alpha + j\omega)Q_1(p)} \\
&= \frac{K_1}{p + \alpha - j\omega} + \frac{K_2}{p + \alpha + j\omega} + \frac{P_1(p)}{Q_1(p)}. \qquad (8.15)
\end{aligned}$$

However, if the first two terms are to combine to form a real-valued rational fraction, they must be conjugates. Since the denominators are conjugates, this can be true only if the numerators are also conjugates. Therefore, the above equation may be written

$$F(p) = \frac{\mathbf{K}}{p + \alpha - j\omega} + \frac{\mathbf{K}^*}{p + \alpha + j\omega} + \frac{P_1(p)}{Q_1(p)}, \qquad (8.16)$$

where

$$\mathbf{K} = K_1 = \text{conjugate of } K_2 = Ke^{j\theta}. \qquad (8.17)$$

Obviously, only one application of Heaviside's theorem is necessary.

It is easily shown that the corresponding time-varying form to Eq. (8.16) is a set of exponentials which reduce to a damped cosine, and

$$f(t) = F(p)\delta(t) = [2Ke^{-\alpha t} \cos (\omega t + \theta)]u(t) + f_1(t). \qquad (8.18)$$

Let us make an important observation here:

> The magnitude and phase angle of the damped cosine are respectively twice the magnitude and once the angle of the complex coefficient of that term corresponding to the root with the positive imaginary part.   (8.19)

Finally, it is simple to show that the connection between the two constants K and θ in Eq. (8.18) with the two constants A and B in Eq. (8.14) is

$$2\mathbf{K} = 2Ke^{j\theta} = A - jB. \qquad (8.20)$$

EXAMPLE 8.9. Find $i(t)$ by both methods of this article when the operational form is

$$I(p) = \frac{290}{(p + 4)(p^2 + 4p + 29)}.$$

Solution.

1.   First method: Use conventional partial fractions for the quadratic factor after finding the coefficient for the real root by Heaviside's method. Completing the square on the quadratic and expanding,

$$I(p) = \frac{290}{(p + 4)[(p + 2)^2 + 5^2]}$$

$$= \frac{\dfrac{290}{(\cancel{p+4})[(-4 + 2)^2 + 5^2]}}{p + 4}$$

$$+ A\frac{p + 2}{(p + 2)^2 + 5^2} + B\frac{5}{(p + 2)^2 + 5^2}$$

$$= \frac{10}{p + 4} + A\frac{p + 2}{(p + 2)^2 + 5^2} + B\frac{5}{(p + 2)^2 + 5^2}.$$

Multiplying through by

$$(p + 4)[(p + 2)^2 + 5^2] = (p + 4)(p^2 + 4p + 29)$$

yields

$$290 = 10(p^2 + 4p + 29) + A(p + 4)(p + 2) + 5B(p + 4)$$

$$= (10 + A)p^2 + (40 + 6A + 5B)p + (290 + 8A + 20B).$$

Equating coefficients of like powers of p and solving yields

$$A = -10 \qquad B = 4$$

so

$$I(p) = \frac{10}{p + 4} - 10\frac{p + 2}{(p + 2)^2 + 5^2} + 4\frac{5}{(p + 2)^2 + 5^2},$$

and

$$i(t) = I(p)\delta(t)$$

$$= [10e^{-4t} + e^{-2t}(-10 \cos 5t + 4 \sin 5t)]u(t). \qquad Ans.$$

2. Second method: Use Heaviside's expansion theorem only. The co-efficient corresponding to the real root was found in 1, so

$$I(p) = \frac{290}{(p + 4)(p + 2 - j5)(p + 2 + j5)}$$

$$= \frac{10}{p + 4} + \frac{\mathbf{K}}{p + 2 - j5} + \frac{\mathbf{K}^*}{p + 2 + j5},$$

where

$$\mathbf{K} = \frac{290}{(-2 + j5 + 4)(\cancel{p+2-j5})(-2 + j5 + 2 + j5)}$$

$$= \frac{290}{(2 + j5)(j10)} = 5.39e^{-j158.2°}.$$

Utilizing (8.19), we have

$$i(t) = I(p)\delta(t)$$

$$= [10e^{-4t} + 10.78e^{-2t} \cos (5t - 158.2°)]u(t). \qquad Ans.$$

3. Check, using Eq. (8.20).

$$2\mathbf{K} = 10.78e^{-j158.2°} = -10.0 - j4.0 = A - jB,$$

and

$$A = -10.0, \qquad B = 4.0. \qquad \text{(Checks)}$$

8.5 OPERATIONAL IMPEDANCES AND ADMITTANCES

The *R-L-C* series circuit integro-differential equation

$$v(t) = Ri(t) + L\frac{di(t)}{dt} + \frac{1}{C}\int_{-\infty}^{t} i(\tau)\, d\tau$$

has the operational form

$$V(p) = RI(p) + L[pI(p) - i(0^-)] + \frac{1}{Cp}[I(p) + i^{(-1)}(0^-)]$$

$$= \left[R + Lp + \frac{1}{Cp}\right]I(p) - Li(0^-) + \frac{v_C(0^-)}{p}$$

$$= Z(p)I(p) - Li(0^-) + \frac{v_C(0^-)}{p}, \qquad (8.21)$$

where

$$Z(p) = R + Lp + \frac{1}{Cp} \qquad (8.22)$$

is called the *operational impedance* of the *R-L-C* series circuit. The function $Z(\ )$ is exactly the same impedance function earlier associated with the *R-L-C* series circuit in the forms $Z(a)$, $Z(m)$, $Z(j\omega)$, etc.

Similarly, for the *G-C-L* parallel circuit

$$I(p) = Y(p)V(p) - Cv(0^-) + \frac{i_L(0^-)}{p}, \qquad (8.23)$$

where

$$Y(p) = G + Cp + \frac{1}{Lp} \qquad (8.24)$$

is the *operational admittance*.

8.6 NETWORK REDUCTIONS

When a network contains a single source and the initial conditions are all zero, all passive branches have operational volt-ampere connections which are special cases of Eqs. (8.21) and (8.23). That is, any passive branch or two-terminal device or network will have the terminal relations

$$V(p) = Z(p)I(p), \qquad (8.25a)$$

or

$$I(p) = Y(p)V(p), \qquad (8.25b)$$

where

$$Y(p) = \frac{1}{Z(p)}. \qquad (8.25c)$$

These operational relationships are formally identical with the cases of direct current with pure resistances and of phasors with complex impedances. Therefore, series-parallel combinations, voltage- and current-divider relationships, and the principle of superposition are handled in the same way.

EXAMPLE 8.10. Find the operational forms of $i(t)$ and $v_2(t)$ in Fig. 8.3(a) by operational methods when

$$V = 1100 \text{ V} \qquad L = 2 \text{ H}$$
$$R_1 = 100 \ \Omega \qquad C = 100 \ \mu\text{F}.$$
$$R_2 = 1000 \ \Omega$$

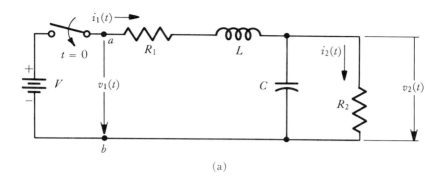

(a)

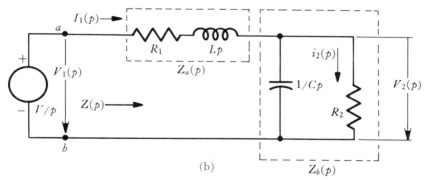

(b)

Fig. 8.3 *Circuit for Example 8.10. (a) Original circuit. (b) Operational form of the circuit.*

Solution. If the circuit has been in equilibrium prior to $t = 0$, all initial conditions are zero, and the network reductions implied by this article apply.

1. Draw the operational form of the network, as in Fig. 8.3(b).

2. Since

$$v_1(t) = \begin{cases} 0, & t < 0 \\ V, & t > 0 \end{cases}$$

it may be adequately described as

$$v_1(t) = Vu(t) = \frac{V}{p}\,\delta(t),$$

so that

$$V_1(p) = \frac{V}{p} = \frac{1100}{p}.$$

3.   Compute $Z_a(p)$, $Z_b(p)$, and $Z(p)$.

$$Z_a(p) = R_1 + Lp = 100 + 2p = 2(p + 50)$$

$$Z_b(p) = \frac{R_2\left(\dfrac{1}{Cp}\right)}{R_2 + \dfrac{1}{Cp}} = \frac{1000\,\dfrac{10^4}{p}}{1000 + \dfrac{10^4}{p}} = \frac{10^4}{p + 10}$$

$$Z(p) = Z_a(p) + Z_b(p)$$

$$= 2(p + 50) + \frac{10^4}{p + 10}$$

$$= 2\,\frac{p^2 + 60p + 5500}{p + 10} = \frac{1}{Y(p)}.$$

4.   Find $I(p)$. By "Ohm's law,"

$$I_1(p) = Y(p)V_1(p)$$

$$= 550\,\frac{p + 10}{p(p^2 + 60p + 5500)}$$

$$= 550\frac{p + 10}{p[(p+30)^2 + 67.8^2]}\ \text{A} \cdot \text{sec.}\qquad Ans.$$

5.   Find $V_2(p)$. Using the voltage-divider relationship,

$$V_2(p) = \frac{Z_b(p)}{Z(p)}\,V_1(p)$$

$$= \frac{\dfrac{10{,}000}{p + 10}\,\dfrac{1100}{p}}{2\,\dfrac{p^2 + 60p + 5500}{p + 10}}$$

$$= \frac{5.5 \times 10^6}{p(p^2 + 60p + 5500)}\ \text{V} \cdot \text{sec.}\qquad Ans.$$

8.7 THÉVENIN–NORTON EQUIVALENT OF ELEMENTS WITH INITIAL STORED ENERGY

For the mesh and nodal methods of analysis in Chapter 6, it was convenient to have all sources in either Thévenin forms or Norton forms, depending on the method of analysis, before writing the system equations.

As energy initially stored in inductances and capacitances will be delivered to the network after $t = 0$, it seems reasonable that such elements should also be representable by Thévenin or Norton equivalents holding for $t \geq 0$. And indeed they are.

For a pure inductance with the terminal voltage drop and current positive in the same direction,

$$v(t) = L \frac{di(t)}{dt}. \tag{8.26}$$

This has the operational form

$$V(p) = LpI(p) - Li(0^-). \tag{8.27}$$

Now recall from Chapter 2 Eqs. (2.9) and (2.12) describing the Thévenin's equivalent for a linear two-terminal network or device. Now rewrite these equations with the terminal voltage drop and current positive in the same direction as shown in the second column of Table 8.1, i.e.,

$$v = z_o i - v_o,$$

where

$$v_o = -v|_{i=0}.$$

The operational equivalent of v_o for the coil with initial current follows from Eq. (8.27).

$$V_o(p) = -V(p)|_{I(p)=0} = Li(0^-) \tag{8.28a}$$

and corresponding to the general impedance, z_o, we have the operational impedance

$$Z_o(p) = Lp. \tag{8.28b}$$

The operational Norton form follows immediately from rewriting Eq. (8.27) as

$$I(p) = \frac{1}{Lp} V(p) + \frac{i(0^-)}{p},$$

from which the operational form of i_o in the general case

$$i = y_o v - i_o$$

becomes

$$I_o(p) = -I(p)|_{V(p)=0} = -\frac{i(0^-)}{p}. \tag{8.29a}$$

Corresponding to y_o we have

$$Y_o(p) = \frac{1}{Lp}. \tag{8.29b}$$

TABLE 8.1 EQUIVALENT OPERATIONAL CIRCUIT REPRESENTATIONS OF INDUCTANCE AND CAPACITANCE

Representation	General	Inductance	Capacitance
a. Actual	$i(t)$, $v(t)$	$i(t)$, L, $v(t)$	$i(t)$, C, $v(t)$
b. Thévenin's equivalent	i, Z_0, v_0, v	$I(P)$, L, $Li(0^-)$, $V(p)$	$I(P)$, C, $v(0^-)/P$, $V(p)$
c. Norton's equivalent	i, i_0, y_0, v	$I(P)$, $i(0^-)/P$, L, $V(p)$	$I(P)$, $Cv(0^-)$, C, $V(p)$

The operational circuit models of these results are shown in the third column of Table 8.1 where the minus sign in Eq. (8.29a) is eliminated by reversing the direction of the source.

In a similar manner for the capacitor,

$$i(t) = C \frac{dv(t)}{dt}$$

leads to

$$I(p) = CpV(p) - Cv(0^-). \tag{8.30}$$

From this equation comes the Norton's equivalent with

$$I_o(p) = Cv(0^-), \tag{8.31a}$$

and

$$Y_o(p) = Cp. \tag{8.31b}$$

It also follows that for the Thévenin's equivalent,

$$V_o(p) = - \frac{v(0^-)}{p}, \tag{8.32a}$$

and

$$Z_o(p) = \frac{1}{Cp}. \tag{8.32b}$$

The schematic forms of these results appear in the fourth column of Table 8.1.

It is also useful at times, and illuminating, to think of the initial conditions as energy sources associated with circuit elements with initial conditions zero. This is done in Table 8.2 by replacing the ideal sources due to initial conditions in Table 8.1 with equivalent ideal sources associated with zero initial conditions, then drawing the time-domain form giving rise to the resulting operational form. That this is valid is easily demonstrated. For example, the time-domain equation corresponding to the Thévenin's equivalent of inductance in Table 8.2 is

$$v(t) = L \frac{di(t)}{dt} - Li_o \delta(t).$$

As initial conditions in the equivalent form are specified to be zero, the operational form is

$$V(p) = LpI(p) - Li_o,$$

and setting $i_o = i(0^-)$ results in Eq. (8.27), demonstrating the equivalence. It should be observed that the directions on the equivalent sources are such as to maintain the terminal flux linkages (or current) at single coils and to maintain the terminal charge (or voltage) at single capacitors.

**TABLE 8.2 EQUIVALENT TIME-DOMAIN CIRCUIT REPRESENTATIONS
OF INDUCTANCE AND CAPACITANCE FOR $t \geq 0$**

Representation	Inductance	Capacitance

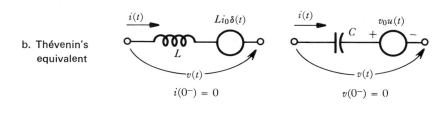

a. Actual

Inductance: $i(0^-) = i_0$

Capacitance: $v(0^-) = v_0$

b. Thévenin's equivalent

Inductance: $L i_0 \delta(t)$, $i(0^-) = 0$

Capacitance: $v_0 u(t)$, $v(0^-) = 0$

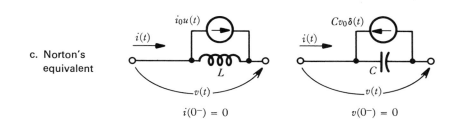

c. Norton's equivalent

Inductance: $i_0 u(t)$, $i(0^-) = 0$

Capacitance: $C v_0 \delta(t)$, $v(0^-) = 0$

EXAMPLE 8.11. Show the networks with (a) equivalent voltage sources and (b) equivalent current sources which with initial conditions zero will yield results identical with those of the network of Fig. 8.4 for $t \geqslant 0$.

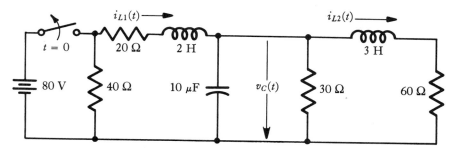

Fig. 8.4 *Circuit for Example 8.11.*

Solution. First, it is observed that equilibrium consists of dc values only. Therefore, the network of Fig. 8.5(a), with inductances short-circuited and capacitors included as open circuits, holds for $t = 0^-$. By standard application of the methods of series-parallel circuits, voltage dividers, etc.

$$i_{L1}(0^-) = 2 \text{ A}$$
$$i_{L2}(0^-) = 2 \text{ A}$$
$$v_C(0^-) = 40 \text{ V}.$$

Using these values in the Thévenin's equivalent of Table 8.2 yields the network of Fig. 8.5(b) with initial conditions zero. The corresponding initially inert network with current sources is that of Fig. 8.5(c).

EXAMPLE 8.12. Find $i_1(t)$ for $t \geqslant 0$ for the network of Fig. 8.6 when

$$V = 2100 \text{ V} \qquad R_1 = \quad 100 \text{ }\Omega \qquad L = \quad 2 \text{ H}$$
$$R_o = 1000 \text{ }\Omega \qquad R_2 = 1000 \text{ }\Omega \qquad C = 100 \text{ }\mu\text{F}.$$

Solution. Since a current value is sought, let us apply the method of mesh currents, which requires Thévenin's equivalent of energy sources. The circuit for $t = 0^-$ is shown in Fig. 8.7(a) and is used to determine the initial inductance current $i_1(0^-)$ and initial condenser voltage $v_2(0^-)$. These are

$$i_1(0^-) = \frac{2100}{1000 + 100 + 1000} = 1$$

$$v_2(0^-) = 1000 i_1(0^-) = 1000(1) = 1000,$$

and the operational Thévenin's equivalent ideal sources for the inductance and capacitance are

$$Li(0^-) = 2(1) = 2$$
$$\frac{v_2(0^-)}{p} = \frac{1000}{p}.$$

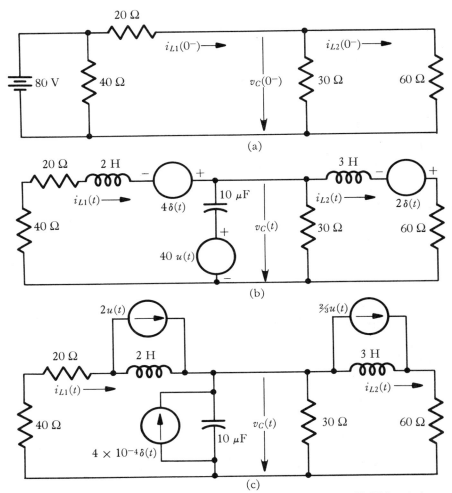

Fig. 8.5 *Equivalent circuits for Fig. 8.4. (a) Equilibrium at* $t = 0^-$. *(b) Thévenin forms for* $t \geqslant 0$. *(c) Norton forms for* $t \geqslant 0$.

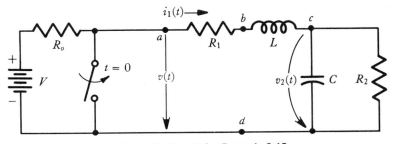

Fig. 8.6 *Circuit for Example 8.12.*

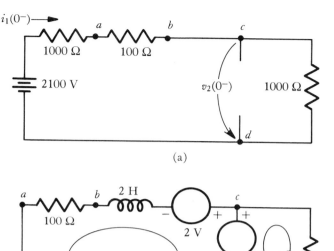

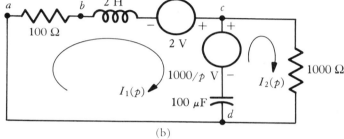

Fig. 8.7 *Equivalent circuits for the network of Fig. 8.6. (a) Equilibrium at t = 0⁻.*
(b) Operational equivalent circuit with Thévenin forms.

These results are entered on Fig. 8.7(b). Mesh current $I_1(p)$ is the operational
form of the required current for $t \geqslant 0$. The mesh forcing voltages are

$$V_{G1}(p) = 2 - \frac{1000}{p}$$

$$V_{G2}(p) = \frac{1000}{p},$$

and the mesh impedances are

$$Z_{11}(p) = 100 + 2p + \frac{10^4}{p}$$

$$Z_{22}(p) = 1000 + \frac{1000}{p}$$

$$Z_{12}(p) = Z_{21}(p) = -\frac{10^4}{p}.$$

The mesh equations in the general operational form are

$$V_{G1}(p) = Z_{11}(p)I_1(p) + Z_{12}(p)I_2(p)$$
$$V_{G2}(p) = Z_{21}(p)I_1(p) + Z_{22}(p)I_2(p),$$

which take on the numerical form

$$2 - \frac{1000}{p} = \left(100 + 2p + \frac{10^4}{p}\right)I_1(p) \qquad - \frac{10^4}{p}I_2(p)$$

$$\frac{1000}{p} = \qquad - \frac{10^4}{p}I_1(p) + \left(1000 + \frac{10^4}{p}\right)I_2(p).$$

Multiplying through the first by $p/2$ and the second by $p/1000$ results in

$$p - 500 = (p^2 + 50p + 5000)I_1(p) - 5000I_2(p)$$
$$1 = \qquad - 10I_1(p) + (p + 10)I_2(p).$$

The solution for $I_1(p)$ by determinants is:

$$I_1(p) = \frac{\begin{vmatrix} p - 500 & -5000 \\ 1 & (p + 10) \end{vmatrix}}{\begin{vmatrix} p^2 + 50p + 5000 & -5000 \\ -10 & p + 10 \end{vmatrix}}$$

$$= \frac{p^2 - 490p}{p^3 + 60p^2 + 5500p}$$

$$= \frac{p - 490}{p^2 + 60p + 5500} = \frac{p - 490}{(p + 30)^2 + 67.8^2}$$

$$= \frac{p - 490}{(p + 30 - j67.8)(p + 30 + j67.8)}$$

$$= \frac{K}{p + 30 - j67.8} + \frac{K^*}{p + 30 + j67.8}.$$

By Heaviside's expansion theorem,

$$K = \left[\frac{p - 490}{(p + 30 - j67.8)(p + 30 + j67.8)}\right]_{p = -30 + j67.8}$$

$$= \frac{-30 + j67.8 - 490}{j2(67.8)}$$

$$= \frac{-520 + j67.8}{j135.6}$$

$$= \frac{524e^{j172.57}}{135.6e^{j90°}}$$

$$= 3.87e^{j82.57°}$$

$$= Ke^{j\theta},$$

where $Ke^{j\theta}$ is used in the same sense as in Eq. (8.17). According to Eq. (8.18), for $t \geq 0$

$$i(t) = I(p)\delta(t)$$
$$= [2Ke^{-30t} \cos(67.8t + \theta)]u(t)$$
$$= [7.74e^{-30t} \cos(67.8t + 82.57°)]u(t) \text{ A.} \quad Ans.$$

PROBLEMS

In Probs. 8.1 through 8.6, solve for the variable indicated, using operational methods.

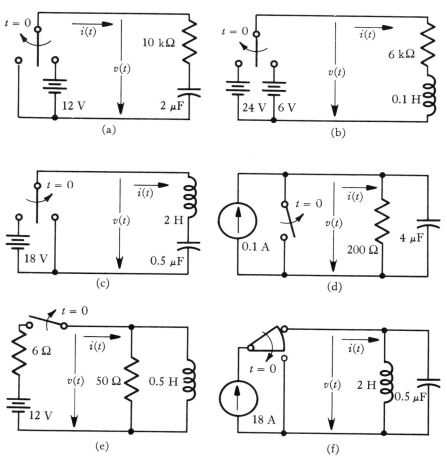

Fig. P.8.1.

8.1   In Fig. P.8.1(a), $i(t)$.
8.2   In Fig. P.8.1(b), $i(t)$.
8.3   In Fig. P.8.1(c), $i(t)$.
8.4   In Fig. P.8.1(d), $v(t)$.
8.5   In Fig. P.8.1(e), $v(t)$.
8.6   In Fig. P.8.1(f), $v(t)$.

In Probs. 8.7 through 8.18, find the explicit function of time, using Heaviside's expansion theorem, corresponding to the given operational form. Show each result as a combination of real exponentials and/or sinusoids.

8.7 $V(p) = \dfrac{100}{p(p + 10)}.$

8.8 $I(p) = \dfrac{5}{(p + 2)(p + 10)}.$

8.9 $I(p) = \dfrac{12(p + 3)}{p(p^2 + 7p + 6)}.$

8.10 $V(p) = \dfrac{80p}{(p + 2)(p^2 + 4p + 10)}.$

8.11 $V(p) = \dfrac{400{,}000}{p(p + 20)(p + 50)(p + 200)}.$

8.12 $V(p) = \dfrac{400(p + 6)(p + 12)}{p(p + 8)(p + 20)}.$

8.13 $V(p) = \dfrac{20p(p + 30)}{p^2 + 50p + 600}.$

8.14 $I(p) = \dfrac{12p^3}{p^4 + 13p^2 + 36}.$

8.15 $V(p) = \dfrac{200p}{(p^2 + 100)(p^2 + 30p + 200)}.$

8.16 $I(p) = \dfrac{64p}{(p + 2)(p^2 + 8p + 16)}.$

8.17 $F(p) = \dfrac{2p^2 + 12p + 10}{8p^2 + 88p + 224}.$

8.18 $I(p) = \dfrac{10p^3 + 100p^2 + 4000p + 2500}{(p^2 + 25)(p^2 + 400)}.$

8.19 Determine the current to and the voltage across the capacitor in Fig. P.8.2 if

a. $R = 5 \text{ k}\Omega$,
b. $R = 4 \text{ k}\Omega$,
c. $R = 2 \text{ k}\Omega$.

(The capacitor is known to be discharged before switching.)

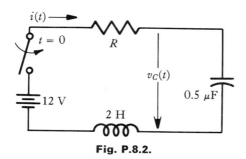

Fig. P.8.2.

8.20 Determine the voltage across the capacitor in Fig. P.8.3 if

a. $R = 5 \text{ k}\Omega$,
b. $R = 4 \text{ k}\Omega$,
c. $R = 2 \text{ k}\Omega$.

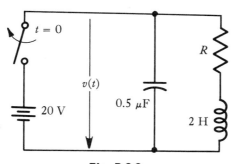

Fig. P.8.3.

8.21 Determine the current to and the voltage across the capacitor in Fig. P.8.4 if $\omega = 10^3$. (The capacitor is known to be discharged before switching.)

8.22 For Fig. P.8.5 determine $i_1(t)$, $i_2(t)$, and $v(t)$ for $t \geq 0$. Also determine $w_{L_1}(0^-)$, $w_{L_2}(0^-)$, $w_{L_1}(0^+)$, $w_{L_2}(0^+)$. Compute the difference in total energy stored in coils at $t = 0^-$ and $t = 0^+$ and attempt a physical explanation of the result.

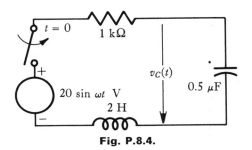

Fig. P.8.4.

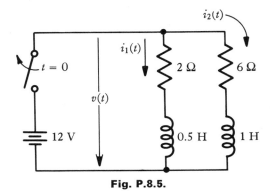

Fig. P.8.5.

8.23 For Fig. P.8.6 assume that $v(t) = 4u(-t) + 2u(t)$ V and solve for $i_1(t)$ and $i_2(t)$ for $t \geqslant 0$. Sketch the two currents including some negative time.

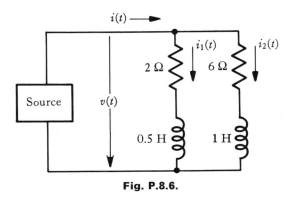

Fig. P.8.6.

8.24 For Fig. P.8.6 assume that $i(t) = 6u(-t) + 2u(t)$ A and solve for $i_1(t)$ and $i_2(t)$ for $t \geqslant 0$. Sketch the two currents including some negative time.

8.25 Prove that Eq. (8.18) follows from Eq. (8.16).

8.26 Prove that Eq. (8.20) follows from Eqs. (8.14) and (8.16).

8.27 The voltage $v(t) = [100 \cos 500t]u(t)$ volts is applied to an initially unexcited coil of 20 H inductance and 0.5 Ω of resistance. Find the current, $i(t)$, for $t \geq 0$.

8.28 Repeat Prob. 8.27 when $v(t) = [100 \sin 500t]u(t)$ volts.

8.29 Repeat Prob. 8.27 when $v(t) = [100 \cos (500t - 45°)]u(t)$ volts.

8.30 In Fig. P.8.1(e) change the switch to close at $t = 0$. Find $i(t)$ and $v(t)$ using the operational impedances in the series-parallel combination.

8.31 Solve for $v(t)$ in Fig. P.8.1(d) using the operational admittance.

8.32 Change the direction of the switch in Fig. P.8.1(f) and solve for $v(t)$ using the operational impedance or admittance.

8.33 Find the operational impedance of the circuit of Fig. P.8.7(a), and use it to find the current $i(t)$ when $v(t) = 10\delta(t)$ volts.

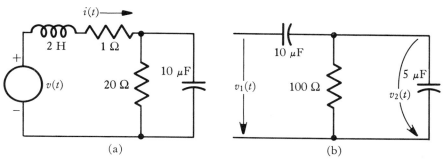

(a)   (b)

Fig. P.8.7.

8.34 In Fig. P.8.7(b), use the operational voltage-divider relationship to find $v_2(t)$ when $v_1(t) = 100u(t)$ volts.

8.35 In Fig. P.8.8, find $i_2(t)$ using operational mesh currents with Thévenin forms for sources and initial conditions.

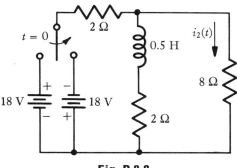

Fig. P.8.8.

8.36 Repeat Prob. 8.35, using Thévenin's equivalent for the network to the left of the 8-Ω resistor.

8.37 Solve for $v_o(t)$ in Fig. P.8.8 utilizing Norton's equivalents for sources and initial conditions and solving by operational nodal analysis.

8.38 In Fig. P.8.9, the rotary switch moves onto its new position just before leaving the old. At $t = 0$ it moves from position 1 to position 2, then 0.5 sec

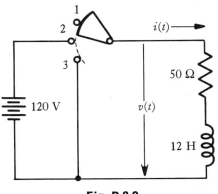

Fig. P.8.9.

later it moves from position 2 to position 3. Find $i(t)$ for all $t \geqslant 0$, utilizing entry 7 in Table 7.2 where its use is indicated. Sketch $v(t)$ and $i(t)$ on the same graph approximately to scale.

8.39 Repeat Prob. 8.38 when the R-L combination is replaced by a 1.0-MΩ, 5-μF R-C series combination.

8.40 Repeat Prob. 8.38 when the R-L combination is replaced by a 60-Ω, 25-H, 50-μF R-L-C series combination.

8.41 Find the operational form of Norton's equivalent of that part of the network of Fig. P.8.10 to the left of the 15-kΩ resistor, and use the result to find $v_a(t)$.

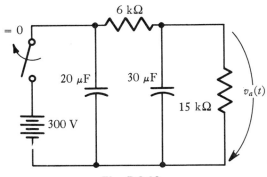

Fig. P.8.10.

8.42 Find the operational Norton's and Thévenin's equivalents for that part of the network of Fig. P.8.11 to the left of the terminating network.

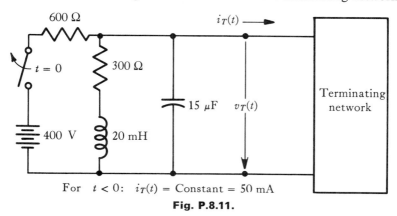

For $t < 0$: $i_T(t) = $ Constant $= 50$ mA

Fig. P.8.11.

8.43 Show the network of Fig. P.8.12 with all initial conditions replaced by current sources.

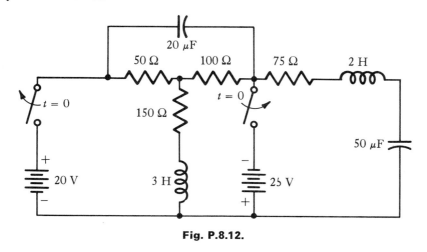

Fig. P.8.12.

8.44 Show the network of Fig. P.8.12 with all initial conditions replaced by voltage sources.

9

The Complex Plane
and System Behavior

9.1 INTRODUCTION

In examples and problems of the previous chapter, the complete function which described some network variable for $t \geqslant 0$ was calculated. This function was really a composite of the responses due to each individual source of energy; and since the networks considered were linear, the complete response was simply the addition of all such component responses. One could determine these component responses by considering the effects of each source of energy individually with all other sources reduced to zero. Of course, each initial condition is a source of energy and must be considered along with the external sources. This is another example of the principle of superposition which is one of the basic properties of linear systems.

The purpose of this chapter is to develop and investigate relationships that describe that portion of the response that is related to one of the external sources of energy. Thus, for our immediate purposes, initial conditions and all external energy sources but one will be presumed to be zero. These investigations will be greatly enhanced by considering the operator p to be a complex variable taking on significant values in the complex plane.

9.2 SYSTEM FUNCTIONS

To obtain response functions, we will be interested in functions of p which operate on an input function to yield the response that the input produces. Such functions will be called *system functions* and are described by the equation

$$R(p) = H(p)F(p), \qquad (9.1)$$

with the following definition of terms:

$H(p)$ is a system function.

$F(p)$ is the operational form of the forcing function and is commonly called the input, the excitation, or the cause.

$R(p)$ is the operational form of that response component caused by the forcing function and is commonly called the output, the result, or the effect.

Equation (9.1) can be rearranged to yield the system function

$$H(p) = \frac{R(p)}{F(p)}. \qquad (9.2)$$

In electrical systems the forcing function can be either a current or a voltage, and the corresponding response can be either a current or a voltage. Thus, Eq. (9.2) can have one of four forms; and it is convenient to name each of these forms and to provide each form with an identifying symbol.

Current Ratio

When both the forcing function and a corresponding response are currents, the system function will be called a *current ratio* and will be given the symbol $H_I(p)$. In other words

$$H_I(p) = \frac{I_R(p)}{I_F(p)}, \qquad (9.3)$$

which results in a dimensionless quantity.

Voltage Ratio

When the system function is a ratio of two voltages, we will use $H_V(p)$ to mean *voltage ratio*; that is,

$$H_V(p) = \frac{V_R(p)}{V_F(p)}, \tag{9.4}$$

which is also dimensionless.

Admittance

Whenever the forcing function is a voltage and the corresponding response is a current, the system function will be referred to as an *admittance*. This is simply an extension of the concept of the admittance function, first introduced in Chapter 4, describing the input current as a response to an input forcing voltage. Again the letter H with a subscript could be employed, but the single letter Y has already been used for the special case of input quantities. Thus,

$$Y(p) = \frac{I_R(p)}{V_F(p)} \; (\Omega^{-1}). \tag{9.5}$$

If the current flows through the same two-terminal network that the voltage appears across, as in Chapter 4, $Y(p)$ is the *driving-point* or *input* admittance of the two-terminal network. If the current flows through some branch *within* the two-terminal network that the voltage appears across, $Y(p)$ is referred to as a *transfer* admittance.

Impedance

The last possibility is a current forcing function and a voltage response. For this case the system function will be called an impedance and symbolized by $Z(p)$, as has been done in a more restricted sense in Chapter 4 and later chapters. That is,

$$Z(p) = \frac{V_R(p)}{I_F(p)} \; (\Omega). \tag{9.6}$$

As with admittance, impedances are divided into two categories and are referred to as driving-point, or input, impedances and as transfer impedances.

EXAMPLE 9.1. List and name the system functions used in working Example 8.10.

Solution. The driving-point impedance of the series R-L combination is

$$Z_a(p) = 2(p + 50) \; \Omega. \qquad \textit{Ans.}$$

The driving-point impedance of the parallel R-C combination is

$$Z_b(p) = \frac{10^4}{p + 10}\ \Omega. \qquad Ans.$$

The imput impedance of the network is

$$Z(p) = 2\frac{p^2 + 60p + 5500}{p + 10}\ \Omega. \qquad Ans.$$

The voltage-divider ratio is

$$H_V(p) = \frac{V_2(p)}{V_1(p)} = \frac{Z_b(p)}{Z(p)}$$

$$= \frac{5000}{p^2 + 60p + 5500}. \qquad Ans.$$

EXAMPLE 9.2. Determine the system function which operates on the input voltage, $V_1(p)\delta(t)$, in Example 8.10 to give the current through resistor R_2, $I_2(p)\delta(t)$.

Solution. Since

$$I_2(p) = \frac{1}{R_2}\,V_2(p)$$

and

$$V_2(p) = H_V(p)V_1(p),$$

substitution gives

$$I_2(p) = \frac{1}{R_2}\,H_V(p)V_1(p).$$

Hence, the transfer admittance relating the resistor current to the input voltage is

$$Y_{21}(p) = \frac{I_2(p)}{V_1(p)} = \frac{1}{R_2}\,H_V(p)$$

$$= \frac{5}{p^2 + 60p + 5500}\ \Omega^{-1}. \qquad Ans.$$

EXAMPLE 9.3. Shown in Fig. 9.1 is a twin-tee coupling network. Determine the system function that relates the output voltage to the input voltage if no current flows through the load (zero load admittance).

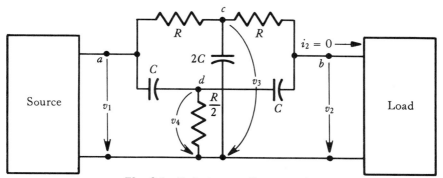

Fig. 9.1 *Twin-tee coupling network.*

Solution. Applying the method of nodal analysis to nodes b, c, and d yields the following current equations in operator form:

$$0 = \left(pC + \frac{1}{R}\right)V_2(p) - \left(\frac{1}{R}\right)V_3(p) - (pC)V_4(p)$$

$$\frac{1}{R}V_1(p) = -\left(\frac{1}{R}\right)V_2(p) + \left(2pC + \frac{2}{R}\right)V_3(p) - (0)V_4(p)$$

$$pCV_1(p) = -(pC)V_2(p) - (0)V_3(p) + \left(2pC + \frac{2}{R}\right)V_4(p).$$

After multiplying each equation by R, $V_2(p)$ can be written in the determinant form

$$V_2(p) = \frac{\begin{vmatrix} 0 & -(1) & -(pRC) \\ V_1(p) & 2(pRC+1) & -(0) \\ pRCV_1(p) & (0) & 2(pRC+1) \end{vmatrix}}{\begin{vmatrix} pRC+1 & -(1) & -(pRC) \\ -(1) & 2(pRC+1) & -(0) \\ -pRC & -(0) & 2(pRC+1) \end{vmatrix}}.$$

Expanding the determinants and simplifying yields

$$V_2(p) = \frac{p^2 + (1/RC)^2}{p^2 + (4/RC)p + (1/RC)^2} V_1(p).$$

Thus, if the load impedance is infinite, the voltage ratio is

$$H_V(p) = \frac{V_2(p)}{V_1(p)} = \frac{p^2 + (1/RC)^2}{p^2 + (4/RC)p + (1/RC)^2}. \qquad Ans.$$

9.3 POLES AND ZEROS

The operational form of a response, or the coefficient of $\delta(t)$ in the operator form, is a ratio of two polynomials which can be written as

$$R(p) = \frac{a_m p^m + a_{m-1} p^{m-1} + \cdots + a_1 p + a_0}{b_n p^n + b_{n-1} p^{n-1} + \cdots + b_1 p + b_0}$$

$$= K \frac{(p - z_1)(p - z_2) \cdots (p - z_m)}{(p - p_1)(p - p_2) \cdots (p - p_n)}, \qquad (9.7)$$

where

$$K = a_m / b_n. \qquad (9.8)$$

This form is an alternative to that which appeared in Chapter 8 where now the numerator as well as the denominator is factored.

The roots of the numerator, represented by z_k's, are called the *zeros* of the function, where the name zero results from the fact that

$$|R(z_k)| = 0. \qquad (9.9)$$

On the other hand, the roots of the denominator, represented by p_k's, are called the *poles* of the function. If p_j is a *pole* of $R(p)$, then

$$\lim_{p \to p_j} |R(p)| \to \infty. \qquad (9.10)$$

In the case of the rational fraction, where $R(p)$ is the ratio of two polynomials as it has been considered here, it is obvious that a pole is simply a value of p which causes the denominator to be zero. It should be remembered, however, that Eq. (9.10) is the more general definition.

In order to obtain a graphical illustration of the poles and zeros of a function, the locations of these roots are plotted in the complex plane as illustrated in Fig. 9.2. The crosses represent the poles; and, of course, the small circles represent the zeros. Including the multiplier, K, with the graphical information causes the function $R(p)$ to be completely specified. In fact, Fig. 9.2 contains

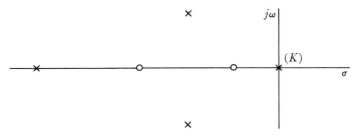

Fig. 9.2 *Illustration of poles and zeros in the p-plane.*

just as much information as does Eq. (9.7). This type of plot is called a *pole-zero (p-z) plot.*

It should be noticed in Fig. 9.2 that the *x*-axis is now designated as the σ-axis and the (jy)-axis is now designated as the $(j\omega)$-axis. It is common practice to refer to this complex plane as the *p-plane*. The reason for the change of notation is to conform to the standard practice of letting $z = x + jy$ be *any* complex variable and letting $p = \sigma + j\omega$ be the special complex variable involved in the integro-differential equations of system behavior.

The operational response $R(p)$ is composed of a system function operating on a forcing function, as illustrated by Eq. (9.1), so its poles and zeros are the poles and zeros of the system function plus the poles and zeros of the forcing function. Even if the forcing function is not explicitly specified, it is still informative to construct a pole-zero plot of the system function.

EXAMPLE 9.4. Construct a pole-zero plot for the voltage ratio in Example 9.3.

Solution. The zeros, or roots of the numerator, are

$$z_1 = j/RC$$
$$z_2 = -j/RC.$$

The poles, or roots of the denominator, are

$$p_1 = -0.268/RC$$
$$p_2 = -3.732/RC.$$

The result is shown in Fig. 9.3.

Fig. 9.3 *Pole-zero plot for the twin-tee coupling network in Fig. 9.1.*

9.4 GRAPHICAL METHODS IN THE COMPLEX PLANE

Plotting poles and zeros requires the extra effort of factoring the numerator, and we need to inquire as to the worth of such a plot. To start our investigation, we will rewrite Eq. (9.7) as

$$R(p) = K\left[k_0 + \frac{k_1}{p - p_1} + \frac{k_2}{p - p_2} + \cdots + \frac{k_n}{p - p_n}\right], \qquad (9.11)$$

where

$$k_0 = \begin{cases} 1, & n = m \\ 0, & n > m. \end{cases} \qquad (9.12)$$

Of course, Eq. (9.11) is an alternative form for Eq. (8.5) with the added restriction that all of the poles are simple. With this restriction and the following example, we will demonstrate how the k_k's of Eq. (9.11) can be determined graphically.

EXAMPLE 9.5. Determine the partial fraction expansion for

$$R(p) = \frac{3p^2 + 18p + 30}{2p^2 + 4p + 4}.$$

Solution. $R(p)$ can be rewritten as

$$R(p) = \frac{3}{2} \frac{p^2 + 6p + 10}{p^2 + 2p + 2}$$

$$= \frac{3}{2} \frac{[p - (-3 + j1)][p - (-3 - j1)]}{[p - (-1 + j1)][p - (-1 - j1)]}$$

$$= \frac{3}{2} \frac{(p - z_1)(p - z_2)}{(p - p_1)(p - p_2)}$$

$$= \frac{3}{2} \left[k_0 + \frac{k_1}{p - p_1} + \frac{k_2}{p - p_2} \right].$$

Note that $R(p)$ has zeros at $p = -3 + j1$ and at $-3 - j1$ and has poles at $-1 + j1$ and at $-1 - j1$, as shown in Fig. 9.4. In this case, $n = m$, so

$$k_0 = 1. \qquad Ans.$$

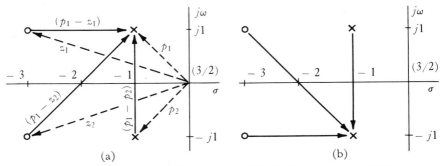

Fig. 9.4 *Graphical evaluation of k's for Example 9.5. (a) Evaluation of k_1. (b) Evaluation of k_2.*

Using the methods of Art. 8.3,

$$k_1 = \frac{(p-p_1)(p-z_1)(p-z_2)}{(p-p_1)(p-p_2)}\bigg|_{p=p_1}$$

$$= \frac{(p_1-z_1)(p_1-z_2)}{(p_1-p_2)}$$

$$= \frac{(2+j0)(2+j2)}{(0+j2)}$$

$$= \frac{2e^{j0°}2\sqrt{2}\,e^{j45°}}{2e^{j90°}}$$

$$= 2\sqrt{2}\,e^{-j45°}. \qquad Ans.$$

Likewise,

$$k_2 = \frac{(p_2-z_1)(p_2-z_2)}{(p_2-p_1)}$$

$$= 2\sqrt{2}\,e^{+j45°}. \qquad Ans.$$

Now we will make use of the pole-zero plot, drawn to scale, to evaluate k_0, k_1, and k_2. Since the number of zeros equals the number of poles

$$k_0 = 1.$$

To obtain k_1, we draw the vector distance to p_1 from every other pole and zero as shown by the solid arrows. (The dashed arrows are for reference purposes.) Then we write an equation for k_1 by placing the complex value of each vector distance from a *zero* in the numerator and the complex value of each vector distance from a *pole* in the denominator. Thus,

$$k_1 = \frac{(p_1-z_1)(p_1-z_2)}{(p_1-p_2)},$$

which, by direct measurement of magnitudes and angles on the pole-zero (*p-z*) plot, becomes

$$k_1 = \frac{2e^{j0°}2\sqrt{2}\,e^{j45°}}{2e^{j90°}}$$

$$= 2\sqrt{2}\,e^{-j45°}$$

and comparison to the previous method illustrates the validity of this second approach. To evaluate k_2, we draw all arrows to p_2; but we notice that every arrow used for k_2 is the conjugate of some arrow used for k_1. Therefore, k_2 must be the conjugate of k_1 whenever p_2 is the conjugate of p_1.

You should have observed by now that what has taken place in the above example is simply a graphical application of Heaviside's expansion theorem of Art. 8.3. This graphical method is useful in determining the coefficients associated with first-order (simple) poles in the function $R(p)$. Let us observe on the p-plane how this theorem works in general by first assuming an arbitrary p-z plot for $R(p)$ as shown in Fig. 9.5.

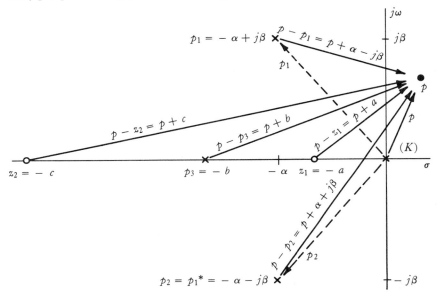

Fig. 9.5 *Showing the factors in numerator and denominator of R(p) at an arbitrary location in the p-plane.*

Having drawn Fig. 9.5, it is apparent that we have assumed that $R(p)$ is

$$R(p) = \frac{K(p+a)(p+c)}{p(p+b)(p+\alpha-j\beta)(p+\alpha+j\beta)}$$

$$= \frac{K(p+a)(p+c)}{p(b+b)[(p+\alpha)^2+\beta^2]}, \qquad (9.13)$$

and all the numerator and denominator factors show up as vectors, or complex numbers, on the p-plane. The point p is chosen arbitrarily to be *any* point anywhere in the p-plane. That these vectors really are factors is apparent if we isolate just one, say the one associated with p_1, as shown in Fig. 9.6. Here we have located the pole p_1 and the arbitrary point p on the p-plane. Now we draw the vector distance from p_1 to p, which we designate as the

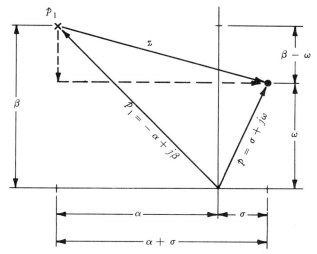

Fig. 9.6 *Example of vector subtraction.*

complex number z. Then we note the real and imaginary components of z in terms of those of p_1 and p to result in

$$z = (\sigma + \alpha) - j(\beta - \omega)$$
$$= (\sigma + j\omega) - (-\alpha + j\beta)$$
$$= p - p_1, \tag{9.14}$$

which is the factor associated with the pole p_1. This is nothing more than an example of the subtraction of complex numbers.

Now how does this illustrate the aforementioned expansion theorem? Simple. To evaluate k_1, for example, simply allow the point p to move onto point p_1. This has reduced the factor $(p - p_1)$ to zero by substituting $p = p_1$, as the theorem dictates, and the remaining vectors are those which make up the coefficient of $1/(p - p_1)$.

If multiple-order zeros had occurred in the previous example, multiple arrows would be assumed to be drawn from the zeros to the pole of interest. If multiple-order poles had occurred in the previous problem, the approach of Eq. (8.11) would have to be used for evaluating all but one of the constants for the multiple poles. Of course, all first-order poles could still be investigated graphically.

Some conclusions concerning the k's become apparent immediately when the poles and zeros are plotted. A zero near a pole, say p_k, tends to reduce the value of k_k, as does a pole far from it. On the other hand, the closer a pole or the farther a zero from a given pole, p_k, the larger is the magnitude of k_k.

Thus, the pole-zero plot gives a quick check on the relative values and importance of the k's. Of particular importance in many network problems is the ability to move a pole or a zero by varying one or more of the network components and thereby affecting the k's. Also it is sometimes convenient either to add or to cancel certain poles and zeros, or to do both, by adding components to the networks.

EXAMPLE 9.6. If in Example 9.3

$$R = 10^6 \ \Omega$$

$$C = 10^{-6} \ \text{F}$$

$$V_1(p) = 10/p \ \text{V} \cdot \sec$$

determine the partial fraction expansion of $V_2(p)$.

Solution. The pole-zero plot of $V_2(p)$ can be constructed from Fig. 9.3. by adding a pole at the origin and changing the multiplier to ten as shown in Fig. 9.7. Using graphical methods and Fig. 9.7, we can write

$$V_2(p) = 10 \left[0 + \frac{\dfrac{1e^{-j90°}1e^{+j90°}}{0.268(3.732)}}{p} \right.$$

$$+ \frac{\dfrac{\sqrt{1.072} \ e^{-j\varphi_1}\sqrt{1.072} \ e^{j\varphi_1}}{3.464(-0.268)}}{p + 0.268}$$

$$\left. + \frac{\dfrac{\sqrt{14.93} \ e^{-j\varphi_2}\sqrt{14.93} \ e^{j\varphi_2}}{(-3.732)(-3.464)}}{p + 3.732} \right]$$

$$= 10 \left[\frac{1}{p} - \frac{1.155}{p + 0.268} + \frac{1.155}{p + 3.732} \right] \text{V} \cdot \sec. \qquad Ans.$$

The angles φ_1 and φ_2 were never evaluated because of the cancellation by $-\varphi_1$ and $-\varphi_2$ respectively.

Fig. 9.7 *Pole-zero plot for Example 9.6.*

9.5 TIME DOMAIN EFFECTS OF POLE LOCATIONS

The operator form of the response, $R(p)$, in Eq. (9.11) represents the time function

$$r(t) = R(p)\delta(t)$$
$$= Kk_0\,\delta(t) + K[k_1 e^{p_1 t} + k_2\, e^{p_2 t} + \cdots + k_m\, e^{p_m t}]u(t), \qquad (9.15)$$

which illustrates that each term in brackets results from some pole. In this respect the role of the zeros is to simply affect the *amplitudes* of the various exponentials, since the exponentials themselves are independent of the zeros.

Our investigation now turns to how the locations of the poles affect the form of the answer. First, consideration will be given to a pole that is located on the real, or sigma, axis. Such a pole must have a real k because the angles on the arrows from all of the complex conjugate zeros and poles cancel and because all other angular contributions, which are from poles and zeros also located on the σ-axis, are either 0° or 180°. Hence, for a pole on the σ-axis, as was the case in the previous example,

$$p_k = \sigma + j0 \qquad (9.16)$$

and

$$k_k = a + j0. \qquad (9.17)$$

Such a pole contributes a component of the form

$$r_k(t) = K\,\frac{a}{p-\sigma}\,\delta(t)$$
$$= Kae^{\sigma t}u(t). \qquad (9.18)$$

If the pole is in the left-half plane (LHP), that is, to the left of the $j\omega$-axis,

$$\sigma = -b. \qquad (9.19)$$

This gives the decaying exponential form,

$$r_k(t) = Kae^{-bt}u(t). \qquad (9.20)$$

If the pole is at the origin,

$$\sigma = 0. \qquad (9.21)$$

This yields the steady-state form,

$$r_k(t) = Kae^{0t}u(t)$$
$$= Ka(1)u(t). \qquad (9.22)$$

Likewise, if the pole is in the right-half plane (RHP), that is, to the right of the $j\omega$-axis,

$$\sigma = +b. \tag{9.23}$$

This produces the increasing exponential form

$$r_k(t) = Kae^{bt}u(t). \tag{9.24}$$

The last component increases without bound, which implies that infinite sources of energy are available. However, such sources are not available; thus, such answers are not possible in any physically realizable passive system.

The second consideration will be given to a pair of complex conjugate poles. The contribution of a pair of such poles is of the form

$$r(t) = K\left[\frac{ae^{j\phi}}{p - (\sigma + j\omega)} + \frac{ae^{-j\phi}}{p - (\sigma - j\omega)}\right]\delta(t)$$

$$= Ka[e^{j\phi}e^{(\sigma + j\omega)t} + e^{-j\phi}e^{(\sigma - j\omega)t}]u(t)$$

$$= K(2a)e^{\sigma t}\frac{e^{j(\omega t + \phi)} + e^{-j(\omega t + \phi)}}{2}u(t)$$

$$= K(2a)e^{\sigma t}\cos(\omega t + \phi)u(t). \tag{9.25}$$

If the pair of poles is in the LHP, σ is negative; and an exponentially decaying cosine is the result. If the pair of poles is on the $j\omega$-axis, they produce a steady-state cosine waveform. Finally, if the pair of poles is in the RHP, an exponentially increasing cosine results which once again implies infinite energy sources not existing in nature.

EXAMPLE 9.7. If the twin-tee coupling network of Example 9.3 has a sinusoidal input voltage, determine the values of R and C which will eliminate any sinusoidal component in the output voltage.

Solution. The input voltage will be of the form

$$v_1(t) = V_m \cos(\omega t + \phi)u(t)$$

$$= V_m(\cos\phi\cos\omega t - \sin\phi\sin\omega t)u(t)$$

$$= V_m \cos\phi\frac{p - \omega\tan\phi}{p^2 + \omega^2}\delta(t).$$

Thus the response function will have the poles and zeros shown in Fig. 9.3 plus a zero on the real axis at $\omega\tan\phi$ and two poles on the $j\omega$-axis. The solution to this problem is to have the zeros of the system function to cancel the poles of the excitation. This approach leads to the result

$$\frac{1}{RC} = \omega, \qquad Ans.$$

and we will have constructed a filter that completely blocks one single frequency. The resulting transient output voltage will then be composed of two decaying exponentials unless the phase shift is such that the zero contributed by the excitation cancels one of the poles on the real axis.

PROBLEMS

In the first ten problems, determine the system function relating each labeled response in the designated figure to the forcing function.

9.1   Figure P.9.1

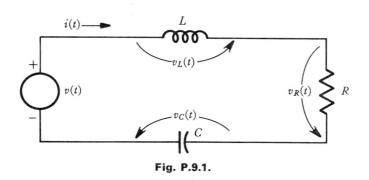

Fig. P.9.1.

9.2   Figure P.9.2.

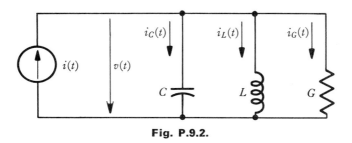

Fig. P.9.2.

9.3 Figure P.9.3.

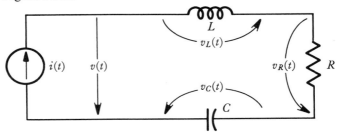

Fig. P.9.3.

9.4 Figure P.9.4.

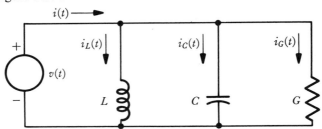

Fig. P.9.4.

9.5 Figure P.9.5.

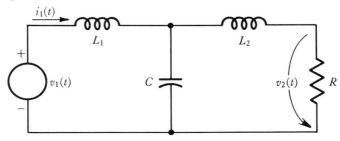

Fig. P.9.5.

9.6 Figure P.9.6.

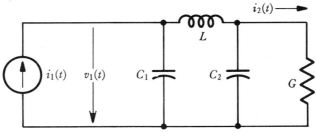

Fig. P.9.6.

9.7 Figure P.9.7.

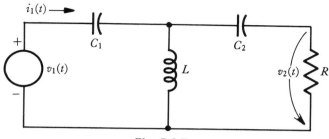

Fig. P.9.7.

9.8 Figure P.9.8.

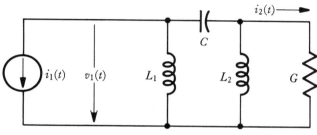

Fig. P.9.8.

9.9 Figure P.9.9.

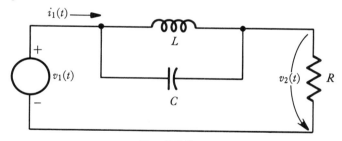

Fig. P.9.9.

9.10 Figure P.9.10.

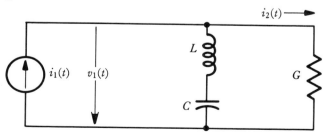

Fig. P.9.10.

9.11 Determine the input impedance, $Z(p)$, of the circuit shown in Fig. P.9.11 and list its poles and zeros.

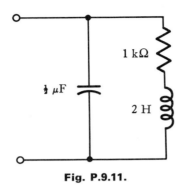

Fig. P.9.11.

9.12 Figure P.9.12(a) contains the pole-zero configuration of a given signal. Employ graphical methods to determine the response signal as a function of time.

9.13 Repeat Prob. 9.12 using Fig. P.9.12(b).

9.14 Repeat Prob. 9.12 using Fig. P.9.12(c).

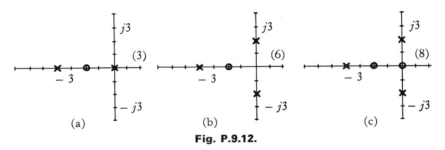

Fig. P.9.12.

In Probs. 9.15 through 9.19, list the poles and zeros for the operational forms designated from the problems for Chapter 8.

9.15 Problem 8.13.
9.16 Problem 8.14.
9.17 Problem 8.15.
9.18 Problem 8.17.
9.19 Problem 8.18.

In Probs. 9.20 through 9.27, find the time-varying form, utilizing graphical methods, corresponding to the operational forms designated from the problems for Chapter 8.

9.20 Problems 8.7 and 8.8.

9.21 Problems 8.9 and 8.10.

9.22 Problems 8.11 and 8.13.

9.23 Problems 8.12 and 8.14.

9.24 Problem 8.15.

9.25 Problems 8.16 and 8.17.

9.26 Problem 8.18.

9.27 Given that

$$H_V(p) = \frac{V_2(p)}{V_1(p)} = \frac{6p^2 + 42p + 60}{(3p + 12)(2p^2 + 8p + 26)}$$

$$v_1(t) = [10 \cos 3t]u(t)$$

determine $V_2(p)$, draw its p-z plot, and determine $v_2(t)$ graphically.

9.28 List the poles and zeros and the constant multiplier in the operational forms for the following functions of time:

a. $f(t) = 100[1 + e^{-2t} - e^{-5t}]u(t)$

b. $f(t) = 200[1 + 5e^{-4t} \cos(10t + 30°)]u(t)$

c. $f(t) = 200[te^{-6t} \cos 10t]u(t)$.

9.29 The operational form of a given signal has a zero at $p = -5$, and poles at $p = -10$, $p = -4 + j10$, and $p = -4 - j10$. List the poles and zeros corresponding to a signal of identical form but occurring twice as fast.

9.30 Show that:

a. In Fig. P.9.13(a), $V_2 = \alpha V_1$ and $I_2 = \alpha I_1$, where

$$\alpha = \frac{R_2}{R_1 + R_2}.$$

b. In Fig. P.9.13(b), $v_C(t) = v_C(0^-)\exp(-t/\tau_{C_o})u(t)$, where

$$\tau_{C_o} = \frac{R_1 R_2}{R_1 + R_2} C$$

$$= (\text{Total resistance in parallel with } C)C.$$

c. In Fig. P.9.13(c), $i_L(t) = i_L(0^-)\exp(-t/\tau_{L_o})u(t)$, where

$$\tau_{L_o} = \frac{L}{R_1 + R_2}$$

$$= \frac{L}{(\text{Total resistance in series with } L)}$$

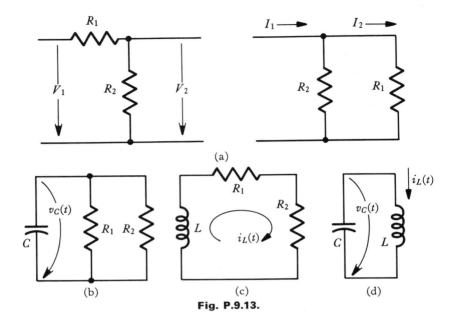

Fig. P.9.13.

d.   In Fig. P.9.13(d), $v_C(t) = V_m \cos(\omega_o t + \theta_v)$ and $i_L(t) = I_m \cos(\omega_o + \theta_i)$, where V_m, I_m, θ_v, and θ_i are constants and

$$\omega_o = \sqrt{\frac{1}{LC}}.$$

The remaining problems require the prior working of Problem 9.30, and the values of R_1, R_2, L, and C are presumed to be those of Prob. 9.30.

9.31 Show that, for Fig. P.9.14(a),

$$H_V(p) = \frac{H(0)}{\dfrac{\alpha}{\omega_o^2}\,p + (\tau_{C_o} + \tau_{L_o})p + 1}$$

$$= \frac{H(0)}{(\tau_{C_o}p + 1)(\tau_{L_o}p + 1) - \alpha^2 \tau_{C_o}\tau_{L_o}p^2},$$

where α, ω_o, τ_{C_o}, and τ_{L_o} are defined as in Prob. 9.30.

9.32 Show that, for Fig. P.9.14 (b),

$$H_V(p) = \frac{H_V(0)(\tau_L p + 1)}{\dfrac{\alpha}{\omega_o^2}\,p^2 + (\tau_{C_o} + \tau_{L_o})p + 1} = \frac{H_V(0)(\tau_L p + 1)}{(\tau_{C_o}p + 1)(\tau_{L_o}p + 1) - \alpha^2 \tau_{C_o}\tau_{Lo}p^2},$$

where $\tau_L = L/R_1$ and the remaining constants are defined as in Prob. 9.30.

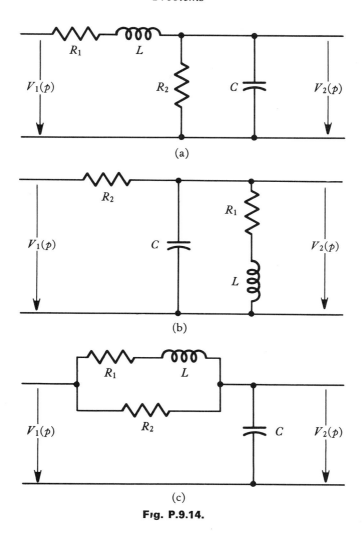

(a)

(b)

(c)

Fig. P.9.14.

9.33 Show that, for Fig. P.9.14(c),

$$H_V(p) = \frac{\tau_{L_o} p + 1}{\dfrac{\alpha}{\omega_o^2} p^2 + (\tau_{C_o} + \tau_{L_o})p + 1}$$

$$= \frac{\tau_{L_o} p + 1}{(\tau_{C_o} p + 1)(\tau_{L_o} p + 1) - \alpha^2 \tau_{C_o} \tau_{L_o} p^2},$$

where the constants are defined as in Prob. 9.30.

9.34 On the basis of the results of Probs. 9.30 through 9.33, attempt to formulate a generalized way of writing the numerator and denominator of a voltage ratio in a network with a single source, a single coil, a single capacitor, and any number of resistors. Check the result with at least one network of your own design.

9.35 Draw two networks on which are defined current ratios having the same denominator as Probs. 9.31 through 9.33.

9.36 Attempt an extension of the generalization of Prob. 9.35 to include *any* system function whose component content is restricted as stated.

9.37 Define Q and ω_n for Probs. 9.31 through 9.33 in terms of α, ω_o, τ_{L_o}, and τ_{C_o}.

10

Special Properties
of the Frequency Response

10.1 INTRODUCTION

In Chapter 8 complete system responses were determined which completely described system variables for $t \geqslant 0$. These responses included the forced components caused by the forcing function and the natural components depending on the initial conditions. In Chapter 9 responses were calculated that included only those components which were caused by a single forcing function applied to an initially unexcited system, so the effects of the initial conditions were not explicitly considered. This chapter will also delete consideration of the effects of the initial conditions by the simple device of making observations only after such effects have vanished, will utilize only sinusoidal forcing functions, and will give particular attention to the steady-state, sinusoidal component of the complete response. In other words, this is a further study of the forced response to sinusoids with which we were concerned in Chapter 5.

The fact that the primary interest of this chapter is in that component of the complete response which results from a pair of complex conjugate poles on the $j\omega$-axis does not imply that the remainder of the complete response is immaterial. On the contrary, the transient portion of a complete response really must be considered first, because every system must be able to survive the transients without breaking down or burning out if it is to reach steady-state operation. Fortunately, in many systems, the engineer eventually obtains enough "feel" or intuition to decide whether or not the transients are important enough to require calculation. He must always bear in mind, however, that there is never a steady-state mode of operation without there having first been a transient condition.

10.2 FREQUENCY RESPONSE FUNCTIONS AND PHASORS

We have seen that the arbitrary sinusoidal signal

$$f(t) = [F_m \cos (\omega t + \theta)]u(t)$$
$$= [\sqrt{2}F \cos (\omega t + \theta)]u(t) \tag{10.1}$$

may be written

$$f(t) = \frac{1}{\sqrt{2}} [Fe^{j\theta}e^{j\omega t} + Fe^{-j\theta}e^{-j\omega t}]u(t). \tag{10.2}$$

The complex quantity

$$\mathbf{F} = Fe^{j\theta} \tag{10.3}$$

is called the *phasor value* of the sinusoidal function $f(t)$, and Eq. (10.2) may be expressed in terms of it as

$$f(t) = \frac{1}{\sqrt{2}} [\mathbf{F}e^{j\omega t} + \mathbf{F}^*e^{-j\omega t}]u(t). \tag{10.4}$$

This same signal may be written in terms of the *complex time function*

$$\mathbf{f}(t) = \frac{1}{\sqrt{2}} \mathbf{F}e^{j\omega t}u(t) = \frac{1}{\sqrt{2}} \frac{\mathbf{F}}{p - j\omega} \delta(t)$$
$$= \mathbf{F}(p)\delta(t) \tag{10.5}$$

as

$$f(t) = \mathbf{f}(t) + \mathbf{f}^*(t). \tag{10.6}$$

Now suppose that $\mathbf{f}(t)$ acts as the forcing function for the system characterized by the system function

$$H(p) = \frac{K(p - z_1)(p - z_2)\cdots(p - z_m)}{(p - p_1)(p - p_2)\cdots(p - p_n)}. \tag{10.7}$$

The operational form of the response to $\mathbf{f}(t)$ will be

$$\mathbf{R}(p) = H(p)\mathbf{F}(p)$$

$$= \frac{H(p)\mathbf{F}}{\sqrt{2}\,(p - j\omega)}. \tag{10.8}$$

The denominator of $\mathbf{R}(p)$ consists of the factor $(p - j\omega)$ plus n factors in the
denominator of $H(p)$, so

$$\mathbf{R}(p) = K_o + \frac{K_{j\omega}}{p - j\omega} + \sum_{k=1}^{n} \frac{K_k}{p - p_k}, \tag{10.9}$$

where

$$K_o = \lim_{p \to \infty} \mathbf{R}(p) = \lim_{p \to \infty} \frac{H(p)\mathbf{F}}{\sqrt{2}\,(p - j\omega)}. \tag{10.10}$$

Using Heaviside's expansion theorem yields

$$K_{j\omega} = (p - j\omega)\frac{H(p)\mathbf{F}}{\sqrt{2}\,(p - j\omega)}\bigg|_{p = j\omega}.$$

$$= \frac{H(j\omega)\mathbf{F}}{\sqrt{2}}, \tag{10.11}$$

and

$$K_k = (p - p_k)\frac{H(p)\mathbf{F}}{\sqrt{2}\,(p - j\omega)}\bigg|_{p = p_k}. \tag{10.12}$$

Thus, the complex time-varying response is

$$\mathbf{r}(t) = \mathbf{R}(p)\delta(t)$$

$$= K_o\,\delta(t) + \left[\frac{H(j\omega)\mathbf{F}}{\sqrt{2}}\,e^{j\omega t} + \sum_{k=1}^{n} K_k\,e^{p_k t}\right]u(t). \tag{10.13}$$

Application of the conjugate of $\mathbf{f}(t)$ to the same system will result in a
response which is the conjugate of Eq. (10.13). By Eq. (10.6), application of
the real function, $f(t)$, may be considered the simultaneous application of $\mathbf{f}(t)$

and its conjugate; and the resulting real response may likewise be considered the combination of the two responses, as follows:

$$r(t) = \mathbf{r}(t) + \mathbf{r}^*(t)$$

$$= (K_o + K_o^*)\delta(t) + \frac{1}{\sqrt{2}} [H(j\omega)\mathbf{F}e^{j\omega t} + H(-j\omega)\mathbf{F}^*e^{-j\omega t}]u(t)$$

$$+ \sum_{k=1}^{n} (K_k e^{p_k t} + K_k^* e^{p_k^* t})u(t). \tag{10.14}$$

If we set

$$H(j\omega) = |H(j\omega)| e^{j\phi}, \tag{10.15}$$

and substitute this equation and Eq. (10.3) into Eq. (10.14), then

$$r(t) = (K_o + K_o^*)\delta(t) + |H(j\omega)| \sqrt{2} F \cos(\omega t + \theta + \phi)u(t)$$

$$+ \sum_{k=1}^{n} (K_k e^{p_k t} + K_k^* e^{p_k^* t})u(t). \tag{10.16}$$

The poles, the p_k, of $H(p)$ will always have negative real parts in physical systems, because such parts result from energy dissipation in the form of heat from resistance or friction; and there is no such thing as a lossless system. These real parts may be quite small, but they are there; and if we wait long enough, they will do their work, which is to reduce the terms in the summation in Eq. (10.16) to zero. That is,

$$(K_o + K_o^*)\delta(t) + \sum_{k=1}^{n} (K_k e^{p_k t} + K_k^* e^{p_k^* t})u(t) \rightarrow 0 \qquad \text{for } t \text{ large enough.} \tag{10.17}$$

The remaining portion of the function, called the *steady-state sinusoidal response*, may be indicated by

$$r(t) \rightarrow r_{ss}(t) \qquad \text{for large } t. \tag{10.18}$$

Relations (10.17) and (10.18) show that for large t Eq. (10.16) becomes the steady-state response

$$r_{ss}(t) = |H(j\omega)| \sqrt{2} F \cos(\omega t + \theta + \phi), \tag{10.19}$$

where the step function is dropped, since its beginning is now so far back in time that it does not concern us.

We may write Eq. (10.19) in the fashion of Eq. (10.4) as

$$r_{ss}(t) = \frac{1}{\sqrt{2}} [\mathbf{R}e^{j\omega t} + \mathbf{R}^*e^{-j\omega t}],$$

where

$$\mathbf{R} = H(j\omega)\mathbf{F}$$
$$= |H(j\omega)|Fe^{j(\theta+\phi)} \tag{10.20}$$

is the *phasor value of the response*. The ratio of the phasor value of the response to the phasor value of the forcing function

$$\frac{\mathbf{R}}{\mathbf{F}} = H(j\omega) = \mathbf{H} \tag{10.21}$$

is called the *frequency response function*. It is very simply formed by replacing p by $j\omega$ in the system function. These results contain as special cases the results embodied in Eqs. (5.38) and (5.39), which two sets of equations formed the basis for the analysis in Chapter 5.

You will recall that

$$H(p) = \frac{R(p)}{F(p)}, \tag{10.22}$$

so one forms the frequency response function of Eq. (10.21) from the system function by replacing the operational forms of the signals by their phasor forms and replacing p in the system function by $j\omega$. You should make note of the fact that the $j\omega$'s are simply a restricted subset of all the p's in the p-plane, where the poles and zeros of $H(p)$ are located. They are the set of p's making up the $j\omega$-axis of the p-plane. This will be exploited in the next article.

10.3 FREQUENCY RESPONSE ON THE COMPLEX PLANE

Suppose the system function connecting a network response variable to the forcing function is the same function of p as $R(p)$ in Eq. (9.13); that is,

$$H(p) = \frac{K(p+a)(p+c)}{p(p+b)(p+\alpha-j\beta)(p+\alpha+j\beta)}. \tag{10.23}$$

Then Fig. 9.5 shows all the numerator and denominator factors of $H(p)$ at the arbitrary point p on the complex plane. The system function is evaluated at this point by simply multiplying the constant multiplier K by the complex numerator factors as measured from the figure, then dividing by the measured denominator factors.

The frequency response function $H(j\omega)$ is nothing more than $H(p)$ with p restricted to that subset of values all of which lie on the imaginary axis. Just one member of this subset is $\omega = \omega_1$, or $p = j\omega_1$, shown in Fig. 10.1, where

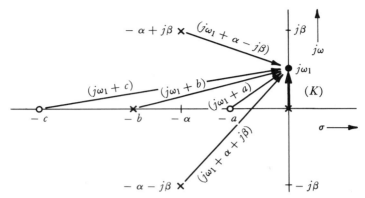

Fig. 10.1   *Showing the numerator and denominator factors of $H(j\omega)$ at an arbitrary ω.*

we have moved the point p from its position in Fig. 9.5 to the point $p = j\omega_1$. Here again all the numerator and denominator factors of the frequency response, evaluated at radian frequency ω_1, may be measured directly from the figure and used to compute $H(j\omega_1)$.

$$H(j\omega_1) = \frac{K(j\omega_1 + a)(j\omega_1 + c)}{j\omega_1(j\omega_1 + b)(j\omega_1 + \alpha - j\beta)(j\omega_1 + \alpha + j\beta)}. \tag{10.24}$$

By following this procedure for successive ω's from 0 to ∞, one obtains the complete frequency response.

$$H(j\omega) = |H(j\omega)|e^{j\phi(\omega)}. \tag{10.25}$$

Plots of $|H(j\omega)|$ and $\phi(\omega)$, with ω as the independent variable, are one effective way of displaying the results.

There are certain aspects of the frequency response which become evident at a glance from the sketch, similar to Fig. 10.1, of the complex plane geometries. For example, in the system represented by Fig. 10.1, the phase shift near $\omega = 0$ is approximately zero, since all factors thereabouts have either zero phase or occur in complex pairs. On the other hand, since there is an excess of poles over zeros of two, the phase shift at large ω's, where each factor has a phase angle approaching $90°$, approaches twice $-90°$, or $-180°$, where the minus signs occur because the excess of factors is in the denominator. Furthermore, one would expect a peak in $|H(j\omega)|$ at some ω in the region of the $j\omega$-axis opposite $-\alpha + j\beta$, since in this region the factor $j\omega_1 + \alpha - j\beta$, a denominator factor, is shrinking at a rate comparatively greater than the rates of change of the remaining factors in $H(j\omega)$. As a matter of fact, if $\alpha = 0$, then $H(j\beta) \to \infty$.

10.4 THE SECOND-ORDER SYSTEM

Quadratic factors which are functions of p will often appear in the numerators and denominators of system functions, and each such factor possesses two characteristic numerics which are readily calculated and which completely specify the quadratic except for a constant multiplier. As an example, let us consider again the simple second-order case, where the system function has a quadratic denominator and a simple numerator which we will designate as the polynomial $P(p)$ for the time being. Such a system function is often written as

$$H(p) = \frac{P(p)}{p^2 + 2\zeta\omega_n p + \omega_n^2},\tag{10.26}$$

where ζ and ω_n are the two characteristic numerics mentioned above.

We will now proceed to investigate the manner in which ζ and ω_n can quickly provide information concerning the locations of the two poles contributed by the quadratic denominator. These poles are

$$p_{1,2} = \frac{-2\zeta\omega_n \pm \sqrt{4\zeta^2\omega_n^2 - 4\omega_n^2}}{2}$$

$$= \omega_n(-\zeta \pm \sqrt{\zeta^2 - 1}).\tag{10.27a}$$

In light of Eq. (10.27a) let us now vary ζ from zero to infinity considering first the range from zero to one, wherein the poles are a complex conjugate pair. In this range it is convenient to use the alternative form

$$p_{1,2} = \omega_n(-\zeta \pm j\sqrt{1 - \zeta^2}).\tag{10.27b}$$

As we saw in Art. 9.5, such a pair of poles contributes a response term

$$r(t) = K(2a)e^{-\zeta\omega_n t}\cos(\omega_n\sqrt{1 - \zeta^2}\,t + \theta)u(t),\tag{10.28}$$

whenever the system is excited. In connection with this response the following terminology has developed:

1. The system is said to be *underdamped* because of the oscillatory nature of the sinusoidal function.
2. The exponential coefficient, $\zeta\omega_n$, is called the *damping coefficient* because it indicates how soon the oscillations will become negligible or will be completely *damped.*
3. The variable zeta, ζ, is dimensionless and is called the *damping ratio.*
4. The frequency term, ω_n, is called the *undamped natural radian frequency* because sustained oscillations would exist at this frequency if damping did not exist ($\zeta = 0$).

In order to determine the distance of these conjugate poles from the origin, we multiply one by its conjugate and take the square root to get

$$|p| = \sqrt{p_1 p_1^*} = \sqrt{p_1 p_2} \Big\} \qquad \zeta < 1.0. \qquad (10.29)$$
$$= \omega_n$$

Thus, we see that the poles lie on a circle which is centered at the origin and which has a radius of ω_n. Since the poles always have a negative real part, they are further restricted to that portion of the circle in the LHP; and the poles form an angle with respect to the negative real axis of value

$$\theta = \cos^{-1} \frac{\omega_n \zeta}{\omega_n} \Big\} \qquad \zeta < 1.0. \qquad (10.30)$$
$$= \cos^{-1} \zeta$$

Equations (10.29) and (10.30) provide a quick and easy way to locate the poles whenever ζ is less than one; but as ζ approaches zero, the angle is difficult to distinguish from 90° using normal computational means. When such is the case, it is easier to use the approximation to Eq. (10.27b)

$$p_{1,2} \simeq \omega_n(-\zeta \pm j1), \qquad |\zeta| \ll 1.0. \qquad (10.31)$$

To be more specific regarding ranges of ζ, Eq. (10.31) is a good approximation by the time ζ has decreased to 0.2. For this value of ζ the imaginary parts of the poles and their magnitudes are within 2% of their true values, as given by Eqs. (10.27); and the angles on the poles have less than 1% error.

By now the student should have realized that when ζ is unity the poles are simply

$$p_1 = p_2 = -\omega_n, \qquad \zeta = 1.0, \qquad (10.32)$$

and the system has a second-order pole. Such a system is said to be *critically damped* because any decrease in damping will cause an oscillatory response component if the system is excited.

For the range of ζ between one and infinity the poles are both real and negative, and the system is said to be *overdamped*. The geometric mean of the poles in Eq. (10.27a) is $-\omega_n$; consequently, one pole is between the origin and $-\omega_n$ and the other is between $-\omega_n$ and $-\infty$. In this range it is illuminating to apply the binomial expansion theorem to Eq. (10.27a), which yields

$$p_{1,2} = \omega_n \Big\{ -\zeta \pm \Big[(\zeta^2)^{1/2} + \tfrac{1}{2}(\zeta^2)^{-1/2}(-1)$$
$$+ \frac{\tfrac{1}{2}(-\tfrac{1}{2})}{2!} (\zeta^2)^{-3/2}(-1)^2 + \cdots \Big] \Big\}, \qquad \zeta > 1$$
$$= \omega_n \Big[-\zeta \pm \Big(\zeta - \frac{1}{2\zeta} - \frac{1}{8\zeta^3} - \frac{1}{16\zeta^5} - \cdots \Big) \Big], \qquad \zeta > 1. \qquad (10.33)$$

For large values of ζ (much, much larger than one) the infinite series converges rapidly, and the poles are approximately

$$p_1 \simeq -\frac{\omega_n}{2\zeta}, \qquad \zeta \gg 1.0 \tag{10.34a}$$

and

$$p_2 \simeq -2\zeta\omega_n, \qquad \zeta \gg 1.0. \tag{10.34b}$$

These approximations are within about 1% of their true value, as given by Eq. (10.27a), when $\zeta = 5$.

Figure 10.2 graphically summarizes the foregoing results by showing the locus of the roots of the quadratic as ζ is varied. Fig. 10.2(d) illustrates the

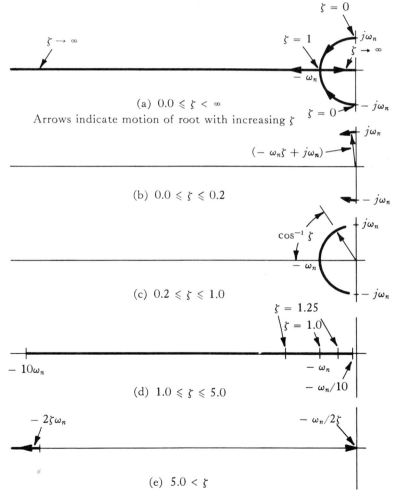

Fig. 10.2 *Root locus of $p^2 + 2\zeta\omega_n + \omega_n^2$ as a function of ζ.*

only range of ζ where Eq. (10.27a) needs to be used to determine the roots. For the remaining values of ζ, the roots can be easily obtained as shown in the figure.

So far nothing has been said about the numerator, $P(p)$, in Eq. (10.26). Of course, the numerator does not contribute any exponential terms to the response, but it does affect the magnitudes of the exponential terms and the magnitude and phase of the frequency response. If the numerator is also a quadratic, the foregoing methods apply in locating the zeros; but the terminology does not apply. *The zeros do not affect the frequencies or the damping coefficients. The zeros do affect the associated magnitudes and phase angles.*

To gain more insight into the effects of the zeros, let us investigate various system functions for Fig. 10.3, a series *R-L-C* network. For this network

$$Y(p) = \frac{I(p)}{V(p)}$$

$$= \frac{1}{Z(p)}$$

$$= \frac{1}{R + pL + \dfrac{1}{pC}}$$

$$= \frac{1}{L} \frac{p}{p^2 + \dfrac{R}{L} p + \dfrac{1}{LC}} \qquad (10.35a)$$

$$H_{V_R}(p) = \frac{V_R(p)}{V(p)}$$

$$= \frac{I(p)Z_R(p)}{V(p)}$$

$$= Y(p)R$$

$$= \frac{R}{L} \frac{p}{p^2 + \dfrac{R}{L} p + \dfrac{1}{LC}} \qquad (10.35b)$$

$$H_{V_L}(p) = Y(p)Z_L(p)$$

$$= \frac{p^2}{p^2 + \dfrac{R}{L} p + \dfrac{1}{LC}}, \qquad (10.35c)$$

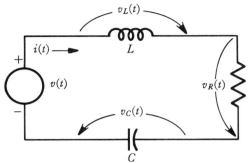

Fig. 10.3 *A simple second-order system.*

and

$$H_{V_C}(p) = Y(p)Z_C(p)$$

$$= \frac{1}{LC}\frac{1}{p^2 + \dfrac{R}{L}p + \dfrac{1}{LC}}. \tag{10.35d}$$

Since

$$\omega_n = \frac{1}{\sqrt{LC}}, \tag{10.36a}$$

and

$$\zeta = \frac{R}{2}\sqrt{\frac{C}{L}} \tag{10.36b}$$

for each of the system functions, we can say that ω_n and ζ are characteristics of the system. On the other hand, the zeros are characteristics of the system function chosen, as is the multiplier.

To illustrate the effects of the zeros, the magnitude and the angle of the frequency response of each system function are shown in Fig. 10.4 when ζ equals 0.2. Here we see that each system function has certain distinct characteristics of its own. For example, although each system function peaks in the vicinity of ω_n (because of the pole near $j\omega_n$) the functions do peak at different frequencies (because of the different zeros). Thus, if we define a *peak frequency* at which the magnitude of a system function is maximum, it would be a characteristic of the system function chosen and not a unique property of the system itself. Similarly, *zero-phase-shift frequency* can be defined only after a system function is selected from the entire set of system functions available in a given system.

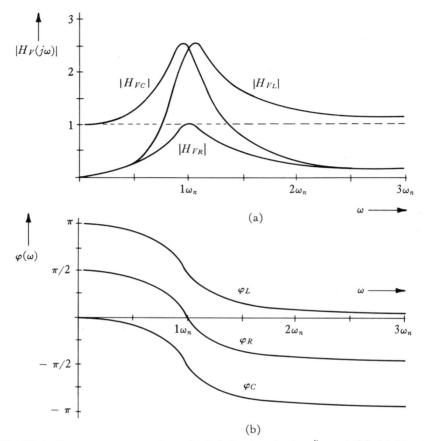

Fig. 10.4 *Frequency response for series R-L-C network when ζ equals 0.2. (a) Magnitude. (b) Phase shift.*

The possibility exists that one could define a peak frequency and a zero-phase-shift frequency for a particular system function such as the impedance or admittance at the input terminals. The second of these is often called the *resonant frequency*, or that finite nonzero frequency of steady-state operation at which the sinusoidal input quantities are in phase. An equivalent definition, which makes the resonant frequency a system characteristic, is that finite nonzero frequency of steady-state operation at which the average kinetic (magnetic) energy equals the average potential (electric) energy. But, alas, there are other definitions of resonant frequency that are almost, but not quite, equivalent to the foregoing. For example, it is not uncommon to consider what we have called peak frequency as marking a resonant condition and, conversely, to refer to the frequency at which there is a minimum in the system function magnitude as marking an antiresonant condition. Hence, in order to avoid ambiguity in our discussions, we will generally focus our attention on ζ and ω_n, which are well defined and mean the same to everyone, and explicitly describe any other frequency in whatever manner seems appropriate.

Other uses for ω_n and ζ may now be easily made apparent to the student. Additional usefulness of ω_n is indicated in Fig. 10.4, where the curves are drawn for only one value of ζ. In that figure the peaking and the maximum rate of change in phase shift occurred at or near ω_n.

Another useful property of the parameter ζ is that it is an indication of the heights of the peaks, the sharpness of the peaks, the closeness of the peaks to ω_n, and the slope of the phase-shift curve at ω_n. To illustrate, the frequency response of the admittance of the series *R-L-C* network, Eq. (10.35a), is shown in Fig. 10.5 for various values of ζ; and it should be noted that *the maximum magnitude and the zero phase angle occur at ω_n because of the simple zero at the origin.*

Another second-order system is shown in Fig. 10.6. For this circuit we will investigate only the impedance of the input terminals, which is

$$Z(p) = \frac{Z_1(p)Z_2(p)}{Z_1(p) + Z_2(p)}$$

$$= \frac{(R + pL)\left(\dfrac{1}{Cp}\right)}{R + pL + \dfrac{1}{Cp}}$$

$$= \frac{1}{C}\frac{p + \dfrac{R}{L}}{p^2 + \dfrac{R}{L}p + \dfrac{1}{LC}}. \tag{10.37}$$

The system function has the same ω_n and ζ as the series *R-L-C* circuit, Eqs. (10.36); but the numerator is different from any of those in Eqs. (10.35). Thus, while we should expect sharp peaking in the frequency response near ω_n whenever ζ is small, there should be some differences because of the zero at $-2\zeta\omega_n$. A plot of the magnitude of the impedance is given in Fig. 10.7, and it should be noted that the maximum magnitude occurs near ω_n for the small ζ's. This peak can be shown to be located at

$$\omega_m = \omega_n[(1 + 8\zeta^2)^{1/2} - 4\zeta^2]^{1/2}, \tag{10.38}$$

which is within 1 % of ω_n when ζ is 0.2 or less.

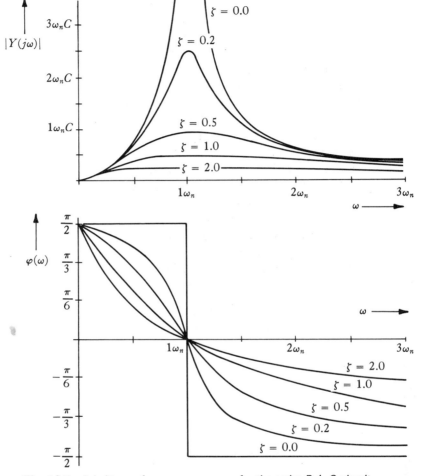

Fig. 10.5 *Admittance frequency response for the series R-L-C circuit.*

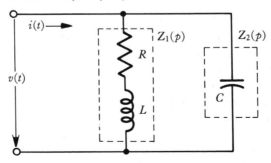

Fig. 10.6 *R-L-C parallel circuit.*

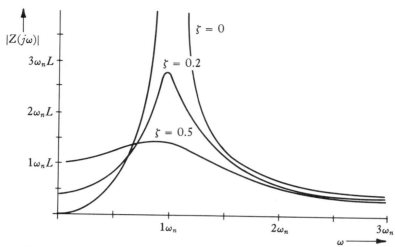

Fig. 10.7 *Impedance frequency response for the R-L-C parallel circuit.*

Investigation of the phase shift shows that zero phase angle, or unity power factor, occurs at yet another frequency which is

$$\omega_u = \omega_n(1 - 4\zeta^2)^{1/2} \tag{10.39}$$

and which represents an error of about 8 % of true ω_n when ζ is 0.2.

It is important to note that ω_n, ω_m, and ω_u are three distinct frequencies in this example because we no longer have a simple zero at the origin. Of course as ζ decreases, the zero $(-2\zeta\omega_n)$ moves toward the origin; and ω_m and ω_u approach ω_n.

An example of a second-order mechanical system is the pendulum. In this system the kinetic energy the pendulum bob possesses because of its motion is changed to potential energy because of its displacement from its lowest position, followed by an exchange of energy in the opposite direction. In practice, the objective of such a system is often to sustain oscillation of a constant frequency with a minimum amount of input energy. Thus, ζ is made as small as possible by minimizing the friction and the periodically applied force is synchronized so that the pendulum can operate at its natural frequency, which is near ω_n.

The suspension system of an automobile provides another example of an oscillating system. Here again the kinetic energy in the masses of the vehicle is changed to potential energy due to compression or elongation of the springs and vice-versa. The objectives in the design of this system are quite the opposite of that of the pendulum. Shock absorbers serving as dampers or " mechanical resistors " are deliberately added to the system to provide overdamping. The quality of the shock absorbers can be checked by jumping on the bumper with a periodic motion which will establish an oscillation and then observing the decay of the oscillations after jumping off the bumper. Note that the jumping frequency must be right or oscillations do not result. When the shock absorbers become worn, the automobile acts much like a pendulum when traveling on a highway where a poor job of paving has resulted in periodic, equally spaced, bumps. If the speed of travel is such that the bumps occur at the natural frequency of the system, the resulting oscillations can become great enough to cause loss of control.

10.5 HIGHER-ORDER SYSTEMS

Generally a higher-order system will, if underdamped, possess one complex pair of poles which will dominate. Its system function may be partially expanded as

$$H(p) = \frac{P(p)}{Q(p)}$$

$$= \frac{P(p)}{(p^2 + 2\zeta\omega_n p + \omega_n^2)Q_1(p)}$$

$$= \frac{P_1(p)}{Q_1(p)} + \frac{Ap + B}{p^2 + 2\zeta\omega_n p + \omega_n^2}. \tag{10.40}$$

The second term in this expression is that part of the system that acts as a simple second-order system. The first term is the remainder of the system having poles which are the zeros of

$$Q_1(p) = \frac{Q(p)}{p^2 + 2\zeta\omega_n p + \omega_n^2},$$

or all the system poles except the dominant complex pair. Often these poles are far enough distant from the origin, compared to the dominant complex pair, that their effects die out very quickly; and the oscillations observed are after a very short time primarily the contribution of the second-order component.

We must recognize, however, that systems can exist with two or more complex pairs of such values that no one can be said to dominate. It is useless, then, to attempt to assign values of ζ and ω_n which characterize the whole system;

and a set of the values must be assigned to each complex pair. For example, a system with two such complex pairs must take the form

$$H(p) = \frac{P(p)}{Q(p)}$$

$$= \frac{P(p)}{Q_1(p)(p^2 + 2\zeta_1\omega_{n1}p + \omega_{n1}^2)(p^2 + 2\zeta_2\omega_{n2}p + \omega_{n2}^2)}$$

$$= \frac{P_1(p)}{Q_1(p)} + \frac{A_1p + B_1}{p^2 + 2\zeta_1\omega_{n1}p + \omega_{n1}^2} + \frac{A_2p + B_2}{p^2 + 2\zeta_2\omega_{n2}p + \omega_{n2}^2}. \quad (10.41)$$

Thus, we add two second-order systems, each with its own set of parameters, to the remainder of the system.

10.6 BANDWIDTH

As has been apparent from our study of steady-state responses to sine waves, physical systems do not respond equally to all frequencies of the forcing function. In the second-order systems, for example, the response was very high near ω_n for small-ζ circuits, but dropped off very rapidly as the frequency became different from ω_n. On the other hand, large-ζ circuits did not respond so greatly at ω_n, but neither did the response drop off so rapidly as the frequency changed from ω_n. If one were to measure the frequency range over which the response exceeded some specified percentage of its maximum value, he would find this range to be much greater for the large-ζ case than for the small-ζ case, even though the sensitivity of the latter to changes in frequency near ω_n is much greater. The large-ζ circuit is consequently said to possess a wider *bandwidth* than the small-ζ circuit.

However, not all systems have their most sensitive regions, or peak responses, at some nonzero finite frequency as does the tuned circuit discussed above. For example, the admittance of the series $R\text{-}L$ circuit is maximum at zero frequency, or has a *low-pass* characteristic. On the other hand, the admittance of the series $R\text{-}C$ circuit is greatest when the frequency is greatest; and it has a *high-pass* characteristic. These are different from the *band-pass* characteristic of the series $R\text{-}L\text{-}C$ admittance.

A general definition of bandwidth may be stated as follows:

> The bandwidth, B, of a system is that range of frequencies over which the magnitude of the frequency response exceeds a specified fraction of some value, occurring within the frequency range, used as a reference.

The fraction specified depends on the application and the performance specifications which go with it, but the most common fraction is that corresponding to the *half-power point* or the *three-db point*.

In linear systems, average power is invariably in proportion to the square of a response variable times the dissipative parameter. For example,

$$P = \begin{cases} V^2 G & \text{for voltage responses} \\ I^2 R & \text{for current responses} \\ V^2 D & \text{for velocity responses} \\ F^2/D & \text{for force responses} \end{cases} \tag{10.42}$$

where V, I, V, and F are the rms values of voltage, current, velocity, and force respectively. In other words, for the arbitrary steady-state sinusoidal response whose phasor value is $\mathbf{X}$ working into dissipative element K, the dissipated power is

$$P = X^2 K. \tag{10.43}$$

If the phasor value of the forcing function is $\mathbf{F}$ at frequency ω, the frequency response is

$$H(j\omega) = \mathbf{H} = \frac{\mathbf{X}}{\mathbf{F}}, \tag{10.44}$$

and

$$|H(j\omega)| = \frac{X}{F}. \tag{10.45}$$

The ratio of the dissipated powers at ω_a and ω_b, when the forcing function has a constant rms value of F, is

$$\frac{P_a}{P_b} = \frac{X_a^2 K}{X_b^2 K}$$

$$= \frac{X_a^2}{X_b^2}$$

$$= \frac{(X_a/F)^2}{(X_b/F)^2}$$

$$= \frac{|H(j\omega_a)|^2}{|H(j\omega_b)|^2}. \tag{10.46}$$

It has become customary in many circles of electrical engineering to express such power ratios in *decibels*. Historically this is a recognition of the fact that the human ear responds to sound power logarithmically; and the decibel, or db, power gain is defined as

$$D_{ab} = 10 \log_{10} \frac{P_a}{P_b},\qquad (10.47\text{a})$$

or, from Eq. (10.46), as

$$D_{ab} = 10 \log_{10} \frac{X_a^2}{X_b^2}$$

$$= 20 \log_{10} \frac{X_a}{X_b} \text{ (db).}\qquad (10.47\text{b})$$

From Eq. (10.46) this is also

$$D_{ab} = 20 \log_{10} \frac{|H(j\omega_a)|}{|H(j\omega_b)|}.\qquad (10.47\text{c})$$

Sometimes the decibel is used as an absolute measure of power by expressing a given power as the ratio it makes with the reference power of 1 mW, which was originally taken as the lowest sound power detectable by the human ear. Such power would be designated in *dbm*, or the *power above 1 mW*.

Now let us return to the half-power criterion for bandwidth. If the power at ω_c is one-half the reference power, P_R, occurring at ω_R, then by Eq. (10.46)

$$\frac{P_c}{P_R} = \frac{|H(j\omega_c)|^2}{|H(j\omega_R)|^2} = \frac{X_c^2}{X_R^2} = \tfrac{1}{2},\qquad (10.48)$$

from which we get

$$|H(j\omega_c)| = \frac{1}{\sqrt{2}} |H(j\omega_R)|,\qquad (10.49\text{a})$$

and

$$X_c = \frac{1}{\sqrt{2}} X_R.\qquad (10.49\text{b})$$

From Eqs. (10.47c) and (10.49a) the decibel change involved here is

$$D_{cR} = 20 \log_{10} \frac{|H(j\omega_c)|}{|H(j\omega_R)|}$$

$$= 20 \log_{10} \frac{1}{\sqrt{2}}$$

$$= -10 \log_{10} 2$$

$$= -3.01 \simeq -3 \text{ db.}\qquad (10.50)$$

Thus, the power is down approximately 3 db at the half-power point. This has given rise to the alternative designation of this point as the 3-*db point*.

Applications of these ideas to the three common systems, with simple examples, follow.

A Low-Pass System

For this system a variable-frequency forcing function having a constant rms value will cause maximum power dissipation at zero frequency. As the frequency of the forcing function is increased, the dissipated power will decrease. At some frequency ω_c the power will be half the maximum power. Consequently, using zero frequency as reference and half power as our bandwidth criterion,

$$\omega_c = \text{Bandwidth of } L\text{-}P \text{ System.} \qquad (10.51)$$

As an example of a low-pass system, consider the power dissipated by an *R-L* circuit. Equation (10.43) becomes

$$P = I^2 R,$$

and Eq. (10.45) is

$$|Y(j\omega)| = \frac{I}{V}.$$

Thus, the power ratio of Eq. (10.48) is a ratio of the square of admittance magnitudes, and the half-power point, ω_c, is where

$$|Y(j\omega_c)| = \frac{1}{\sqrt{2}} |Y(j0)|.$$

As

$$Y(p) = \frac{1}{R + pL}$$

$$= \frac{1}{L} \frac{1}{p + R/L}, \qquad (10.52)$$

we can write

$$\left| \frac{1}{L} \frac{1}{\frac{R}{L} + j\omega_c} \right| = \frac{1}{\sqrt{2}} \left| \frac{1}{L} \frac{1}{\frac{R}{L} + j0} \right|, \qquad (10.53)$$

which has the solution

$$\omega_c = \frac{R}{L} \text{ rad/sec.} \qquad (10.54)$$

Hence, the bandwidth is

$$B = \frac{R}{L} = \frac{1}{T},$$ (10.55)

where T is the time constant of the R-L circuit.

The magnitude plot of the admittance is shown in Fig. 10.8.

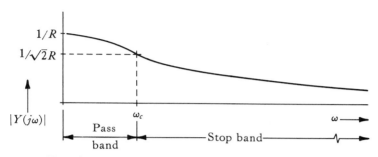

Fig. 10.8 *The low-pass series R-L admittance function.*

A High-Pass System

We will rapidly cover this system and leave some work for the student. For our example, we will use the series R-C circuit, letting the reference frequency be measured as

$$\omega_R \to \infty.$$ (10.56)

For this system, then,

$$|Y(j\omega_c)| = \frac{1}{\sqrt{2}}|Y(j\infty)|,$$

which gives

$$\omega_c = \frac{1}{RC} = \frac{1}{T} \text{ rad/sec.}$$ (10.57)

Here the pass band is from ω_c to infinity (infinite bandwidth), and the low end of the frequency spectrum from zero to ω_c is called the *width of the stop-band*. This frequency response is plotted in Fig. 10.9.

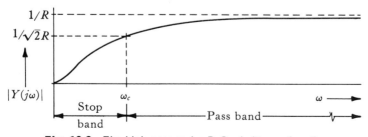

Fig. 10.9 *The high-pass series R-C admittance function.*

A Band-Pass System

This type of system has maximum power dissipation at some nonzero finite frequency; and there are two half-power points, one on either side of the maximum. Hence, we set

$$\omega_c = \begin{cases} \omega_1 & \text{at the lower half-power point} \\ \omega_2 & \text{at the upper half-power point.} \end{cases} \tag{10.58}$$

For an example we will consider the series R-L-C circuit. Once again the three-db points occur when

$$|Y(j\omega_c)| = \frac{1}{\sqrt{2}} |Y(j\omega)|_{max}.$$

In Fig. 10.5 this admittance is seen to peak at ω_n. This fact and Eq. (10.35a) provide the alternative form

$$\left| \frac{1}{L} \frac{j\omega_c}{\omega_n^2 - \omega_c^2 + j2\zeta\omega_n\omega_c} \right| = \frac{1}{\sqrt{2}} \left| \frac{1}{L} \frac{j\omega_n}{\omega_n^2 - \omega_n^2 + j\zeta\omega_n\omega_n} \right|,$$

$$= \frac{1}{\sqrt{2}} \frac{1}{L} \frac{1}{2\zeta\omega_n},$$

which has the solution

$$\omega_c = \omega_n(\sqrt{1 + \zeta^2} \pm \zeta). \tag{10.59a}$$

Equation (10.58) then gives the two values of ω_c

$$\omega_1 = \omega_n(\sqrt{1 + \zeta^2} - \zeta), \tag{10.59b}$$

and

$$\omega_2 = \omega_n(\sqrt{1 + \zeta^2} + \zeta). \tag{10.59c}$$

The pass band is said to be from ω_1 to ω_2; therefore, the bandwidth is

$$B = \omega_2 - \omega_1$$

$$= 2\zeta\omega_n, \tag{10.60}$$

with ω_n being the geometric mean of the cutoff frequencies. This is illustrated in Fig. 10.10.

We now return briefly to the time-honored circuit parameter, Q, which has already been introduced in Art. 5.11. It has long been the custom of communication engineers to indicate the quality of their band-pass systems by the sharpness of tuning, or narrowness of the pass band. This quality is traditionally indicated by the quality factor, or the Q, of the system, which we shall define as

$$Q = \frac{\omega_n}{B}. \tag{10.61a}$$

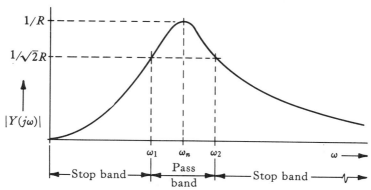

Fig. 10.10 *The band-pass series R-L-C admittance function.*

This definition contains Eq. (5.105), previously encountered, as a special case, and we see that Eqs. (5-102) and Eqs. (10-59) are equivalent.

In the series R-L-C or parallel G-L-C circuits, where $\omega_m = \omega_n$, this is equivalent to

$$Q = \frac{\text{average stored energy}}{\text{energy loss per radian}}\Bigg|_{\omega = \omega_n}, \qquad (10.61b)$$

which is often taken as the defining relationship for Q, rather than Eq. (10.61a). In the special cases just cited, where there is a single zero at the origin,

$$Q = \frac{1}{2\zeta}. \qquad (10.62)$$

This expression also holds to a good approximation for the second-order system with no finite zeros as well as for the second-order system with a zero very close to the origin compared to the nearest pole.

The example we have been considering is that of a narrow-band system used in practice to provide great frequency selectivity by having a system respond freely to signal frequencies in the very close neighborhood of a specified frequency with very little response to frequencies outside this neighborhood. Such systems may be either series or parallel, or combinations thereof, but are nearly always high Q or small ζ for good selectivity.

On the other hand, band-pass systems which are wide-band also form a large class of systems whose practical applications and associated problems are quite the opposite of those of the narrow-band system. An example of such a system lies in the circuit of Fig. 10.11, which is very similar to the small-signal equivalent circuit of the capacitor-coupled vacuum tube amplifier stage.

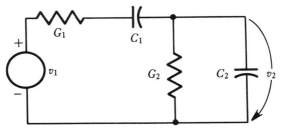

Fig. 10.11   *A wide-band system.*

By setting

$$G_{sh} = G_1 + G_2, \qquad (10.63)$$

it develops that the system function relating the response $v_2(t)$ to the forcing function $v_1(t)$ is

$$H_V(p) = \frac{V_2(p)}{V_1(p)} = \frac{G_1}{C_2} \frac{p}{p^2 + \left(\dfrac{G_{sh}}{C_2} + \dfrac{G_1}{C_1}\right)p + \dfrac{G_1}{C_1}\dfrac{G_2}{C_2}}. \qquad (10.64)$$

A typical set of parameters for circuits of this type might be the following:

$$G_1 = 3 \ \mu(\Omega^{-1}) \qquad C_1 = 0.02 \ \mu F$$
$$G_2 = 2 \ \mu(\Omega^{-1}) \qquad C_2 = 20 \ \mu\mu F.$$

For this second-order system we calculate

$$\omega_n = \sqrt{15(10^6)} = 3.87 \times 10^3 \ \text{rad/sec}$$

$$\zeta = \frac{0.25(10^6)}{2(3.87)10^3} = 32.3.$$

Because ζ is larger than five, we can use the pole locations as given in Eqs. (10.34) to give

$$H_V(p) \simeq K_T \frac{p}{\left(p + \dfrac{\omega_n}{2\zeta}\right)(p + 2\zeta\omega_n)}, \qquad (10.65)$$

where

$$K_T = \frac{G_1}{C_2}. \qquad (10.66)$$

The pole-zero plot of this function is sketched in Fig. 10.12(a).

The magnitude of the pole at $-2\zeta\omega_n$ is $4\zeta^2$, which in this case equals 4173, times the magnitude of the pole at $-\omega_n/2\zeta$. It is convenient to consider the

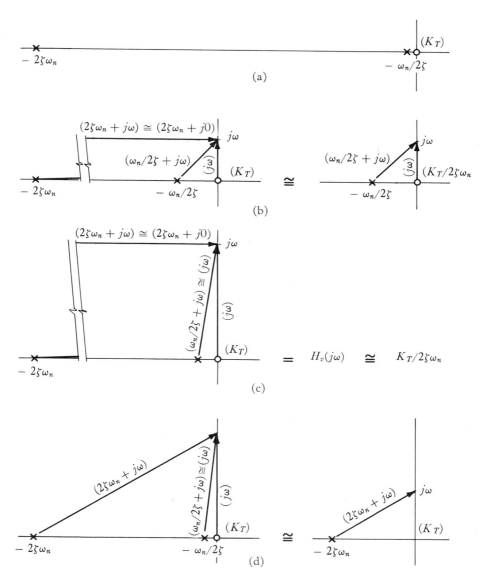

Fig. 10.12 *The p-z plot of Eq. (10.61) and various approximations. (a) Actual p-z plot. (b) Low-frequency equivalent. (c) Mid-frequency equivalent. (d) High-frequency equivalent.*

frequency response for different ranges of ω. Starting with the lowest frequencies, we use Fig. 10.12(b), which is the same pole-zero plot shown in (a) of the figure with the neighborhood of the origin greatly expanded. In this frequency region the distance on the complex plane from $-2\zeta\omega_n$ to the $j\omega$-axis remains essentially constant in magnitude and angle, and the $j\omega + 2\zeta\omega_n$ term in $H_V(j\omega)$ can be written as

$$j\omega + 2\zeta\omega_n \simeq 2\zeta\omega_n, \qquad \omega \ll 2\zeta\omega_n. \tag{10.67}$$

Consequently,

$$H_V(j\omega) \simeq \frac{K_T j\omega}{2\zeta\omega_n\left(j\omega + \dfrac{\omega_n}{2\zeta}\right)}, \qquad \omega \ll 2\zeta\omega_n. \tag{10.68}$$

The next range of frequencies where approximations can simplify the frequency response function is illustrated in Fig. 10.12(c). In this frequency band Eq. (10.67) still applies; but the frequencies are large enough that the vector distance from the pole at $-\omega_n/2\zeta$ to the point being considered on the $j\omega$-axis essentially cancels the distance from the zero at the origin to the point in question; that is

$$j\omega + \frac{\omega_n}{2\zeta} \simeq j\omega, \qquad \omega \gg \frac{\omega_n}{2\zeta}. \tag{10.69}$$

Therefore, the system function is simplified to

$$H_V(j\omega) \simeq \frac{K_T}{2\zeta\omega_n} = \frac{G_1}{G_2}, \qquad \frac{\omega_n}{2\zeta} \ll \omega \ll 2\zeta\omega_n. \tag{10.70}$$

The last range of frequencies to be considered is shown in Fig. 10.12(d). In this range the $j\omega + 2\zeta\omega_n$ term is no longer constant; but Eq. (10.69) still applies; that is, the pole close to the origin cancels the effects of the zero at the origin. The system function then becomes

$$H_V(j\omega) \simeq \frac{K_T}{j\omega + 2\zeta\omega_n}, \qquad \omega \gg \frac{\omega_n}{2\zeta}. \tag{10.71}$$

In effect, what we have done is to consider three approximations to the circuit shown in Fig. 10.11. These approximations are given in Fig. 10.13, and the student should calculate the system function for each circuit shown and compare the results to Eqs. (10.68), (10.69), and (10.71). The student is cautioned to remember that these approximations are valid only when the magnitude of one pole is a great deal larger than that of the other, as in the case when ζ is greater than about five.

The circuit in Fig. 10.13(a) is a high-pass circuit because the coupling capacitor, C, impedes the low-frequency currents while offering little impedance to the high-frequency currents. The system function for this circuit, Eq. (10.68),

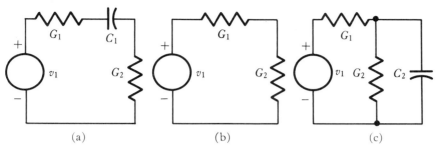

Fig. 10.13 *Equivalent circuits for Fig. 10.11 when ζ is greater than five. (a) Low-frequency equivalent. (b) Mid-frequency equivalent. (c) High-frequency equivalent.*

has the high-pass magnitude characteristic shown in Fig. 10.9; and the frequency at which the function is 0.707 of its maximum value can be shown to be

$$\omega_c = \omega_1 = \frac{\omega_n}{2\zeta}.$$ (10.72a)

This is a half-power frequency from the standpoint that the second-stage amplifier, represented by G_2 and C_2, receives one-half of the maximum power that is available at the higher frequencies, assuming that $\mathbf{V}_1$ is a constant.

The circuit in Fig. 10.13(c) is a low-pass circuit because the shunting capacitor, C_2, provides a low impedance path for high-frequency source currents. The system function for this circuit, Eq. (10.71), has the low-pass magnitude characteristic illustrated in Fig. 10.8, and a half-power frequency of

$$\omega_c = \omega_2 = 2\zeta\omega_n.$$ (10.72b)

The high-pass and low-pass characteristics are combined in Fig. 10.14 to show the over-all frequency response. The semilog coordinate system was used

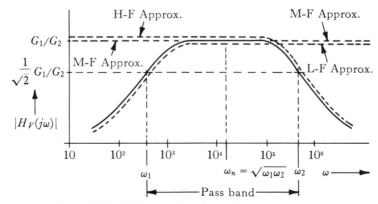

Fig. 10.14 *Wide-band band-pass frequency response.*

in order that high-frequency and low-frequency effects may be shown together on a reasonable scale.

The bandwidth of this response is clearly bounded by the lower and upper half-power points given in Eqs. (10.72); that is,

$$B = 2\zeta\omega_n - \frac{\omega_n}{2\zeta}$$

$$= \omega_n\left(2\zeta - \frac{1}{2\zeta}\right)$$

$$\simeq 2\zeta\omega_n, \qquad \zeta \gg 1. \tag{10.73}$$

This provides a pass band in the order of hundreds of kilohertz compared to the few hertz possible in the band-pass system considered previously. Notice that this is a very low-Q system.

10.7 EFFECT OF BANDWIDTH ON TRANSIENT RESPONSE

Consideration of the wide-band example in the previous article can lead to some qualitative conclusions about the interrelationships between transient response and system bandwidth.

First of all, a glance at the p-z plot of Fig. 10.12(a) leads to some immediate conclusions. For example, if the system is excited by a step function the zero at the origin is cancelled by the pole introduced by the step function, leaving only the poles at $-2\zeta\omega_n = -\omega_2$ and $-\omega_n/2\zeta = -\omega_1$. The coefficients in the partial fraction expansion are then equal, but opposite in sign. However, the exponential due to $-2\zeta\omega_n$ will decay very rapidly, showing its effects very near the origin, whereas the exponential due to $-\omega_n/2\zeta$ will decay very slowly, taking a long time to show its effects. Furthermore, in a more complex system, any pole in the neighborhood of $-\omega_2$ will cause behavior similar to that due to $-2\zeta\omega_n$ while any pole in the neighborhood of $-\omega_1$ will cause behavior similar to that due to $-\omega_n/2\zeta$. From these observations we may conclude that

"The largeness of ω_2 determines the rapidity of system response to abrupt disturbances while the smallness of ω_1 determines the duration of trailing effects following the disturbance."

Getting a little more specific, we observe that Eqs. (10.64) and (10.65) may be written

$$H_V(p) = K_T \frac{p}{(p + \omega_1)(p + \omega_2)}. \tag{10.74}$$

Applying the step function

$$v_2(t) = Vu(t) \tag{10.75}$$

to the system results in the operational form of the response

$$V_2(p) = K_T \frac{V}{(p + \omega_1)(p + \omega_2)}$$

$$= \frac{K_T V}{\omega_2 - \omega_1} \left[\frac{1}{p + \omega_1} - \frac{1}{p + \omega_2} \right]$$

$$= \frac{K_T V}{B} \left[\frac{1}{p + \omega_1} - \frac{1}{p + \omega_2} \right]. \tag{10.76}$$

The transient response to this step function is thus

$$v_2(t) = \frac{K_T V}{B} \left[e^{-\omega_1 t} - e^{-\omega_2 t} \right] u(t)$$

$$= \frac{K_T V}{B} e^{-\omega_1 t} \left[1 - e^{-(\omega_2 - \omega_1)t} \right] u(t)$$

$$= \frac{K_T V}{B} e^{-\omega_1 t} \left[1 - e^{-Bt} \right] u(t), \tag{10.77}$$

where from Eqs. (10.64), (10.66), and (10.73) it may be shown that

$$\frac{K_T}{B} = \frac{G_1/G_2}{1 - \dfrac{\omega_1}{\omega_2}}, \tag{10.78a}$$

or

$$\frac{K_T}{B} \simeq G_1/G_2, \qquad \omega_2 \gg \omega_1 \qquad \text{or} \qquad \zeta \gg 1. \tag{10.78b}$$

In Table 10.1, responses under several different cutoff conditions are re-corded. These values result from application of Eqs. (10.77) and (10.78). The results, for relatively narrow band cases, are shown in Fig. 10.15.

Consideration of these results leads to the following conclusions for this system response to abrupt changes in input signal.

1. The greater the upper bound of the pass band is, the shorter will be the *rise time* for the response.
2. The smaller the lower bound of the pass band is, the longer will be the *fall time* of the response.
3. The wider the pass band is, the more nearly the response will approach the ideal of having a form identical to the input signal.

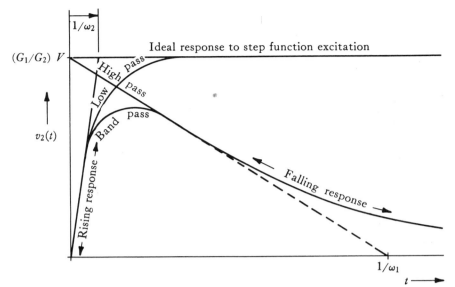

Fig. 10.15 *Illustrating effects of pass bands on step function response.*

TABLE 10.1   EFFECT OF BANDWIDTH CRITERIA ON TRANSIENT RESPONSE

System condition	Criterion	Response $v_0(t)$ when $v_g(t) = Vu(t)$
Ideal	$\omega_1 = 0$ $B \to \infty$	$\dfrac{G_1}{G_2} Vu(t)$
Low-pass	$\omega_1 = 0$ $B = \omega_2$	$\dfrac{G_1}{G_2} V(1 - e^{-Bt})u(t)$
High-pass	$\omega_1 \neq 0$ $B \to \infty$	$\dfrac{G_1}{G_2} Ve^{-\omega_1 t}u(t)$
Band-pass (Wide)	$\omega_1 \neq 0$ $B = \omega_2 - \omega_1$	$\dfrac{G_1}{G_2} Ve^{-\omega_1 t}(1 - e^{-Bt})u(t)$

It should be obvious that the highest-quality response results from the shortest rise time and the longest fall time. This becomes extremely important, for example, in video amplifiers used in television, where the signal must often change from " black " level to " white " level quickly (fast rise time) without fading (slow fall time) during a complete line on the raster.

If one considers a higher-ordered wide-band system, he comes to the conclusion that the qualitative interrelationships between bandwidth and transient response discovered here for the second-order system will hold in general.

10.8 ASYMPTOTIC FREQUENCY PLOTS

Let us return to the frequency response function given in Eq. (10.23). In terms of ζ and ω_n this function becomes

$$H(j\omega) = |H(j\omega)|e^{j\phi(\omega)} = \frac{K(j\omega + a)(j\omega + c)}{j\omega(j\omega + b)(\omega_n^2 - \omega^2 + j2\zeta\omega_n\omega)}. \qquad (10.79)$$

A rough sketch illustrating how the magnitude and angle vary with frequency can be quickly constructed by use of the pole-zero plot of Fig. 10.1. To obtain a more accurate magnitude plot requires determination of $H(j\omega)$ at many different values of ω, and for each value of frequency the magnitude and angle contributions of all poles and zeros must be calculated and combined by multiplication and division before $|H(j\omega)|$ and $\phi(\omega)$ are known.

This tedious process of multiplication and division may be circumvented by the use of logarithms, since multiplication and division are thereby replaced by addition and subtraction respectively. To be consistent with our previous use of logarithms in this chapter, we shall utilize the base of ten and will calculate the magnitude in terms of decibels, i.e.,

$$H_{\text{db}} = 20 \log_{10} |H(j\omega)|. \qquad (10.80)$$

Then we shall see how the results of a very few simple examples of $H(j\omega)$ can be combined to quickly yield results for more complicated examples, such as that of Eq. (10.23).

The Constant System Function

In this trivial example,

$$H(p) = K = \text{constant}, \qquad (10.81)$$

and Eq. (10.80) becomes

$$H_{\text{db}} = 20 \log_{10} K, \qquad (10.82)$$

and

$$\phi(\omega) = 0.$$

Singularities at the Origin

Suppose the *p-z* plot of $H(p)$ consists of just an *n*th order pole at the origin, or

$$H(p) = \frac{K}{p^n}, \qquad n = 1, 2, 3, \cdots. \tag{10.83}$$

Then

$$H(j\omega) = \frac{K}{(j\omega)^n}, \tag{10.83a}$$

and

$$H_{db} = 20 \log_{10} \left| \frac{K}{(j\omega)^n} \right| = 20 \log_{10} \frac{K}{\omega^n},$$

or

$$H_{db} = 20 \log_{10} K - 20 \log_{10} \omega^n$$
$$= 20 \log_{10} K - 20n \log_{10} \omega. \tag{10.84}$$

Let us now define the *decade* as

$$u = \log_{10} \omega, \tag{10.85}$$

so called because a ten-fold change in ω creates a unit change in u. Then Eq. (10.84) becomes

$$H_{db} = 20 \log_{10} K - 20nu = 20n[\log_{10} \sqrt[n]{K} - u]. \tag{10.86}$$

Obviously, H_{db}, plotted as a function of u, is a straight line with its

$$\text{slope} = -20n \text{ decibels/decade.} \tag{10.87}$$

Let us allow ourselves one more convenient definition:

$$\omega_o = \omega \,|_{H_{db}=0} = \sqrt[n]{K}, \tag{10.88a}$$

with its corresponding value in decades,

$$u_o = \log_{10} \omega_o = \log_{10} \sqrt[n]{K} = u \,|_{H_{db}=0}. \tag{10.88b}$$

These define the intercepts of H_{db} on the $\log_{10} \omega$ and u axes. Now Eq. (10.86) may be written

$$H_{db} = -20n(u - u_o), \tag{10.89}$$

which is a straight line with a slope of $-20n$ db/decade and an intercept of u_o decades from the origin ($u = 0$).

The phase shift function is

$$\phi(\omega) = \underline{/H(j\omega)} = \underline{/\frac{K}{(j\omega)^n}} = \underline{/\frac{K}{\omega^n e^{jn\pi/2}}}.$$

Thus,

$$\phi(\omega) = -n\frac{\pi}{2} \text{ for all } \omega. \tag{10.90}$$

Figure 10.16 shows the frequency plots for the constant system function previously mentioned and for system functions consisting solely of

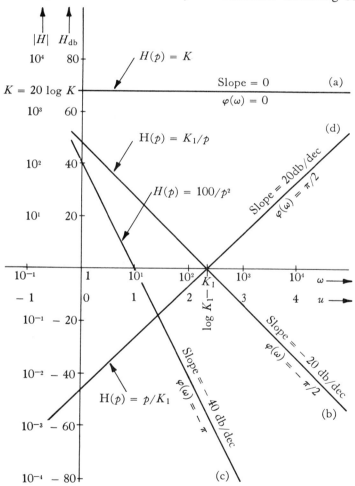

Fig. 10.16 *Logarithmic frequency responses for a constant H(p) and for functions with singularities at the origin.*

singularities (poles or zeros) at the origin. The obvious results for the constant are shown by curve (a). On the plots for $n = 1$ and $K = K_1$ in curve (b) and for $n = 2$ and $K = 100$ in curve (c), one can recognize Eqs. (10.84) and (10.89) as well as alternative forms for each. Each curve is also marked with the slope, indicated by Eq. (10.87), and the phase shift, indicated by Eq. (10.90).

TABLE 10.2 VARIABLES AND GRAPH COORDINATES RESULTING IN STRAIGHT LINE PLOTS FOR FREQUENCY RESPONSE FUNCTIONS WITH SINGULARITIES ONLY AT THE ORIGIN

Type of Plot	Graph Paper	Abscissa	Ordinate
H_{db} vs ω	Semilog	Linear	Logarithmic
H_{db} vs u	Rectilinear	Linear	Linear
$|H|$ vs ω	Log-log	Logarithmic	Logarithmic
$|H|$ vs u	Semilog	Logarithmic	Linear

A study of the equations and their graphs should make clear the entries in Table 10.2. The fourth entry, a plot of $|H|$ vs u on semilog paper, is seldom encountered in engineering literature but is included for completeness. The four possibilities result from a simple listing of the ways in which the two choices of independent variables in Fig. 10.16 can be paired off with the two choices of dependent variables.

Now consider the function consisting of an nth-order zero at the origin, which we shall write in the form

$$H(p) = Kp^n. \tag{10.91}$$

It is easy to show, in a manner similar to that for the nth-order pole, that the decibel value can be written as

$$H_{db} = 20 \log_{10} K + 20 \log_{10} \omega^n$$
$$= 20 \log_{10} K + 20n \log_{10} \omega, \tag{10.92}$$

or as

$$H_{db} = 20n(u - u_o). \tag{10.93}$$

In this expression

$$u_o = u \,|_{H_{db}=0} = \log_{10} \omega_o = \log_{10} \frac{1}{\sqrt[n]{K}}, \tag{10.94}$$

where

$$\omega_o = \frac{1}{\sqrt[n]{K}}. \tag{10.95}$$

Equations (10.92) and (10.93) are straight lines with

$$\text{slope} = +20n \text{ db/decade}, \tag{10.96}$$

intersecting the abscissa at ω_o (or u_o). In Fig. 10.16, curve (d) shows such a response with $n = 1$ and $K = 1/K_1$.

Real-Axis Singularities

Let us now study the system function whose *p-z* plot consists of simply a pole on the negative real axis:

$$H(p) = \frac{a}{p + a} \quad \frac{1}{1 + \dfrac{p}{a}}. \tag{10.97}$$

The frequency response is

$$H(j\omega) = \frac{a}{a + j\omega} = \frac{1}{1 + \dfrac{j\omega}{a}}, \tag{10.97a}$$

having the magnitude

$$|H(j\omega)| = \frac{1}{\left|1 + j\dfrac{\omega}{a}\right|} = \frac{1}{\sqrt{1 + \dfrac{\omega^2}{a^2}}}, \tag{10.97b}$$

and the angle

$$\phi(\omega) = -\tan^{-1}\frac{\omega}{a}. \tag{10.97c}$$

From Eq. (10.97b)

$$H_{db} = 20 \log_{10} \frac{1}{\sqrt{1 + \dfrac{\omega^2}{a^2}}} = -20 \log_{10}\sqrt{1 + \frac{\omega^2}{a^2}}. \tag{10.98}$$

It is extremely useful to note that Eq. (10.98) leads to

$$H_{db} = \begin{cases} 0, & \omega \ll a \\[2mm] -20 \log_{10}\sqrt{2} \simeq -3 \text{ db} & \omega = a \\[2mm] \left(-20 \log_{10}\dfrac{\omega}{a} = 20 \log_{10} a - 20 \log_{10} \omega\right) & \omega \gg a. \end{cases} \tag{10.99}$$

The decibel value thus is seen to correspond with the axis (zero db) for frequencies much less than the *corner frequency*, $\omega = a$. At frequencies much larger than the corner frequency, it corresponds with a straight line of -20 db/decade slope intercepting the zero-db line at $\omega = a$, as can be seen by comparing the third form of Eq. (10.99) with Eq. (10.84) after setting $K = a$ and $n = 1$. Another way of looking at it is that

$$H(p) \simeq \frac{a}{p}, \qquad |p| \gg a,$$

which is the same form, for large p, as the case of a pole at the origin. The equation form is perhaps more apparent when the result above is expressed in terms of decades after setting

$$u_a = \log_{10} a. \tag{10.100}$$

Then

$$H_{\mathrm{db}} = \begin{cases} 0, & u \ll u_a \\ -3 \text{ db}, & u = u_a \\ -20(u - u_a), & u \gg u_a. \end{cases} \tag{10.101}$$

Similarly, but more simply, Eq. (10.97c) leads to

$$\phi(\omega) = \begin{cases} 0, & \omega \ll a \quad (u \ll u_a) \\ -\dfrac{\pi}{4}, & \omega = a \quad (u = u_a) \\ -\dfrac{\pi}{2}, & \omega \gg a \quad (u \gg u_a), \end{cases} \tag{10.102}$$

and we have defined the asymptotes of the magnitude and angle for the very low frequencies and the very high frequencies. It is going to be very useful for us that the deviation of the frequency response magnitude from its asymptote occurs over a relatively small range of frequency and is of relatively small value. Thus the frequency response and its asymptotes coincide, or nearly do, over much of the total frequency range, and the two asymptotes may be combined into an approximation of the frequency response itself. This approximation may be stated as

$$H_{\mathrm{db}} \simeq \begin{cases} 0 & \omega < a \\ 20 \log_{10} a - 20 \log_{10} \omega, & \omega > a, \end{cases} \tag{10.103a}$$

or as

$$H_{db} \simeq \begin{cases} 0, & u < u_a \\ -20(u - u_a), & u > u_a. \end{cases} \qquad (10.103b)$$

A much cruder approximation is involved in a similar statement for the angle on the frequency response based on Eq. (10.102):

$$\phi(\omega) \simeq \begin{cases} 0, & \omega < a \quad (u < u_a) \\ -\dfrac{\pi}{2}, & \omega > a \quad (u > u_a). \end{cases} \qquad (10.104)$$

The above approximations, along with the actual values, are plotted as the curves marked (a) on Fig. 10.17. It is left as a student exercise to show that

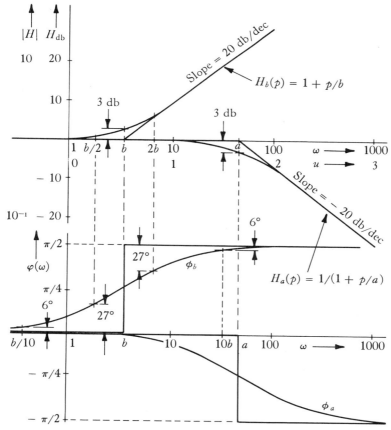

Fig. 10.17 *Logarithmic frequency responses for a real-axis pole and a real-axis zero.*

the errors between the actual curves and their asymptotic approximations one
decade and one octave (a doubling or halving of frequency) away from the
corner frequency are

$$
\text{error in } H_{\text{db}} \simeq
\begin{cases}
0 \text{ db}, & \omega < a/10 & [u < (u_a - 1)] \\
-1 \text{ db}, & \omega = a/2 & \\
-3 \text{ db}, & \omega = a & (u = u_a) \\
-1 \text{ db}, & \omega = 2a & \\
0 \text{ db}, & \omega > 10a & [u > (u_a + 1)]
\end{cases}
\tag{10.105a}
$$

$$
\text{error in } \phi(\omega) \simeq
\begin{cases}
-6°, & \omega = a/10 & (u = u_a - 1) \\
-27°, & \omega = a/2 & \\
+27°, & \omega = 2a & \\
+6°, & \omega = 10a & (u = u_a + 1).
\end{cases}
\tag{10.105b}
$$

It now becomes quite simple to very rapidly obtain a logarithmic frequency response curve which is quite accurate. The asymptote approximations are
rapidly drawn in with a straight edge and the easily-memorized errors of
Eqs. (10.105) are added back in to obtain points on the actual curve in that
frequency range containing the only significant deviation from the asymptotes.

Suppose the system function consists of a single real-axis zero so that it
takes the form

$$
H(p) = \frac{p + a}{a} = 1 + \frac{p}{a}.
\tag{10.106}
$$

Then

$$
H(j\omega) = 1 + \frac{j\omega}{a},
\tag{10.107}
$$

and it is easy to show that

$$
H_{\text{db}} =
\begin{cases}
0, & \omega \ll a \\
20 \log_{10} \sqrt{2} \simeq 3 \text{ db}, & \omega = a \\
20 \log_{10} \dfrac{\omega}{a} = -20 \log_{10} a + 20 \log_{10} \omega, & \omega \gg a,
\end{cases}
\tag{10.108}
$$

or

$$
H_{\text{db}} =
\begin{cases}
0, & u \ll u_a \\
3 \text{ db}, & u = u_a \\
20(u - u_a), & u \gg u_a,
\end{cases}
\tag{10.109}
$$

and that

$$\phi(\omega) = \begin{cases} 0, & \omega \ll a \quad (u \ll u_a) \\ +\dfrac{\pi}{4}, & \omega = a \quad (u = u_a) \\ +\dfrac{\pi}{2}, & \omega \gg a \quad (u \gg u_a). \end{cases}$$ (10.110)

Obviously, the result, for both magnitude and angle, is simply the negative of that for a pole in the same location as the given zero, so nothing more needs to be said. A typical example is included in Fig. 10.17 as the curve marked (b).

A Complex Pair of Singularities

The remaining type of singularity which we should study is the complex pole, or zero. Again we will consider a system function whose only singularity is of the type we wish to study; in this case

$$H(p) = \frac{\omega_n^2}{p^2 + 2\zeta\omega_n p + \omega_n^2} = \frac{1}{\left(\dfrac{p}{\omega_n}\right)^2 + 2\zeta\left(\dfrac{p}{\omega_n}\right) + 1}.$$ (10.111)

The frequency response is

$$H(j\omega) = \frac{1}{1 - \left(\dfrac{\omega}{\omega_n}\right)^2 + j2\zeta\left(\dfrac{\omega}{\omega_n}\right)}.$$ (10.112)

This leads to

$$H_{db} = -20 \log_{10} \left| 1 - \left(\frac{\omega}{\omega_n}\right)^2 + j2\zeta\frac{\omega}{\omega_n} \right|$$

$$= \begin{cases} 0, & \omega \ll \omega_n \\ -20 \log_{10} 2\zeta = 20 \log_{10} \dfrac{1}{2\zeta}, & \omega = \omega_n \\ -20 \log_{10} \left(\dfrac{\omega}{\omega_n}\right)^2 = 40 \log_{10} \omega_n - 40 \log_{10} \omega, & \omega \gg \omega_n, \end{cases}$$ (10.113)

or

$$H_{db} = \begin{cases} 0, & u \ll u_n \\ +20 \log_{10} \dfrac{1}{2\zeta}, & u = u_n \\ -40(u - u_n), & u \gg u_n, \end{cases}$$ (10.114)

where

$$u_n = \log_{10} \omega_n. \tag{10.115}$$

The asymptotic approximations for the amplitude in this case are

$$H_{db} \simeq \begin{cases} 0 & \omega < \omega_n \\ 40 \log_{10} \omega_n - 40 \log_{10} \omega, & \omega > \omega_n, \end{cases} \tag{10.116a}$$

or

$$H_{db} \simeq \begin{cases} 0, & u < u_n \\ 40(u - u_n), & u > u_n. \end{cases} \tag{10.116b}$$

The approximation above is plotted in Fig. 10.18, along with the actual plot for various values of the damping ratio. The most striking difference between this case and the previous one is that the deviation of the actual curve from the asymptotic approximation now depends on the damping ratio, ζ. It is left for the student to show that

$$\text{error in } H_{db} \simeq \begin{cases} 0, & \omega < 0.1\omega_n, & [u < (u_n - 1)] \\ 20 \log_{10} \dfrac{1}{2\zeta}, & \omega = \omega_n, & (u = u_n) \\ 0, & \omega > 10\omega_n, & [u > (u_n + 1)], \end{cases} \tag{10.117}$$

and it may also be occasionally helpful if he were to satisfy himself that

$$\text{error in } H_{db} = 20 \log_{10} \frac{1}{2\zeta\sqrt{1 - \zeta^2}}, \quad \omega = \omega_m, \quad 0 < \zeta < \frac{1}{\sqrt{2}}, \tag{10.118`}$$

where

$$\omega_m = \omega_n \sqrt{1 - 2\zeta^2}, \quad 0 < \zeta < \frac{1}{\sqrt{2}} \tag{10.119}$$

is the frequency at which the peak value occurs. Such peaking occurs only when $\zeta < 0.707$, because 0.707 is the largest damping ratio yielding real values for ω_m in Eq. (10.119).

The phase angle is

$$\phi(\omega) = -\tan^{-1} \frac{2\zeta\omega_n\omega}{\omega_n^2 - \omega^2}, \tag{10.120}$$

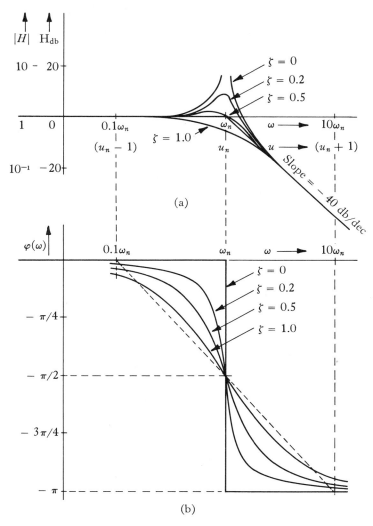

Fig. 10.18 *Actual and asymptote plots for a complex pair of poles with several different damping ratios.*

from which

$$\phi(\omega) = \begin{cases} 0, & \omega \ll \omega_n \quad (u \ll u_n) \\ -\dfrac{\pi}{2}, & \omega = \omega_n \quad (u = u_n) \\ -\pi, & \omega \gg \omega_n \quad (u \gg u_n). \end{cases} \quad (10.121)$$

The asymptotic representations are

$$\phi(\omega) \simeq \begin{cases} 0, & \omega < \omega_n/10 \\ -\pi, & \omega > 10\omega_n. \end{cases} \tag{10.122}$$

Any error values applied at particular frequencies for the above angle, such as those of Eqs. (10.105b) for the real-axis pole, would be at least as great a bother to apply as a simple spotting of a few points on the actual curve, so they are omitted. However, by reference to Fig. 10.18(b), where the actual curves are plotted for several damping ratios, one can sketch his own curves accurately enough for many purposes.

In the case of a complex pair of zeros of the form

$$H(p) = \frac{p^2 + 2\zeta\omega_n\, p + \omega_n^2}{\omega_n^2}, \tag{10.123}$$

the result is simply a mirror image about the frequency axis of those for the complex pair of poles. That is, the signs on H_{db} and $\phi(\omega)$ change.

More Complicated *P-Z* Plots

Let us now return to Eq. (10.23), with which the discussions of this article started. This may be rewritten in the form of

$$H(p) = \left(\frac{K_o}{p}\right)(1 + p/a)\left(\frac{1}{1 + p/b}\right)(1 + p/c)\left[\frac{1}{(p/\omega_n)^2 + 2\zeta(p/\omega_n) + 1}\right]$$

$$= H_o(p)H_a(p)H_b(p)H_c(p)H_n(p), \tag{10.124}$$

where

$$H_o(p) = K_o/p, \qquad K_o = \frac{Kac}{b\omega_n^2} \tag{10.124a}$$

$$H_a(p) = 1 + p/a \tag{10.124b}$$

$$H_b(p) = \frac{1}{1 + p/b} \tag{10.124c}$$

$$H_c(p) = 1 + p/c \tag{10.124d}$$

$$H_n(p) = \frac{1}{\left(\dfrac{p}{\omega_n}\right)^2 + 2\zeta\left(\dfrac{p}{\omega_n}\right) + 1}, \tag{10.124e}$$

and it is assumed that

$$0 < a < b < c < d < \omega_n < \infty. \tag{10.124f}$$

From Eq. (10.124)

$$H_{db} = 20 \log_{10} |H(j\omega)|$$
$$= H_{odb} + H_{adb} + H_{bdb} + H_{cdb} + H_{ndb}. \qquad (10.125)$$

Each of the components of this equation is of a type covered in the preceding sections and is shown separately on Fig. 10.19, with a damping ratio in the

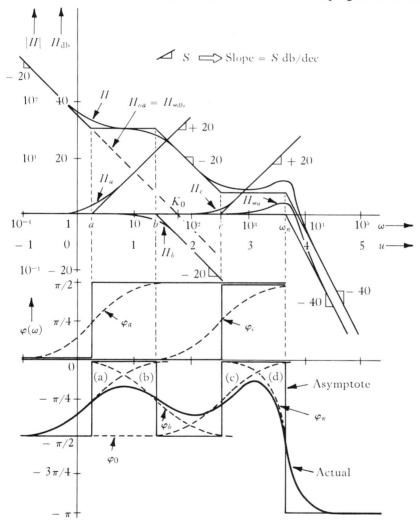

Fig. 10.19 *Asymptote and actual plots of magnitude and angle for the system function*

$$H(p) = \frac{K_1(1 + p/a)(1 + p/c)}{p(1 + p/b)\,[(p/\omega_n)^2 + 2\zeta(p/\omega_n) + 1]}$$

order of 0.2 assumed for the complex pair. The total frequency response, H_{db}, is then obtained by a simple addition of the components, as shown. The manner of combination yields the asymptote approximation

$$H_{db} \simeq \begin{cases} H_{odb} = 20 \log_{10} K_o - 20 \log_{10} \omega & 0 < \omega < a \\[2mm] H_{1db} = H_{odb} + H_{adb} = H_{odb} + 20 \log_{10} \dfrac{\omega}{a}, & a < \omega < b \\[2mm] H_{2db} = H_{1db} + H_{bdb} = H_{1db} - 20 \log_{10} \dfrac{\omega}{b}, & b < \omega < c \\[2mm] H_{3db} = H_{2db} + H_{cdb} = H_{2db} + 20 \log_{10} \dfrac{\omega}{c}, & c < \omega < \omega_n \\[2mm] H_{db} = H_{3db} + H_{ndb} = H_{3db} - 40 \log_{10} \dfrac{\omega}{\omega_n}, & \omega_n < \omega < \infty. \end{cases}$$

$$(10.126)$$

In terms of decades, the asymptotic approximation is

$$H_{db} \simeq \begin{cases} -20(u - u_o), & 0 < u < u_a \\[1mm] -20(-u_o + u_a), & u_a < u < u_b \\[1mm] -20(u - u_o + u_a - u_b), & u_b < u < u_c \\[1mm] -20(-u_o + u_a - u_b + u_c), & u_c < u < u_n \\[1mm] -40\left(u - \dfrac{u_o}{2} + \dfrac{u_a}{2} - \dfrac{u_b}{2} + \dfrac{u_c}{2} - u_n\right), & u_n < u < \infty, \end{cases} \quad (10.127)$$

where

$$u_o = \log_{10} K_o \qquad (10.127a)$$

$$u_q = \log_{10} q, \qquad q = a, b, c \qquad (10.127b)$$

$$u_n = \log_{10} \omega_n. \qquad (10.127c)$$

The angle on the frequency response is

$$\phi(\omega) = \phi_o(\omega) + \phi_a(\omega) + \phi_b(\omega) + \phi_c(\omega) + \phi_n(\omega). \qquad (10.128)$$

The component angles, asymptotes, and actual plots are shown on Fig. 10.19. They combine to give a total angle whose asymptotes are

$$\phi(\omega) \cong \begin{cases} -\dfrac{\pi}{2}, & 0 < \omega < a & (0 < u < u_a) \\[2mm] 0, & a < \omega < b & (u_a < u < u_b) \\[2mm] -\dfrac{\pi}{2}, & b < \omega < c & (u_b < u < u_c) \\[2mm] 0, & c < \omega < \omega_n & (u_c < u < u_n) \\[2mm] -\pi, & \omega_n < \omega < \infty & (u_n < u < \infty). \end{cases} \qquad (10.129)$$

These asymptotes, along with the actual angle variation, are plotted in Fig.
10.19. Note there the manner in which sketches of the actual angle variations
due to individual poles or zeros superimposed on the total asymptote aid in
the sketching of the total variation. Dotted curve (a) indicates the manner in
which the zero at $-a$ carries the actual curve from the $-\pi/2$ phase shift (due
to the pole at the origin) at low frequencies toward a phase shift of zero, while
dotted curve (b) indicates the effect of the pole at $-b$ in turning the actual
variation away from zero back towards $-\pi/2$. However, before (b) completes
its work, (c), due to the zero at $-c$, is again forcing the variation toward zero,
only to be overcome in turn by (d), due to the complex pair of poles a distance
ω_n from the origin. The sketch of actual variation, then, is a simple visual
combination of the dotted individual variations which are easily sketched onto
the asymptotes as indicated in the figure.

A helpful bit of information which shows the interdependence of the magnitude and angle plots can be summarized by introducing the notation:

$$P_\omega = \text{the number of poles at a distance}$$
$$\text{less than } \omega \text{ from the origin,} \qquad (10.130\text{a})$$

$$Z_\omega = \text{the number of zeros at a distance}$$
$$\text{less than } \omega \text{ from the origin,} \qquad (10.130\text{b})$$

$$S_\omega = \text{slope of the magnitude asymtotes}$$
$$\text{in db/decade at } \omega, \qquad (10.130\text{c})$$

$$\phi_\omega = \text{value of the angle asymptote at } \omega. \qquad (10.130\text{d})$$

The following relationships then hold:

$$S_\omega = 20(Z_\omega - P_\omega) \qquad (10.131\text{a})$$

$$\phi_\omega = \frac{\pi}{2}(Z_\omega - P_\omega). \qquad (10.131\text{b})$$

Equations (10.131) allow the total magnitude and angle asymptotes to be
drawn immediately without the necessity of first drawing in the individual
component asymptotes.

The student is cautioned that these techniques have been applied to an
example which had all its poles and zeros in the left-half plane. *When there are
zeros in the right-half plane (the so-called nonminimum-phase functions)
additional considerations are required before the knowledge of these techniques
is complete.* Nonminimum-phase functions will not be considered in this
course, however.

PROBLEMS

10.1 For the system function

$$H(p) = \frac{10}{p + 10},$$

construct an accurate *p-z* plot to a rather large scale, then plot $|H(j\omega)|$ as a function of ω, evaluating H by products and quotients of directed line lengths measured from the *p-z* plot in the manner indicated by Fig. 10.1.

10.2 Repeat Prob. 10.1 when

$$H(p) = \frac{10p}{p + 10}.$$

10.3 Repeat Prob. 10.1 when

$$H(p) = \frac{20}{(p + 2)(p + 5)}.$$

10.4 Repeat Prob. 10.1 when

$$H(p) = \frac{20p}{(p + 2)(p + 5)}.$$

10.5 Repeat Prob. 10.1 for the system function

$$H(\omega) = \frac{p}{p^2 + 2\zeta\omega_n p + \omega_n^2},$$

when $\omega_n = 1$ and when

a. $\zeta = 1.0$,   b. $\zeta = 0.5$,

c. $\zeta = 0.2$,   d. $\zeta = 0$,

e. $\zeta = 5$.

10.6 Verify the curves in Fig. 10.4 by graphical methods.

10.7 Verify the curves in Fig. 10.7 by graphical methods.

10.8 By graphical methods, plot $|H(j\omega)|$ for the system function

$$H(p) = \frac{p}{(p^2 + 2p + 10)(p^2 + 2p + 65)}.$$

Note. In Probs. 10.9 through 10.17, find the half-power point (or points) in radians per second, provided a well-defined half-power point exists.

10.9 The system function of Prob. 10.1.

10.10 The system function of Prob. 10.3.

10.11 The system function of Prob. 10.4.

10.12 $H(p) = \dfrac{10(p + 2)}{p + 10}.$

10.13 $H(p) = \dfrac{2(p + 10)}{p + 2}.$

10.14 $H(p) = \dfrac{10}{p^2 + 2p + 10}.$

10.15 $H(p) = \dfrac{10}{(p + 1)(p + 2)}.$

10.16 $H(p) = \dfrac{p(p + 2)}{(p + 10)(p + 20)}.$

10.17 $H(p) = \dfrac{p + 10}{p^2 + 8p + 116}.$

10.18 Show that Eqs. (5.102) are equivalent to Eqs. (10.59).

10.19 A 10-mH coil of 18 Ω resistance is in series with a capacitor of 25 μF. List the poles and zeros of the admittance and find the damping ratio, the undamped natural frequency, the quality factor, and the bandwidth and half-power points in radians per second.

10.20 Find the bandwidth and half-power points, in radians per second, if

$$H(p) = \frac{100p}{p^2 + 10^5 p + 10^6}.$$

10.21 Repeat Prob. 10.19, except connect the coil and capacitor in parallel and find the indicated quantities, except quality factor, for the impedance function.

10.22 Give ω_1, ω_2, B, ω_n, and ζ for $H_V(p)$ in the network of Fig. P.10.1. (Any approximations which do not result in significant loss of accuracy may be used.)

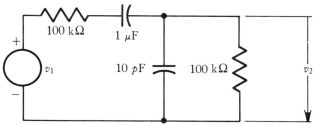

Fig. P.10.1.

10.23 The system of Fig. P.10.2 is to be used to provide a low-pass transfer relationship between v_1 and v_2. What value of R produces a bandwidth of 1000 Hz?

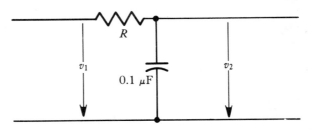

Fig. P.10.2.

10.24 The *R-L-C* combination shown in Fig. P.10.3 represents a relay that pulls in whenever the relay current exceeds 50 mA (rms) and drops out

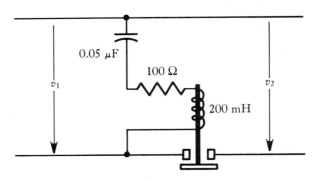

Fig. P.10.3.

whenever the relay current is less than 50 mA (rms). Input voltage is $v_1(t) = \sqrt{2}\, V_1 \cos \omega t$. Plot $|H(j\omega)| = |\mathbf{V}_2/\mathbf{V}_1|$ as a function of ω when V_1 equals 10 and when V_1 equals 20.

10.25 For the circuit of Fig. P.10.4:

a. Find the transfer function relating the response v_2 to the forcing function v_1.

b. Find ω_1 and/or (depending on whether the system is *L-P*, *H-P*, or *B-P*) ω_2.

c. What is the bandwidth?

d. Give the response to the step function $v_1(t) = Vu(t)$. (If applicable, approximations indicated by frequency characteristics may be used.)

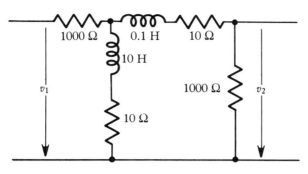

Fig. P.10.4.

10.26 Give the *p-z* plots for the low- and high-frequency approximations to the system having the complete *p-z* plot shown in Fig. P.10.5(a). Sketch

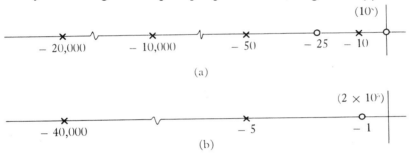

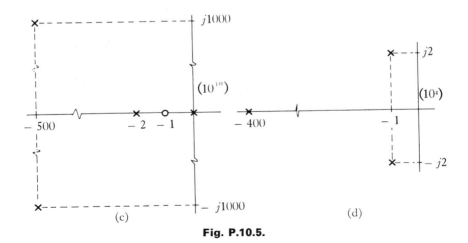

Fig. P.10.5.

approximately to scale on rectangular coordinates the frequency responses for each approximation.

10.27 Repeat Prob. 10.26, except refer to Fig. P.10.5(b).

10.28 Repeat Prob. 10.26, except refer to Fig. P.10.5(c).

10.29 Repeat Prob. 10.26, except refer to Fig. P.10.5(d).

10.30 Derive Eqs. (10.38) and (10.39).

10.31 Derive Eq. (10.117).

10.32 Derive Eqs. (10.118) and (10.119).

10.33 Show that $\omega_n = \sqrt{\omega_1\omega_2}$ = geometric mean of ω_1 and ω_2.

10.34 Show that if

$$F(p) = \frac{KP(p)}{p^n Q(p)} = \frac{K\prod_{k=1}^{m}(p+z_k)}{p^n\prod_{j=1}^{n}(p+p_j)},$$

where $P(p)$ and $Q(p)$ are polynomials with nonzero roots, then the low-frequency asymptote of F_{db} has a slope of $-20n$ db/decade and its extension intersects the zero-db axis at

$$\omega = \left\{\frac{K\prod_{k=1}^{m}z_k}{\prod_{j=1}^{n}p_j}\right\}^{1/n}.$$

10.35 A certain transfer function has poles at $p = -50$ and $p = -50{,}000$, a zero at $p = 0$, and has a magnitude of 10 at $p = j1600$.

a.   Plot on semilog paper both asymptotic and actual values of the magnitude in decibels and the phase shift in degrees.

b.   Assume the *rise time* is the time it takes the response to a step function to rise to 63% of its ideal value (a step function) and the *fall time* is the time it takes for it to drop to 37% of its ideal level. Find each.

c.   What is the bandwidth of this system?

Note. For Probs. 10.36 through 10.43, draw on semilog paper the asymptotes and sketch the actual plots of magnitude in decibels and the phase angle of the given system function.

10.36 $H(p) = \dfrac{10}{p+5}$.

10.37 $H(p) = \dfrac{200}{(p+1)(p+2)(p+20)}$.

10.38 $H(p) = \dfrac{250p}{(p+10)(p+15)}$.

10.39 $H(p) = \dfrac{2500p}{(p+10)(p+2000)}$.

10.40 $H(p) = \dfrac{250(p+1)}{(p+5)(p+10)(p+100)}$.

10.41 $H(p) = \dfrac{50}{p^2(p+5)}$.

10.42 $H(p) = \dfrac{10^6 p}{p^2 + 100p + 10^6}$.

10.43 $H(p) = \dfrac{10^6 p}{p^2 + 10,000p + 10^6}$.

10.44 If

$$H(p) = \frac{150p(p+1)}{(p+3)(p^2+6p+25)}:$$

a. Give the equation of each section of the H_{db} asymptote and specify the radian frequency over which it applies.

b. Compute, without plotting, the radian frequency, or frequencies, if any, at which the asymptote crosses the zero-db line.

10.45 Repeat Prob. 10.44 for the function

$$H(p) = \frac{2.5 \times 10^5 p(p+5)}{(p+50)(p^2+20p+10^4)(p+200)}.$$

10.46 Plot on semilog paper the asymptote and actual values of H_{db} and $\phi(\omega)$ when $H(p)$ has the *p-z* plot of Fig. P.10.5(a).

10.47 Repeat Prob. 10.46, but refer to Fig. P.10.5(b).

10.48 Repeat Prob. 10.46, but refer to Fig. P.10.5(c).

10.49 Repeat Prob. 10.46, but refer to Fig. P.10.5(d).

11

Matrix Analysis of
Networks

11.1 INTRODUCTION

The solution of the simultaneous equations that occur in network analysis can be a tedious process even when the networks are relatively simple, the sizes of the components are explicitly specified, the equations describing the forcing functions are given, and the initial conditions are known. The trail one follows toward a solution may become virtually obscured by the forest of detail, in the form of many equations and transformations of variables, accompanying the march forward.

Through the use of matrices we are able to lump great masses of this troublesome detail into single algebraic entities providing the vehicles for carrying us in an organized manner along the road to a solution. Now a single algebraic symbol will represent an entire set of forcing functions, of response functions, or of system parameters; and the algebra of matrices will formalize to simple algebraic operations the procedures which otherwise require the laborious writing and rewriting of many succeeding sets of ordinary equations, with all the confusion that must result from such a cluttered process.

The matrix solution to a system will result in an indication of the manner in which a set of response variables is related to a set of forcing functions and will indicate, as a simple inverse operation, the manner in which they are to be solved to yield explicit values for the response functions. This final step is the equivalent of the solution of a set of equations by determinants and involves an equivalent amount of "arithmetic." The beauty of matrices has been in the ease with which they have brought us to this final step.

11.2 REVIEW OF SOLUTION OF LINEAR EQUATIONS BY DETERMINANTS

This review seems advisable, not only as a refresher but also as an introduction to some of the notation which will be convenient in the work to follow.

Let us start by considering a system of three linear equations expressing the knowns (dependent variables) y_1, y_2, and y_3 in terms of the unknowns (independent variables) x_1, x_2, and x_3:

$$y_1 = a_{11}x_1 + a_{12}x_2 + a_{13}x_3 \tag{11.1a}$$

$$y_2 = a_{21}x_1 + a_{22}x_2 + a_{23}x_3 \tag{11.1b}$$

$$y_3 = a_{31}x_1 + a_{32}x_2 + a_{33}x_3. \tag{11.1c}$$

A word about the meaning of the subscripts is in order here. The subscripts on the x and y variables are simply identifying tags. In the terminology of physical systems, the y's may be considered *effects* due to the *causes* identified as the x's. The a's, on the other hand, provide a measure of that portion of a particular *effect* which is due to a specified *cause*. The following statement, then, holds:

If

$$y_j = \text{the } j\text{th effect} \tag{11.2a}$$

$$x_k = \text{the } k\text{th cause,} \tag{11.2b}$$

then

$$a_{jk} = \text{the units of change in the } j\text{th effect per unit of change in the } k\text{th cause.} \tag{11.2c}$$

Equation (11.2c) is evident when you observe, from Eqs. (11.1), that, for example

$$a_{jk} = \frac{\partial y_j}{\partial x_k}. \tag{11.2d}$$

Thus, in the coefficients of the independent variable, the first subscript locates the effect and the second the cause. It should be realized that the terms "cause" and "effect" are somewhat loosely applied here, because it is simple to solve for the x's in Eqs. (11.1) in terms of the y's (providing the determinant is not zero). In this case we should want the *form* of the results to be the same as far as subscripting is concerned. For example, the solution for x_2 might be

$$x_2 = b_{21} y_1 + b_{22} y_2 + b_{23} y_3,$$

where the b's now describe effects due to y's on x's and are subscripted according to the same conventions used when the reverse was true.

The determinant of Eqs. (11.1) is

$$|A| = \begin{vmatrix} a_{11} & a_{12} & a_{13} \\ a_{21} & a_{22} & a_{23} \\ a_{31} & a_{32} & a_{33} \end{vmatrix}. \tag{11.3}$$

Note that the subscripts as defined are such that the first identifies a row in the determinant while the second identifies a column. Note also in Eqs. (11.1) that the second subscript on an a is repeated in the associated x.

Now let us solve Eqs. (11.1) for x_1 using determinants:

$$x_1 = \frac{1}{|A|} \begin{vmatrix} y_1 & a_{12} & a_{13} \\ y_2 & a_{22} & a_{23} \\ y_3 & a_{32} & a_{33} \end{vmatrix}$$

$$= \frac{1}{|A|} \left[\begin{vmatrix} a_{22} & a_{23} \\ a_{32} & a_{33} \end{vmatrix} y_1 - \begin{vmatrix} a_{12} & a_{13} \\ a_{32} & a_{33} \end{vmatrix} y_2 + \begin{vmatrix} a_{12} & a_{13} \\ a_{22} & a_{23} \end{vmatrix} y_3 \right]. \tag{11.4}$$

But

$$\begin{vmatrix} a_{22} & a_{23} \\ a_{32} & a_{33} \end{vmatrix} = A_{11} = \text{cofactor of } a_{11} \tag{11.5a}$$

$$-\begin{vmatrix} a_{12} & a_{13} \\ a_{32} & a_{33} \end{vmatrix} = A_{21} = \text{cofactor of } a_{21} \tag{11.5b}$$

$$\begin{vmatrix} a_{12} & a_{13} \\ a_{22} & a_{23} \end{vmatrix} = A_{31} = \text{cofactor of } a_{31}, \tag{11.5c}$$

so Eq. (11.4) may be written

$$x_1 = \frac{A_{11}}{|A|} y_1 + \frac{A_{21}}{|A|} y_2 + \frac{A_{31}}{|A|} y_3. \tag{11.6}$$

If we say that, in general, cofactors such as those in Eqs. (11.5) are designated

$$A_{jk} = \text{cofactor of } a_{jk}, \tag{11.7}$$

then the solutions for the remaining two variables are

$$x_2 = \frac{A_{12}}{|A|} y_1 + \frac{A_{22}}{|A|} y_2 + \frac{A_{32}}{|A|} y_3 \qquad (11.8)$$

$$x_3 = \frac{A_{13}}{|A|} y_1 + \frac{A_{23}}{|A|} y_2 + \frac{A_{33}}{|A|} y_3 . \qquad (11.9)$$

To get these solutions into a form where the subscripts on the coefficients obey the rules we have established, we will set

$$(a^{-1})_{jk} = \frac{A_{kj}}{|A|}, \qquad (11.10)$$

so that Eqs. (11.6), (11.8), and (11.9) become

$$x_1 = (a^{-1})_{11} y_1 + (a^{-1})_{12} y_2 + (a^{-1})_{13} y_3 \qquad (11.11a)$$

$$x_2 = (a^{-1})_{21} y_1 + (a^{-1})_{22} y_2 + (a^{-1})_{23} y_3 \qquad (11.11b)$$

$$x_3 = (a^{-1})_{31} y_1 + (a^{-1})_{32} y_2 + (a^{-1})_{33} y_3 . \qquad (11.11c)$$

These, then, are the results of solving a system of three linear equations in three unknowns. We may abbreviate these results and at the same time extend them to any number of unknowns, say to a system of n equations in n unknowns. If the dependent variables are $y_1, y_2, \ldots, y_j, \ldots, y_n$ and the independent variables are $x_1, x_2, \ldots, x_n$, then the jth equation in a set like that of Eqs. (11.1) is

$$y_j = \sum_{k=1}^{n} a_{jk} x_k, \qquad j = 1, 2, 3, \ldots, n, \qquad (11.12)$$

where j is any one of the integers from 1 to n inclusive listed along with the equation. To cite an example: In Eqs. (11.1) $n = 3$, and for the second equation $j = 2$. With the value of n known, exactly the same information is included in the abbreviated form of Eq. (11.12) as in Eqs. (11.1), and it would be just as simple if there were independent equations involving six or 126 unknowns.

When j and k range over the same value, it is possible to solve for the x's, providing the determinant is not zero. When j and k do not range over the same value, the determinant does not exist. This means that a complete set of *independent* equations has not been written. In brief, for independent equations

$$\text{If } y_j = \sum_{k=1}^{n} a_{jk} x_k, \qquad j = 1, 2, \ldots, m \neq n, \qquad (11.13)$$

no complete solution for the x's is possible.

The determinant of Eq. (11.12) is

$$|A| = \begin{vmatrix} a_{11} & a_{12} \cdots a_{1k} \cdots a_{1n} \\ a_{21} & a_{22} \cdots a_{2k} \cdots a_{2n} \\ \vdots & \vdots & \vdots & \vdots \\ a_{j1} & a_{j2} & a_{jk} & a_{jn} \\ \vdots & \vdots & \vdots & \vdots \\ a_{n1} & a_{n2} & a_{nk} & a_{nn} \end{vmatrix}. \tag{11.14}$$

With the (a^{-1}) or *inverse* coefficients defined as in Eq. (11.10) in terms of the cofactors of Eq. (11.7), the solutions of the Eqs. (11.12) become, in the summation form

$$x_j = \sum_{k=1}^{n} (a^{-1})_{jk} y_k, \qquad j = 1, 2, \ldots, n. \tag{11.15}$$

These results are important enough and will be used enough in the work to come to merit bringing them together in one place for easy reference. Therefore, they are summarized below:

If the set of n linear equations in n unknowns,

$$y_j = \sum_{k=1}^{n} a_{jk} x_k, \qquad j = 1, 2, \ldots, n, \tag{11.16a}$$

has the nonzero determinant $|A|$ whose elements have cofactors according to the notation

$$A_{jk} = \text{cofactor of } a_{jk} \tag{11.16b}$$

then the solutions for the x's are

$$x_j = \sum_{k=1}^{n} (a^{-1})_{jk} y_k, \qquad j = 1, 2, 3, \ldots, n, \tag{11.16c}$$

where

$$(a^{-1})_{jk} = \frac{A_{kj}}{|A|} \tag{11.16d}$$

are the *inverse* coefficients corresponding to the original coefficients a_{jk}.

11.3 MATRICES

The manipulations of the preceding article have been formalized to a certain extent by the introduction of the summation forms and indexed parameters of Eqs. (11.16). This formalization may be simplified and extended through the concept of a *matrix* and certain defined operations forming an *algebra of matrices* (or matrix algebra).

Definition of a Matrix

In the broadest sense, a matrix is any collection of *elements* each requiring two ordered markers, or tags, or indices, for its identification. Generally, however, this concept is narrowed to suggest an *array* of elements arranged in rows and columns so that the first of the two indices associated with an element identifies the row in which it appears and the second the column in which it appears. An example of such a matrix is the *coefficient matrix* of Eqs. (11.1), which is formed by the a's which are the coefficients of the independent variables, i.e.,

$$\mathscr{A} = \begin{bmatrix} a_{11} & a_{12} & a_{13} \\ a_{21} & a_{22} & a_{23} \\ a_{31} & a_{32} & a_{33} \end{bmatrix}. \tag{11.17}$$

Note the use of the script letter to identify the matrix and the brackets, [—], enclosing the array. This is the notation which will generally be used in our treatment. Other symbolisms sometimes used include the use of bold-face type or bracketed single letters as identifiers and the use of (—) or ||—|| as enclosures of the array of elements.

Once we know what a matrix is, the following statement prescribes our notation:

a_{jk} is the element in the jth row and kth column of the matrix. $\tag{11.18}$

In other words, unless we specifically state otherwise, the subscripted lower-case type letter designating the elements will be the same letter as that in script identifying the matrix.

Matrix Forms

A. Rectangular Matrix—This is the general matrix form in which the number of rows is not necessarily equal to the number of columns. This is an appropriate place to introduce the following bit of nomenclature:

A matrix with m rows and n columns is called an m by n (or $m \times n$) matrix. $\tag{11.19}$

An example of a 2×3 matrix is

$$\mathscr{A} = \begin{bmatrix} a_{11} & a_{12} & a_{13} \\ a_{21} & a_{22} & a_{23} \end{bmatrix} \tag{11.20a}$$

and of a 3 × 2 matrix is

$$\mathscr{B} = \begin{bmatrix} b_{11} & b_{12} \\ b_{21} & b_{22} \\ b_{31} & b_{32} \end{bmatrix}. \tag{11.20b}$$

B. Square Matrix—This is the matrix with the number of rows equal to the number of columns; an $m \times m$ matrix. The matrix of Eq. (11.17), a 3 × 3 matrix, provides an example. A square matrix is *symmetric* if $a_{jk} = a_{kj}$.

C. Column Matrix—The rectangular matrix with but one column, the $m \times 1$ matrix, is the *column matrix*. With but one column, the second, or column-identifying index, is redundant and is generally not written. This special matrix will be identified by the lower-case script letter. An example is

$$x = \begin{bmatrix} x_{11} \\ x_{21} \\ x_{31} \end{bmatrix} = \begin{bmatrix} x_1 \\ x_2 \\ x_3 \end{bmatrix}. \tag{11.21}$$

The elements of such a matrix might be the independent variables of Eqs. (10.11), for example.

D. Row Matrix—A matrix with but one row, a $1 \times m$ matrix, is a *row matrix*. In this case, the row-identifying, or first, index is redundant and is generally dropped. The symbol used for such a matrix will be the lower-case script with the "tilde", i.e.,

$$\tilde{x} = [x_{11} \quad x_{12} \quad x_{13}] = [x_1 \quad x_2 \quad x_3]. \tag{11.22}$$

E. Diagonal Matrix—This is a square matrix with all the off-diagonal terms zero. An example of a 3 × 3 diagonal matrix is

$$\mathscr{D} = \begin{bmatrix} d_{11} & 0 & 0 \\ 0 & d_{22} & 0 \\ 0 & 0 & d_{33} \end{bmatrix}. \tag{11.23}$$

F. The Unit Matrix—This is the diagonal matrix with the nonzero terms equal to unity. The elements of this matrix are those of the "Kronecker deltas," which satisfy the relationship

$$\delta_{jk} = \begin{cases} 1, & j = k \\ 0, & j \neq k. \end{cases} \tag{11.24a}$$

The symbol $\mathscr{U}$ will be reserved for the unit matrix, an example of which is

$$\mathscr{U} = \begin{bmatrix} \delta_{11} & \delta_{12} & \delta_{13} \\ \delta_{21} & \delta_{22} & \delta_{23} \\ \delta_{31} & \delta_{32} & \delta_{33} \end{bmatrix} = \begin{bmatrix} 1 & 0 & 0 \\ 0 & 1 & 0 \\ 0 & 0 & 1 \end{bmatrix}. \tag{11.24b}$$

G. The Null Matrix—The matrix with all elements zero is the null matrix. We shall reserve it for the symbol $\mathcal{O}$, using upper case for rectangular matrices, lower case for column or row matrices, i.e.,

$$\mathcal{O} = \begin{bmatrix} 0 & 0 & 0 \\ 0 & 0 & 0 \\ 0 & 0 & 0 \end{bmatrix} \qquad o = \begin{bmatrix} 0 \\ 0 \\ 0 \end{bmatrix} \qquad \tilde{o} = [0 \quad 0 \quad 0]. \qquad (11.25)$$

11.4 MATRIX ALGEBRA

The rules of matrix algebra necessary for our purposes are few and simple, and it appears simplest to briefly state all we will need before applying them to the problems at hand.

Equality of Matrices

Two matrices will be defined as equal only when they have the same number of rows and columns and corresponding elements are equal. That is,

$$\text{If } \mathcal{A} \doteq \mathcal{B}, \qquad \text{then } a_{jk} = b_{jk}. \qquad (11.26)$$

An example is provided by the equation

$$\begin{bmatrix} a_{11} & a_{12} \\ a_{21} & a_{22} \end{bmatrix} = \begin{bmatrix} 4 & x \\ 3 & x+2 \end{bmatrix},$$

which states that

$$a_{11} = 4 \qquad a_{12} = x$$
$$a_{21} = 3 \qquad a_{22} = x+2.$$

Multiplication by a Constant or Linear Operator

Suppose K is either a constant or a linear operator such as the differentiation operator, the integration operator, or a system function. Multiplication by, or operation on, the matrix $\mathcal{A}$ by K is defined as follows:

$$\text{If } \mathcal{B} = K\mathcal{A}, \qquad \text{then } b_{jk} = Ka_{jk}. \qquad (11.27)$$

An example is

$$K\begin{bmatrix} a_{11} & a_{12} \\ a_{21} & a_{22} \end{bmatrix} = \begin{bmatrix} Ka_{11} & Ka_{12} \\ Ka_{21} & Ka_{22} \end{bmatrix}.$$

Addition of Matrices

Addition of matrices is defined for two $m \times n$ matrices in this way:

If both $\mathscr{A}$ and $\mathscr{B}$ are $m \times n$ matrices, then their sum is

$$\mathscr{C} = \mathscr{A} + \mathscr{B} \tag{11.28}$$

having the elements $c_{jk} = a_{jk} + b_{jk}$.

For example,

$$\begin{bmatrix} 2 & 3 & 4 \\ 4 & 3 & 2 \end{bmatrix} + \begin{bmatrix} 1 & 0 & 6 \\ 7 & 2 & 3 \end{bmatrix} = \begin{bmatrix} 3 & 3 & 10 \\ 11 & 5 & 5 \end{bmatrix}.$$

Matrix Products

Matrix multiplication may be defined as follows:

If $\mathscr{A}$ is an $m \times n$ matrix and $\mathscr{B}$ is an $n \times p$ matrix, the two matrices are said to be *conformable* and have as their product the $m \times p$ matrix

$$\mathscr{C} = \mathscr{A}\mathscr{B}$$

defined so that its elements are

$$c_{jk} = \sum_{r=1}^{n} a_{jr} b_{rk}, \qquad \begin{Bmatrix} j = 1, 2, \ldots, m \\ k = 1, 2, \ldots, p \end{Bmatrix}. \tag{11.29a}$$

Stated another way:

If $\mathscr{C} = \mathscr{A}\mathscr{B}$, then the element in the jth row and kth column of $\mathscr{C}$ is found by multiplying the elements in the jth row of $\mathscr{A}$ by the corresponding elements in the kth column of $\mathscr{B}$ and adding the products so formed. $\tag{11.29b}$

Thus, we see that multiplication is defined for two matrices only when the number of columns of the first, or *premultiplying*, matrix is equal to the number of rows in the second, or *post-multiplying*, matrix. These concepts of premultiplication and postmultiplication in general do not commute. That is,

As it is generally true that

$$\sum_{r=1}^{n} a_{jr} b_{rk} \neq \sum_{r=1}^{n} b_{jr} a_{rk}, $$

it is also true that generally

$$\mathscr{A}\mathscr{B} \neq \mathscr{B}\mathscr{A}. \tag{11.29c}$$

The multiplication rule is easily extended to multiple products, as can be seen by premultiplying the matrix $\mathscr{C}$ in the definition (11.29a) by the matrix $\mathscr{D}$ (conformable with $\mathscr{C}$). The resulting matrix $\mathscr{F}$ will have the elements

$$f_{jk} = \sum_{s=1}^{q} d_{js} c_{sk}$$

$$= \sum_{s=1}^{q} d_{js} \sum_{r=1}^{n} a_{sr} b_{rk}$$

$$= \sum_{s=1}^{q} \sum_{r=1}^{n} d_{js} a_{sr} b_{rk}, \qquad (11.30a)$$

and may be written

$$\mathscr{F} = \mathscr{D}\mathscr{C}$$
$$= \mathscr{D}(\mathscr{A}\mathscr{B})$$
$$= (\mathscr{D}\mathscr{A})\mathscr{B}$$
$$= \mathscr{D}\mathscr{A}\mathscr{B}. \qquad (11.30b)$$

The student should satisfy himself that the *associative properties* indicated here for the matrix product are valid.

An example of matrix multiplication is

$$\mathscr{C} = \begin{bmatrix} \rule[0.5ex]{0pt}{0pt}\!\!-a_{11}\!\!-\!\!a_{12}\!\!-\!\!a_{13}\!\rightarrow \\ a_{21} \quad a_{22} \quad a_{23} \end{bmatrix} \qquad \begin{bmatrix} b_{11} & b_{12} & b_{13} \\ b_{21} & b_{22} & b_{23} \\ b_{31} & b_{32} & b_{33} \end{bmatrix},$$

$$\mathscr{C} = \begin{bmatrix} (a_{11}b_{11} + a_{12}b_{21} + a_{13}b_{31}) & (a_{11}b_{12} + a_{12}b_{22} + a_{13}b_{32}) \\ & (a_{11}b_{13} + a_{12}b_{23} + a_{13}b_{33}) \\ (a_{21}b_{11} + a_{22}b_{21} + a_{23}b_{31}) & (a_{21}b_{12} + a_{22}b_{22} + a_{23}b_{32}) \\ & (a_{21}b_{13} + a_{22}b_{23} + a_{23}b_{33}) \end{bmatrix}$$

The arrows indicate the combination forming element c_{12}.

You should observe in the index forms of Eqs. (11.29) and (11.30) that the summing index is always repeated, occurring once in the first position and once in the second. When it does not do this, the summation does not define a matrix multiplication. For example, the summation

$$\sum_{r=1}^{n} a_{jr} b_{kr}$$

does not represent a conformable product. Another truth about indices which is often convenient is that the letters used are immaterial, and an index may be replaced or interchanged with another throughout an expression without changing the nature of the expression.

If you will recall the position of the missing indices in the row and column matrices of Eqs. (11.21) and (11.22), then you will recognize the following as conformable matrix products:

$$\text{If } y_j = \sum_{r=1}^{n} a_{jr} x_r, \qquad \text{then } y = \mathscr{A}x. \tag{11.31a}$$

$$\text{If } y_k = \sum_{r=1}^{n} x_r a_{rk}, \qquad \text{then } \tilde{y} = \tilde{x}\mathscr{A}. \tag{11.31b}$$

Another very important product is the special case of the general product involving the row and column matrices:

$$\left(\tilde{x}y = \tilde{y}x = \sum_{r=1}^{n} x_r y_r = \text{inner product of } x \text{ and } y \right). \tag{11.32}$$

Finally, we list two special products involving the unit matrix, $\mathscr{U}$, and the null matrix, $\mathscr{O}$, which are very easily shown:

$$\mathscr{U}\mathscr{A} = \mathscr{A}\mathscr{U} = \mathscr{A}, \tag{11.33}$$

$$\mathscr{O}\mathscr{A} = \mathscr{A}\mathscr{O} = \mathscr{O}. \tag{11.34}$$

Thus, the unit matrix and the null matrix have the same significance in matrix algebra as the numbers one and zero in conventional algebra.

Transpose of a Matrix

The transpose of a matrix is formed by interchanging its rows and columns, $\tag{11.35a}$

or

If

$$c_{jk} = \tilde{a}_{jk} = a_{kj},$$

then

$$\mathscr{C} = \tilde{\mathscr{A}} = \text{transpose of } \mathscr{A}. \tag{11.35b}$$

Furthermore,

If

$$c_{jk} = \sum_{r=1}^{n} a_{jr} b_{rk} \quad \text{or} \quad \mathscr{C} = \mathscr{A}\mathscr{B},$$

then

(11.36a)

$$\tilde{c}_{jk} = c_{kj} = \sum_{r=1}^{n} a_{kr} b_{rj} = \sum_{r=1}^{n} \tilde{b}_{jr} \tilde{a}_{rk}.$$

This represents the matrix product

$$\widetilde{\mathscr{C}} = \widetilde{\mathscr{A}\mathscr{B}} = \widetilde{\mathscr{B}}\widetilde{\mathscr{A}}, \tag{11.36b}$$

and we see that the transpose of a product of two matrices is the reversed product of the transposed matrices.

An example of a transposed matrix is

$$\widetilde{\begin{bmatrix} 1 & 2 & 3 \\ 4 & 5 & 6 \\ 7 & 8 & 9 \end{bmatrix}} = \begin{bmatrix} 1 & 4 & 7 \\ 2 & 5 & 8 \\ 3 & 6 & 9 \end{bmatrix}.$$

Before leaving the subject of transposed matrices, we note that the symmetric matrix transposes into itself; that is, transposing a symmetric matrix yields the original matrix. Also, we note that a row matrix, $\tilde{x}$, is a transpose of a column matrix, x, justifying the use of the tilde in identifying both the row matrix and the transpose.

Determinant and Adjoint of a Matrix

These two definitions are important primarily because they lead to the very important inverse defined next. First,

The determinant of the square matrix, $\mathscr{A}$, designated $|A|$, is the determinant having the same rows, columns, and elements as the matrix.   (11.37)

For example,

$$\text{determinant of } \begin{bmatrix} a_{11} & a_{12} \\ a_{21} & a_{22} \end{bmatrix} = \begin{vmatrix} a_{11} & a_{12} \\ a_{21} & a_{22} \end{vmatrix} = |A|.$$

Next,

The adjoint of the matrix $\mathscr{A}$ is the transpose of the matrix formed by the cofactors of $\mathscr{A}$.   (11.38a)

Or

> If $\mathscr{A}^a$ having elements $(a^a)_{jk}$ is the adjoint of $\mathscr{A}$ and A_{jk} is the cofactor of a_{jk}, then $(a^a)_{jk} = A_{kj}$. $\qquad$ (11.38b)

There is a definite relationship between the determinant and the adjoint. You will recall that the expansion of a determinant according to the elements of the jth row is

$$
\begin{aligned}
|A| &= a_{j1}A_{j1} + a_{j2}A_{j2} + \cdots + a_{jn}A_{jn} \\
&= a_{j1}(a^a)_{1j} + a_{j2}(a^a)_{2j} + \cdots + a_{jn}(a^a)_{nj} \\
&= \sum_{r=1}^{n} a_{jr}(a^a)_{rj}, \qquad j = 1, 2, 3, \ldots, n.
\end{aligned}
$$

By using the Kronecker delta of Eq. (11.24a), this may be made into the conformable product

$$
|A|\,\delta_{jk} = \sum_{r=1}^{n} a_{jr}(a^a)_{rk} \qquad \begin{array}{l} j = 1, 2, 3, \ldots, n \\ k = 1, 2, 3, \ldots, n, \end{array} \qquad (11.39a)
$$

where k can also be one of the integers from 1 through n independent of j. The array of Kronecker deltas using all possible combinations of j and k is the unit matrix of Eq. (11.24b). The summation on the right is the definition of a matrix product as given in Eq. (11.29a). Thus, the matrix form of this equation is

$$
|A|\,\mathscr{U} = \mathscr{A}\mathscr{A}^a. \qquad (11.39b)
$$

Similarly, we find that by expanding the determinant by columns we have

$$
|A|\,\delta_{jk} = \sum_{r=1}^{n} (a^a)_{jr}\, a_{rk} \qquad \begin{array}{l} j = 1, 2, 3, \ldots, n \\ k = 1, 2, 3, \ldots, n, \end{array} \qquad (11.39c)
$$

or

$$
|A|\,\mathscr{U} = \mathscr{A}^a\mathscr{A}. \qquad (11.39d)
$$

The Inverse of a Matrix

This is an important one:

The inverse of $\mathscr{A}$, designated $\mathscr{A}^{-1}$, is defined such that

$$
\mathscr{A}^{-1}\mathscr{A} = \mathscr{A}\mathscr{A}^{-1} = \mathscr{U}. \qquad (11.40)
$$

Now let us try our hand at a little matrix algebra. First, multiply both sides of Eq. (11.40) by the determinant of $\mathscr{A}$ to get

$$
|A|\,\mathscr{A}^{-1}\mathscr{A} = |A|\,\mathscr{U}.
$$

Substituting in Eq. (11.39d) yields

$$|A| \mathscr{A}^{-1} \mathscr{A} = \mathscr{A}^a \mathscr{A},$$

and postmultiplying by $\mathscr{A}^{-1}$ and applying Eq. (11.40) produces

$$|A| \mathscr{A}^{-1} = \mathscr{A}^a.$$

Now divide both sides by $|A|$ to get

$$\mathscr{A}^{-1} = \frac{\mathscr{A}^a}{|A|}. \tag{11.41}$$

By definition (11.38), the element in the jth row and kth column of $\mathscr{A}^{-1}$ is, then,

$$(a^{-1})_{jk} = \frac{(a^a)_{jk}}{|A|} = \frac{A_{kj}}{|A|}, \tag{11.42a}$$

and we may state the rule for forming the inverse of a matrix as follows:

> The element in the jth row and the kth column of the inverse
> of a matrix is equal to the cofactor of the element in the   (11.42b)
> kth row and jth column of the matrix divided by the deter-
> minant of the matrix.

An example

$$
\begin{bmatrix} 1 & 2 & 1 \\ 3 & 2 & 4 \\ 6 & 4 & 1 \end{bmatrix}^{-1} = \frac{\begin{bmatrix} \begin{vmatrix} 2 & 4 \\ 4 & 1 \end{vmatrix} & -\begin{vmatrix} 2 & 1 \\ 4 & 1 \end{vmatrix} & \begin{vmatrix} 2 & 1 \\ 2 & 4 \end{vmatrix} \\ -\begin{vmatrix} 3 & 4 \\ 6 & 1 \end{vmatrix} & \begin{vmatrix} 1 & 1 \\ 6 & 1 \end{vmatrix} & -\begin{vmatrix} 1 & 1 \\ 3 & 4 \end{vmatrix} \\ \begin{vmatrix} 3 & 2 \\ 6 & 4 \end{vmatrix} & -\begin{vmatrix} 1 & 2 \\ 6 & 4 \end{vmatrix} & \begin{vmatrix} 1 & 2 \\ 3 & 2 \end{vmatrix} \end{bmatrix}}{\begin{vmatrix} 1 & 2 & 1 \\ 3 & 2 & 4 \\ 6 & 4 & 1 \end{vmatrix}}
$$

$$
= \begin{bmatrix} -\dfrac{1}{2} & \dfrac{1}{14} & \dfrac{3}{14} \\[2ex] \dfrac{21}{28} & -\dfrac{5}{28} & -\dfrac{1}{28} \\[2ex] 0 & \dfrac{2}{7} & -\dfrac{1}{7} \end{bmatrix}.
$$

It is left as an exercise for the student to show, using the operations already defined, that the inverse of a product is equal to the reversed product of the inverses. That is,

$$(\mathscr{A}\mathscr{B})^{-1} = \mathscr{B}^{-1}\mathscr{A}^{-1}. \tag{11.43}$$

TABLE 11.1 MATRIX FORMS AND OPERATIONS

Entry No.	Form or operation	Matrix form	The element in row j and column k
1.	Rectangular matrix	$\mathscr{A}$ (or $[A]$)	a_{jk}, $\begin{cases} j = 1, 2, 3, \ldots, m \\ k = 1, 2, 3, \ldots, n \end{cases}$
2.	Square matrix	$\mathscr{A}$ (or $[A]$)	a_{jk}, $\begin{cases} j = 1, 2, 3, \ldots, m \\ k = 1, 2, 3, \ldots, m \end{cases}$
3.	Column matrix	x (or x])	$x_j = x_{j(\,)}$, $\ j = 1, 2, 3, \ldots, m$
4.	Row matrix	$\tilde{x}$ (or $\underline{x}$])	$x_k = x_{(\,)k}$, $\ k = 1, 2, 3, \ldots, m$
5.	Kronecker delta	$\ldots$	$\delta_{jk} = \begin{cases} 1, j = k \\ 0, j \neq k \end{cases}$
6.	Unit matrix	$\mathscr{U}$	δ_{jk}, $\begin{cases} j = 1, 2, 3, \ldots, m \\ k = 1, 2, 3, \ldots, m \end{cases}$
7.	Diagonal matrix	$\mathscr{D}$	$d_{jk}\delta_{jk}$, $\begin{cases} j = 1, 2, 3, \ldots, m \\ k = 1, 2, 3, \ldots, m \end{cases}$
8.	Transpose of $\mathscr{A}$	$\tilde{\mathscr{A}}$ (or $[A]^t$)	$\tilde{a}_{jk} = a_{kj}$
9.	Multiplication by a constant	$K\mathscr{A}$	Ka_{jk}
10.	Addition	$\mathscr{A} + \mathscr{B}$	$a_{jk} + b_{jk}$
11.	Multiplication by $\mathscr{A}$		
(a)	General	$\mathscr{C} = \mathscr{A}\mathscr{B}$	$c_{jk} = \sum\limits_{r=1}^{n} a_{jr}b_{rk}$
(b)	Column	$y = \mathscr{A}x$	$y_j = \sum\limits_{r=1}^{n} a_{jr}x_r$
(c)	Row	$\tilde{y} = \tilde{x}\mathscr{A}$	$y_j = \sum\limits_{r=1}^{n} x_r a_{rj}$
12.	Inner product	$\tilde{x}y = \tilde{y}x$	$\sum\limits_{r=1}^{n} x_r y_r$ (a scalar)
13.	Cofactor of element a_{jk}	$\ldots$	Designated A_{jk}
14.	Inverse of $\mathscr{A}$	$\mathscr{A}^{-1}$	$(a^{-1})_{jk} = \dfrac{A_{kj}}{|A|}$

The matrix definitions and operations which are important in the manipulative algebra of networks are summarized in Table 11.1. In this table are also shown a common alternative notation which we may use to symbolize a matrix should an occasion arise where the script notation is awkward.

11.5 MATRIX ALGEBRA AND LINEAR EQUATIONS

The linear equations of Eq. (11.1) have the general form of Eq. (11.12) which defines the matrix relationship

$$y = \mathscr{A}x. \tag{11.44}$$

In the case of Eq. (11.1) the complete form of this is

$$\begin{bmatrix} y_1 \\ y_2 \\ y_3 \end{bmatrix} = \begin{bmatrix} a_{11} & a_{12} & a_{13} \\ a_{21} & a_{22} & a_{23} \\ a_{31} & a_{32} & a_{33} \end{bmatrix} \begin{bmatrix} x_1 \\ x_2 \\ x_3 \end{bmatrix}. \tag{11.45}$$

Premultiplying both sides by the inverse of $\mathscr{A}$ results in

$$\mathscr{A}^{-1}y = \mathscr{A}^{-1}\mathscr{A}x.$$

But

$$\mathscr{A}^{-1}\mathscr{A}x = \mathscr{U}x = x,$$

so

$$x = \mathscr{A}^{-1}y. \tag{11.46a}$$

The jth element of the matrix, x, is, from the definition of the product,

$$x_j = \sum_{r=1}^{n} (a^{-1})_{jr}\, y_r, \tag{11.46b}$$

where

$$(a^{-1})_{jk} = \frac{A_{kj}}{|A|}. \tag{11.46c}$$

Notice that this is exactly the result indicated by Eqs. (11.16); but notice also how much less work, now that we have formulated a few rules of matrix algebra, is involved in arriving at this point. It is just this manipulation of sets of linear equations which has motivated our study of matrices.

EXAMPLE 11.1. The dependent variables in Eqs. (11.1) are considered to be the independent variables in the new set of equations

$$\begin{aligned} y_1' &= b_{11}y_1 + b_{12}y_2 + b_{13}y_3 \\ y_2' &= b_{21}y_1 + b_{22}y_2 + b_{23}y_3 \\ y_3' &= b_{31}y_1 + b_{32}y_2 + b_{33}y_3. \end{aligned} \tag{A}$$

Using matrix algebra, find the equations expressing the new dependent variable in terms of the x's in Eqs. (11.1).

Solution. The matrix form of Eqs. (11.1) as given in Eq. (11.44) is

$$y = \mathscr{A}x, \tag{B}$$

and, similarly, that of Eq. (A) is

$$y' = \mathscr{B}y. \tag{C}$$

Substituting Eq. (B) into Eq. (C) results in

$$y' = \mathscr{B}\mathscr{A}x. \tag{D}$$

This indicates the result sufficiently, but we will expand the coefficient matrix, $\mathscr{B}\mathscr{A}$, to see just what the coefficients of the x's are in Eq. (D). Thus, we get

$$\mathscr{B}\mathscr{A} = \begin{bmatrix} b_{11} & b_{12} & b_{13} \\ b_{21} & b_{22} & b_{23} \\ b_{31} & b_{32} & b_{33} \end{bmatrix} \begin{bmatrix} a_{11} & a_{12} & a_{13} \\ a_{21} & a_{22} & a_{23} \\ a_{31} & a_{32} & a_{33} \end{bmatrix}$$

$$= \begin{bmatrix} (b_{11}a_{11} + b_{12}a_{21} + b_{13}a_{31}) & (b_{11}a_{12} + b_{12}a_{22} + b_{13}a_{32}) & (b_{11}a_{13} + b_{12}a_{23} + b_{13}a_{33}) \\ (b_{21}a_{11} + b_{22}a_{21} + b_{23}a_{31}) & (b_{21}a_{12} + b_{22}a_{22} + b_{23}a_{32}) & (b_{21}a_{13} + b_{22}a_{23} + b_{23}a_{33}) \\ (b_{31}a_{11} + b_{32}a_{21} + b_{33}a_{31}) & (b_{31}a_{12} + b_{32}a_{22} + b_{33}a_{32}) & (b_{31}a_{13} + b_{32}a_{23} + b_{33}a_{33}) \end{bmatrix}.$$

Ans.

These are the coefficients which relate the new y's to the x's. You will have more confidence in this method and more appreciation for the work it saves if you will obtain the same results by substituting Eqs. (11.1) in Eqs. (A) of this example and collecting terms to achieve the same ends.

EXAMPLE 11.2. Use matrix methods to solve the set of equations

$$10 = 5x_1 + 3x_2 + 4x_3$$
$$5 = 3x_1 + 4x_2 + 2x_3$$
$$5 = 4x_1 + 2x_2 + 1x_3.$$

Solution. These equations may be put in the matrix form

$$y = \mathscr{A}x, \tag{A}$$

which, with its elements shown, is

$$\begin{bmatrix} 10 \\ 5 \\ 5 \end{bmatrix} = \begin{bmatrix} 5 & 3 & 4 \\ 3 & 4 & 2 \\ 4 & 2 & 1 \end{bmatrix} \begin{bmatrix} x_1 \\ x_2 \\ x_3 \end{bmatrix}. \tag{B}$$

The determinant of the coefficient matrix is

$$|A| = \begin{vmatrix} 5 & 3 & 4 \\ 3 & 4 & 2 \\ 4 & 2 & 1 \end{vmatrix} = -25.$$

The inverse of the coefficient matrix is

$$\mathscr{A}^{-1} = -\frac{1}{25} \begin{bmatrix} \begin{vmatrix} 4 & 2 \\ 2 & 1 \end{vmatrix} & -\begin{vmatrix} 3 & 4 \\ 2 & 1 \end{vmatrix} & \begin{vmatrix} 3 & 4 \\ 4 & 2 \end{vmatrix} \\ -\begin{vmatrix} 3 & 2 \\ 4 & 1 \end{vmatrix} & \begin{vmatrix} 5 & 4 \\ 4 & 1 \end{vmatrix} & -\begin{vmatrix} 5 & 4 \\ 3 & 2 \end{vmatrix} \\ \begin{vmatrix} 3 & 4 \\ 4 & 2 \end{vmatrix} & -\begin{vmatrix} 5 & 3 \\ 4 & 2 \end{vmatrix} & \begin{vmatrix} 5 & 3 \\ 3 & 4 \end{vmatrix} \end{bmatrix}$$

$$= -\frac{1}{25} \begin{bmatrix} 0 & 5 & -10 \\ 5 & -11 & 2 \\ -10 & 2 & 11 \end{bmatrix}.$$

The solution is $x = \mathscr{A}^{-1}y$, or

$$\begin{bmatrix} x_1 \\ x_2 \\ x_3 \end{bmatrix} = -\frac{1}{25} \begin{bmatrix} 0 & 5 & -10 \\ 5 & -11 & 2 \\ -10 & 2 & 11 \end{bmatrix} \begin{bmatrix} 10 \\ 5 \\ 5 \end{bmatrix}$$

$$= -\frac{1}{25} \begin{bmatrix} -25 \\ 5 \\ -35 \end{bmatrix} = \begin{bmatrix} 1.0 \\ -0.2 \\ 1.4 \end{bmatrix}.$$

The solutions for the x's are, from the equality rule for matrices,

$$x_1 = 1.0, \qquad x_2 = -0.2 \qquad x_3 = 1.4. \qquad Ans.$$

In the work that follows, we shall find that the time saved by the use of matrix algebra will more than compensate for the time spent in establishing its basic rules. Also, we will find that our ability to quickly grasp the general problems, where the values are not explicitly given, may be enhanced.

11.6 NODE AND MESH MATRICES

In Chapter 6 it was shown that for a system of node voltages the equation for the jth node was

$$i_j = \sum_{k=1}^{n} y_{jk} v_k. \tag{11.47a}$$

In the manner of Eqs. (11.31), this defines an element in the column matrix

$$i = \mathscr{Y}v,$$ (11.47b)

where

$$i = \begin{bmatrix} i_1 \\ i_2 \\ \vdots \\ i_n \end{bmatrix} = \begin{Bmatrix} \text{node forcing} \\ \text{current matrix} \end{Bmatrix}, \qquad v = \begin{bmatrix} v_1 \\ v_2 \\ \vdots \\ v_n \end{bmatrix} = \begin{Bmatrix} \text{node voltage} \\ \text{matrix} \end{Bmatrix}$$

$$\mathscr{Y} = \begin{bmatrix} y_{11} & y_{12} & y_{13} & \cdots & y_{1n} \\ y_{21} & y_{22} & y_{23} & \cdots & y_{2n} \\ y_{31} & y_{32} & y_{33} & \cdots & y_{3n} \\ \vdots & \vdots & \vdots & & \vdots \\ y_{n1} & y_{n2} & y_{n3} & \cdots & y_{nn} \end{bmatrix} = \begin{Bmatrix} \text{node} \\ \text{admittance} \\ \text{matrix} \end{Bmatrix}.$$

The solution for the node voltages is indicated by solving Eq. (11.47b) for

$$v = \mathscr{Y}^{-1}i.$$ (11.48)

It was also shown in Chapter 6 that

$$p(t) = \sum_{j=1}^{n} i_j(t)v_j(t).$$ (11.49a)

According to Eq. (11.32), this is the inner product

$$p(t) = \tilde{i}(t)v(t) = \tilde{v}(t)i(t).$$ (11.49b)

Similarly, mesh current analysis is described by the following matrix equations

$$v = \mathscr{Z}i$$ (11.50)

$$i = \mathscr{Z}^{-1}v$$ (11.51)

$$p(t) = \tilde{v}(t)i(t) = \tilde{i}(t)v(t).$$ (11.52)

11.7 BRANCH MATRICES

In Chapter 6 a network branch was considered to consist simply of a single network element or ideal source. This simple definition of the branch had the advantage that none of the details of circuit behavior became hidden behind the mathematical manipulations leading to a solution. You will recall, however, that in the switch to the formalized nodal and mesh analyses such entities as the node between a series voltage source and impedance and the loop consisting of a parallel current source and admittance were absorbed by elimination of variables prior to the appearance of the formalized forms.

The above observations lead one to believe that there may be some advantages, in formalized analysis, in considering the two-terminal networks consisting of series voltage sources and impedances or of parallel current sources and admittances as single network branches. The topological properties of such networks would be identical with those whose branches are made up of single elements. In fact, for the purposes of this chapter, it can be advantageous to go one step further and admit the following statement:

> Any two-terminal element, device, or subnetwork may be
> considered a branch of the network of which it is a part.

A branch defined in this way will, in general, have a Thévenin's equivalent and a Norton's equivalent, as illustrated in Fig. 11.1 for branch j of some

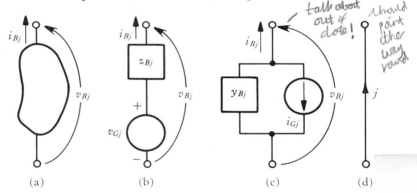

talk about out of date! should point other way round

Fig. 11.1 *Branch j and three of its models. (a) Branch j. (b) Thévenin's equ.*
(c) Norton's equivalent. (d) Directed-line representation.

network. In these equivalents, positive directions have been chosen so that the ideal sources deliver positive power when the associated voltages and currents are positive and so that passive branches, for which i_{Gj} and v_{Gj} are zero, will have voltage drop and current positive in the same direction. A third model is the directed line segment in (d) of the figure drawn in the network position of branch j and with a direction assigned that corresponds with the positive direction for i_{Bj} and v_{Bj}.

The Norton form of the branch gives rise to the equation

$$i_{Bj} = y_{Bj} v_{Bj} - i_{Gj}. \qquad (11.53)$$

If we set

$$y_{Bjk} = y_{Bj}\delta_{jk} = \begin{cases} y_{Bj}, & j=k \\ 0, & j \neq k \end{cases} \tag{11.54}$$

then

$$i_{Bj} = \sum_{k=1}^{n_B} y_{Bjk} v_{Bk} - i_{Gj}. \tag{11.55}$$

If all branches in the network are in the Norton form this describes the jth element in the n_B-element column matrix

$$i_B = \mathscr{Y}_B v_B - i_G, \tag{11.56}$$

which is called the *branch current matrix*. It is expressed in terms of the n_B-element *generated current matrix*, i_G, the n_B-element *branch voltage matrix*, v_B, and the $n_B \times n_B$ branch admittance matrix, $\mathscr{Y}_B$. The branch admittance matrix is a diagonal matrix, a fact which is obvious from Eq. (11.54).

The total power delivered to the network is

$$p(t) = \sum_{j=1}^{n_B} i_{Gj}(t)v_{Bj}(t), \tag{11.57a}$$

which describes the matrix inner product

$$p(t) = \tilde{i}_G(t)v_B(t) = \tilde{v}_B(t)i_G(t). \tag{11.57b}$$

When all the network branches are in their Thévenin form, then

$$v_{Bj} = \sum_{k=1}^{n_B} z_{Bjk} i_{Bk} - v_{Gj}, \tag{11.58}$$

where

$$z_{Bjk} = z_{Bj}\delta_{jk} = \begin{cases} z_{Bj}, & j=k \\ 0, & j \neq k \end{cases}. \tag{11.59}$$

Thus

$$v_B = \mathscr{Z}_B i_B - v_G, \tag{11.60}$$

where the $n_B \times n_B$ *branch impedance matrix*, $\mathscr{Z}_B$, is a diagonal matrix.

The total generated power in terms of the Thévenin formulation is

$$p(t) = \tilde{v}_G(t)i_B(t) = \tilde{i}_B(t)v_G(t). \tag{11.61}$$

Finally, let's premultiply each side of Eq. (11.56) by the inverse of the admittance matrix to get

$$\mathscr{Y}_B^{-1} i_B = \mathscr{Y}_B^{-1}\mathscr{Y}_B v_B - \mathscr{Y}_B^{-1} i_G = v_B - \mathscr{Y}_B^{-1} i_G.$$

Rearranging,

$$v_B = \mathscr{Y}_B^{-1} i_B + \mathscr{Y}_B^{-1} i_G .$$

Comparing this equation with Eq. (11.60), we see that

$$\mathscr{Z}_B = \mathscr{Y}_B^{-1}, \tag{11.62}$$

and

$$v_G = -\mathscr{Z}_B i_G . \tag{11.63}$$

Since the elements of the inverse of a diagonal matrix are the reciprocal of the elements of the original matrix,

$$z_{Bj} = \frac{1}{y_{Bj}}, \tag{11.64}$$

as, of course, we knew all along.

11.8 MATRIX FORMULATION OF NETWORK TOPOLOGY

The topological properties of networks may be assembled in an extraordinarily neat and concise way through the use of matrices. A brief look at such properties should help the student to an appreciation of the power of matrix analysis as well as open the door to more advanced readings in networks.

Directed Graphs

When the circuit model of the network is redrawn with all branches represented by directed line segments, as in Fig. 11.1(d), we have the model known as the directed graph of the network. This graph has the same configuration as does the undirected graph previously used, except that each branch now carries a direction arrow. The graph may be subdivided into trees and links in the conventional manner.

Figure 11.2 shows the directed graph of Fig. 6.9 with the series combination of y_8 and v_{G1} considered a single branch and the parallel combination of y_6 and i_{G2} considered a single branch.

The basic difference between the two types of graphs lies in the fact that the undirected graph may be drawn for the inert network, but the directed graph cannot be drawn until positive directions have been assigned to branch variables after the fashion of Sec. 11.7.

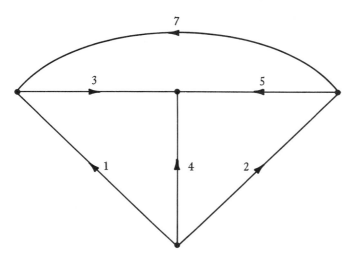

Fig. 11.2 *The directed graph of the network in Fig. 6.9 with the two possible two-terminal subnetworks considered single branches.*

Tree-Branch and Node Variables from Branch Variables

Let us now consider the matrix relations between branch quantities and tree-branch quantities (and, similarly, nodal quantities).

Figure 11.3 shows just the portion of a network tree which is adjacent to basic loop j in the network. All the basic cuts intersecting link j are also shown. Tree branches may be considered to have been labeled 1, 2, 3, ..., n_T and

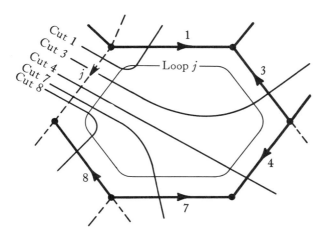

Fig. 11.3 *The jth basic loop in a network and portions of the basic cuts intersecting its links.*

network branches, of which the tree branches are a subset, to have been labeled $1, 2, 3, \ldots, j, \ldots, n_B$.

When we set out to express all branch voltages in terms of tree-branch voltages, those branches which are tree branches are easy; they simply consist of a single tree-branch voltage. However, those branches which are links require combinations of tree-branch voltages, which are easily formed by taking KVL about basic loops. Branch j, for example, is

$$v_{Bj} = 1v_1 + 0v_2 - 1v_3 + 1v_4 + 0v_5 + 0v_6 - 1v_7 + 1v_8 + \cdots + 0v_{n_T},$$

$$(11.65a)$$

which may be shortened to the form

$$v_{Bj} = \sum_{k=1}^{n_T} n_{jk} v_k, \qquad (11.65b)$$

describing the jth branch voltage in terms of the n_T tree-branch voltages.

Now consider the application of KCL at the n_T basic cuts with the equations written as *the summation of the currents crossing the cut in the direction of its associated tree branch*. A list showing the way i_{Bj} enters into KCL at cuts follows.

Cut 1: $\cdots + 1i_{Bj} + \cdots = 0$

Cut 2: $\cdots + 0i_{Bj} + \cdots = 0$

Cut 3: $\cdots - 1i_{Bj} + \cdots = 0$

Cut 4: $\cdots + 1i_{Bj} + \cdots = 0$

Cut 5: $\cdots + 0i_{Bj} + \cdots = 0$

Cut 6: $\cdots + 0i_{Bj} + \cdots = 0$

Cut 7: $\cdots - 1i_{Bj} + \cdots = 0$

Cut 8: $\cdots + 1i_{Bj} + \cdots = 0$

$$\vdots \qquad\qquad \vdots \qquad\qquad \vdots$$

Cut n_T: $\cdots + 0i_{Bn_T} + \cdots = 0.$

Note carefully that the column of coefficients of i_{Bj} in this list corresponds, one-to-one, with the row of coefficients of tree-branch voltages in Eq. (11.65a). Therefore, the kth equation in the above list may be written in the form

$$\sum_{j=1}^{n_B} n_{jk} i_{Bj} = 0, \qquad (11.66)$$

where n_{jk} has the same meaning as in Eq. (11.65b), having the value -1, 0, or $+1$.

It is left for the student to show that equations similar to (11.65b) and (11.66) relate nodal quantities to branch quantities. As the results are identical, we shall state them as they apply to both cases.

Equation (11.65b) is in the form of entry 11(b) in Table 11.1 and therefore represents a column matrix which is the product of a rectangular (not necessarily square) matrix and another column matrix. The results embodied by Eq. (11.65a) may then be stated in terms of matrices as follows:

"The network branch voltages in terms of tree-branch (or node-to-datum) voltages are represented by the column matrix

$$v_B = \mathcal{N} v \tag{11.67}$$

where v is the tree-branch (or node) voltage matrix and $\mathcal{N}$ is a matrix each element of which is -1, 0, or $+1$."

Equation (11.66) is not a conformable product, but setting $n_{jk} = \tilde{n}_{kj}$ creates the conformable product

$$\sum_{j=1}^{n_B} \tilde{n}_{kj} i_j = 0, \tag{11.68}$$

which describes a valid matrix product. Thus we may state the meaning of Eq. (11.66) as follows:

The set of KCL equations for basic cuts (or nodes), written as the summation of branch currents crossing the cut (or approaching the node) in the direction of the associated tree-branch (or node) voltage, is given by the matrix form

$$\tilde{\mathcal{N}} i_B = o \tag{11.69}$$

where i_B is the branch current matrix.

The generated currents from branches crossing cuts opposite the associated tree-branch direction (or approaching nodes in a direction opposite the node voltage) combine exactly as total branch currents do, but the result of the combination is not zero. We represent the result of this combination as

$$i = \tilde{\mathcal{N}} i_G, \tag{11.70}$$

which we shall call the *tree-branch* (or *node*) *forcing current*.

Now premultiply both sides of Eq. (11.56) by $\tilde{\mathcal{N}}$ and apply Eq. (11.69) to get

$$\tilde{\mathcal{N}} i_B = \tilde{\mathcal{N}} \mathcal{Y}_B v_B - \tilde{\mathcal{N}} i_G = o.$$

Substituting Eqs. (11.67) and (11.70) results in

$$\tilde{\mathcal{N}} \mathcal{Y}_B \mathcal{N} v - i = o.$$

Hence

$$i = \mathscr{Y}v \qquad (11.71)$$

where

$$\mathscr{Y} = \mathscr{N}\mathscr{Y}_B\mathscr{N}. \qquad (11.72)$$

Equation (11.71) is nothing more than Eq. (11.47b), except that now it has been extended to include the method of tree-branch voltages and the admittance matrix has been explicitly tied to the basic branch admittance matrix through Eq. (11.72).

Substituting Eq. (11.67) (in its time-varying form) into Eq. (11.57b) yields

$$p(t) = \tilde{\imath}_G(t)\mathscr{N}v(t).$$

But from Eq. (11.70)

$$\tilde{\imath} = \tilde{\imath}_G\mathscr{N}$$

so

$$p(t) = \tilde{\imath}(t)v(t), \qquad (11.73)$$

which attaches greater generality to Eq. (11.49b), stated for nodal analysis only.

Link and Mesh Variables from Branch Variables

In Fig. 11.4 are shown just those links intersecting the basic cut associated with tree-branch j in the network. All basic loops adjacent to tree-

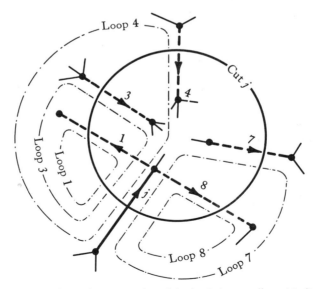

Fig. 11.4 *The jth basic cut in a network and the basic loops adjacent to its tree branch.*

branch j are also shown. Links have been labeled 1, 2, 3, ..., n_L and again tree branches have been tagged 1, 2, 3, ..., j, ..., n_B, with the n_L links a subset of the n_B branches.

The branch currents are either link currents or can be expressed as combinations of link currents by applying KCL at basic cuts. Branch j is an example of the latter, where

$$i_{Bj} = 1i_1 + 0i_2 - 1i_3 - 1i_4 + 0i_5 + 0i_6 + 1i_7 + 1i_8 + \cdots + 0i_{n_L},$$

or

$$i_{Bj} = \sum_{k=1}^{n_L} m_{jk} i_k. \tag{11.74}$$

Next, we prepare a list showing the way v_{Bj} enters into KVL around the n_L basic loops with the equations written as *the summation of the voltage drops around the loop in the direction of its associated link*:

$$\begin{aligned}
\text{Loop 1:} &\quad \cdots + 1v_{Bj} + \cdots = 0 \\
\text{Loop 2:} &\quad \cdots + 0v_{Bj} + \cdots = 0 \\
\text{Loop 3:} &\quad \cdots - 1v_{Bj} + \cdots = 0 \\
\text{Loop 4:} &\quad \cdots - 1v_{Bj} + \cdots = 0 \\
\text{Loop 5:} &\quad \cdots + 0v_{Bj} + \cdots = 0 \\
\text{Loop 6:} &\quad \cdots + 0v_{Bj} + \cdots = 0 \\
\text{Loop 7:} &\quad \cdots + 1v_{Bj} + \cdots = 0 \\
\text{Loop 8:} &\quad \cdots + 1v_{Bj} + \cdots = 0 \\
&\quad\vdots \\
\text{Loop } n_L: &\quad \cdots + 0v_{Bj} + \cdots = 0.
\end{aligned}$$

The kth equation in this list is of the form

$$\sum_{j=1}^{n_B} m_{jk} v_{Bj} = 0 \tag{11.75}$$

where m_{jk} has the value -1, 0, or $+1$.

A similar development can be made for meshes, and in a manner very similar to that followed for voltage variables, we may state, as a result of Eq. (11.74)

"The network branch currents in terms of link (or mesh) currents are represented by the column matrix

$$i_B = \mathcal{M}i, \tag{11.76}$$

where i is the link (or mesh) current matrix and $\mathcal{M}$ is a matrix each element of which is -1, 0, or $+1$."

From Eq. (11.75), and the step leading up to it, we also deduce that

> The set of KVL equations for basic loops (or meshes), written as the sum of branch voltages around the loop in the direction of the associated link (or mesh) current, is given by the matrix form

$$\tilde{\mathcal{M}} v_B = o \tag{11.77}$$

> where v_B is the branch voltage matrix.

The sum of the generated voltages from branches adjacent to the basic loop (or mesh) around the loop (or mesh) opposite the direction of the associated link (or mesh) current is

$$v = \tilde{\mathcal{M}} v_G. \tag{11.78}$$

This is the *link* (or mesh) *forcing voltage.*

In a manner analogous to that used for establishing Eq. (11.71), we may now easily show, starting with Eq. (11.60), that

$$v = \mathscr{L} i, \tag{11.79}$$

where

$$\mathscr{L} = \tilde{\mathcal{M}} \mathscr{L}_B \mathcal{M}, \tag{11.80}$$

and that

$$p(t) = \tilde{v}(t) i(t). \tag{11.81}$$

Equations (11.79) and (11.81) repeat Eqs. (11.50) and (11.52), but we have now shown them to cover a more general class of situations.

PROBLEMS

In the following problems

$$\mathcal{A} = \begin{bmatrix} 1 & -1 & 0 \\ 2 & 3 & -1 \\ -3 & 0 & 1 \end{bmatrix}, \quad \mathcal{B} = \begin{bmatrix} 3 & 2 & 2 \\ -1 & 0 & 2 \\ 2 & 1 & 1 \end{bmatrix}, \quad y = \begin{bmatrix} x_1 \\ x_2 \\ x_3 \end{bmatrix}, \quad x = \begin{bmatrix} y_1 \\ y_2 \\ y_3 \end{bmatrix}.$$

Perform the indicated operation, evaluation, or expansion, writing the result with each element expressed as a simple numerical or as the simplest combination of x's and y's.

11.1 Find $\mathcal{C} = \mathcal{A} + \mathcal{B}$.
11.2 Find $\mathcal{F} = \mathcal{A} - \mathcal{B}$.
11.3 Find $\mathcal{C} = \mathcal{A}\mathcal{B}$.

11.4 Find $\mathscr{D} = \mathscr{B}\mathscr{A}$.

11.5 Write $y = \mathscr{A}x$ as an equation of column matrices.

11.6 Write $\tilde{\mathscr{A}}$.

11.7 Write $\tilde{x}$ and $\tilde{y}$.

11.8 Find $\widetilde{\mathscr{A}\mathscr{B}}$ and $\tilde{\mathscr{B}}\tilde{\mathscr{A}}$ and compare.

11.9 Find $|A|$ and $|B|$.

11.10 Find $\mathscr{A}^{-1}$.

11.11 Find $\mathscr{B}^{-1}$.

11.12 Find $(\mathscr{A}\mathscr{B})^{-1}$ and $\mathscr{B}^{-1}\mathscr{A}^{-1}$ and compare.

11.13 Write $40\,\mathscr{A}$.

11.14 Show that $\mathscr{A}\mathscr{U} = \mathscr{A}$.

11.15 Write $\tilde{x}y$ and $\tilde{y}x$.

11.16 If $y = \mathscr{A}x$, find x.

11.17 If $y = \mathscr{A}x$, $z = \mathscr{B}y$, and $z = \mathscr{M}x$, find $\mathscr{M}$ in terms of $\mathscr{A}$ and $\mathscr{B}$.

11.18 Expand $k = \tilde{x}\mathscr{A}x$.

11.19 Show that $\tilde{x}\mathscr{A}y = \tilde{y}\tilde{\mathscr{A}}x$.

11.20 Show that $|A| \times |B| = |AB|$.

11.21 Show that in a resistive network with the voltage sources only, the power expended is

$$p = \tilde{\imath}\mathscr{R}i,$$

where i is the mesh current matrix and $\mathscr{R}$ is the mesh resistance matrix.

11.22 Show that in a resistive network with current sources only, the power expended is

$$p = \tilde{v}\mathscr{G}v,$$

where v is the node voltage matrix and $\mathscr{G}$ is the nodal conductance matrix.

11.23 Show that in a network under steady-state sinusoidal excitation by voltage sources only, described in terms of mesh currents, the vector volt-amperes are

$$\mathbf{S} = \underline{\mathbf{I}^*}\ \mathbf{V}] = \underline{\mathbf{I}^*}\ [\mathbf{Z}]\mathbf{I}].$$

11.24 Solve the network of Fig. P.6.2 by using Eq. (11.51). Find the dissipated power using Eq. (11.52) and check using the results of Prob. 11.21.

11.25 Solve the network of Fig. P.6.3 using Eq. (11.51).

11.26 Solve the network of Fig. P.6.4 using Eq. (11.51).

11.27 Solve the network of Fig. P.6.5 using Eq. (11.51).

11.28 Solve the network of Fig. P.6.6 using Eq. (11.51).

11.29 Solve the network of Fig. P.6.8 for the indicated mesh currents by use of Eq. (11.51) and find the total vector volt-amperes by the results of Prob. 11.23.

11.30 Repeat Prob. 11.29 for the network of Fig. P.6.9.

11.31 Solve the network of Fig. P.6.1 by using Eq. (11.48). Then use Eq. (11.49b) to find the total dissipated power in the vertical resistors and check using the results of Prob. 11.22.

11.32 Solve the network of Fig. P.6.3 using Eq. (11.48).

11.33 Solve the network of Fig. P.6.4 using Eq. (11.48).

11.34 Solve the network of Fig. P.6.5 using Eq. (11.48).

11.35 Solve the network of Fig. P.6.6 using Eq. (11.48).

11.36 Solve the network of Fig. P.6.7 for the indicated voltages utilizing a two-by-two nodal admittance matrix.

11.37 Solve for the voltages across the capacitor and the inductance in Fig. P.6.8 by way of a second-order matrix equation.

11.38 Indicate the results of Prob. 6.44 in matrix form utilizing the $\mathscr{R}$, $\mathscr{L}$, and $\mathscr{S}$ (where $S_{jk} = 1/C_{jk}$) matrices. Show the array of elements corresponding to each matrix used.

11.39 Repeat Prob. 11.38 for Prob. 6.47.

11.40 Indicate the results of Prob. 6.45 in matrix form utilizing the $\mathscr{G}$, $\mathscr{C}$, and $\mathscr{B}$ (where $\Gamma_{jk} = 1/L_{jk}$) matrices. Show the array of elements corresponding to each matrix used.

11.41 Repeat Prob. 11.40 for Prob. 6.46.

11.42 For Fig. P.6.3, show the arrays of elements corresponding to the matrix quantities of Eq. (11.56). Find the matrix $\mathscr{N}$, and check its results using Eqs. (11.67), (11.70), and (11.72) against those of Prob. 11.32.

11.43 For Fig. P.6.2, show the arrays of elements corresponding to the matrices in Eq. (11.60). Find the matrix $\mathscr{M}$, and check its results using Eqs. (11.76), (11.78), and (11.80) against those of Prob. 11.24.

12

Special Topics

12.1 INTRODUCTION

In a chapter entitled as this one is, one should not expect to find any new basic material. Rather he should expect to find previously established basic relationships organized in such a way as to exploit the underlying unity that all systems of the class studied have because of their common characteristics.

By now the observant student is beginning to suspect that Mother Nature's splendid variety of appearances is due more to her wardrobe than to her form. He finds that a phenomenon in the dress of a mechanical system, an acoustical system, or a nodal system will reduce, for example, to the very same mathematical form as that taken by a system of mesh currents. He is discovering that certain general *forms*, which are, oddly enough, often specializations of more general *properties* basic to the system, will be identical for every network studied. This chapter recognizes and exploits those properties, as well as forms, which are common to all systems, and catalogs as *theorems* or *principles* certain relationships which occur again and again as the equations resulting from the basic volt-ampere and energy relationships are manipulated.

12.2 MAXIMUM POWER TRANSFER

In low-energy circuits, such as those used in communication elec-
tronics, it is often desirable that the maximum possible power flow from one
part of the network to another. This is important, for example, when one
wishes to transfer the maximum amount of the limited power available in a
microphone or a phonograph pickup through the succeeding stages of ampli-
fication into the final speaker system.

Suppose that we desire to transfer the maximum possible power out of the
two-terminal network whose Thévenin's equivalent is shown in Fig. 12.1 into
the impedance $Z(j\omega)$ by the proper selection of $Z(j\omega)$.

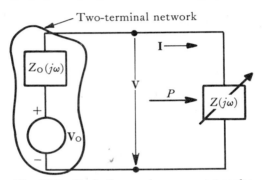

Fig. 12.1 *Illustrating maximum power transfer.*

At a given radian frequency, ω, Thévenin's equivalent impedance of the
two-terminal network is

$$Z_o(j\omega) = \mathbf{Z_o}$$
$$= R_o + jX_o. \tag{12.1}$$

The *load impedance* on the network is

$$Z(j\omega) = \mathbf{Z}$$
$$= R + jX, \tag{12.2}$$

where R and X are to be varied to maximize the transferred power, which is

$$P = \text{Re}\,[\mathbf{I^*V}]$$
$$= \text{Re}\,[\mathbf{I^*IZ}]$$
$$= I^2R$$
$$= \frac{V_o^2 R}{(R + R_o)^2 + (X + X_o)^2}$$
$$= P(R, X). \tag{12.3}$$

At a maximum P changes both with respect to R and with respect to X are zero, since such a change in either direction ($-$ or $+$) must reduce P. Therefore, at such a point,

$$\frac{\partial P}{\partial R} = 0 \qquad\qquad\qquad (12.4a)$$

$$\frac{\partial P}{\partial X} = 0. \qquad\qquad\qquad (12.4b)$$

From Eq. (12.3)

$$\frac{\partial P}{\partial R} = V_o^2 \frac{(R + R_o)^2 + (X + X_o)^2 - 2R(R + R_o)}{[(R + R_o)^2 + (X + X_o)^2]^2} \qquad (12.5a)$$

$$\frac{\partial P}{\partial X} = -2V_o^2 R \frac{X + X_o}{[(R + R_o)^2 + (X + X_o)^2]^2}. \qquad (12.5b)$$

Setting these partial derivatives equal to zero and solving for R and X results in

$$R = R_o \qquad\qquad\qquad (12.6a)$$

$$X = -X_o, \qquad\qquad\qquad (12.6b)$$

or, more briefly,

$$\mathbf{Z} = \mathbf{Z}_o^*. \qquad\qquad\qquad (12.7)$$

Thus, the impedance which extracts maximum power from the *source network* is that impedance which is the conjugate of the Thévenin's equivalent impedance (or *output impedance*) of the network. Alternatively, the admittance which extracts maximum power from the source network is the conjugate of the Norton's equivalent admittance (or *output admittance*) of the network. Operating under these conditions, the *load* is said to be *matched* to the source network.

In some applications, such a free choice of parameters is not admitted. A common exception occurs when the magnitude only of the load impedance can be varied, with the phase angle, θ, fixed. Under these conditions, Eq. (12.3) becomes

$$P = \frac{V_o^2 Z \cos \theta}{Z^2 + Z_o^2 + 2kZ \cos \theta}$$

$$= P(Z) \qquad\qquad\qquad (12.8)$$

where both θ and

$$k = R_o + \frac{X}{R} X_o$$

$$= R_o + X_o \tan \theta$$

are constants. To find Z for maximum P, set

$$\frac{dP}{dZ} = 0,$$

or

$$V_o^2 \cos \theta \, \frac{Z_o^2 - Z^2}{[Z^2 + Z_o^2 + 2kZ \cos \theta]^2} = 0. \qquad (12.9)$$

This results in

$$Z = Z_o, \qquad (12.10)$$

and we see that under the condition of constant phase angle on the load, the load is matched for maximum power transfer when the magnitude of the load impedance is equal to the magnitude of the output impedance of the source network.

A word of caution is in order regarding the use of this *maximum power transfer theorem*. The student must remember that matching at a particular frequency does not infer matching at all frequencies. In general, maximum power transfer occurs at one frequency only.

12.3 EQUIVALENT THREE-TERMINAL NETWORKS

Any passive three-terminal linear network may be represented by one of the networks shown in Fig. 12.2. Actually, there are only two configurations shown, since the π- and T-networks are identical respectively to the Δ- and Y-networks, the different nomenclature being suggested by the slightly different, but equivalent, ways of drawing the network.

Two three-terminal networks are said to be *equivalent* if they cannot be determined to be different by measurements taken at their respective terminals.

It is left as an exercise for the student to show that the networks in Fig. 12.2 are equivalent insofar as they are viewed externally through the three terminals, providing that the T (or Y) impedances are defined in terms of the π (or Δ) impedances as

$$z_1 = \frac{z_a z_b}{z_a + z_b + z_c}, \qquad (12.11a)$$

$$z_2 = \frac{z_b z_c}{z_a + z_b + z_c}, \qquad (12.11b)$$

$$z_3 = \frac{z_c z_a}{z_a + z_b + z_c}, \qquad (12.11c)$$

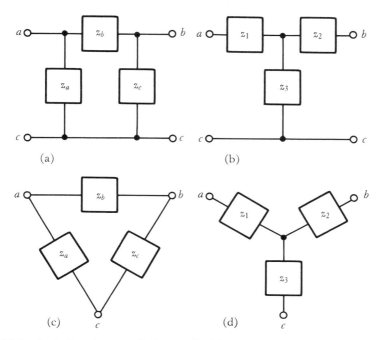

Fig. 12.2 *Equivalent three-terminal networks. (a) π-configuration. (b) T-configuration.
(c) Δ-configuration. (d) Y-configuration.*

or, conversely,

$$y_a = \frac{y_3\,y_1}{y_1 + y_2 + y_3}, \tag{12.12a}$$

$$y_b = \frac{y_1 y_2}{y_1 + y_2 + y_3}, \tag{12.12b}$$

$$y_c = \frac{y_2\,y_3}{y_1 + y_2 + y_3}. \tag{12.12c}$$

Again, the lower case y's and z's indicate *some* linear operation for which a reciprocal has meaning, such as $Y(p)$, $Z(j\omega)$, R, G, $\mathbf{Z}$, and the like.

Although Eqs. (12.11) and (12.12) appear complicated, reference to the equations and to Fig. 12.3 allows one to state the rules for their formation, one from the other, as follows:

1. The equivalent wye impedance connecting to a given point on the delta being replaced is equal to the product of the two delta impedances connecting to the point divided by the sum of the delta impedances.

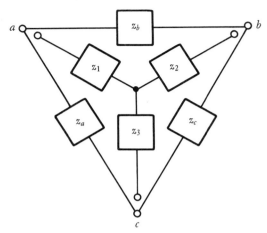

Fig. 12.3 *Equivalent networks overlaid.*

2. The equivalent delta admittance connected between a given pair of external points on the wye being replaced is equal to the product of the two wye admittances connected to the points divided by the sum of the wye admittances.

EXAMPLE 12.1. Find the resistance between terminals a and b of the given network in Fig. 12.4.

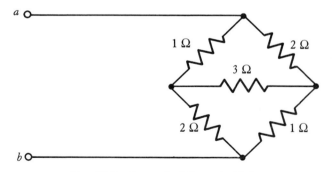

Fig. 12.4 *Network of Example 12.1.*

Solution. One is first inclined in a network with no sources to use progressive applications of the formation of series and parallel circuits. However, in this example, he is faced immediately with the fact that no one resistor is in simple parallel or simple series with any other. Although he can assume a forcing voltage (or current) and solve by routine methods, it is likely to be less work to apply the results of this section by computing the equivalent single resistor.

Applying the delta-wye transformation to the delta formed by the upper three resistors results in

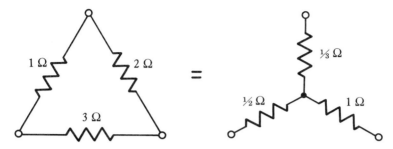

which transforms the original network into that shown in Fig. 12.5. The total resistance then becomes, by application of series-parallel combinations,

$$R = \frac{1}{3} + \frac{(2 + \frac{1}{2})(1 + 1)}{2 + \frac{1}{2} + 1 + 1}$$

$$= \frac{1}{3} + \frac{10}{9}$$

$$= \frac{39}{27} = \frac{13}{9}$$

$$= 1.44 \ \Omega. \qquad Ans.$$

Fig. 12.5 *Network externally equivalent to that of Fig. 12.4.*

12.4 SUPERPOSITION AND TRANSFER QUANTITIES

In Sec. 3.5, where the principle of superposition was introduced, it was shown that the jth response current of a system of n generated signals was

$$i_j = \sum_{k=1}^{n} i_{jk}, \tag{12.13}$$

where

$$i_{jk} = i_j \big|_{\text{all except the } k\text{th generated signal zero}}. \tag{12.13a}$$

Similarly, the ith response voltage was

$$v_i = \sum_{k=1}^{n} v_{ik}, \tag{12.14}$$

where

$$v_{ik} = v_i \big|_{\text{all except the } k\text{th generated signal zero}}. \tag{12.14a}$$

In Eq. (12.13), i_{jk} is proportional to the kth exciting function, whether it be a forcing voltage or a forcing current. We recognize this by setting

$$i_{jk} = \begin{cases} y_{Tjk} v_{Sk}, & k\text{th source a voltage} \\ h_{Ijk} i_{Sk}, & k\text{th source a current.} \end{cases} \tag{12.15}$$

The operator

$$h_{Ijk} = \frac{i_{jk}}{i_{Sk}} = \frac{i_j}{i_{Sk}} \bigg|_{\text{all sources but the } k\text{th zero}} \tag{12.16}$$

is called the *transfer current ratio* relating current response j to forcing current k. The admittance operator becomes

$$y_{Tjk} = \frac{i_{jk}}{v_{Sk}} \quad \frac{i_j}{v_{Sk}} \bigg|_{\text{all sources but the } k\text{th zero}}$$

$$= \begin{cases} \textit{transfer admittance} \text{ from source} \\ k \text{ to response } j, j \neq k \\ \textit{driving-point admittance} \text{ to} \\ \text{source } k, j = k \end{cases}. \tag{12.17}$$

Similarly, in Eq. (12.14)

$$v_{ik} = \begin{cases} z_{Tik} i_{Sk}, & k\text{th source a current} \\ h_{Vik} v_{Sk}, & k\text{th source a voltage.} \end{cases} \tag{12.18}$$

We define as the *transfer voltage* ratio between voltage response i and forcing voltage k the operator

$$h_{Vik} = \frac{v_{ik}}{v_{Sk}} = \frac{v_i}{v_{Sk}} \bigg|_{\text{all sources except the } k\text{th zero}} . \tag{12.19}$$

The impedance operator is

$$z_{Tik} = \frac{v_{ik}}{i_{Sk}} = \frac{v_i}{i_{Sk}} \bigg|_{\text{all sources except the } k\text{th zero}}$$

$$= \begin{pmatrix} transfer\ impedance\ \text{from source} \\ k\ \text{to response } i,\ i \neq k \\ \\ driving\text{-}point\ impedance\ \text{to} \\ \text{source } k,\ i = k \end{pmatrix} . \tag{12.20}$$

If one were to generalize the principles here by denoting the kth source (or forcing function) by f_{Sk}, whether voltage or current, and the jth response by r_k, whether voltage or current, then

$$r_j = \sum_{k=1}^{n} r_{jk} = \sum_{k=1}^{n} h_{Tjk} f_{Sk} , \tag{12.21}$$

where

$$h_{Tjk} = \frac{r_{jk}}{f_{Sk}} = \frac{r_j}{f_k} \bigg|_{\text{all sources except the } k\text{th zero}} . \tag{12.22}$$

In these expressions, h_{Tjk} is a *transfer system function* which in a particular case may be h_{Ijk}, y_{Tjk}, h_{Vjk}, or z_{Tjk}.

As an example, suppose a system has m voltage sources resulting in p current responses. If source variables are identified with the subscript S, the jth current response will be the special form of Eq. (12.21),

$$i_j = \sum_{r=1}^{m} y_{Tjr} v_{Sr} , \qquad j = 1, 2, \ldots, p. \tag{12.23a}$$

Equation (12.23a) describes the matrix form

$$i = \mathscr{Y}_T v_S , \tag{12.23b}$$

where the subscript, T, is employed to differentiate between the transfer admittance, which may be singular, and the branch or nodal admittance matrices, which are nonsingular.

In a similar way, the current responses to current sources, the voltage responses to voltage sources, and the voltage responses to current sources may be expressed by superposition. The first four entires in Table 12.1 list

TABLE 12.1 SOME SPECIAL SOURCE-RESPONSE COMBINATIONS

Entry No.	Source matrix, f_S	Response matrix, $\imath$	Transfer matrix, $\mathscr{H}_T$	Name of Transfer Matrix	Units on h_{Tjk}
1.	i_S	v	$\mathscr{Y}_T$	Transfer admittance	Ohm^{-1}
2.	i_S	i	$\mathscr{H}_I$	Current ratio	Unitless
3.	v_S	v	$\mathscr{H}_V$	Voltage ratio	Unitless
4.	v_S	i	$\mathscr{Z}_T$	Transfer impedance	Ohms
5.	f	φ	$\mathscr{P}_T$	Transfer permeance	Henries

these, along with the result embodied in Eq. (12.23b). The table establishes the symbolism which will henceforth be used to designate the various transfer matrices.

Entry No. 5 is included in the table because it will be useful to us later on. Equation (1.50) for the magnetic circuit is repeated here in its general form for convenience.

$$\phi = \mathscr{P}Ni. \tag{12.24}$$

This is the equation for the magnetic flux in a single-coil system. The flux, ϕ, is a response to the magnetic potential source, Ni. In a system of more than one coil, the various magnetic branches will contain fluxes which are the superposed effects of all coil currents in the system. For this case the principle of superposition states that, if the system has m coil currents,

$$\phi_j = \sum_{r=1}^{m} \phi_{jr} = \sum_{r=1}^{m} \mathscr{P}_{Tjr} F_r, \tag{12.25}$$

where

$$F_r = N_r i_r. \tag{12.25a}$$

Equation (12.25) is the conformable product whose matrix representation is

$$\varphi = \mathscr{P}_T f, \tag{12.26}$$

which explains the fifth entry in the table.

It must be recognized that some electric networks will have mixed current and voltage sources and also that both current and voltage responses sometimes need to be determined. This means that some elements of the transfer matrix will have the dimensions of admittance, some will have the dimensions of impedance, and some will be voltage ratios or current ratios with no dimensions. In these cases it is often desirable to use the same subscript to identify a voltage as has been used to identify a current. For example, it is certainly desirable to identify all quantities associated with Branch No. 3 with the subscript, 3. For this reason, we shall adopt a system of variable numbering that allows such duplication of subscripts for mixed systems. This is illustrated by the following example of a system with m voltage sources, n current sources, p desired current responses, and q desired voltage responses:

$$
\begin{bmatrix}
i_1 \\ i_2 \\ \vdots \\ i_p \\ \hline v_1 \\ v_2 \\ \vdots \\ v_q
\end{bmatrix}
=
\left[
\begin{array}{cccc|cccc}
y_{T11} & y_{T12} & \cdots & y_{T1m} & h_{I11} & h_{I12} & \cdots & h_{I1n} \\
y_{T21} & y_{T22} & \cdots & y_{T2m} & h_{I21} & h_{I22} & \cdots & h_{I2n} \\
\vdots & \vdots & & \vdots & \vdots & \vdots & & \vdots \\
y_{Tp1} & y_{Tp2} & \cdots & y_{Tpm} & h_{Ip1} & h_{Ip2} & \cdots & h_{Ipn} \\
\hline
h_{V11} & h_{V12} & \cdots & h_{V1m} & z_{T11} & z_{T12} & \cdots & z_{T1n} \\
h_{V21} & h_{V22} & \cdots & h_{V2m} & z_{T21} & z_{T22} & \cdots & z_{T2n} \\
\vdots & \vdots & & \vdots & \vdots & \vdots & & \vdots \\
h_{Vq1} & h_{Vq2} & \cdots & h_{Vqm} & z_{Tq1} & z_{Tq2} & \cdots & z_{Tqn}
\end{array}
\right]
\begin{bmatrix}
v_{S1} \\ v_{S2} \\ \vdots \\ v_{Sm} \\ \hline i_{S1} \\ i_{S2} \\ \vdots \\ i_{Sn}
\end{bmatrix} . \quad (12.27)
$$

The dotted lines partition this complete matrix into those which would have resulted with but one kind of source present and with but one kind of response included in the set of desired response variables.

EXAMPLE 12.2. Find the transfer admittance matrix relating all indicated response currents in Fig. 12.6 to the forcing voltages.

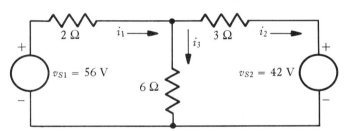

Fig. 12.6 *Circuit for Example 12.2.*

Solution. Let us solve by direct application of superposition, utilizing Fig. 12.7, where the effects of the two sources are separated. It is not necessary

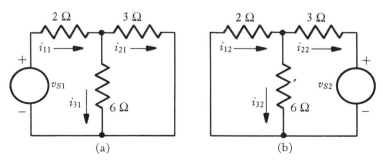

Fig. 12.7 *The separate effects in the circuit of Fig. 12.6.*

to use the operational form here, since all operations are simply multiplications by constants.

Using standard resistance network reductions,

$$y_{T11} = \frac{i_{11}}{v_{S1}} = \frac{1}{2 + \dfrac{3(6)}{3+6}} = \frac{1}{4} = 0.250 \ \Omega^{-1},$$

$$y_{T21} = \frac{i_{21}}{v_{S1}} = \frac{6}{3+6}\frac{i_{11}}{v_{S1}} = \frac{2}{3}\left(\frac{1}{4}\right) = \frac{1}{6} = 0.167 \ \Omega^{-1},$$

$$y_{T31} = \frac{i_{31}}{v_{S1}} = \frac{3}{3+6}\frac{i_{11}}{v_{S1}} = \frac{1}{3}\left(\frac{1}{4}\right) = \frac{1}{12} = 0.0833 \ \Omega^{-1},$$

$$y_{T22} = \frac{i_{22}}{v_{S2}} = \frac{-1}{3 + \dfrac{2(6)}{2+6}} = -\frac{8}{15} = -0.533 \ \Omega^{-1},$$

$$y_{T12} = \frac{i_{12}}{v_{S2}} = \frac{6}{2+6}\frac{i_{22}}{v_{S2}} = \frac{3}{4}\left(-\frac{8}{15}\right) = -\frac{6}{15} = -0.400 \ \Omega^{-1},$$

$$y_{T32} = \frac{i_{32}}{v_{S2}} = \frac{-2}{2+6}\frac{i_{22}}{v_{S2}} = -\frac{1}{4}\left(-\frac{8}{15}\right) = \frac{2}{15} = 0.133 \ \Omega^{-1}.$$

Therefore,

$$Y_T = \begin{bmatrix} y_{T11} & y_{T12} \\ y_{T21} & y_{T22} \\ y_{T31} & y_{T32} \end{bmatrix} = \begin{bmatrix} 0.250 & -0.400 \\ 0.167 & -0.533 \\ 0.0833 & 0.133 \end{bmatrix} \Omega^{-1}. \qquad Ans.$$

EXAMPLE 12.3. Find v_3 and i_3 in Fig. 12.8 by the principle of superposition and find the four transfer quantities relating v_3 and i_3 to sources v_{S1} and i_{S2}.

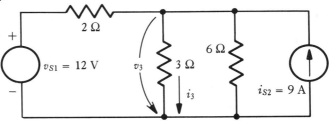

Fig. 12.8 *Circuit for Example 12.3.*

Solution. Since this is a resistance network with mixed sources and responses, the matrix form of the system responses is

$$\begin{bmatrix} i_3 \\ v_3 \end{bmatrix} = \begin{bmatrix} y_{T31} & h_{I32} \\ h_{V31} & z_{T32} \end{bmatrix}\begin{bmatrix} v_{S1} \\ i_{S2} \end{bmatrix} = \begin{bmatrix} G_{T31} & H_{I32} \\ H_{V31} & R_{T32} \end{bmatrix}\begin{bmatrix} v_{S1} \\ i_{S2} \end{bmatrix}.$$

Here we have acknowledged the purely direct-current nature of this problem by the use of actual resistive operators, which have in the past been indicated by capital letters, such as G for the conductance (dc admittance) and R for the resistance (dc impedance), as well as the use of the capital H in the same sense.

Expanding the right side, equating elements on the left to elements on the right, and expressing each response in terms of component responses results in

$$i_3 = G_{T31} v_{S1} + H_{I32} i_{S2} = i_{31} + i_{32}$$
$$v_3 = H_{V31} v_{S1} + R_{T32} i_{S2} = v_{31} + v_{32}.$$

It is not necessary here to use the operational form, because all operations are simply multiplications by constants. The circuit for observing the effects of v_{S1} is the circuit above with $i_{S2} = 0$, shown in Fig. 12.9 with resulting responses labeled.

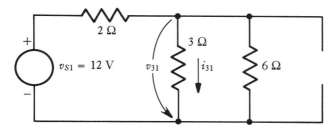

Fig. 12.9 *Circuit for finding response due to voltage source in Fig. 12.8.*

From voltage-divider relationships,

$$v_{31} = \frac{\dfrac{3(6)}{3+6}}{2 + \dfrac{3(6)}{3+6}} v_{S1} = \frac{1}{2} v_{S1} = 6 \text{ V},$$

and

$$i_{31} = \frac{v_{31}}{3} = \frac{6}{3} = 2 \text{ A}.$$

Thus, from Eq. (12.21),

$$G_{T31} = \frac{i_{31}}{v_{S1}} = \frac{2}{12} = \frac{1}{6} \Omega^{-1} \qquad Ans.$$

$$H_{V31} = \frac{v_{31}}{v_{S1}} = \frac{6}{12} = \frac{1}{2} \frac{\text{volt}}{\text{volt}}. \qquad Ans.$$

The circuit for the effects of i_{S2} with $v_{S1} = 0$ is shown in Fig. 12.10 with responses labeled.

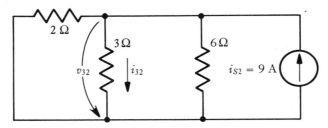

Fig. 12.10   *Circuit for finding response due to current source in Fig. 12.8.*

Using current-divider relationships,

$$i_{32} = \frac{\frac{1}{3}}{\frac{1}{2} + \frac{1}{3} + \frac{1}{6}} i_{S2} = \frac{1}{3} i_{S2} = \frac{9}{3} = 3 \text{ A},$$

and

$$v_{32} = 3i_{32} = 3(3) = 9 \text{ V}.$$

The transfer quantities become

$$z_{T32} = R_{T32} = \frac{v_{32}}{i_{S2}} = \frac{9}{3} = 3 \ \Omega \qquad Ans.$$

$$H_{I32} = \frac{i_{32}}{i_{S2}} = \frac{3}{9} = \frac{1}{3} \frac{\text{ampere}}{\text{ampere}}. \qquad Ans.$$

The combined effects of v_{S1} and i_{S2} are

$$i_3 = i_{31} + i_{32} = 2 + 3 = 5 \text{ A} \qquad Ans.$$
$$v_3 = v_{31} + v_{32} = 6 + 9 = 15 \text{ V}. \qquad Ans.$$

12.5 TWO-PORT NETWORKS

Networks with but two pairs of terminals through which energy exchange occurs, as illustrated in Fig. 12.11, are called *two-port*, or *two-terminal-pair*, or, inaccurately, *four-terminal* networks with the first-mentioned the apparent current favorite. Such networks are generally the sole connection between two other networks and usually only the terminal responses, as illustrated in the figure, are of interest. Thus, for the problem at hand internal voltages and currents of the two-port network are of secondary

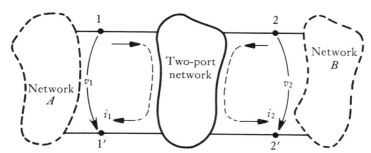

Fig. 12.11   *Two-port network used in the cascaded connection.*

importance. This indicates the possibility of establishing an equivalent circuit, from the standpoint of terminal responses, for the two-port network.

If the two-port network has no independent energy sources, including initial conditions, then the mesh current equation for the two-port network is

$$
\begin{bmatrix} v_1 \\ v_2 \\ 0 \\ \vdots \\ 0 \end{bmatrix} = \begin{bmatrix} z_{11} & z_{12} & \cdots & z_{1n} \\ z_{21} & z_{22} & \cdots & z_{2n} \\ z_{31} & z_{32} & \cdots & z_{3n} \\ \vdots & \vdots & & \vdots \\ z_{n1} & z_{n2} & \cdots & z_{nn} \end{bmatrix} \begin{bmatrix} i_1 \\ i_2 \\ i_3 \\ \vdots \\ i_n \end{bmatrix},
\tag{12.28}
$$

where i_3 through i_n are mesh currents within the two-port network and where v_1 and v_2 represent the only sources of energy available, networks A and B. Solving for i_1 and i_2 in terms of inverse impedances results in

$$
\begin{bmatrix} i_1 \\ i_2 \end{bmatrix} = \begin{bmatrix} (z^{-1})_{11} & (z^{-1})_{12} \\ (z^{-1})_{21} & (z^{-1})_{22} \end{bmatrix} \begin{bmatrix} v_1 \\ v_2 \end{bmatrix},
\tag{12.29a}
$$

which can be written as the superposition of the effect of the two voltage sources,

$$
\begin{bmatrix} i_1 \\ i_2 \end{bmatrix} = \begin{bmatrix} y_{T11} & y_{T12} \\ y_{T21} & y_{T22} \end{bmatrix} \begin{bmatrix} v_1 \\ v_2 \end{bmatrix},
\tag{12.29b}
$$

where

$$
\begin{aligned}
y_{Tjk} &= (z^{-1})_{jk} \\
&= \frac{\text{cofactor of } z_{kj}}{\text{determinant of the impedance matrix}} \\
&= \frac{|Z_{kj}|}{|Z|}.
\end{aligned}
\tag{12.30}
$$

In the literature the T subscript is usually deleted, but we will continue to use it for a while to represent transfer quantities and to emphasize that y_{Tjk} is not a reciprocal of z_{jk}.

An active circuit model satisfying Eq. (12.29b) is shown in Fig. 12.12. The model is comparable to Norton's equivalent of a one-port network. In fact, from Eq. (12.29b),

$$y_{T11} = \frac{i_1}{v_1}\bigg|_{v_2 = 0} \tag{12.31}$$

is the input admittance of terminals 1 and 1' when v_2 is zero (terminals 2 and 2' are shorted together), and the dependent generator $y_{T12}\,v_2$ is the short-circuit current of terminals 1 and 1'. The same is true of the other half of the model, and the four parameters have been named the *short-circuit admittance parameters*.

The two generators in Fig. 12.12 depend on the terminal voltages. Thus, these voltages should appear as unknown variables in the analysis of the

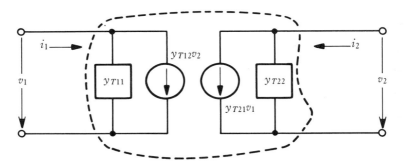

Fig. 12.12 *Active circuit model for a two-port network.*

complete system, as shown in Fig. 12.11. This suggests the use of solution by tree-branch voltages (or nodal analysis, *providing* one input and one output terminal are at the same potential and can be called a common datum node). Now v_1 and v_2 are two of the unknown tree branch (or node) voltages. Of course, the possibility exists that the mesh method of analysis is more adaptable to the problem at hand, and an equivalent circuit comparable to Thévenin's equivalent for a one-port with generators dependent upon mesh currents would be more advantageous. Such an equivalent would have occurred had we written nodal equations for the two-port network. This would have resulted in

$$\begin{bmatrix} v_1 \\ v_2 \end{bmatrix} = \begin{bmatrix} z_{T11} & z_{T12} \\ z_{T21} & z_{T22} \end{bmatrix} \begin{bmatrix} i_1 \\ i_2 \end{bmatrix}, \tag{12.32}$$

TABLE 12.2 TWO-PORT NETWORK PARAMETERS AND MODELS

Model	Transfer-parameter form of the response functions (Note: Reappearing symbols in this column have different meanings; i.e., z_{T11} in (c) is not equal to z_{T11} in (d).)	Response functions with transfer parameters replaced by conventional two-port parameters
(a) Actual network (i_1, v_1, i_2, v_2)		**Transmission Parameters** $$\begin{bmatrix} v_1 \\ i_1 \end{bmatrix} = \begin{bmatrix} A & B \\ C & D \end{bmatrix} \begin{bmatrix} v_2 \\ -i_2 \end{bmatrix}$$
(b) (model with y_{T11}, $y_{T12}v_2$, $y_{T21}v_1$, y_{T22})	$$\begin{bmatrix} i_1 \\ i_2 \end{bmatrix} = \begin{bmatrix} y_{T11} & y_{T12} \\ y_{T21} & y_{T22} \end{bmatrix} \begin{bmatrix} v_1 \\ v_2 \end{bmatrix}$$	**Short circuit Admittance Parameters (y-parameters)** $$\begin{bmatrix} i_1 \\ i_2 \end{bmatrix} = \begin{bmatrix} y_{11} & y_{12} \\ y_{21} & y_{22} \end{bmatrix} \begin{bmatrix} v_1 \\ v_2 \end{bmatrix}$$
(c) (model with z_{T11}, $z_{T12}i_2$, $z_{T21}i_1$, z_{T22})	$$\begin{bmatrix} v_1 \\ v_2 \end{bmatrix} = \begin{bmatrix} z_{T11} & z_{T12} \\ z_{T21} & z_{T22} \end{bmatrix} \begin{bmatrix} i_1 \\ i_2 \end{bmatrix}$$	**Open circuit Impedance Parameters (z-parameters)** $$\begin{bmatrix} v_1 \\ v_2 \end{bmatrix} = \begin{bmatrix} z_{11} & z_{12} \\ z_{21} & z_{22} \end{bmatrix} \begin{bmatrix} i_1 \\ i_2 \end{bmatrix}$$
(d) (model with z_{T11}, $h_{v12}v_2$, $h_{I21}i_1$, y_{T22})	$$\begin{bmatrix} v_1 \\ i_2 \end{bmatrix} = \begin{bmatrix} z_{T11} & h_{v12} \\ h_{I21} & y_{T22} \end{bmatrix} \begin{bmatrix} i_1 \\ v_2 \end{bmatrix}$$	**Hybrid parameters (h-parameters)** $$\begin{bmatrix} v_1 \\ i_2 \end{bmatrix} = \begin{bmatrix} h_{11} & h_{12} \\ h_{21} & h_{22} \end{bmatrix} \begin{bmatrix} i_1 \\ v_2 \end{bmatrix}$$
(e) (model with y_{T11}, $h_{I12}i_2$, $h_{v21}v_1$, z_{T22})	$$\begin{bmatrix} i_1 \\ v_2 \end{bmatrix} = \begin{bmatrix} y_{T11} & h_{I12} \\ h_{v21} & z_{T22} \end{bmatrix} \begin{bmatrix} v_1 \\ i_2 \end{bmatrix}$$	**(g-parameters)** $$\begin{bmatrix} i_1 \\ v_2 \end{bmatrix} = \begin{bmatrix} g_{11} & g_{12} \\ g_{21} & g_{22} \end{bmatrix} \begin{bmatrix} v_1 \\ i_2 \end{bmatrix}$$

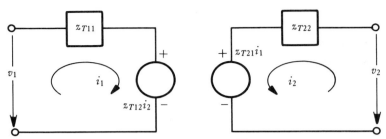

Fig. 12.13 *Another active circuit model for a two-port network.*

which has the model shown in Fig. 12.13. These parameters are called the *open-circuit impedance parameters*, and they are obviously related to the previous parameters by

$$\mathscr{Z}_T = \mathscr{Y}_T^{-1}. \tag{12.33}$$

Thus, z_{Tjk} is not generally a reciprocal of y_{Tjk}.

Since the models essentially separate the system into two parts, with the effect of one part upon another represented by a dependent generator, one does not have to use mesh currents or node voltages to describe the entire system. Table 12.2 provides other models and their corresponding equations; and after deciding which method of analysis is most convenient for networks *A* and *B* one picks the appropriate model. Then, if one set of parameters is known or is easier to obtain, these known parameters are used to obtain the desired parameters by rewriting the equations to fit the model being used.

12.6   THE RECIPROCITY THEOREM

Whenever the mesh impedance matrix of Eq. (12.28) is symmetrical, as it will be if the two-port network is passive, the inverse matrix is also symmetrical because the cofactor of z_{jk} is equal to the cofactor of z_{kj}. As by Eq. (12.30) the *y*-parameters are inverse impedances, symmetry also implies that

$$y_{T12} = y_{T21}. \tag{12.34a}$$

This is one statement of the *reciprocity theorem*, which also states the similarly established fact that

$$z_{T12} = z_{T21}. \tag{12.34b}$$

Under the condition of reciprocity two more equivalent circuits exist, as shown in Fig. 12.14, that can be used to represent a two-port network. It is

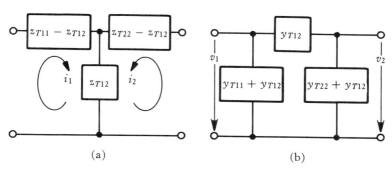

(a) (b)

Fig. 12.14 *Equivalent circuits for two-port networks when the reciprocity theorem holds.*

left as a student exercise to verify that the models do satisfy the z- and y-parameter equations and that the delta-wye transformation is applicable.

12.7 DUALITY

Two networks are said to be *dual networks* if the nodal equations for one have the same mathematical form as the mesh equations for the other, and vice-versa. If the coefficients of the currents in the one are also numerically the same as those of the voltages in the other, they are said to be *exact duals*.

A simple example of duality is the series R-L-C circuit, whose dual is the parallel G-C-L circuit. In general, to form a dual of a given network, one simply provides for the dual network a node and node voltage for each mesh and mesh current, provides one extra node as a reference node, provides a node forcing current generator for each mesh forcing voltage generator, and provides node self and mutual admittances corresponding to mesh self and mutual impedances. Or he can do the reverse.

For example, if in the original network mesh No. 3 has the equation

$$V_3(p) = -(R_a + L_a p)I_1(p) - R_b I_2(p) + \left(R_c + L_c p + \frac{1}{C_c p}\right)I_3(p),$$

then in the dual network node 3 has the equation

$$I_3(p) = -(G_a + C_a p)V_1(p) - G_b V_2(p) + \left(G_c + C_c p + \frac{1}{L_c p}\right)V_3(p).$$

For every mesh in a network there is a node in its dual plus a reference node; to each voltage source in the network there corresponds a current source in the dual and vice-versa, and to every R, L, or C there corresponds a G, C, or L. Therefore, a schematic construction directly from the original network is suggested. This is illustrated in Fig. 12.15, where a network,

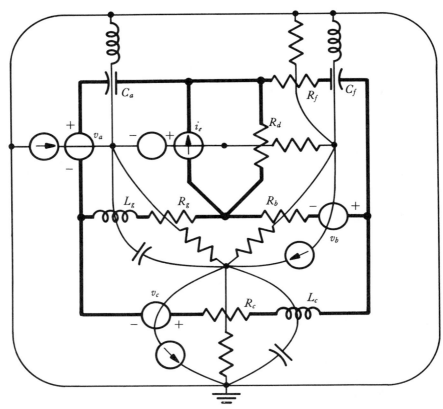

Fig. 12.15 *Construction of a dual network.*

drawn in heavy lines, has its dual overlaid in light lines. In constructing the dual, you must remember that node voltages are defined so that mutual admittances always have negative signs. The directions of sources in the dual are much more easily correlated with those in the original network if you imagine that all mesh currents circulate in the same direction, say clockwise, so that the mutual impedances are also all negative.

In Fig. 12.16 the two networks are shown together, with the dual redrawn and its components labeled, so that they may be more easily compared. That they are indeed duals can be demonstrated by writing the mesh equations for

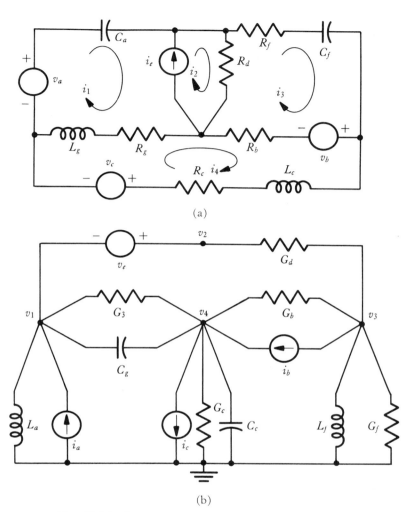

(a)

(b)

Fig. 12.16 *A network and its dual. (a) Original. (b) Dual.*

the one and the node equations for the other and comparing the two sets of equations.

The duality concept can be extended to elements, matrices, and topological concepts as illustrated in Table 12.3. This, in part, explains why so often in this text we have been able to save time by developing general voltage responses to current excitations by analogy to previously developed current responses to voltage excitations, or vice-versa.

TABLE 12.3 DUAL NETWORK RELATIONSHIPS

Quantity	Dual
voltage	current
series connection	parallel connection
tree branch	link
loop	node pair
node	mesh
Thévenin's equivalent	Norton's equivalent
R	G
L	C
$\mathcal{M}$	$\mathcal{N}$

12.8 CONVOLUTION AND THE RELATION BETWEEN IMPULSE RESPONSE AND SYSTEM FUNCTION

Although the common mathematical operation known as *convolution* may be simply defined, it seems that there is merit in a physical consideration which gives it some motivation. To this end, consider a system, H, whose response to the prelimit form of an impulse, $\delta_T(t)$, is $h_T(t)$. In the limit as $T \to 0, h_T(t) \to h(t)$, as indicated by the equality of block diagrams of Fig. 12.17,

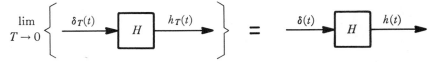

Fig. 12.17 *Illustrating system impulse response.*

where $h(t)$ is known as the *impulse response*, or, for reasons which should soon be apparent, the *weighting function*, of the system.

Suppose the arbitrary forcing function, $f(t)$, shown in Fig. 12.18, is applied to system H. The forcing function is approximated by superposing $N + 1$ rectangular pulses, each of the form of $f_n(t)$, so that

$$f(t) \simeq \sum_{n=0}^{N} f_n(t),$$

with the approximation becoming more and more exact as N is made a larger and larger number.

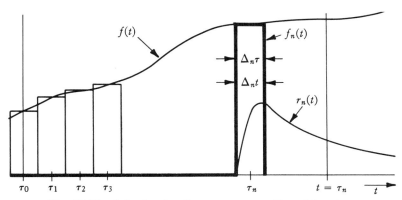

Fig. 12.18 *A forcing function as a superposition of impulses.*

Because the pulse $f_n(t)$ is symmetric about $t = \tau_n$ it satisfies the specification of the prelimit form of the impulse at $t = \tau_n$ except for the area it bounds, which is $f(\tau_n)\Delta_n\tau$ rather than unity. Therefore,

$$f_n(t) = f(\tau_n)\delta_T(t - \tau_n)\Delta_n\tau.$$

According to Fig. 12.17, the response to a forcing function of this type will be

$$r_n(t) = f(\tau_n)h_T(t - \tau_n)\Delta_n\tau.$$

The combined responses to all $N + 1$ of the $f_n(t)$ will be the approximate value of the response to $f(t)$ evaluated at t; that is,

$$r(t) \simeq \sum_{n=0}^{N} r_n(t) = \sum_{n=0}^{N} f(\tau_n)h_T(t - \tau_n)\Delta_n\tau.$$

If we let $N \to \infty$, the approximation becomes exact and $\Delta_n\tau = T \to 0$ so that $\delta_T(t) \to \delta(t)$ and $h_T(t) \to h(t)$. Thus

$$r_t = \int_0^t f(\tau)h(t - \tau)\, d\tau. \tag{12.35a}$$

In this expression $r(t)$ is expressed as the *convolution of* $f(t)$ *with* $h(t)$.

An alternative form of the *convolution integral* in Eq. (12.35a) is evident after the substitution

$$t_1 = t - \tau,$$

which leads to

$$r(t) = -\int_t^0 f(t - t_1)h(t_1)\, dt_1$$

$$= \int_0^t f(t - t_1)h(t_1)\, dt_1.$$

As the variable of integration may be a symbol of our own choosing, the above may be written

$$r(t) = \int_0^t h(\tau)f(t - \tau)\, d\tau, \tag{12.35b}$$

which is another form of the convolution integral showing its commutability for *linear* systems.

Our previous work has shown us that in this case the response and forcing function are related operationally as

$$R(p) = H(p)F(p). \tag{12.36}$$

Thus we see that the system function, $H(p)$, is the operational form of the impulse response of the system.

As $h(t)$ can be *any* function of time, we make the general statement, based on Eqs. (12.35) and (12.36), that:

if

$$f(t) = \int_0^t f_1(\tau)f_2(t - \tau)\, d\tau \tag{12.37a}$$

then

$$F(p) = F_1(p)F_2(p). \tag{12.37b}$$

PROBLEMS

12.1 In Fig. P.3.2(c), $i = I = 10$ A, $G_1 = 0.2\ \Omega^{-1}$, and $G_2 = 0.05\ \Omega^{-1}$. What value of G_3 will extract maximum power and what will be the maximum power?

12.2 In Fig. P.3.2(d), $v = V = 160$ V, $R_2 = 20$ kΩ, $R_1 = 5$ kΩ, and $R_4 = 4$ kΩ. What value of R_3 will extract maximum power, and what will be the maximum power?

12.3 In Fig. P.3.3(a), the ideal generator, v_S, is replaced by a constant voltage V_S in series with a resistance having the value R_S. R_o has been chosen so that

$$R_o = \sqrt{R_1 R_2 + \frac{R_1^2}{4}}.$$

What value of R_S will cause maximum power to be delivered to R_o?

12.4 Repeat Prob. 12.3, except refer to Fig. P.3.3(b).

12.5 In Fig. P.3.4, replace the 6-Ω resistor with the resistor which will absorb maximum power from the remainder of the network, and compute the power absorbed by the replacement.

12.6 In Fig. P.3.5, replace the 3-Ω resistor with the resistor which will absorb maximum power, and compute the power absorbed by the replacement.

12.7 In Fig. P.3.6, the 12-V source is replaced by a short-circuit and the adjacent 6-Ω resistor by a variable resistor, R_x. Find the value of R_x which will absorb maximum power, and compute the efficiency ($\eta = P_{out}/P_{in}$) with which this maximum power is transmitted from the 24-V source to R_x.

12.8 In Fig. P.3.7, an ideal 30-V source is connected with its (+) terminal to point a and its (−) terminal to point b. What resistor replacing the 5-Ω resistor will extract maximum power?

12.9 What value of R in Fig. P.12.1 will extract maximum power, and what will be the maximum power?

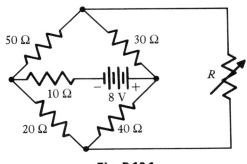

50 Ω   30 Ω

10 Ω   8 V R

20 Ω   40 Ω

Fig. P.12.1.

12.10 One electromechanical generator, which converts mechanical to electrical energy, can be represented by an ideal voltage source, representing the total conversion of mechanical to electrical energy, in series with an R-L series circuit. If the ideal source is

$$v_s(t) = 200 \sin 500t \text{ V},$$

$R = 10$ Ω, and $L = 0.1$ H, what series combination of components will cause maximum mechanical power to be transferred? What will be the efficiency of this system if the externally connected electrical components are considered the load and the mechanical power the power input?

12.11 What parallel combination of the two components will accomplish the same task as the series combination in Prob. 12.10?

12.12 In Prob. 5.52, the 20-Ω resistor is changed to the value which will absorb maximum average power. What is the new value of resistance?

12.13 In Fig. P.12.2, $v_{1ss}(t) = 50 \cos 5000t$. Determine the series R-L or R-C combination which will extract maixmum average power from the terminals at the right and the amount of power extracted.

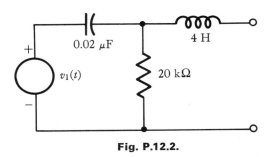

Fig. P.12.2.

12.14 In Fig. P.12.3, $f = 1000$ Hz and $\mathbf{V}_1 = 100 + j0$ V. Find the value of $\mathbf{Z}_L$ which will absorb maximum power under the following conditions:

a. $\mathbf{Z}_L$ is a pure resistance.
b. $\mathbf{Z}_L = Z_L e^{j\pi/6}$.
c. $\mathbf{Z}_L$ may be any series combination of resistance, capacitance, and/or inductance.

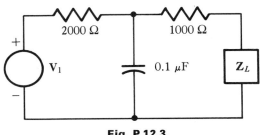

Fig. P.12.3.

12.15 In Fig. P.12.4, find the parallel combination of resistance and reactance that will transfer the greatest average power through terminals a and b, and indicate whether the reactance is capacitive or inductive.

12.16 A certain signal source has an output impedance consisting of 100 Ω of resistance in series with 1.0 H of inductance. When operating at 100 rad/sec, determine:

a.   The series R-C load for maximum power transfer.
b.   The parallel R-C load for maximum power transfer.

12.17 Find the resistance between terminals a and b in Fig. P.3.7 by employing a Y-Δ transformation.

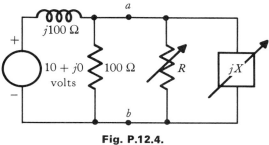

Fig. P.12.4.

12.18 Find the resistance between terminals a and b in Fig. P.3.7 by employing a Δ-Y transformation.

12.19 Find the complex impedance between terminals $a-b$ in Fig. P.12.5.

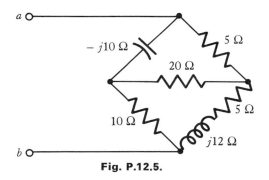

Fig. P.12.5.

12.20 Find the complex impedance of the two-terminal network of Fig. P.12.6.

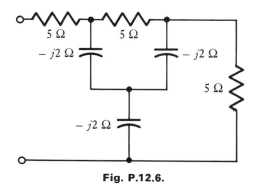

Fig. P.12.6.

12.21 Find the equivalent capacitance of the combination in Fig. P.12.7.

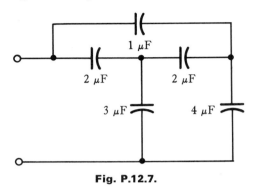

Fig. P.12.7.

12.22 Write the matrix equation connecting the four current responses in Fig. P.6.1 to the two sources, showing the result in the form of Eq. (12.27) with numeral values in the transfer matrix.

12.23 In Fig. P.6.2, let v_a and v_b be respectively the voltage to the right across the 6-Ω resistor and downward across the 10-Ω resistor and identify the sources with the subscripts 1 and 2, left to right. Write the matrix equation connecting the above two voltage responses and the current responses indicated on the figure to the two sources. Show the result in the form of Eq. (12.27) with numerical values in the transfer matrix.

12.24 In Fig. P.6.4, let v_1 and v_2 be respectively the voltages downward across the 40-Ω resistor and the current source, and let i_1 and i_2 be respectively the currents to the right through the 25-Ω resistor and the 10-Ω resistor. Label the sources No. 1, No. 2, and No. 3, left to right, with positive directions as shown. Write the transfer matrix, relating the four responses to the forcing functions, with numerical elements, in the form of Eq. (12.27).

12.25 Write, with complex numerical elements, the transfer matrix, in the form of that in Eq. (12.27), connecting the downward phasor voltage drop and current associated with the capacitor in Fig. P.5.16 with the two sources, identified with the subscripts 1 and 2, left to right.

12.26 In Fig. P.5.17, let $\mathbf{V}_a$ be the downward phasor voltage drop across the current source. Write a matrix equation, in the form of Eq. (12.27), relating phasor responses $\mathbf{I}_a$ and $\mathbf{V}_a$ to the two sources, showing complex numerical elements in the transfer matrix.

12.27 In Fig. P.6.7, replace the source on the right by $\mathbf{V}_{Sa}$ upward and the source on the left by $\mathbf{V}_{Sb}$ upward. Write the transfer matrix, with complex numerical elements, connecting the responses $\mathbf{V}_a$, $\mathbf{V}_b$, and $\mathbf{V}_c$ to the two sources.

12.28 For the network of Fig. P.12.8, find

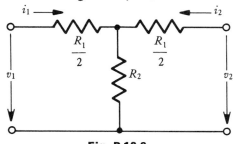

Fig. P.12.8.

a. The transmission parameter matrix.
b. The y-parameter matrix.
c. The z-parameter matrix.
d. The h-parameter matrix.
e. The g-parameter matrix.

12.29 Repeat Prob. 12.28 for the network of Fig. P.12.9.

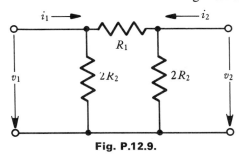

Fig. P.12.9.

12.30 Repeat Prob. 12.28 for the network of Fig. P.12.10, in which R is some specified resistance.

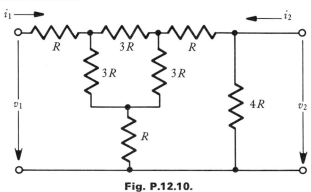

Fig. P.12.10.

12.31 Repeat Prob. 12.28 for the network of Fig. P.12.11.

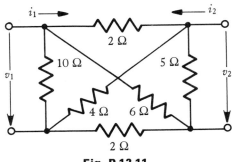

Fig. P.12.11.

12.32 For the network of Fig. P.12.12, find the operational forms of the five parameter-matrices.

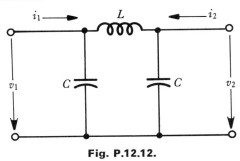

Fig. P.12.12.

12.33 For the network of Fig. P.12.13, find:

a. The transmission parameter matrix.
b. The y-parameter matrix.
c. The z-parameter matrix.

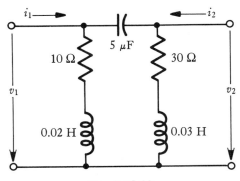

Fig. P.12.13.

12.34 For the network of Fig. P.12.14:

a. Find the y-parameter matrix.

b. Find the h-parameter matrix.

c. Show the pole-zero plot of $h_{11}(p)$ and $h_{12}(p)$ and sketch the magnitude and phase angles of $h_{11}(j\omega)$ and $h_{12}(j\omega)$. (*Note.* The inconsistent lower case h for these forms is due to deference to convention.)

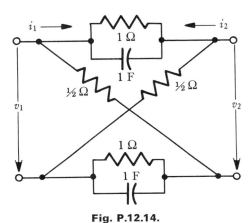

Fig. P.12.14.

12.35 Find the "T" configuration [Fig. 12.14(a)] equivalent to the network of Fig. P.12.10.

12.36 Find the "π" configuration [Fig. 12.14(b)] for the network of Fig. P.12.10.

12.37 Repeat Prob. 12.35 for the network of Fig. P.12.11.

12.38 Repeat Prob. 12.36 for the network of Fig. P.12.11.

12.39 Show in operational form the "T" network equivalent to the network of Fig. P.12.12.

12.40 Construct the dual of the network of Fig. 6.1.

12.41 Construct the dual of the network of Fig. 6.15(a).

12.42 Construct the dual of the network of Fig. P.6.7.

12.43 Construct the dual of the network of Fig. P.6.8.

12.44 Construct the dual of the network of Fig. P.6.10.

12.45 Construct the duals of:

a. The network of Fig. P.6.11.

b. The network of Fig. P.6.12.

12.46 Construct the dual of the network of Fig. P.8.3. (What is the dual of an open switch?)

12.47 Construct the dual of Fig. P.8.1(f).

12.48 Find the weighting function of the R-C series circuit current response to voltage inputs in terms of R and C. If the applied voltage is

$$v(t) = Ve^{-at}u(t),$$

find $i(t)$ by convolution.

12.49 Repeat Prob. 12.48 when

$$v(t) = V[u(t) - u(t - T)].$$

12.50 Repeat Prob. 12.48 when

$$v(t) = \frac{V}{T} t[u(t) - u(t - T)].$$

12.51 For Prob. 12.48, sketch on one graph $v(\tau)$ and $h(-\tau)$ and $h(t - \tau)$. Show all time-dimensioned variables and constants. What are the units on $H(p)$?

12.52 Suppose it were possible to design a network such that the weighting function relating output voltage $v_o(t)$ to the input voltage $v_i(t)$ was

$$h(t) = \begin{cases} 0, & t < 0 \\ 4, & 0 < t < 2 \\ 0, & t > 2. \end{cases}$$

What will be $v_o(t)$ when

$$v_1(t) = \begin{cases} 0, & t < 0 \\ 5, & 0 < t < 4 \\ 0, & t > 0? \end{cases}$$

13

Magnetically Coupled Circuits

13.1 INTRODUCTION

In previous chapters, mutual impedances have been connected in the network with leads which were common to two meshes in the network, with the actual current being the algebraic combination of the mesh currents. When there are coils in close proximity to one another, however, an effect in one mesh due to currents in another may be observed when there is no such electrical connection between the meshes. This effect is usually observed as a voltage due to the action of Faraday's law through flux linkages whose origin is outside the coil under observation. In this chapter we develop the parameters which are a measure of such *coupling* of one circuit part with another.

13.2 NETWORK FOR MAGNETIC CIRCUITS

The network laws for magnetic circuits present but a small problem to the student who has arrived at this point, providing that he recognizes that they are already at hand. Such recognition should be forthcoming after a short perusal of Secs. 1.6 and 1.8 which show how quantities associated with the conductive medium and quantities associated with the magnetic medium respectively correspond to the general flow quantities. As a consequence of these two correspondences and taking proper notes of Eqs. (1.21) and (1.22), as compared with Eqs. (1.46) and (1.47), the correspondences below follow:

$$\phi \qquad \Rightarrow i$$
$$Ni \qquad \Rightarrow v$$
$$\mathscr{P} = \frac{1}{\mathscr{R}} \Rightarrow G = \frac{1}{R} \qquad (13.1)$$
$$\mu \qquad \Rightarrow \sigma = \frac{1}{\rho}.$$

You will recall that the only volt-ampere relationship of interest in purely conductive networks involved Ohm's law and the conductance (or resistance) parameter. These simple volt-ampere relationships, along with Kirchhoff's current law and Kirchhoff's voltage law, formed the entire basis for the analysis of such networks. As each of the quantities for the electric conductive network has an exact analogue in the magnetic circuit, one may immediately come to the conclusion that the conductive electric circuit has its exact counterpart in the magnetic circuit. This means that every rule and network generalization applicable to the first can be adapted to the second. The following statement expresses this fact:

> All circuit laws, network theorems, transfer relationships, reduction processes, and generalized methods which may be applied to conductive electric networks have exact counterparts in the magnetic network provided the correspondences of Eqs. (13.1) are observed.

This means that all the tools for working with linear magnetic circuits are already at our disposal.

13.3 THE INDUCTANCE PARAMETERS

First consider a simple system of two current-carrying coils as shown in Fig. 13.1(a). Each of these coils will, of course, produce a given amount of

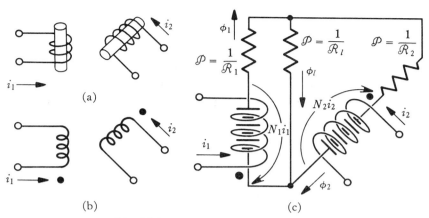

Fig. 13.1 *Magnetically coupled coils.*

flux, part of which will "link" the other coil. Thus, the total flux linking one of the coils is composed of the flux created by the current in that coil and a portion of the flux created by the current in the other coil. Whether these two flux components add or subtract depends on the relative directions of fluxes produced by the two currents; which in turn depends on the relative positions of the coil axes, on the directions of the windings, and on the directions of the currents. A common method for illustrating whether the flux components aid or oppose one another is shown in Fig. 13.1(b) by the heavy dots at one terminal of each coil. These dots are called *polarity marks*, and their significance is this: *currents entering* (or leaving) *identical polarity marks on a pair of coils produce fluxes in the same direction along either coil axis.* These marks depend entirely on system geometry; and when there are more than one pair of coils, it may be necessary to adopt different marks for each pair.

In Fig. 13.1 there will be three gross flux paths: one through each coil and one missing both coils. However, the three paths must be connected so that a loop formed by any two must link at least one of the coils. This is shown, schematically, using circuit symbols, in Fig. 13.1(c).

In the schematic, the path permeances are shown as lumped parameter elements. If the paths should consist of a ferromagnetic material of high enough permeability that fluxes in air could be neglected, these permeances could be easily calculated from the geometry, using the fact that $\mathscr{P} = \mu A / l$. If the paths are in air, the fluxes distribute nonuniformly and the indicated permeances may be difficult or impossible to calculate. Fortunately, we can talk about them whether we know them or not, thereby arriving at parameters which we can either calculate or determine by experiment.

The abstract flow quantity, flux, through each coil is given the direction of the flux produced in that coil by its own current. The *magnetomotive force, Ni,* for each coil is represented by the same symbol that was used for a battery in the electric circuit, with its positive terminal in the direction of positive H for the current assumed in the coil. This is necessary in order to maintain the correspondence between electric and magnetic circuits.

The concept of *transfer permeance* has already been introduced in the discussions leading to entry 5 in Table 12.1 and to Eq. (12.26). Since each of the two coil fluxes depends on both currents for its value, the principle of superposition may be applied to designate them

$$\phi_1 = \phi_{11} + \phi_{12}$$
$$= \mathscr{P}_{T11} N_1 i_1 + \mathscr{P}_{T12} N_2 i_2, \tag{13.2a}$$

and

$$\phi_2 = \phi_{21} + \phi_{22}$$
$$= \mathscr{P}_{T21} N_1 i_1 + \mathscr{P}_{T22} N_2 i_2, \tag{13.2b}$$

where $\mathscr{P}_{T12} = \mathscr{P}_{T21}$ is the transfer permeance corresponding to transfer conductance in the electric circuit and $\mathscr{P}_{T11}$ and $\mathscr{P}_{T22}$ are the driving-point permeances.

The flux linkages in the two coils are

$$\lambda_1 = N_1 \phi_1$$
$$= N_1 \phi_{11} + N_1 \phi_{12}$$
$$= \lambda_{11} + \lambda_{12}$$
$$= N_1^2 \mathscr{P}_{T11} i_1 + N_1 N_2 \mathscr{P}_{T12} i_2$$
$$= L_{11} i_1 + L_{12} i_2 \tag{13.3a}$$

$$\lambda_2 = N_2 \phi_2$$
$$= N_2 \phi_{21} + N_2 \phi_{22}$$
$$= \lambda_{21} + \lambda_{22}$$
$$= N_1 N_2 \mathscr{P}_{T21} i_1 + N_2^2 \mathscr{P}_{T22} i_2$$
$$= L_{21} i_1 + L_{22} i_2. \tag{13.3b}$$

In these expressions:

$$L_{11} = \frac{\lambda_{11}}{i_1} = N_1^2 \mathscr{P}_{T11} \qquad = \text{self inductance of coil 1,} \tag{13.4a}$$

$$L_{12} = \frac{\lambda_{12}}{i_2} = N_1 N_2 \mathscr{P}_{T12} = \begin{array}{l}\text{mutual inductance between} \\ \text{coil 1 and coil 2,}\end{array} \tag{13.4b}$$

$$L_{21} = \frac{\lambda_{21}}{i_1} = N_1 N_2 \mathscr{P}_{T21} = \begin{array}{l}\text{mutual inductance between} \\ \text{coil 2 and coil 1,}\end{array} \tag{13.4c}$$

$$L_{22} = \frac{\lambda_{22}}{i_2} = N_2^2 \mathscr{P}_{T22} \qquad = \text{self inductance of coil 2.} \tag{13.4d}$$

The reciprocity theorem states that

$$\mathscr{P}_{T12} = \mathscr{P}_{T21},\tag{13.5}$$

so it is obvious that

$$L_{21} = L_{12}.\tag{13.6}$$

Oftentimes, when only two coils are under consideration, the magnitude of the mutual inductance is given the designation

$$M = |L_{21}| = |L_{12}|.\tag{13.7}$$

In this example, the mutual inductances are positive numbers. Had either one of the currents been reversed, the mutual inductances would have been negative because the transfer permeances would have had negative signs. Clearly, then, the magnitudes of the mutuals are independent of current but their signs are not. We can state the following rule for remembering the signs on mutual inductances:

> When the assigned currents in two coils produce additive fluxes, the signs on the mutual inductances are positive; or, when the currents in both coils flow into (or out of) polarity marks, the mutual inductances are positive. Otherwise, they are negative.

When there are n coils in the system, the flux linking the jth one is

$$\phi_j = \sum_{k=1}^{n} \phi_{jk}$$

$$= \sum_{k=1}^{n} \mathscr{P}_{Tjk} N_k i_k.$$

The jth coil flux linkages are

$$\lambda_j = N_j \phi_j$$

$$= \sum_{k=1}^{n} N_j N_k \mathscr{P}_{Tjk} i_k.\tag{13.8}$$

The *inductance parameters* are defined

$$L_{jk} = N_j N_k \mathscr{P}_{Tjk}$$

$$= \begin{cases} \text{mutual inductance,} & j \neq k \\ \text{self inductance,} & j = k \end{cases}.\tag{13.9}$$

The jth coil flux linkages then may be expressed in terms of inductance parameters and currents as

$$\lambda_j = \sum_{k=1}^{n} L_{jk} i_k,\tag{13.10}$$

with the signs on the L's determined by the above rule on signs.

13.4 MATRIX FORMULATION OF MAGNETICALLY COUPLED COILS

The organization of the matrix relationships for magnetically coupled coils is suggested by the foregoing equations. In the following development the student should continually check the matrix results with the algebraic equations developed in the preceding article.

If in an electromagnetic system of n coils one forms a column matrix of the coil currents

$$i = \begin{bmatrix} i_1 \\ i_2 \\ \vdots \\ i_n \end{bmatrix}, \tag{13.11}$$

and forms the system *turns matrix*

$$\mathcal{N} = \begin{bmatrix} N_1 & 0 & 0 & \cdots & 0 \\ 0 & N_2 & 0 & \cdots & 0 \\ 0 & 0 & N_3 & \cdots & 0 \\ \vdots & \vdots & \vdots & & \vdots \\ 0 & 0 & 0 & \cdots & N_n \end{bmatrix}, \tag{13.12}$$

where N_j is the number of turns in coil j, then the *magnetomotive force matrix* is

$$f = \mathcal{N}i. \tag{13.13}$$

If the *transfer permeance matrix* for the magnetic network is $\mathscr{P}_T$, the *coil flux matrix* is that of Eq. (12.26), i.e.,

$$\begin{aligned} \varphi &= \mathscr{P}_T f \\ &= \mathscr{P}_T \mathcal{N}i. \end{aligned} \tag{13.14}$$

The flux linkage matrix is

$$\lambda = \mathcal{N}\varphi, \tag{13.15}$$

or, upon substitution of Eq. (13.14),

$$\lambda = \mathcal{N}\mathscr{P}_T \mathcal{N}i. \tag{13.16}$$

Defining the inductance matrix as

$$\mathscr{L} = \mathcal{N}\mathscr{P}_T \mathcal{N} \tag{13.17}$$

introduces the alternative form of the flux linkage matrix,

$$\lambda = \mathscr{L}i. \tag{13.18}$$

The last two equations correspond with algebraic Eqs. (13.9) and (13.10), respectively.

If each branch impedance is at most a simple R-L-C series combination, and if we admit the possibility that the branch inductances may be magnetically coupled to one another, the matrix form of the volt-ampere equation is still that of Eq. (11.60), which, rearranged, is

$$v_B + v_G = \mathscr{Z}_B i_B. \tag{13.19a}$$

If the inductances do not vary with time, the volt-ampere equations can be written in their time-varying form as

$$v_B(t) + v_G(t) = \left[\mathscr{R}_B + \mathscr{L}_B \frac{d}{dt} + \mathscr{S}_B \int_{-\infty}^{t} (\ ) \, d\tau \right] i_B(t)$$

$$= \mathscr{R}_B i_B(t) + \mathscr{L}_B \frac{d i_B(t)}{dt} + \mathscr{S}_B \int_{-\infty}^{t} i_B(\tau) \, d\tau$$

$$= \mathscr{R}_B i_B(t) + \frac{d}{dt} \lambda_B(t) + \mathscr{S}_B \int_{-\infty}^{t} i_B(\tau) \, d\tau, \tag{13.19b}$$

where

$$\lambda_B(t) = \mathscr{L}_B i_B(t) \tag{13.20}$$

is the branch flux linkage matrix, usually the same as the flux linkage matrix in Eq. (13.18). Since the inductance matrix is no longer diagonal, the branch impedance matrix will now have nonzero elements off the diagonal; and these elements represent the coupling between branches, or indicate the manner in which the current in one branch affects the voltage in another branch.

13.5 MAGNETIC COUPLING IN GENERALIZED ANALYSIS

The generalized analyses covered in Chapters 6 and 11 were generally discussed on the basis of no magnetic coupling between branches. This was done to keep the discussion simple, but their extension to include magnetic coupling is not difficult, once the nature of inductance is understood.

The principal difficulty, if it may be considered to be one, in extending the generalized methods to include magnetic coupling lies in the fact that the branch parameter matrices are no longer diagonal. As inductance enters in a direct way into the impedance concept and in an inverse manner into the admittance concept, it seems that the most convenient doorway to opening the discussion of these new problems is the use of methods involving the impedance matrices; that is, with the network model which has its branches in the Thévenin form.

The suspicion cited above is borne out if one considers the Thévenin matrix form of the branch equations in Eq. (11.60)

$$v_B = \mathscr{Z}_B\, i_B - v_G \tag{13.21}$$

in comparison with the Norton form of Eq. (11.56)

$$i_B = \mathscr{Y}_B\, v_B - i_G. \tag{13.22}$$

The generated currents in the Norton form are related to the generated voltages in the Thévenin form by Eq. (11.63),

$$v_G = -\mathscr{Z}_B\, i_G = -\mathscr{Y}_B^{-1} i_G, \tag{13.23}$$

where

$$\mathscr{Y}_B = \mathscr{Z}_B^{-1}. \tag{13.24}$$

When the branch impedance matrix was a diagonal matrix, the above inverse had elements which were simply the reciprocals of corresponding elements in the impedance matrix. Now that magnetic coupling is present, the elements of the branch impedance matrix are still simple R-L-C series combinations, but there are now inductance terms forming off-diagonal elements. This means that the branch admittance matrix will no longer consist of simple G, C, or L elements, even when a branch is defined to contain but one kind of element, because now $Y_{jk}(p)$ will be the ratio of two polynomials in p, the denominator polynomial being the determinant of $\mathscr{Z}_B(p)$. Thus, the advantage of considering the Thévenin form first is evident. Then if one desires the admittance matrix, he has access to it through Eq. (13.24).

Mesh-current variables are particularly adaptable to the analysis of networks with magnetic coupling, because it is often possible to establish them in such a way that the total current in a coil is one of the mesh currents. Even when this is not possible, it is usually a simple matter to arrive at the mesh mutual inductance terms by inspection.

The methods of Chapter 8 regarding initial conditions apply exactly when one recognizes that the initial flux linkages in coil j, magnetically coupled with $n-1$ other coils, are

$$\lambda_j(0^-) = \sum_{k=1}^{n} L_{jk}\, i_k(0^-). \tag{13.25}$$

The correspondence between the original coil and the one with initial conditions replaced by equivalent sources is shown in Fig. 13.2. After thus re-

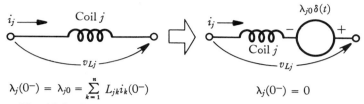

$$\lambda_j(0^-) = \lambda_{j0} = \sum_{k=1}^{n} L_{jk} i_k(0^-) \qquad\qquad \lambda_j(0^-) = 0$$

Fig. 13.2 *Equivalent sources when magnetic coupling is present.*

placing all coils with initial conditions by equivalent sources and coils without initial conditions, the equation for mesh j takes the form

$$V_j(p) = \sum_{k=1}^{n} Z_{jk}(p) I_k(p), \qquad (13.26)$$

where $V_j(p)$ is the mesh forcing voltage for the modified network including the equivalent sources for the initial conditions.

EXAMPLE 13.1. Set up by inspection the mesh-current equations for the network of Fig. 13.3 for $t \geqslant 0$.

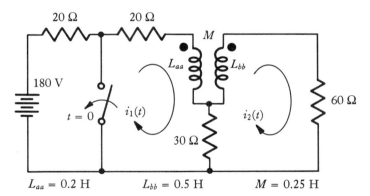

Fig. 13.3 *Network for Example 13.1.*

Solution. The mesh current matrix is

$$i = \begin{bmatrix} i_1 \\ i_2 \end{bmatrix}.$$

As

$$i_1(0^-) = \frac{180}{60} = 3 \text{ A},$$

and

$$i_2(0^-) = \frac{30}{30 + 60}\, i_1(0^-) = \frac{1}{3}(3) = 1 \text{ A},$$

the initial mesh current matrix is

$$i(0^-) = \begin{bmatrix} 3 \\ 1 \end{bmatrix} \text{ A}.$$

The mesh resistance matrix is

$$\mathscr{R} = \begin{bmatrix} 50 & -30 \\ -30 & 90 \end{bmatrix},$$

and the mesh inductance matrix is

$$\mathscr{L} = \begin{bmatrix} L_{aa} & L_{ab} \\ L_{ba} & L_{bb} \end{bmatrix} = \begin{bmatrix} 0.2 & -0.25 \\ -0.25 & 0.5 \end{bmatrix},$$

so we may write the operational mesh impedance matrix

$$\mathscr{Z}(p) = \mathscr{R} + \mathscr{L}p = \begin{bmatrix} 50 + 0.2p & -(30 + 0.25p) \\ -(30 + 0.25p) & 90 + 0.5p \end{bmatrix}.$$

The instantaneous mesh voltages are

$$v(t) = \mathscr{R}i(t) + \frac{d\lambda(t)}{dt},$$

where

$$\lambda = \mathscr{L}i = \begin{bmatrix} 0.2 & -0.25 \\ -0.25 & 0.5 \end{bmatrix}\begin{bmatrix} i_1 \\ i_2 \end{bmatrix}.$$

The operator form of the mesh voltages is

$$V(p)] = \mathscr{R}I(p)] + p\Lambda(p)] - \lambda(0^-)$$
$$= (\mathscr{R} + \mathscr{L}p)I(p)] - \lambda(0^-),$$

or

$$V'(p)] = \mathscr{Z}(p)I(p)],$$

where

$$V'(p)] = V(p)] + \lambda(0^-) = V(p)] + \mathscr{L}i(0^-)$$

$$= \begin{bmatrix} 0 \\ 0 \end{bmatrix} + \begin{bmatrix} 0.2 & -0.25 \\ -0.25 & 0.5 \end{bmatrix}\begin{bmatrix} 3 \\ 1 \end{bmatrix} = \begin{bmatrix} 0.35 \\ -0.25 \end{bmatrix}.$$

Thus the solution is that of the operational matrix equation

$$\begin{bmatrix} 0.35 \\ -0.25 \end{bmatrix} = \begin{bmatrix} 50 + 0.2p & -(30 + 0.25p) \\ -(30 + 0.25p) & 90 + 0.5p \end{bmatrix}\begin{bmatrix} I_1(p) \\ I_2(p) \end{bmatrix},$$

or of the set of operational mesh equations formed by expanding the matrix into its elements,

$$0.35 = (50 + 0.2p)I_1(p) - (30 + 0.25)I_2(p)$$
$$-0.25 = -(30 + 0.25)I_1(p) + (90 + 0.5p)I_2(p).$$

EXAMPLE 13.2. Set up the modified network equivalent to that of Fig. 13.3 for $t \geqslant 0$ with initial conditions replaced by equivalent sources.

Solution. Applying the equivalents of Fig. 13.2 produces the network of Fig. 13.4. Note how simply the mesh equations requested in the previous example may be written by inspection of this network.

EXAMPLE 13.3. Set up the branch impedance matrix for the network of Fig. 13.4, establish $\mathscr{M}$ and transform branch impedances to arrive at the mesh impedance matrix of Example 13.1.

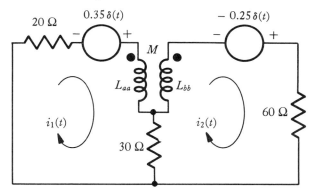

Fig. 13.4 *Modified network equivalent to that of Fig. 13.3.*

Solution. The branch impedance matrix associated with branch currents indicated on the figure is

$$\mathscr{Z}_B(p) = \begin{bmatrix} 20 + 0.2p & -0.25p & 0 \\ -0.25p & 60 + 0.5p & 0 \\ 0 & 0 & 30 \end{bmatrix}.$$

Inspection of the network shows that

$$\begin{bmatrix} i_{B1} \\ i_{B2} \\ i_{B3} \end{bmatrix} = \begin{bmatrix} 1 & 0 \\ 0 & 1 \\ 1 & -1 \end{bmatrix} \begin{bmatrix} i_1 \\ i_2 \end{bmatrix},$$

and since

$$i_B = \mathcal{M}i,$$

it is apparent that

$$\mathcal{M} = \begin{bmatrix} 1 & 0 & 1 \\ 0 & 1 & -1 \end{bmatrix}.$$

The mesh impedance matrix is then

$$\mathcal{Z}(p) = \mathcal{\tilde M}\mathcal{Z}_B(p)\mathcal{M}$$

$$= \begin{bmatrix} 1 & 0 & 1 \\ 0 & 1 & -1 \end{bmatrix} \begin{bmatrix} (20 + 0.2p) & -0.25p & 0 \\ -0.25p & (60 + 0.5p) & 0 \\ 0 & 0 & 30 \end{bmatrix} \begin{bmatrix} 1 & 0 \\ 0 & 1 \\ 1 & -1 \end{bmatrix}$$

$$= \begin{bmatrix} (50 + 0.2p) & -(30 + 0.25p) \\ -(30 + 0.25p) & (90 + 0.5p) \end{bmatrix},$$

which agrees with the matrix previously established.

13.6 COEFFICIENT OF COUPLING

In a given pair of coils, tagged as coil 1 and coil 2, the flux linking one because of the other will be some fixed fraction of the total flux produced by the causing coil. That is,

$$|\phi_{21}| = k_{21}\phi_{11} \qquad 0 < k_{21} < 1 \tag{13.27a}$$

$$|\phi_{12}| = k_{12}\phi_{22} \qquad 0 < k_{12} < 1. \tag{13.27b}$$

For the system of Fig. 13.1 the current-divider relationship reveals that

$$k_{21} = +\frac{\mathscr{P}_2}{\mathscr{P}_l + \mathscr{P}_2}. \tag{13.28a}$$

$$k_{12} = +\frac{\mathscr{P}_1}{\mathscr{P}_l + \mathscr{P}_1}. \tag{13.28b}$$

By Eqs. (13.4)

$$|L_{12}| = \frac{|\lambda_{12}|}{|i_2|}$$

$$= \left|\frac{N_1\phi_{12}}{i_2}\right|$$

$$= k_{12}\frac{N_1\phi_{22}}{i_2}. \tag{13.29a}$$

Similarly,

$$|L_{21}| = k_{21}\frac{N_2\,\phi_{11}}{i_1}.$$

(13.29b)

Then

$$L_{12}^2 = |L_{12}|\,|L_{21}|$$

$$= k_{12}\,k_{21}\left(\frac{N_1\phi_{11}}{i_1}\right)\left(\frac{N_2\phi_{22}}{i_2}\right)$$

$$= k_{12}\,k_{21}L_{11}L_{22}\,,$$

(13.30)

which can be written

$$M = |L_{12}| = k\sqrt{L_{11}L_{22}}\,,$$

(13.31)

where

$$k = \sqrt{k_{12}\,k_{21}}$$

(13.32)

is called the *coefficient of coupling* between the two coils, 1 and 2.

13.7 LEAKAGE INDUCTANCE

Although the concept of leakage inductance may be adapted to the n-coil system, its greatest use is in connection with systems with but two coils, which case will be covered in this article.

The *leakage flux* of a coil is that component of its self-produced flux which links only the producing coil and no other coil in the system. In Fig. 13.1, for example, such fluxes will penetrate the permeance shown schematically as $\mathscr{P}_l$. The total flux in this leg will be

$$\phi_l = \phi_{l1} + \phi_{l2}\,,$$

(13.33)

where ϕ_{l1} and ϕ_{l2} are the leakage fluxes of coil 1 and coil 2 respectively and the letter l is used to indicate a quantity associated with the leakage path symbolically represented by $\mathscr{P}_l$.

According to the flux-divider relationship (by comparison with the current-divider relationship),

$$|\phi_{l1}| = \frac{\mathscr{P}_l}{\mathscr{P}_l + \mathscr{P}_2}\,\phi_{11}$$

$$= \frac{\mathscr{P}_l}{\mathscr{P}_l + \mathscr{P}_2}\,\mathscr{P}_{T11}N_1i_1$$

$$= (1 - k_{21})\mathscr{P}_{T11}N_1i_1$$

$$= |\mathscr{P}_{Tl1}|\,N_1i_1\,.$$

(13.34)

Here $\mathscr{P}_{Tl1}$ is the transfer permeance connecting branch l with source (or coil mmf) No. 1. The coil No. 1 flux linkages due to its leakage flux alone are

$$
\begin{aligned}
\lambda_{l1} &= N_1 |\phi_{l1}| \\
&= N_1^2 |\mathscr{P}_{Tl1}| \, i_1 \\
&= L_1 i_1,
\end{aligned} \tag{13.35}
$$

where

$$
L_1 = N_1^2 |\mathscr{P}_{Tl1}| \tag{13.36}
$$

is the *leakage inductance* of coil 1.

The total flux produced by coil 1 is

$$
\phi_{11} = |\phi_{l1}| + |\phi_{21}|,
$$

and the total flux linkages produced by coil 1 are

$$
\begin{aligned}
\lambda_{11} &= N_1 \phi_{11} \\
&= N_1 |\phi_{l1}| + N_1 |\phi_{21}| \\
&= N_1^2 |\mathscr{P}_{Tl1}| \, i_1 + N_1^2 |\mathscr{P}_{T21}| \, i_1 \\
&= \left(N_1^2 |\mathscr{P}_{Tl1}| + \frac{N_1}{N_2} N_2 N_1 |\mathscr{P}_{T21}| \right) i_1 \\
&= L_{11} i_1.
\end{aligned} \tag{13.37}
$$

Substituting Eqs. (13.4c), (13.7), and (13.36) and equating the coefficients of i_1 results in

$$
L_{11} = L_1 + a|L_{21}| = L_1 + aM, \tag{13.38}
$$

where

$$
a = \frac{N_1}{N_2} = \text{turns ratio.} \tag{13.39}
$$

In a similar manner, we may show that the leakage inductance of coil 2 is

$$
L_2 = N_2^2 |\mathscr{P}_{Tl2}|,
$$

and that

$$
L_{22} = L_2 + \frac{|L_{12}|}{a} = L_2 + \frac{M}{a}. \tag{13.40}
$$

13.8 THE LOSSLESS-CORE TRANSFORMER

The transformer is a collection of stationary coils used to change the voltage and current levels between a power source and its load or to change the ac impedance level of a load attached to a power source.

The magnetic configuration of a two-winding transformer is shown in Fig. 13.5(a) and its magnetic schematic is Fig. 13.5(b). The core may be either air or some magnetic material such as laminated sheet steel or sintered

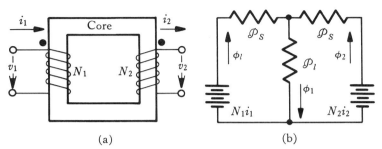

Fig. 13.5 *The two-winding transformer.*

powdered iron. In high-frequency applications, the core is usually air, while it is invariably laminated steel in power transformers and either laminated steel or powdered iron in audio-frequency applications.

The schematic indicates the magnetic symmetry of this type of device and shows the leakage path permeance $\mathscr{P}_l$. In magnetic-core transformers, $\mathscr{P}_l$ is usually very small while $\mathscr{P}_s$ is very high, due to the tendency of the flux to remain in the high-permeance core with very little "leaking" across the air path between coils.

There are two sources of heat, or loss, in the core. The first, hysteresis loss, is due to the resistance of dipoles to alignment changes, discussed in Art. 1.8. The second, eddy-current loss, is due to circulating currents in the core due to voltages caused by changing flux in the core, and such loss is generally reduced by breaking up current paths by "laminating" the core or through the use of powdered iron or sintered cores. Although these losses can be significant, they are assumed to be negligible in this analysis.

If i_1 and i_2 are assumed to be mesh currents and v_1 and v_2 generated voltages, the operational mesh-current equations are, in matrix form,

$$\begin{bmatrix} V_1(p) \\ -V_2(p) \end{bmatrix} = \begin{bmatrix} R_1 + L_{11}\,p & L_{12}\,p \\ L_{21}\,p & R_2 + L_{22}\,p \end{bmatrix} \begin{bmatrix} I_1(p) \\ I_2(p) \end{bmatrix}, \qquad (13.41a)$$

or, in expanded form,

$$\begin{aligned} V_1(p) &= (R_1 + L_{11}\,p)I_1(p) & - Mp I_2(p) \\ -V_2(p) &= \qquad - Mp I_1(p) + (R_2 + L_{22}\,p)I_2(p) \end{aligned}. \qquad (13.41b)$$

Substituting Eqs. (13.38) and (13.40) produces

$$V_1(p) = (R_1 + L_1 p + aMp)I_1(p) \qquad\qquad - MpI_2(p)$$

$$-V_2(p) = \qquad - MpI_1(p) + \left(R_2 + L_2 p + \frac{M}{a} p\right)I_2(p).$$

Now multiply and divide the second term in the first equation by the turns ratio, a; multiply both sides of the second equation by a; and multiply and divide the second term of the second equation by a. The result may be written

$$V_1(p) = (R_1 + L_1 p + aMp)I_1(p) \qquad\qquad - aM\frac{I_2(p)}{a}$$

$$-aV_2(p) = \qquad - aMpI_1(p) + (a^2R_2 + a^2L_2 p + aMp)\frac{I_2(p)}{a}.$$

$$(13.42)$$

The *magnetizing inductance* is defined

$$L_M = aM = \frac{N_1}{N_2} N_1 N_2 |\mathscr{P}_{T12}| = N_1^2 |\mathscr{P}_{T12}|, \qquad (13.43)$$

which in Eqs. (13.42) results in

$$V_1(p) = (R_1 + L_1 p + L_M p)I_1(p) \qquad\qquad - L_M p\frac{I_2(p)}{a}$$

$$-aV_2(p) = \qquad - L_M pI_1(p) + (a^2R_2 + a^2L_2 p + L_M p)\frac{I_2(p)}{a}.$$

$$(13.44)$$

These equations form the mesh equations for the circuit of Fig. 13.6. This circuit has exactly the same behavior with respect to its input terminals as does the actual transformer.

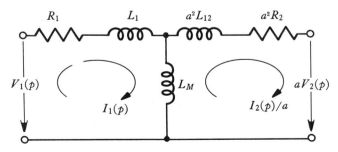

Fig. 13.6 *Equivalent circuit of the two-winding lossless-core transformer, referred to Coil 1.*

13.9   THE IDEAL TRANSFORMER

When the permeance of the coil in the lossless-core transformer becomes very high, so that $\mathscr{P}_s \to \infty$ and $\mathscr{P}_l \to 0$, and when its coil resistance becomes very low, it approaches the *ideal transformer*, which is often used as an approximation to the actual transformer in analysis. Under these conditions

$$R_1 + L_1 p \simeq 0, \qquad R_2 + L_2 p \simeq 0, \qquad L_M \to \infty. \qquad (13.45)$$

Then the equivalent circuit of the transformer whose circuit schematic is shown in Fig. 13.7(a) approaches the circuit of Fig. 13.7(b). Obviously, in such a transformer

$$\frac{V_1(p)}{V_2(p)} = a = \frac{N_1}{N_2} \qquad (13.46a)$$

$$\frac{I_1(p)}{I_2(p)} = \frac{1}{a} = \frac{N_2}{N_1}. \qquad (13.46b)$$

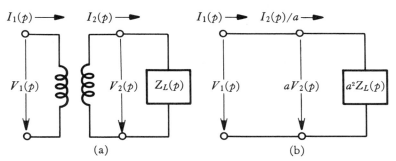

Fig. 13.7   *The ideal transformer, with load impedance.* (a) *Circuit schematic.* (b) *Equivalent circuit.*

An interesting and very useful property of the transformer is the manner in which its input impedance is affected by its load impedance. The good quality audio or power transformer approaches the ideal in this regard, and in the ideal transformer the input impedance is

$$Z_i(p) = \frac{V_1(p)}{I_1(p)} = \frac{a V_2(p)}{I_2(p)/a} = a^2 \frac{V_2(p)}{I_2(p)} = a^2 Z_L(p). \qquad (13.47)$$

In other words, the input impedance is the load impedance multiplied by the square of the turns ratio. This property finds important applications in the *matching* of a given load for maximum power from a given source. An example would be the choosing of a transformer to place between a loud-speaker and an audio amplifier to cause maximum power to be transferred to the speaker.

EXAMPLE 13.4. A power amplifier having an output impedance of 1000 Ω is to deliver maximum power to a speaker having an impedance of 10 Ω. What must be the turns ratio of the matching transformer between them?

Solution. The circuit is shown in Fig. 13.8, where the power amplifier is represented by its Thévenin's equivalent. According to the maximum power transfer theorem, for maximum power to the transformer

$$Z_i(p) = R_o.$$

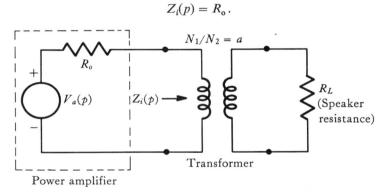

Fig. 13.8 *Circuit for Example 13.4.*

If the transformer approaches the ideal, essentially all this power is transferred to the load. As in this case

$$Z_i(p) = R_o = a^2 R_L,$$

the turns ratio must be

$$a = \sqrt{\frac{R_o}{R_L}} = \sqrt{\frac{1000}{10}} = 10. \qquad Ans.$$

13.10 TRANSFORMERS WITH LOSSY CORES

So far, the generation of heat in the core of the transformer has been ignored, but the picture remains incomplete without its consideration. Such heat losses will generally be of the same order of magnitude as the copper losses (the power dissipated in R_1 and R_2), and they cannot properly be ignored in large power transformers where efficiencies are important. Such losses also modify the circuit characteristics of transformers, so they may be important in applications other than power transfer.

The core losses arise from two separate phenomena:

1. There are *eddy-current* losses due to the fact that the metal core is a conductor influenced by changing magnetic fields, so that short-circuited voltages are induced and currents flow, causing conductive heating.

2. There are *hysteresis losses*, which arise from the phenomenon of magnetic hysteresis, which was discussed in Sec. 1.8.

Let us discuss these phenomena briefly and somewhat qualitatively as applied to the transformer of Fig. 13.5 when *the secondary is open-circuited and the primary leakage flux and resistance are presumed negligible.* Under these assumptions,

$$\phi_1(t) = -\phi_2(t) = \phi(t) \tag{13.48}$$

and

$$v_1(t) = N_1 \frac{d\phi(t)}{dt}. \tag{13.49}$$

The changing flux in the core will cause voltages of the same directions as those in coil 1 to be induced in the core; but these voltages are short-circuited by the metal core, producing currents circulating inside the core in such a way that each elemental current path encircles a fixed portion of the total flux, $\phi(t)$. Consequently, the voltage forcing the circulating current is a fixed constant times the derivative of the total core flux, so the kth incremental current is proportional to the derivative of flux and to the applied voltage as follows:

$$\Delta_k i \propto \frac{d\phi}{dt} \propto v_1,$$

or, in terms of phasors

$$\Delta_k I \propto j\omega\Phi \propto V_1,$$

and the incremental average rate of eddy-current loss is

$$P_e = \sum_k \Delta_k P_e \propto \sum_k (\Delta_k I)^2 \propto V_1^2.$$

Thus, the eddy-current power is

$$P_e = k_e V_1^2. \tag{13.50}$$

As from Eq. (13.49)

$$\mathbf{V}_1 = j\omega N_1 \mathbf{\Phi}$$

and as

$$\mathbf{\Phi} = \mathbf{B}A_c,$$

where A_c is the cross-sectional area of the core, we may write

$$V_1 = \omega N_1 \Phi = \frac{\omega N_1 \Phi_m}{\sqrt{2}} = \frac{2\pi f N_1 B_m A_c}{\sqrt{2}}.$$

and an alternative form of Eq. (13.50) is

$$P_e = K_e B_m^2 f^2. \tag{13.51}$$

Thus, eddy-current loss is proportional to the squares of both maximum flux density and frequency, or, alternatively, to the square of the applied voltage alone. It is reduced to a minimum in transformer design by *laminating* the core into thin sheets parallel to the core flux. This forces the circulating, or *eddy*, currents into long narrow loops having high resistance and linking small amounts of flux. Consequently, the eddy currents are reduced to much smaller values than would exist in solid iron cores. Similar effects are obtained in small transformers used in electronic circuitry by employing powdered-iron cores.

Now let us look at hysteresis loss. You will recall that the magnetic field intensity is the magnetic potential drop per unit of length. [See Eq. (1.10) for the general case.] According to Ampere's law, Eq. (1.49), we have, consequently, for our transformer core

$$H(t)l_c = N_1 i_1(t),$$

or

$$i_1(t) = \frac{l_c}{N_1} H(t), \tag{13.52}$$

where l_c is the mean length of the core. The instantaneous power may be computed in the absence of eddy-current loss as

$$p_h(t) = v_1(t)i_1(t)$$

$$= \left[N_1 \frac{d\phi(t)}{dt} \right] \left[\frac{l_c}{N_1} H(t) \right]$$

$$= l_c A_c H(t) \frac{dB(t)}{dt}$$

$$= (\text{core volume})H(t) \frac{dB(t)}{dt}.$$

The hysteresis energy lost *per unit of core volume per cycle of the hysteresis loop*

$$w_h(t) = \frac{1}{(\text{core volume})} \int_{\substack{\text{hyst.} \\ \text{loop}}} p_h(t)\, dt = \int_{\substack{\text{hyst.} \\ \text{loop}}} H(t)\, dB(t)$$

$$= (\text{area of hysteresis loop}). \tag{13.53}$$

The power is the energy lost per unit of time, so under steady-state periodic variations in $H(t)$ and $B(t)$, the average power is the total energy lost per cycle times the number of cycles per second, i.e.,

$$P_h = (\text{core volume})(\text{area of hysteresis loop})\, f. \tag{13.54}$$

Experimental results show that

$$(\text{area of hysteresis loop}) \propto B_m^n, \tag{13.55}$$

where n, the *Steinmetz constant* for the core material, usually lies between 1.5 and 2.0 and is often taken to be 1.6. Thus, we see that the average rate of hysteresis loss under periodic excitation is proportional to B_m^n and to f, so

$$P_h = K_h B_m^n f. \tag{13.56}$$

Equation (13.56) holds for any periodic waveform of frequency f. For steady-state sinusoids, then, the total core loss is the combination of hysteresis and eddy-current losses,

$$P_{\text{core}} = P_e + P_h$$
$$= K_e B_m^2 f^2 + K_h B_m^n f. \tag{13.57}$$

Equation (13.57) may be rewritten as

$$P_{\text{core}} = K_e(B_m f)^2 + K_h f^{1-n}(B_m f)^n.$$

We have seen that $V_1 \propto B_m f$, so we may write the above equation as

$$P_{\text{core}} = k_e V_1^2 + k_h f^{1-n} V_1^n.$$

When the Steinmetz constant is considered approximately equal to 2 and the frequency is constant, the core loss may be considered to be approximately proportional to the square of the applied voltage. Formalizing this, we have

$$P_{\text{core}} \simeq K_c V_1^2, \qquad \left\{\begin{matrix} f = \text{constant} \\ n \simeq 2 \end{matrix}\right\}. \tag{13.58}$$

The above approximation allows us to account for the total core loss as the loss in a resistor properly added in the equivalent circuit of the transformer. It must be remembered that the relationship is only approximate and it is frequency dependent. These factors are of small consequence, however, in power transformers, which operate at constant frequencies and nearly constant terminal voltages.

Now that we recognize that the nature of core losses allows them to be accounted for by circuit constants to a good approximation, let us account for the core as though it produced the effects of a short-circuited one-turn coil with no leakage flux, a concept with the merit of a pretty fair correspondence with reality. In order to save time, let us first consider the transformer of Fig. 13.5 with the secondary open. Under the assumptions we are accepting, the unit now becomes a two-winding transformer, the secondary of which is the no-leakage winding representing the core. The equivalent circuit for such a system is that created by modifying the equivalent circuit of Fig. 13.6 to suit the case at hand by setting

$$a_2 R_2 = R_M$$
$$a^2 L_2 = 0 \qquad \text{(the no-leakage condition)}$$
$$a V_2 = 0 \qquad \text{(the short-circuited turn).}$$

The inductances are replaced, in the figure, by reactances and phasor values are used to remind us of the constant-frequency character of the representation. The result is the circuit of Fig. 13.9. Note that the result is identical to

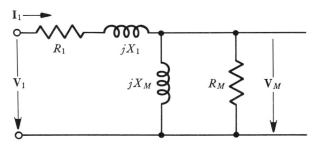

Fig. 13.9 *The transformer with core losses at no load.*

that of the active part of the circuit of Fig. 13.6 with no secondary current, except that the resistor, R_M, now appears in parallel with the magnetizing reactance, X_M.

Now allow current to flow in coil 2, the secondary. Since X_M is a measure of the core flux, which still excites the secondary, it is to be expected that the secondary circuit will continue to appear across X_M, as shown in Fig. 13.10. To find the core losses, one simply computes the power dissipated in resistor R_M. Thus we complete a somewhat intuitive deduction of the circuit effects of core losses. Note that the end result is that of Fig. 13.6 with the *magnetizing resistance, R_M,* added.

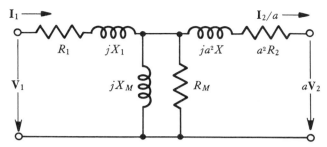

Fig. 13.10 *Equivalent circuit for the transformer with core losses.*

PROBLEMS

13.1   In Fig. P.13.1, the core is of magnetic material having an effective relative permeability of 5000 under operating conditions. Assuming that all flux remains in the core, compute all self and mutual inductances if the coil turns are $N_1 = 400$, $N_2 = 400$, and $N_3 = 2000$.

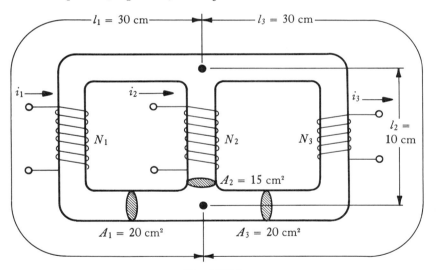

Fig. P.13.1.

13.2   Repeat Prob. 13.1 when $N_1 = 800$, $N_2 = 2000$, and $N_3 = 2000$ while all other constants remain unchanged.

13.3   Repeat Prob. 13.1 when

$N_1 = 400$	$N_2 = 400$	$N_3 = 2000$
$l_1 = 30$ cm	$l_2 = 10$ cm	$l_3 = 30$ cm
$A_1 = 40$ cm^2	$A_2 = 15$ cm^2	$A_3 = 40$ cm^2.

13.4 Coil 1 has a resistance of 5 Ω and an inductance of 0.5 mH. It is located near Coil 2, which has a resistance of 20 Ω and an inductance of 4.0 mH. The magnitude of the mutual inductance is 1.0 mH. Coil 2 is short-circuited and a constant 50 V is applied to Coil 1 at $t = 0$. Find the currents in both coils for $t > 0$.

13.5 Repeat Prob. 13.4 when the applied voltage is

$$v_1(t) = \begin{cases} -100, & -\infty < t < 0 \\ 50, & 0 < t < \infty. \end{cases}$$

13.6 Find the poles and zeros of the voltage transfer ratio of the two-coil system of Prob. 13.4, then plot the asymptote and actual H_{db} and angle plots on semilog coordinates. What are the half-power points?

13.7 A two-coil system has negligible resistances and $L_{11} = 0.2$ mH, $L_{22} = 1.2$ mH, and $M = 0.3$ mH. One current flows into a polarity mark, the other out of a polarity mark, and voltage drops are taken positive in the same directions as the coil currents. Find in operational form:

a.   The transmission parameters.
b.   The y-parameters.
c.   The h-parameters.

13.8 A capacitor is placed across the terminals of Coil 2 in Prob. 13.7 which resonates with Coil 2 at 20 kHz when Coil 1 is open-circuited. Find the voltage transfer ratio, $H_V(p) = V_2(p)/V_1(p)$. Sketch the frequency response.

13.9 In Fig. P.13.2, $L_{aa} = 1.0$ H, $L_{bb} = 5.0$ H, and $M = 2.0$ H. Find $v_2(t)$ and $i_1(t)$ for $t > 0$.

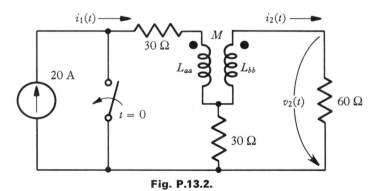

Fig. P.13.2.

13.10 In Prob. 13.9, replace the 60-Ω resistor with a 20-μF capacitor, then find $I_1(p)$ and $V_2(p)$.

13.11 In Fig. P.13.3, $R_a = 2\,\Omega$, $R_b = 10\,\Omega$, $L_{aa} = 1\,H$, $L_{bb} = 5\,H$, $M = 2\,H$, and $R = 440\,\Omega$. Find the pole-zero configuration of

$$H_V(p) = V_2(p)/V_1(p)$$

and sketch the magnitude in decibels and angle of the frequency response on semilog paper.

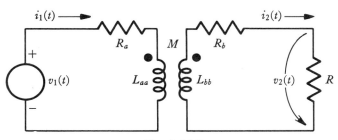

Fig. P.13.3.

13.12 In Fig. P.13.3, $v_1(t) = 5u(t)$ with the same circuit constants as in Prob. 13.11. Find $v_2(t)$ for $t > 0$.

13.13 In Fig. P.13.3, $v_1(t) = 5u(-t)$ with the same circuit constants as in Prob. 13.11. Find $v_2(t)$ for $t > 0$.

13.14 Show that the input impedance to the network of Fig. P.13.3 is

$$Z(p) = R_a \frac{(1 - k^2)\tau_1\tau_2\, p^2 + (\tau_1 + \tau_2)p + 1}{\tau_2\, p + 1},$$

where k is the coefficient of coupling and τ_1 and τ_2 are the time constants of the first (left) and second meshes acting alone.

13.15 In Fig. P.13.4 the switch changes position without opening the circuit to the right. Solve for $i_2(t)$ for $t \geqslant 0$.

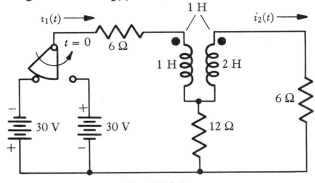

Fig. P.13.4.

13.16 For the circuit of Fig. P.13.5

a.   Find $i_2(t)$ for $t \geqslant 0$.

b.   Find the energy dissipated as heat and radiation in the opening of the switch.

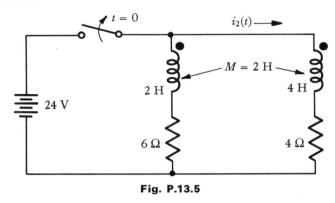

Fig. P.13.5

13.17 Reverse the polarity of the 4-H coil in Fig. P.13.5, then repeat Prob. 13.16.

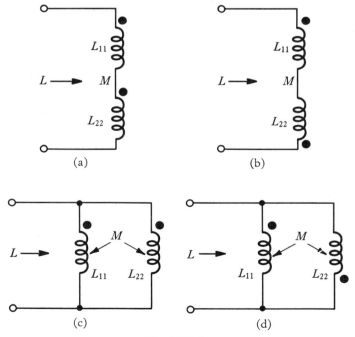

Fig. P.13.6.

13.18 Show that the following are true:

a.   In Fig. P.13.6(a), $L = L_{11} + L_{22} + 2M$
b.   In Fig. P.13.6(b), $L = L_{11} + L_{22} - 2M$

c.   In Fig. P.13.6(c), $L = \dfrac{L_{11}L_{22} - M^2}{L_{11} + L_{22} - 2M}$

d.   In Fig. P.13.6(d), $L = \dfrac{L_{11}L_{22} - M^2}{L_{11} + L_{22} + 2M}$.

13.19 Give the pole-zero plot for $V_2(p)/I_1(p)$ in Fig. P.13.7 when $L_{11} = 10\,\text{mH}$, $L_{22} = 5\,\text{mH}$, $M = 4\,\text{mH}$, $C_1 = 1\,\mu\text{F}$, and $C_2 = 5\,\mu\text{F}$. Sketch the frequency response on a linear frequency scale.

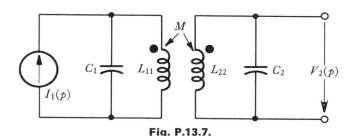

Fig. P.13.7.

13.20 In Fig. P.13.7, $L_{11} = L_{22} = 1\,\text{H}$, and $C_1 = C_2 = 1\,\text{F}$. Find the poles and zeros for $Z_{T21}(p) = V_2(p)/I_1(p)$ and sketch the frequency response on a linear frequency scale when the coefficient of coupling is

a. $k = 1$
b. $k = 1/\sqrt{2}$
c. $K = 1/\sqrt{5}$
d. k is very small.

Also,

e.   What changes in the L's and C's would expand the pole-zero plot by a factor of 10^6, thereby causing the significant frequencies to lie in the megacycle ranges? The circuit should now utilize more usual values of inductance and capacitance.

13.21 Repeat Prob. 13.20, except for part (e), when C_2 is increased to 2 F.

13.22 In Fig. P.13.7, $C_1 = C_2 = 1$ F and the coefficient of coupling is $1/\sqrt{5}$. Find the poles and zeros of $Z_{T21} = V_2(p)/I_1(p)$ and sketch the frequency response on a linear frequency scale when

a. $L_{11} = L_{22} = 2\,\text{H}$
b. $L_{11} = 4\,\text{H}, \qquad L_{22} = 1\,\text{H}$
c. $L_{11} = 8\,\text{H}, \qquad L_{22} = 1/2\,\text{H}.$

13.23 The two-winding transformer of Fig. P.13.8 has a core which will yield a deliberately high leakage reactance, such as might be used in current

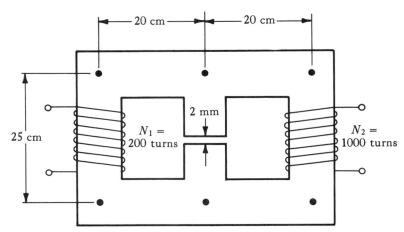

Fig. P.13.8.

limiting applications, rather than the low leakage reactance of the conventional transformer. Mean core-section lengths are given, and the cross-sectional core area is 100 cm² throughout. The core material has an effective relative permeability of 1500 H/m, and air-gap flux is uniformly distributed with negligible fringing. Find the leakage inductances and the magnetizing inductance.

13.24 Repeat Prob. 13.23 when the numerals 1 and 2, identifying the coils, are interchanged.

13.25 Repeat Prob. 13.23 when the air-gap length is doubled.

13.26 Repeat Prob. 13.23 when the core area of the two outside legs is halved.

13.27 Show that in transformers wound on symmetric cores

$$L_1 = a^2 L_2, \qquad \text{where } a = N_1/N_2.$$

13.28 The input inductance of a symmetric-core audio transformer with a 3:1 turns ratio measures 9.1 H when the secondary is open-circuited and 0.3 H when the secondary is short-circuited. What are the magnetizing, mutual, self, and leakage inductances?

13.29 The ideal audio matching transformer of Example 13.4 must in practice be an actual transformer. Suppose the actual transformer has negligible core losses and the following parameters:

$$R_1 = 200 \ \Omega \qquad M = 0.5 \text{ H}$$
$$R_2 = 2 \ \Omega \qquad L_1 = 50 \text{ mH}$$
$$L_2 = 0.5 \text{ mH}.$$

Find the pole-zero configuration of $V_L(p)/V_a(p)$, where $V_L(p)$ is the downward voltage drop across the load resistor. Find the half-power frequencies and the bandwidth. Sketch the db amplitude and phase shift on semilog coordinates, assuming both polarity marks are at the top.

13.30 A 10 : 1 ratio audio transformer with negligible core losses has $L_1 = 0.1$ H, $L_M = 9$ H, $R_1 = 500 \ \Omega$ and $R_2 = 5 \ \Omega$. If it is terminated with 40 Ω of pure resistance, find the upper and lower half-power points and the bandwidth, in Hz, of

$$H_V(p) = V_2(p)/V_1(p).$$

13.31 An audio transformer has negligible core losses and has the following parameters:

$$a = N_1/N_2 = 5 \qquad L_M = 40 \text{ H}$$
$$L_1 = 0.4 \text{ H} \qquad R_1 = 20 \ \Omega$$
$$R_2 = 1 \ \Omega.$$

The primary is excited by a voltage source whose output impedance is 10 kΩ of pure resistance and whose open-circuit voltage is v_S. A variable resistance, R_L, is connected across the secondary. Both primary and secondary voltage drops are considered positive away from the polarity marks.

a.   Give the approximate range of frequencies over which R_L " sees " a pure resistance when looking back into the secondary.
b.   Find the value of R_L which will extract maximum power at frequencies near the center of the range determined in (a).
c.   With R_L set as in (b), find the poles and zeros of $H(p) = V_2(p)/V_S(p)$.
d.   Sketch the asymptotic and actual decibel values and angles of $H(j\omega)$ on semilog coordinates.

13.32 This problem introduces the student to some approximations which can be extremely useful in applications of broadband transformers. In such transformers, the behavior takes on characteristics peculiar to one of three ranges of frequency:

1. The low-frequency range, where $\begin{cases} L_1 p = a^2 L_2 p \simeq 0 \\ L_M p \text{ is finite} \end{cases}$

2. The mid-frequency range, where $\begin{cases} L_1 p = a^2 L_2 p \simeq 0 \\ L_M |p| \simeq \infty \end{cases}$

3. The high-frequency range, where $\begin{cases} L_1 p = a^2 L_2 p \text{ is nonzero} \\ L_M |p| \simeq \infty. \end{cases}$

Find the constraints between L_1, L_2, L_M, and ω for such ranges to exist separate from one another. Draw the equivalent circuit for each frequency range when the approximations above are valid.

13.33 From the results of part (c) of Prob. 13.31, find the approximate *p-z* plot for the transformer in the three frequency ranges, as was done for the example of Fig. 10.12. Then compute the *p-z* plots using the three approximate equivalent circuits of Prob. 13.32, and compare the two sets of results.

13.34 Suppose the transformer of Fig. 13.5 has negligible core losses, has the constants a, L_1, L_M, R_1, and R_2 known, and is terminated, at the secondary, with a resistance, R_L. Let $H(p) = V_2(p)/V_1(p)$, and assume that:

1. In the low-frequency range, $H(p) = H_l(p)$
2. In the mid-frequency range, $H(p) = H_m = a$ constant
3. In the high-frequency range, $H(p) = H_h(p)$.

Do the following:

a. Show that

$$H_l(p) = \frac{H_m \, p}{p + \omega_1}$$

$$H_h(p) = \frac{H_m \, \omega_2}{p + \omega_2}.$$

b. Express H_m, ω_1, and ω_2 in terms of the transformer constants and R_L.

c. Show that for *all* values of p

$$H(p) = \frac{1}{H_m} H_l(p) H_h(p).$$

13.35 An audio transformer with negligible losses matches $10 \, \Omega$ of resistance to a $10{,}000\text{-}\Omega$ source for maximum power transfer in the mid-frequency range. Experiment shows a lower 3-db point at 300 rad/sec and an upper 3-db point at 30,000 rad/sec. What are L_{11}, L_{22}, and M?

13.36 A $10:1$ ratio transformer has $L_1 = 0.05$ H and $L_M = 10$ H. Core and copper losses are negligible. The inter-winding and inter-turn capacitances plus secondary circuit capacitance have the approximate effect of a 0.05-μF capacitor across the secondary terminals. The source feeding the primary has the operational Thévenin equivalent of an ideal source, $V_S(p)$, in series with a 10-kΩ resistor, and the transformer delivers maximum power to a pure resistance on the secondary at the middle frequencies. Find the poles and zeros of $H(p) = V_2(p)/V_S(p)$, and sketch asymptotic and actual values of H_{db} and the angle on $H(j\omega)$ as functions of ω on semilog coordinates.

13.37 Rework Prob. 13.36 neglecting the capacitance, and compare the results with those of Prob. 13.36.

13.38 Show that the energy stored in the magnetic fields of a set of interacting coils is

$$w_m = \tfrac{1}{2}\tilde{\imath}\,\mathscr{L}i,$$

where i is the current matrix and $\mathscr{L}$ the inductance matrix.

13.39 Let the currents $i_1(t)$ and $i_2(t)$ indicated in Fig. P.13.2 be the two mesh currents for $t \geqslant 0$, when $L_{aa} = 1$H, $L_{bb} = 5$ H, and $M = 2$ H. Solve for the mesh current matrix by conventional matrix methods, finding first the operational matrix current, then the corresponding time-varying current matrix. Find the instantaneous stored energy by application of the results of Prob. 13.38.

13.40 Repeat Prob. 13.39, except utilize Fig. P.13.3 with the circuit constants of Prob. 13.11 and with $v_1(t) = 10u(t)$.

13.41 Repeat Prob. 13.39, except refer to Fig. P.13.4.

13.42 Write the operational matrix form of the mesh equations leading to a solution for the network of Fig. P.13.9.

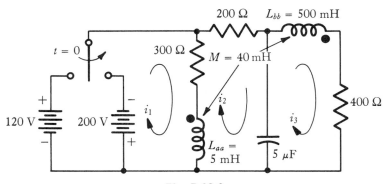

Fig. P.13.9.

13.43 Establish the mesh operational impedance matrix for the network of Fig. P.13.10.

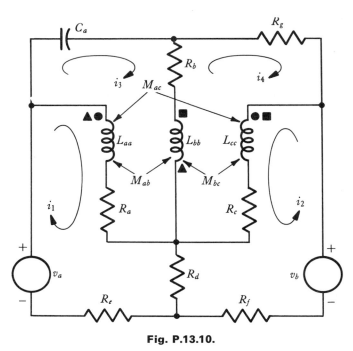

Fig. P.13.10.

13.44 Magnetically coupled coils No. 1, No. 2, and No. 3 have the inductance matrix

$$\mathscr{L} = \begin{bmatrix} 3 & \pm 2 & \pm 3 \\ \pm 2 & 2 & \pm 1 \\ \pm 3 & \pm 1 & 4 \end{bmatrix}.$$

Show all possible series combinations of the three coils, using as polarity marks circular dots for the 1-2 combination, triangular dots for the 2-3 combination, and square dots for the 3-1 combination. Give the inductance of each combination.

13.45 Find $i_2(t)$ and $v_2(t)$ for $t \geqslant 0$ in Fig. P.13.11.

13.46 Reverse the connections on the 4-H coil in Fig. P.13.11 and repeat Prob. 13.45.

13.47 In Fig. P.13.11, replace the battery-switch combination by a steady-state 60-Hz source with 120 rms terminal volts. What will be the source current?

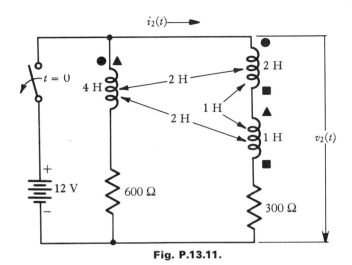

Fig. P.13.11.

13.48 A certain power transformer has the following constants:

$$R_1 = 0.3 \ \Omega \qquad X_1 = \omega L_1 = 0.7 \ \Omega$$
$$R_2 = 0.003 \ \Omega \qquad X_2 = \omega L_2 = 0.007 \ \Omega$$
$$R_M = 300 \ \Omega \qquad X_M = \omega L_M = 1200 \ \Omega.$$

Let us now consider the input, or No. 1, coil to be that which was the output, or No. 2, coil when the above data were listed. Relist the data to fit the new coil designations.

13.49 A certain transformer has, at rated voltage and frequency, a core loss of 600 W, equally divided between hysteresis and eddy-current losses. Find the core losses under each of the following conditions:

a. At rated frequency, but one-half rated voltage.

b. At rated voltage, but twice rated frequency.

The remaining problems apply to power transformers, in which, at normal frequency,

$$|R_1 + j\omega L_1| \simeq a^2 |R_2 + j\omega L_2| \ll |R_M \text{ in parallel with } j\omega L_M|.$$

This inequality is so pronounced that little error occurs if the magnetizing impedance, which is R_M in parallel with $j\omega L_M$, as it occurs in Fig. 13.10, is either moved ahead of $R_1 + j\omega L_1$ to appear across $\mathbf{V}_1$ or moved behind $R_2 + j\omega L_2$ to appear directly across $\mathbf{V}_2$. The student is invited to exploit these approximations to the derived equivalent circuit in the problems that follow.

13.50 Explain why the inequality above justifies the approximations suggested for the equivalent circuit. Show that as the inequality becomes more and more severe, the transformer more and more approaches the ideal transformer, in which

$$\frac{V_1}{V_2} = \frac{I_2}{I_1} = \frac{N_1}{N_2} = a.$$

13.51 The following data are collected for a 7200/2400-V, 500-kVA transformer from measurements at the terminals of the low-voltage side:

High-voltage side Short-circuited	High-voltage side Open-circuited
$V = 50$ V	$V = 2400$ V
$I = 208$ A	$I = 7.0$ A
$P = 6$ kW	$P = 7$ kW

The unit is operated with the high-voltage side as the primary.

a.   Find the efficiency when delivering 300 kVA at 0.8 pf lag and rated voltage.

b.   What primary voltage is required for rated secondary voltage when the load is 500 kVA at 0.6 pf lag?

c.   What is the voltage regulation in (b)?

13.52 Repeat parts (b) and (c) of Prob. 13.51 when the load is 500 kVA at 0.6 pf lead.

13.53 Show the equivalent circuit of the transformer of Prob. 13.51.

14

Fourier Methods

14.1 INTRODUCTION

In Chapter 10, the characteristics of systems under sinusoidal excitations were studied in considerable detail. It became obvious there that the amplitude and phase angle of the response were, in general, frequency dependent. It may also have been noted that only in those systems in which this frequency dependence was absent, as in pure resistance networks, could one expect the form of the output for nonsinusoidal excitation functions to be identical with the form of the input. This alone would lead one to suspect that the form of a signal depends somehow on its "frequency content." We shall see in this chapter that it does, indeed, and does so uniquely. Such a fortuitous circumstance allows us to apply the well-organized methods special to sinusoidal excitations to the problems of nonsinusoidal excitations.

The study of the frequency characteristics of signals comes under the broad heading of *Fourier Methods*. Also under this heading, or one closely related to it, comes the Laplace transform, which in a sense may replace, and certainly extends, the operator concept that we have been using to solve our systems. Both are considered in this chapter, as well as related time-domain methods.

14.2 FOURIER EXPANSION OF PERIODIC FUNCTIONS

As an indication of the probability that a given periodic function may be at least approximated by a series of sinusoids, consider the square wave of Fig. 14.1, which is a periodic function of period 2π, expressible as

$$f(t) = f(t \pm 2\pi n) = \begin{Bmatrix} 1, & 0 < t < \pi \\ 0, & \pi < t < 2\pi \end{Bmatrix}, \qquad n = 0, 1, 2, 3, \dots . \quad (14.1)$$

The wave has a nonzero average value, so we would expect that one term of any series expansion approximating it would be a constant.

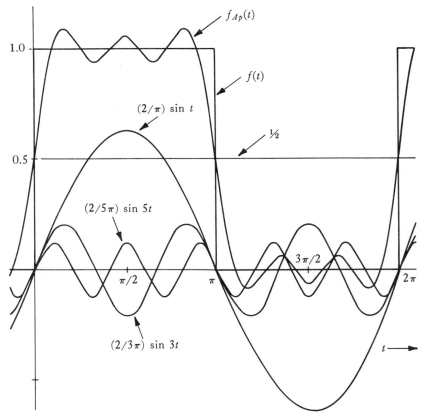

Fig. 14.1 *Approximation of a square wave by a series of sinusoids.*

Assuming that it is possible to complete the expansion as a series of sinu-soids, as suspected in the introduction, they would need to be waves which behave in a manner to produce a slope at $t = \pi$ negative to that at $t = 0$. One such sinusoid is a sine wave with zero phase angle and the same frequency as the given periodic function. A little reflection will reveal that the only sinusoids behaving in this way are sine waves of zero or 180° phase shift and of frequencies which are odd multiples of that of the given periodic function. As a matter of fact, considerable looking ahead reveals that such a series yielding a good approximation is

$$f_{Ap}(t) = \frac{1}{2} + \frac{2}{\pi} \sin t + \frac{2}{3\pi} \sin 3t + \frac{2}{5\pi} \sin 5t. \tag{14.2}$$

This function is also plotted in Fig. 14.1, and the closeness with which these few terms approximate the original function compels us to explore further this type of representation of periodic functions. We might even suspect that our approximation becomes better and better as we add more and more properly selected terms.

Let us consider the periodic signal of period T,

$$f(t) = f(t \pm T) = f\left(t \pm \frac{2\pi}{\omega}\right), \tag{14.3}$$

where

$$\omega = \frac{2\pi}{T} \tag{14.4}$$

is called the *fundamental radian frequency* and is 2π times the *fundamental frequency*. On the basis of our scanty experience with the square wave, we will assume, rather presumptuously, that $f(t)$ may be expressed in the form

$$f(t) = F_0 + \sqrt{2} \sum_{n=1}^{\infty} F_n \cos(\omega_n t + \phi_n). \tag{14.5}$$

The amplitudes of the terms in this series are expressed in terms of their rms values, F_n; and the nth sinusoid in the series is presumed to be a cosine of amplitude $\sqrt{2}\, F_n$, radian frequency ω_n, and phase angle ϕ_n.

The right-hand side of Eq. (14.5) must also be periodic just as the left-hand side is, so, corresponding to Eq. (14.3), we have

$$F_0 + \sqrt{2} \sum_{n=1}^{\infty} F_n \cos(\omega_n t + \phi_n) = F_0 + \sqrt{2} \sum_{n=1}^{\infty} F_n \cos\left[\omega_n\left(t \pm \frac{2\pi}{\omega}\right) + \phi_n\right].$$

This can be true for all values of t only if the arguments of the cosines are correspondingly equal or differ by some integral number of 2π's. Thus

$$\omega_n t \pm 2\pi k + \phi_n = \omega_n \left(t \pm \frac{2\pi}{\omega} \right) + \phi_n, \qquad k = 1, 2, 3, \ldots,$$

which leads to

$$\omega_n = k\omega, \qquad k = 1, 2, 3, \ldots.$$

Thus the component frequencies are integral multiples of the fundamental frequency. Since each such frequency has a particular amplitude and phase angle associated with it, it seems advisable to identify the component frequencies with these associated quantities by setting $k = n$, so that

$$\omega_n = n\omega. \tag{14.6}$$

The index, n, now identifies what is called the nth *harmonic* in the approximating series.

The form of the series representation, Eq. (14.5), now becomes any one of the equivalent forms

$$f(t) = F_o + \sqrt{2} \sum_{n=1}^{\infty} F_n \cos (n\omega t + \phi_n) \tag{14.7a}$$

$$f(t) = \sum_{n=-\infty}^{\infty} \mathbf{f}_n e^{jn\omega t} = \sum_{n=-\infty}^{\infty} \mathbf{f}_n^* e^{-jn\omega t} \tag{14.7b}$$

$$f(t) = \frac{a_o}{2} + \sum_{n=1}^{\infty} (a_n \cos n\omega t + b_n \sin n\omega t), \tag{14.7c}$$

where

$$\mathbf{f}_n = \mathbf{f}_{-n}^* = \frac{a_n - jb_n}{2} = \frac{\mathbf{F}_n}{\sqrt{2}} = \frac{F_n e^{j\phi_n}}{\sqrt{2}}, \qquad n = 1, 2, 3, \ldots \tag{14.7d}$$

$$\mathbf{f}_o = F_o = \frac{a_o}{2} \tag{14.7e}$$

$$a_n = 2 \operatorname{Re} \mathbf{f}_n = \sqrt{2} \operatorname{Re} \mathbf{F}_n = \sqrt{2} F_n \cos \phi_n \tag{14.7f}$$

$$b_n = -2 \operatorname{Im} \mathbf{f}_n = -\sqrt{2} \operatorname{Im} \mathbf{F}_n = -\sqrt{2} F_n \sin \phi_n. \tag{14.7g}$$

The last form of Eq. (14.7b) follows from the preceding form from the facts that the same series results when n is replaced by $-n$ and that $\mathbf{f}_{-n} = \mathbf{f}_n^*$. The student should by all means satisfy himself that the above series are indeed equivalent when the coefficients are related as indicated in the last four equations. Forms a and c are two versions of the *trigonometric* form of the series while form b is the *exponential* form.

Now let us multiply each side of Eq. (14.7b) by $e^{-jm\omega t}$, m being an integer, then average the result over any interval of time equal to one period of $f(t)$, to get

$$\frac{1}{T} \int_{t_1}^{t_1 + T} f(t) e^{-jm\omega t} \, dt = \frac{1}{T} \sum_{n=1}^{\infty} \mathbf{f}_n \int_{t_1}^{t_1 + T} e^{j(n-m)\omega t} \, dt. \qquad (14.8)$$

It is left for the student to show that

$$\frac{1}{T} \int_{t_1}^{t_1 + T} e^{j(n-m)\omega t} \, dt = \begin{cases} 1, & m = n \\ 0, & m \neq n \end{cases} = \delta_{nm}, \qquad (14.9)$$

which shows that the set of functions

$$\frac{1}{\sqrt{T}}, \quad \frac{e^{j\omega t}}{\sqrt{T}}, \quad \frac{e^{j2\omega t}}{\sqrt{T}}, \ldots, \quad \frac{e^{jn\omega t}}{\sqrt{T}}, \ldots$$

forms an *orthonormal* set of functions over the interval T. This follows from the definition of *orthonormality* of functions, which states that two possibly complex functions $\phi_n(t)$ and $\phi_m(t)$ are orthonormal over the interval from a to b if

$$\int_a^b \phi_n^*(x) \phi_m(x) \, dx = \delta_{nm}.$$

Substituting Eq. (14.9) into Eq. (14.8) results in

$$\frac{1}{T} \int_{t_1}^{t_1 + T} f(t) e^{-jm\omega t} \, dt = \sum_{n=1}^{\infty} \mathbf{f}_n \delta_{nm}. \qquad (14.10)$$

The only nonzero term on the right occurs when $m = n$, so

$$\mathbf{f}_n = \frac{1}{T} \int_{t_1}^{t_1 + T} f(t) e^{-jn\omega t} \, dt. \qquad (14.11)$$

Equations (14.7b) and (14.11) constitute the complete exponential periodic *Fourier pair*:

$$f(t) = \sum_{n=-\infty}^{\infty} \mathbf{f}_n e^{jn\omega t} \qquad (14.12a)$$

$$\mathbf{f}_n = \frac{1}{T} \int_{t_1}^{t_1+T} f(t) e^{-jn\omega t}\, dt, \qquad (14.12b)$$

in which Eq. (14.12b) defines the coefficients in the series of Eq. (14.12a).

As from Eqs. (14.7), $a_n - jb_n = 2\mathbf{f}_n$ when $n = 1, 2, 3, \ldots$, and $a_0 = 2\mathbf{f}_0$, Eq. (14.12b) yields

$$a_n - jb_n = \frac{2}{T} \int_{t_1}^{t_1+T} f(t)(\cos n\omega t - j \sin n\omega t)\, dt.$$

Equating reals and imaginaries here and noting Eq. (14.7c) leads to an alternative form of Eqs. (14.12), which is the trigonometric form of the Fourier series:

$$f(t) = \frac{a_0}{2} + \sum_{n=1}^{\infty} (a_n \cos n\omega t + b_n \sin n\omega t) \qquad (14.13a)$$

where

$$a_n = \frac{2}{T} \int_{t_1}^{t_1+T} f(t)(\cos n\omega t)\, dt \qquad (14.13b)$$

$$b_n = \frac{2}{T} \int_{t_1}^{t_1+T} f(t)(\sin n\omega t)\, dt. \qquad (14.13c)$$

It is simple to show that the following useful form is also valid:

$$f(t) = F_0 + \sqrt{2} \sum_{n=1}^{\infty} F_n \cos(n\omega t + \phi_n) \qquad (14.14a)$$

where

$$F_n e^{j\phi_n} = \frac{\sqrt{2}}{T} \int_{t_1}^{t_1+T} f(t) e^{-jn\omega t}\, dt \qquad (14.14b)$$

$$F_0 = \frac{1}{T} \int_{t_1}^{t_1+T} f(t)\, dt. \qquad (14.14c)$$

Rather than attempt to remember all three forms in detail, the student is advised to be certain that he has the exponential form well in hand, since it is the simplest to compute and the other two forms follow easily from it.

Let us return now to the example at the beginning of this article and observe just what was established by such foresight as was there apparent. The exponential coefficients stemming from the original signal described by

Eq. (14.1) are found by utilizing Eq. (14.12b) and letting t_1 be conveniently zero:

$$\mathbf{f}_n = \frac{1}{2\pi} \left[\int_0^\pi e^{-jnt}\, dt + \int_\pi^{2\pi} 0 e^{-jnt}\, dt \right]$$

$$= \frac{1}{j2\pi n} \left[-e^{-jn\pi} + 1 \right]$$

$$= \frac{e^{-jn(\pi/2)}\, e^{jn(\pi/2)} - e^{-jn(\pi/2)}}{\pi n} \cdot \frac{1}{2j}$$

$$= \frac{e^{-jn(\pi/2)}}{2} \frac{\sin \dfrac{n\pi}{2}}{\dfrac{n\pi}{2}}$$

$$= \begin{cases} \frac{1}{2}, & n = 0 \\ 0, & n = 2, 4, 6, \ldots \\ -\dfrac{j}{n\pi}, & n = 1, 3, 5, \ldots \end{cases} = \begin{cases} \dfrac{a_0}{2}, & n = 0 \\ \dfrac{a_n - jb_n}{2}, & n \neq 0 \end{cases}.$$

Notice the manipulations necessary here to evaluate the indeterminate 0/0 for $n = 0$ by utilizing

$$\lim_{n \to 0} \frac{\sin x}{x} = 1.$$

It follows from the above results that

$$\frac{a_0}{2} = \frac{1}{2}$$

$$a_n = 0, \qquad n = 1, 2, 3, \ldots$$

$$b_n = \begin{cases} 0, & n = 2, 4, 6, \ldots \\ \dfrac{2}{n\pi}, & n = 1, 3, 5, \ldots, \end{cases}$$

so that

$$f(t) = \frac{1}{2} + \frac{2}{\pi} \sum_{n=1}^\infty \frac{1}{n} \sin nt, \qquad n = 1, 3, 5, \ldots$$

$$= \frac{1}{2} + \frac{2}{\pi} \sum_{k=1}^\infty \frac{1}{2k-1} \sin (2k-1)t, \qquad k = 1, 2, 3, \ldots.$$

The example cited approximates the original function by terminating the series so that n varies just to 5 (or k ranges just to 3).

One cannot help wondering if the coefficients determined by Eq. (14.12b) still give the most accurate representation of $f(t)$ when only a finite number of terms are utilized, as was done in the example. In a later article, this question is considered in a way that should also increase one's confidence in the validity of the Fourier representation.

In the introduction we spoke of the implied *frequency content* of the signal. The strength of a particular harmonic is indicated by f_n which may be plotted at those discrete points along the abscissa identifying multiples of the fundamental frequency. Such a plot is called the *frequency spectrum* of the given signal.

In our example

$$f_n = |\mathbf{f}_n| = \left| \frac{e^{-jn(\pi/2)}}{2} \frac{\sin \frac{n\pi}{2}}{\frac{n\pi}{2}} \right| = \frac{1}{2} \left| \frac{\sin \frac{n\pi}{2}}{\frac{n\pi}{2}} \right|.$$

This particular frequency spectrum is plotted in Fig. 14.2. Note especially the decrease in strength as one moves up the frequency scale. This could be of great practical importance, for it tells us that a system function whose fre-

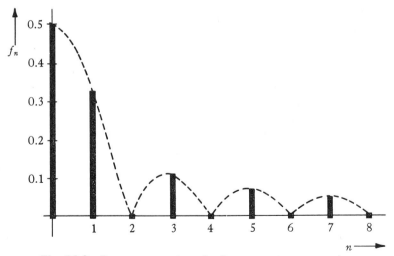

Fig. 14.2 *Frequency spectrum for the square-wave example.*

quency response is essentially a constant at radian frequencies below about eight will create a response to our square wave to a good approximation. It also leads to the intuitive feeling that the error introduced by terminating the series with the seventh harmonic should be small.

EXAMPLE 14.1. Find the Fourier series expansion of the wave in Fig. 14.3 and plot the frequency spectrum.

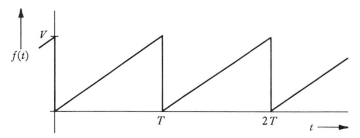

Fig. 14.3 *A periodic signal.*

Solution. The mathematical description of the signal is

$$f(t) = f(t \pm T) = \frac{V}{T}t, \qquad 0 < t < T. \tag{A}$$

From Eq. (14.12b) with $t_1 = 0$

$$\mathbf{f}_n = \frac{1}{T} \int_0^T f(t) e^{-jn\omega t}\, dt$$

$$= \frac{1}{T} \int_0^T \frac{V}{T} t e^{-j(2n\pi/T)t}\, dt. \tag{B}$$

Integration by parts yields

$$\mathbf{f}_n = -\frac{V}{j2n\pi T} \left[te^{-j(2n\pi/T)t} + \frac{T}{2n\pi} e^{-j(2n\pi/T)t} \right]_0^t$$

$$= -\frac{V}{j2n\pi} \left[e^{-j2n\pi} + \frac{1}{j2n\pi}(e^{-j2n\pi} - 1) \right]$$

$$= j\frac{V}{2n\pi} \left[e^{-j2n\pi} - e^{-jn\pi} \frac{\sin n\pi}{n\pi} \right]. \tag{C}$$

As

$$\lim_{x \to 0} \frac{\sin x}{x} = 1,$$

$\mathbf{f}_0$ is indeterminate in (C), but it is quickly calculated from (B). For $n \neq 0$

$$\frac{\sin n\pi}{n\pi} = 0,$$

and we have

$$\mathbf{f}_n = \begin{cases} \dfrac{V}{2}, & n = 0 \\[3mm] j\,\dfrac{V}{2n\pi}\,e^{-j2n\pi} = j\,\dfrac{V}{2n\pi}, & n = 1, 2, 3, \ldots. \end{cases} \qquad \text{(D)}$$

From Eqs. (14.7c) and (14.7d)

$$\frac{a_\mathrm{o}}{2} = \frac{V}{2},$$

and

$$\frac{a_n - jb_n}{2} = j\,\frac{V}{2n\pi}, \qquad n = 1, 2, 3, \ldots,$$

so that

$$\left.\begin{array}{l} a_n = 0 \\[2mm] b_n = -\dfrac{V}{n\pi} \end{array}\right\}, \qquad n = 1, 2, 3, \ldots.$$

Thus the desired Fourier series is

$$f(t) = \frac{a_\mathrm{o}}{2} + \sum_{n=1}^{\infty} (a_n \cos n\omega t + b_n \sin n\omega t)$$

$$= V\left[\frac{1}{2} - \frac{1}{\pi}\sum_{n=1}^{\infty}\frac{1}{n}\sin\frac{2n\pi}{T}t\right]. \qquad Ans.$$

The frequency spectrum, f_n, is plotted in Fig. 14.4.

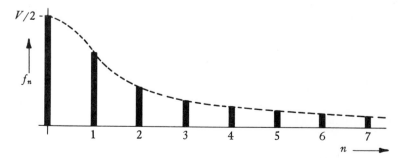

Fig. 14.4 *Frequency spectrum of the periodic function in Fig. 14.3.*

14.3 SYMMETRY EFFECTS

Certain symmetries in periodic functions will result in simplification of the Fourier series due to the vanishing of particular classes of terms. These symmetries are listed in what follows, with illustrations in Fig. 14.5. The

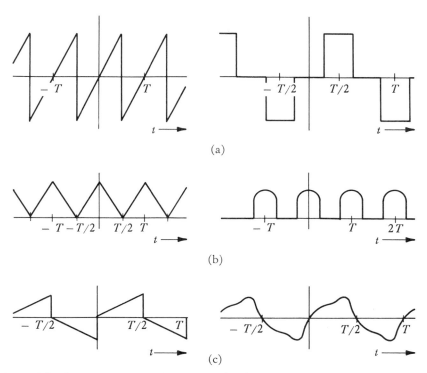

Fig. 14.5 *Symmetries in periodic functions. (a) Odd functions, sine terms only. (b) Even functions, cosine terms only. (c) Odd-harmonic functions.*

defining property of the particular symmetry is given along with its effects on the Fourier series. Substantiation that a given result follows from a given symmetry condition is left as a student exercise.

Odd Functions

An odd function is one for which

$$f(t) = -f(-t). \tag{14.15a}$$

When an odd function is periodic, then

$$a_n = 0 \qquad \text{for all } n, \tag{14.15b}$$

and the Fourier expansion contains only sine terms without phase angles.

Even Functions

For an even function

$$f(t) = f(-t), \tag{14.16a}$$

leading to

$$b_n = 0 \qquad \text{for all } n, \tag{14.16b}$$

and only cosines without phase angles and a possible constant exist in the Fourier series.

Odd-Harmonic Functions

When

$$f(t) = -f\left(t \pm \frac{T}{2}\right), \tag{14.17a}$$

as in Fig. 14.5(c), then

$$\mathbf{f}_n = \mathbf{f}_{2k-1} \qquad \text{for all } k, \tag{14.17b}$$

and the Fourier series contains odd harmonics only.

14.4 SYSTEM ANALYSIS BY FOURIER SERIES

Suppose a given system has the system function

$$H(p) = \frac{R(p)}{F(p)}, \tag{14.18}$$

where $F(p)$ and $R(p)$ are the operational forms of forcing and response functions, and the forcing function is in the Fourier series form of Eq. (14.14a), or

$$f(t) = F_o + \sqrt{2} \sum_{n=1}^{\infty} F_n \cos(n\omega t + \phi_n), \tag{14.19}$$

where the nth harmonic has the phasor value

$$\mathbf{F}_n = F_n e^{j\phi_n}. \tag{14.20}$$

Then if

$$H(jn\omega) = H_n e^{j\theta_n} = \mathbf{H}_n, \tag{14.21}$$

the response to the nth harmonic is also a sinusoid having the phasor value

$$\mathbf{R}_n = \mathbf{H}_n \mathbf{F}_n$$
$$= H_n F_n e^{j(\theta_n + \phi_n)}. \tag{14.22}$$

The Fourier expansion of the response to periodic function $f(t)$ is the sum of its harmonic responses, or

$$r(t) = R_o + \sqrt{2} \sum_{n=1}^{\infty} R_n \cos(n\omega t + \phi_{R_n})$$

$$= H_o F_o + \sqrt{2} \sum_{n=1}^{\infty} H_n F_n \cos(n\omega t + \theta_n + \phi_n). \tag{14.23}$$

14.5 BEST APPROXIMATION BY A TRUNCATED SERIES

Suppose we approximate $f(t)$ by a series of the same form as the Fourier series, but with just a finite number of terms. We shall not be bound by the previous definition of the coefficients of such a series, but will select coefficients which will cause the least error, on a least-square basis, between $f(t)$ and the approximating series.

We shall begin with the truncated form of Eq. (14.7b), which is the approximation to $f(t)$,

$$f_{Ap}(t) = \sum_{n=-N}^{N} \mathbf{f}_n e^{jn\omega t} = \sum_{n=-N}^{N} \mathbf{f}_n^* e^{-jn\omega t}. \tag{14.24}$$

The square of the rms value (or mean-square value) of the approximating function is

$$F_{Ap}^2 = \frac{1}{T} \int_{t_1}^{t_1 + T} f_{Ap}^2(t) \, dt$$

$$= \frac{1}{T} \int_{t_1}^{t_1 + T} \left(\sum_{n=-N}^{N} \mathbf{f}_n e^{jn\omega t} \right)^2 dt.$$

But

$$\left(\sum_n a_n \right)^2 = \sum\sum_{nm} a_n a_m = \sum_n a_n \sum_m a_m,$$

so

$$F_{Ap}^2 = \frac{1}{T}\int_{t_1}^{t_1+T} \sum_{n=-N}^{N} \mathbf{f}_n e^{jn\omega t} \sum_{m=-N}^{N} \mathbf{f}_m e^{jm\omega t}\, dt$$

$$= \frac{1}{T}\int_{t_1}^{t_1+T} \sum_{n=-N}^{N} \mathbf{f}_n e^{jn\omega t} \sum_{m=-N}^{N} \mathbf{f}_m^* e^{-jm\omega t}\, dt$$

$$= \sum_{n=-N}^{N} \sum_{m=-N}^{N} \mathbf{f}_m^* \mathbf{f}_n \left[\frac{1}{T}\int_{t_1}^{t_1+T} e^{j(n-m)\omega t}\, dt\right].$$

According to Eq. (14.10), this becomes

$$F_{Ap}^2 = \sum_{n=-N}^{N} \sum_{m=-N}^{N} \mathbf{f}_m^* \mathbf{f}_n \, \delta_{mn}.$$

The only surviving terms occur when $m = n$, so

$$F_{Ap}^2 = \sum_{n=-N}^{N} \mathbf{f}_n \mathbf{f}_n^*$$

$$= \left[f_o^2 + 2\sum_{n=1}^{N} f_n^2 \right]$$

$$= F_o^2 + \sum_{n=1}^{N} F_n^2$$

$$= \sum_{n=0}^{N} F_n^2. \qquad (14.25)$$

Thus the rms value of the approximate function is the square root of the sum of the squares of the rms values of its single-frequency components.

Next we must choose the coefficients which yield the best possible approximation to the original function but in order to do so we must first choose a criterion for the quality of approximation. To this end, we shall call the best approximation that which minimizes the rms value of the error it makes with respect to the original. That is, if the error is

$$\varepsilon(t) = f(t) - f_{Ap}(t), \qquad (14.26)$$

then the optimum $f_{Ap}(t)$ is that which makes the rms error

$$E = \sqrt{\frac{1}{T}\int_{t_1}^{t_1+T} \varepsilon^2(t)\, dt} \qquad (14.27)$$

a minimum.

Let us investigate the exponential form of approximation in light of this accuracy criterion. The error is, from Eqs. (14.24) and (14.26),

$$\varepsilon(t) = f(t) - \sum_{n=-N}^{N} \mathbf{f}_n e^{jn\omega t}, \tag{14.28}$$

and the square of the rms error, usually called the *mean-square error*, is

$$E^2 = \frac{1}{T} \int_{t_1}^{t_1+T} [f(t) - f_{Ap}(t)]^2 \, dt$$

$$= \frac{1}{T} \int_{t_1}^{t_1+T} f^2(t) \, dt + \frac{1}{T} \int_{t_1}^{t_1+T} f_{Ap}^2(t) \, dt - \frac{2}{T} \int_{t_1}^{t_1+T} f(t) f_{Ap}(t) \, dt$$

$$= F^2 + F_{Ap}^2 - \frac{2}{T} \int_{t_1}^{t_1+T} f(t) f_{Ap}(t) \, dt. \tag{14.29}$$

Substituting Eqs. (14.25) and (14.24) into Eq. (14.29) results in

$$E^2 = F^2 + \sum_{n=-N}^{N} \mathbf{f}_n^* \mathbf{f}_n - \frac{2}{T} \sum_{n=-N}^{N} \mathbf{f}_n \int_{t_1}^{t_1+T} f(t) e^{jn\omega t} \, dt. \tag{14.30}$$

If a particular $\mathbf{f}_n$, say $\mathbf{f}_k$, is adjusted to make a mean-square (and consequently the rms) error a minimum, then the adjustment is optimum when

$$\frac{\partial E^2}{\partial \mathbf{f}_k} = 0. \tag{14.31}$$

Applying this relationship to Eq. (14.30), we have

$$0 + 2\mathbf{f}_k^* - \frac{2}{T} \int_{t_1}^{t_1+T} f(t) e^{jk\omega t} \, dt = 0.$$

This equation obviously produces a minimum mean-square error, not a maximum, because E^2 can be made arbitrarily large by choosing "approximations" that clearly are not approximations at all. Hence, for minimum rms error

$$\mathbf{f}_k^* = \frac{1}{T} \int_{t_1}^{t_1+T} f(t) e^{jk\omega t} \, dt, \tag{14.32a}$$

or

$$\mathbf{f}_k = \frac{1}{T} \int_{t_1}^{t_1+T} f(t) e^{-jk\omega t} \, dt, \tag{14.32b}$$

substantiating the fact that $\mathbf{f}_{-n} = \mathbf{f}_n^*$. We are pleased to note that the coefficients which yield the best truncated series are *exactly* those of the first N terms in the complete Fourier series. This is reassuring, because one would expect that however large N is, this is still true, and it should therefore be true also for the complete series.

We have now selected the coefficients yielding the best approximation with a series of N harmonic components. Let us return to a consideration of the size of the error remaining. In Eq. (14.29) we have the term

$$\frac{2}{T} \int_{t_1}^{t_1+T} f(t) f_{Ap}(t) \, dt = \frac{2}{T} \int_{t_1}^{t_1+T} f(t) \sum_{n=-N}^{N} \mathbf{f}_n e^{jn\omega t} \, dt$$

$$= 2 \sum_{n=-N}^{N} \mathbf{f}_n \frac{1}{T} \int_{t_1}^{t_1+T} f(t) e^{jn\omega t} \, dt.$$

From Eqs. (14.25) and (14.32) in the above we have

$$\frac{2}{T} \int_{t_1}^{t_1+T} f(t) f_{Ap}(t) \, dt = 2 \sum_{n=-N}^{N} \mathbf{f}_n^* \mathbf{f}_n = 2F_{Ap}^2,$$

which causes Eq. (14.29) to be

$$E^2 = F^2 - F_{Ap}^2. \tag{14.33}$$

We are now further reassured by the fact that the error in truncating the series is completely in the omitted terms.

It may, in fact, be shown that if the Dirichlet conditions prevail, that is, if $f(t)$ has at most a finite number of finite discontinuities and a finite number of maxima and minima in a given period, and that if

$$\int_{t_1}^{t_1+T} |f(t)| \, dt = \text{finite value},$$

a *complete* series, which is a series with an infinite number of terms, leads to

$$\lim_{N \to \infty} E = 0, \tag{14.34}$$

except at discontinuities in $f(t)$, where jumps known as *Gibbs' phenomenon* occur.

Let us return again to the original square-wave example, which had the exact rms value,

$$F = \sqrt{\frac{1}{T} \int_{t_1}^{t_1+T} f^2(t) \, dt} = \sqrt{\tfrac{1}{2}} = 0.707.$$

The rms value indicated by the approximation is, by Eq. (14.25),

$$F_{Ap} = \sqrt{\sum_{n=0}^{5} F_n^2}$$

$$= \sqrt{\frac{1^2}{2} + \left(\frac{2}{\sqrt{2\pi}}\right)^2 [1^2 + 0^2 + (\tfrac{1}{3})^2 + 0^2 + (\tfrac{1}{5})^2]}$$

$$= \sqrt{0.483} = 0.695.$$

The rms error is given by Eq. (14.33)

$$E = \sqrt{0.500 - 0.483}$$
$$= \sqrt{0.017} = 0.13.$$

The student should investigate the further reduction of this already-small error by the addition of just one more harmonic in the approximation.

14.6 FOURIER TRANSFORM

In this treatment, the Fourier transform is of interest chiefly as a stepping stone to the generally (not always) more useful transform of the following article, the Laplace transform.

The Fourier transform arises when one attempts to consider the nonperiodic function as a special case of the periodic function with a period approaching infinity. For example, the nonperiodic function of Fig. 14.6(d) may be considered the *limiting* case of a periodic square wave with its period approaching infinity (or, equivalently, its fundamental frequency approaching zero).

An Illustrative Example

Figure 14.6 provides an example of the manner in which the frequency spectrum of a simple bounded function, a rectangular pulse, may be deduced from the limit of a sequence of periodic trains of such pulses with ever-greater periods.

The mathematical description of any pulse train in Fig. 14.6 is

$$f_P(t) = \begin{cases} 0, & -\dfrac{T}{2} < t < -\dfrac{W}{2} \\[2mm] A, & -\dfrac{W}{2} < t < +\dfrac{W}{2} \\[2mm] 0, & \dfrac{W}{2} < t < \dfrac{T}{2} \end{cases}, \qquad T > W. \qquad (14.35)$$

Of course,

$$\lim_{T \to \infty} f_P(t) = f(t), \qquad (14.36)$$

where $f(t)$ is the nonperiodic pulse of Fig. 14.6(d).

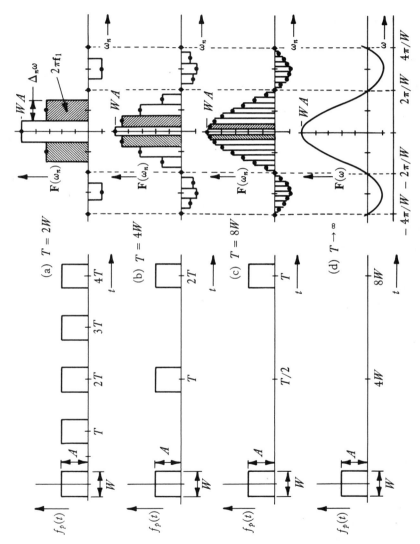

Fig. 14.6 *Illustration of the Fourier transform as a limiting case of the Fourier series.*

If we differentiate the fundamental frequency of the pulse train from *any* ω by use of the subscript 1, then

$$\omega_1 = \frac{2\pi}{T}. \qquad (14.37)$$

The nth Fourier coefficient of $f_P(t)$ is then

$$\mathbf{f}_n = -\frac{\omega_1}{2\pi} \int_{-W/2}^{W/2} A e^{-jn\omega_1 \tau} \, d\tau$$

$$= \frac{\omega_1 W A}{2\pi} \frac{\sin \dfrac{W n \omega_1}{2}}{\dfrac{W n \omega_1}{2}}. \qquad (14.38)$$

Now let us set

$$\mathbf{f}_n = \frac{1}{2\pi} \omega_1 \mathbf{F}(n\omega_1), \qquad (14.39a)$$

so that $\mathbf{F}(n\omega_1)$ must be

$$\mathbf{F}(n\omega_1) = W A \frac{\sin \dfrac{W}{2} n\omega_1}{\dfrac{W}{2} n\omega_1}. \qquad (14.39b)$$

It will now be convenient to introduce new notation identifying the nth harmonic as

$$\omega_n = n\omega_1, \qquad (14.40a)$$

and the *harmonic separation* as

$$\Delta_n \omega = \omega_1. \qquad (14.40b)$$

Equations (14.39) then may be written

$$\mathbf{f}_n = \frac{1}{2\pi} \mathbf{F}(\omega_n) \Delta_n \omega \qquad (14.41a)$$

$$\mathbf{F}(\omega_n) = W A \frac{\sin \dfrac{W}{2} \omega_n}{\dfrac{W}{2} \omega_n}. \qquad (14.41b)$$

The function $\mathbf{F}(\omega_n)$ is plotted in Fig. 14.6 for $T = 2W$, $T = 4W$, and $T = 8W$. The discrete points on $\mathbf{F}(\omega_n)$ are shown as heavy dots. It is interesting to note that when one constructs a rectangle of height $\mathbf{F}(\omega_n)$ and a width equal to the harmonic separation, its area is 2π times the Fourier coefficient $\mathbf{f}_n$. If such a rectangle is constructed on each point representing $\mathbf{F}(\omega_n)$, as shown in the figure, the entire set of rectangles will fill, without overlapping, the area under a curve connecting the discretely located points. This suggests that $\mathbf{F}(\omega_n)$ may be considered a line density function, having the units of $\mathbf{f}_n$ per radian of abscissa.

The usefulness of such a density function over the direct Fourier coefficient when the period becomes very long, compared to pulse width, is apparent when one observes that as the period gets larger and larger, $\mathbf{f}_n$ gets smaller and smaller. On the other hand, the curve through the discrete values of $\mathbf{F}(\omega_n)$ remains fixed in shape and amplitude as the period increases, the only change being an increase in the density of discrete points throughout a fixed interval. If we let the period approach infinity, so that the harmonic separation becomes zero (as does $\mathbf{f}_n$), then ω_n may be considered *any* ω, and

$$\mathbf{F}(\omega) = WA \, \frac{\sin \dfrac{W}{2} \omega}{\dfrac{W}{2} \omega}, \tag{14.42}$$

which, according to Eq. (14.36), must be the harmonic density function corresponding to the single pulse, $f(t)$. Now the points are no longer discrete and merge into the continuous curve of Fig. 14.6(d).

The General Case

Let us now consider an arbitrary nonperiodic function bounded in such a way that on *some* scale of observation the function is zero for $t < -W/2$ and $t > W/2$, where W is some arbitrarily large finite number. If the function is considered to be one of a train of identical pulses, the periodic function so formed may be written, in a manner similar to that for the previous special case,

$$f_P(t) = \begin{cases} 0, & -\dfrac{T}{2} < t < -\dfrac{W}{2} \\[2mm] f(t), & -\dfrac{W}{2} < t < \dfrac{W}{2} \\[2mm] 0, & \dfrac{W}{2} < t < \dfrac{T}{2} \end{cases}, \qquad T > W. \tag{14.43}$$

Its nth Fourier coefficient is

$$\mathbf{f}_n = \frac{\omega_1}{2\pi} \int_{-W/2}^{W/2} f_P(\tau) e^{-jn\omega_1 \tau} \, d\tau,$$

which, with the nth harmonic and harmonic separation designated as for the preceding special case, is

$$\mathbf{f}_n = \frac{1}{2\pi} \int_{-W/2}^{W/2} f_P(\tau) e^{-j\omega_n \tau} \, d\tau \Delta_n \omega$$

$$= \frac{1}{2\pi} \int_{-\infty}^{\infty} f_P(\tau) e^{-j\omega_n \tau} \, d\tau \Delta_n \omega$$

$$= \frac{1}{2\pi} \mathbf{F}(\omega_n) \Delta_n \omega, \tag{14.44}$$

where

$$\mathbf{F}(\omega_n) = \int_{-\infty}^{\infty} f_P(\tau) e^{-j\omega_n \tau} \, d\tau. \tag{14.45}$$

Again

$$f_P(t) = \sum_{n=-\infty}^{\infty} \mathbf{f}_n e^{j\omega_n t}$$

$$= \lim_{N \to \infty} \sum_{n=-N}^{N} \mathbf{f}_n e^{j\omega_n t}$$

$$= \frac{1}{2\pi} \lim_{N \to \infty} \sum_{n=-N}^{N} \mathbf{F}(\omega_n) e^{j\omega_n t} \Delta_n \omega. \tag{14.46}$$

Although $f_P(t)$ appears to be a definite integral, it is not, cause the smallness of $\Delta_n \omega$ is independent of the largness of N. However, the function $f(t)$ may be written as a definite integral providing the limit in Eq. (14.36) implies that

$$\lim_{N \to \infty} \Delta_n \omega = 0.$$

Referring again to the previous special case, it is clear from Eq. (14.38), as plotted in Fig. 14.6, that $\mathbf{f}_n$ becomes negligible after some finite value of ω_n. A consideration of Eq. (14.44) should reveal that any other function of the class we are now considering, which may be "boxed in" by a rectangular pulse of width W and finite height, will produce $\mathbf{f}_n$'s which will shrink more rapidly with increasing ω_n than did the square pulse of width W. Thus $\mathbf{f}_n$ may be considered bounded so that it becomes negligible for all ω_n greater than some finite number, say B. Then $N \to \infty$ within the finite interval from $-B$ to B only if $\Delta_n \omega \to 0$, which also means that $T \to \infty$ and that $f_P(t) \to f(t)$

anywhere within our scale of observation. Therefore, Eq. (14.36) may be written

$$f(t) = \frac{1}{2\pi} \lim_{\substack{N \to \infty \\ (\Delta_n \omega \to 0)}} \sum_{n=-N}^{N} \mathbf{F}(\omega_n) e^{j\omega_n t} \, \Delta_n \, \omega$$

$$= \frac{1}{2\pi} \int_{-B}^{B} \mathbf{F}(\omega) e^{j\omega t} \, d\omega.$$

The just-mentioned boundedness condition allows this to be written

$$f(t) = \frac{1}{2\pi} \int_{-\infty}^{\infty} \mathbf{F}(\omega) e^{j\omega t} \, d\omega \tag{14.47a}$$

where, from Eq. (14.45),

$$\mathbf{F}(\omega) = \int_{-\infty}^{\infty} f(\tau) e^{-j\omega\tau} \, d\tau. \tag{14.47b}$$

Equations (14.47) constitute what is called a *Fourier transform pair*. $\mathbf{F}(\omega)$ is called the *Fourier transform* of $f(t)$, and conversely, $f(t)$ is expressed here as the *inverse Fourier transform* of $\mathbf{F}(\omega)$.

Symbolically this is often written

$$f(t) = \mathscr{F}^{-1}[\mathbf{F}(\omega)] = \text{inverse Fourier transform of } \mathbf{F}(\omega) \tag{14.48a}$$

$$\mathbf{F}(\omega) = \mathscr{F}[f(t)] \quad = \text{Fourier transform of } f(t). \tag{14.48b}$$

The Fourier transform is often used in system analysis, but it has the disadvantage that $f(t)$ must be closed, or absolutely convergent on the entire time domain. That is, it must be *bounded* so that

$$\int_{-\infty}^{\infty} |f(t)| \, dt = \text{a finite value} \tag{14.49}$$

for the transform to be defined. This greatly restricts its usefulness. Techniques are available for forcing convergence of the integral for a somewhat larger class of functions, but in general the Laplace transform, covered in the next article, has replaced the Fourier transform in such cases, since it is not so restricted. This is particularly true when forcing functions are initiated no sooner than $t = 0$.

The frequency content of nonperiodic functions is indicated by $\mathbf{F}(\omega)$ in the same sense that the spectrum of the periodic function was indicated by $\mathbf{f}_n$. For the nonperiodic function, however, the spectrum is continuous, since the fundamental frequency has approached zero and the harmonic separation has disappeared.

EXAMPLE 14.2. Find the frequency spectrum of the rectangular pulse in Fig. 14.7.

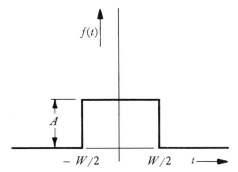

Fig. 14.7 *A rectangular pulse.*

Solution. From Eq. (14.47b)

$$\mathbf{F}(\omega) = \int_{-\infty}^{\infty} f(t)e^{-j\omega t}\, dt$$

$$= A \int_{-W/2}^{W/2} e^{-j\omega t}\, dt$$

$$= \frac{A}{j\omega}(e^{j\omega(W/2)} - e^{-j\omega(W/2)})$$

$$= \frac{2A}{\omega} \sin \frac{\omega W}{2}$$

$$= AW \frac{\sin \omega \dfrac{W}{2}}{\dfrac{\omega W}{2}}. \qquad Ans.$$

Thus the frequency spectrum varies as the common form $(\sin x)/x$. It is plotted in Fig. 14.6(d).

In the above example, an important fact of nature is immediately apparent, that *the more narrow is the pulse, the wider is its frequency spectrum*. Since the entire frequency spectrum must be transmitted if the form of the pulse is to be preserved, it is evident that preserving shapes of narrow pulses through systems requires systems of wide bandwidth. For example, a rectangular pulse of 1-μsec width will require a system bandwidth in the order of 2 megacycles for transmission without substantial distortion.

The student will find it instructive to compare the $\mathbf{F}(\omega)$ of Example 14.2 with the $\mathbf{f}_n$ for a periodic function formed by a train of rectangular pulses of width W when the period of the periodic function is much greater than W.

14.7 LAPLACE TRANSFORMS

Suppose we desire to find the Fourier transform of a piecewise regular (not impulsive) function $f(t)$, but are frustrated by the fact that $f(t)$ cannot be depended on to satisfy the boundedness condition. However, $f(t)$ is known to be of *exponential order*; that is, there exists a finite constant, a, such that

$$\int_0^\infty e^{-at} |f(t)|\, dt = \text{a finite value} \tag{14.50}$$

thus assuring boundedness on the right of the function $e^{-\sigma t} f(t)$ as long as $\sigma > a$.

Let us generate from $f(t)$ a new function which is bounded on the right by virtue of the exponential order of $f(t)$ and bounded on the left by virtue of being zero for $t < 0$. To do so we may use the prelimit form of the unit step function, designated $u_T(t)$ in Chapter 7, to form the function

$$f_T(t) = e^{-\sigma t} f(t) u_T(t), \qquad \sigma > a, \qquad T > 0, \tag{14.51}$$

where, from its definition in Chapter 7,

$$u_T(t) = \begin{cases} 0, & t \leqslant -T \\ \tfrac{1}{2}, & t = 0 \\ 1, & t \geqslant T. \end{cases}$$

The new function, $f_T(t)$, is Fourier-transformable, having the transform

$$\mathbf{F}_T(\omega) = \int_{-\infty}^\infty f_T(t) e^{-j\omega t}\, dt$$

$$= \int_{-\infty}^\infty f(t) e^{-(\sigma + j\omega)t} u_T(t)\, dt$$

$$= \int_{-T}^T f(t) e^{-(\sigma + j\omega)t} u_T(t) + \int_T^\infty f(t) e^{-(\sigma + j\omega)t}\, dt. \tag{14.52}$$

Substituting

$$s = \sigma + j\omega, \tag{14.53}$$

we have

$$F_T(s) = \mathbf{F}_T(-j[s - \sigma])$$

$$= \int_{-T}^T f(t) e^{-st} u_T(t)\, dt + \int_T^\infty f(t) e^{-st}\, dt. \tag{14.54}$$

The inverse Fourier transform of $\mathbf{F}_T(\omega)$ is

$$f_T(t) = \frac{1}{2\pi} \int_{-\infty}^{\infty} \mathbf{F}_T(\omega) e^{j\omega t}\, d\omega,$$

so we may write

$$e^{-\sigma t} f(t) u_T(t) = \frac{1}{2\pi} \int_{-\infty}^{\infty} \mathbf{F}_T(\omega) e^{j\omega t}\, d\omega.$$

Consequently, by multiplying both sides of the above equation by $e^{\sigma t}$, we have

$$f(t) u_T(t) = \frac{1}{2\pi} \int_{-\infty}^{\infty} \mathbf{F}_T(\omega) e^{(\sigma + j\omega)t}\, d\omega. \tag{14.55}$$

Changing variables according to Eq. (14.53) requires the substitution

$$d\omega = \frac{1}{j}\, ds$$

and a change in limits from

$$\omega = -\infty \qquad \text{and} \qquad \omega = \infty$$

to the limits

$$s = \sigma - j\infty \qquad \text{and} \qquad s = \sigma + j\infty.$$

Furthermore, the substitution of Eq. (14.54) is in order. Thus Eq. (14.55) takes the form

$$f(t) u_T(t) = \frac{1}{2\pi j} \int_{\sigma - j\infty}^{\sigma + j\infty} \mathbf{F}_T(s) e^{st}\, ds. \tag{14.56}$$

Now let T approach, but not pass, zero. Because $f(t) u_T(t)$ is continuous in the interval from $-T$ to T, the first integral in Eq. (14.54) becomes zero, and if we define

$$F(s) = \lim_{T \to 0} F_T(s), \tag{14.57}$$

Eqs. (14.54) and (14.56) become

$$F(s) = \int_{0}^{\infty} f(t) e^{-st}\, dt \qquad\Bigg\} \tag{14.58a}$$
$$\qquad\qquad\qquad\qquad\qquad\qquad \sigma = \operatorname{Re} s > a.$$
$$f(t) u(t) = \frac{1}{2\pi j} \int_{\sigma - j\infty}^{\sigma + j\infty} F(s) e^{st}\, ds \tag{14.58b}$$

Equations (14.58) constitute what is known as the *Laplace transform pair.* The *Laplace transform* of $f(t)$ is

$$F(s) = \mathscr{L}[f(t)] = \mathscr{L}[f(t)u(t)] = \int_{0^+}^{\infty} f(t)e^{-st}\,dt, \qquad (14.59a)$$

and

$$f(t)u(t) = \mathscr{L}^{-1}[F(s)] = \frac{1}{2\pi j}\int_{\sigma-j\infty}^{\sigma+j\infty} F(s)e^{st}\,ds \qquad (14.59b)$$

is the *inverse Laplace transform* of $F(s)$, and we have a symbolic expression of Eqs. (14.58) in which

$$\mathscr{L}\mathscr{L}^{-1} = \mathscr{L}^{-1}\mathscr{L} = 1.$$

The use of $f(t)$ and $f(t)u(t)$ interchangeably in Eq. (14.59a) recognizes that the definition of the Laplace transform literally "chops off" the negative part of any time function extending backwards across the ordinate and excludes it from consideration.

Let us now consider the Laplace transform of the derivative. First we observe that

$$\mathscr{L}\left[\frac{df(t)}{dt}u(t)\right] = \int_0^\infty \frac{df(t)}{dt} e^{-st}\,dt.$$

Integration by parts yields

$$\int_0^\infty \frac{df(t)}{dt} e^{-st}\,dt = f(t)e^{-st}\Big]_0^\infty + s\int_0^\infty f(t)e^{-st}\,dt$$

$$= 0 - f(0^+) + sF(s),$$

where the 0^+ symbol is used to emphasize that zero is approached from the right, as indicated by the limiting process which led to the definition of the transform. Thus

$$\mathscr{L}\left[\frac{df(t)}{dt}u(t)\right] = sF(s) - f(0^+). \qquad (14.60)$$

Turning to the Laplace transform of the integral, we write

$$\mathscr{L}\left[\int_{-\infty}^t f(\tau)\,d\tau u(t)\right] = \int_0^\infty \int_{-\infty}^t f(\tau)\,d\tau e^{-st}\,dt.$$

Integration by parts yields:

$$\mathscr{L}\left[\int_{-\infty}^{t} f(\tau)\, d\tau u(t)\right] = -\frac{1}{s}\int_{-\infty}^{t} f(\tau)\, d\tau e^{-st}\Big]_{0}^{\infty} + \frac{1}{s}\int_{0}^{\infty} f(t)e^{-st}\, dt$$

$$= \frac{1}{s}\int_{-\infty}^{0} f(\tau)\, d\tau + \frac{F(s)}{s}.$$

(14.61)

We have previously used the notation

$$\int_{-\infty}^{t} f(\tau)\, d\tau = f^{(-1)}(t),$$

which allows the abbreviated form of Eq. (14.61)

$$\mathscr{L}\left[\int_{-\infty}^{t} f(\tau)\, d\tau u(t)\right] = \frac{F(s)}{s} + \frac{f^{(-1)}(0^{+})}{s}.$$

(14.62)

Consider now a particular function, $f(t)$. In Chapter 7, we find from Table 7.2 and Eq. (7.74) that, under proper conditions of $f(t)$,

$$f(t) = F(p)\delta(t)$$

$$F(p) = \int_{0}^{\infty} f(t)e^{-pt}\, dt$$

$$\frac{df(t)}{dt} = [pF(p) - f(0^{-})]\delta(t)$$

$$\int_{-\infty}^{t} f(\tau)\, d\tau = \left[\frac{1}{p}F(p) + \frac{f^{(-1)}(0^{-})}{p}\right]\delta(t).$$

For this same function, we have now discovered that

$$f(t)u(t) = \mathscr{L}^{-1}F(s)$$

$$F(s) = \int_{0}^{\infty} f(t)e^{-st}\, dt$$

$$\mathscr{L}\left[\frac{df(t)}{dt}u(t)\right] = sF(s) - f(0^{+})$$

$$\mathscr{L}\left[\int_{-\infty}^{t} f(\tau)\, d\tau u(t)\right] = \frac{F(s)}{s} + \frac{f^{(-1)}(0^{+})}{s}$$

We can see immediately that the *forms* of the transforms are identical with those of the corresponding operational forms with 0^{-} replaced with 0^{+}.

There are a number of important little niceties involved in this innocent looking distinction between the Laplace transform and the operational form. However, we shall not discuss them further here. Suffice it to say that we protected ourselves from worry on this score in practical problems when, in Art. 4.2, we discovered that around any loop

$$\sum \lambda(0^+) = \sum \lambda(0^-)$$

and at any node

$$\sum q(0^+) = \sum q(0^-).$$

It should also be mentioned that for consistency with operator form, the transforms of impulsive functions must carry the implication that

$$\mathscr{L}[\delta(t)] = \lim_{T \to 0} \mathscr{L}[\delta(t - T)], \qquad T > 0. \tag{14.63}$$

This means that an "impulse at the origin" implies an impulse just to the right of the origin, not centered about the origin as in Chapter 7. It is only under this assumption that we may write

$$\mathscr{L}[\delta(t)] = 1. \tag{14.64}$$

PROBLEMS

14.1 Give the Fourier expansion, in all three of the forms of Eqs. (14.7), for the periodic function of Fig. P.14.1. Plot the frequency spectrum.

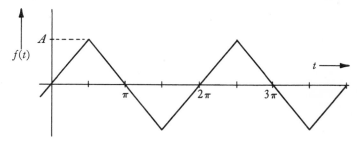

Fig. P.14.1.

14.2 Repeat Prob. 14.1, except refer to Fig. P.14.2.

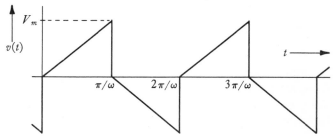

Fig. P.14.2.

14.3 Repeat Prob. 14.1, except refer to Fig. P.14.3.

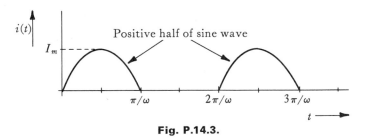

Fig. P.14.3.

14.4 Repeat Prob. 14.1, except refer to Fig. P.14.4.

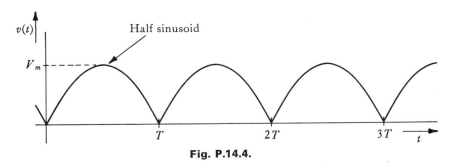

Fig. P.14.4.

14.5 Establish the Fourier series for the wave of Fig. P.14.4 using the results of Prob. 14.3.

14.6 Establish the Fourier series for the periodic function of period $2\pi/\omega$,

$$
i(t) = \begin{cases}
0, & -\pi < \omega t < -\dfrac{\pi}{18} \\[2mm]
I_m\left(\cos \omega t - \cos \dfrac{\pi}{18}\right), & -\dfrac{\pi}{18} < \omega t < \dfrac{\pi}{18} \\[2mm]
0, & \dfrac{\pi}{18} < \omega t < \pi.
\end{cases}
$$

This is typical of the periodic plate currents in "Class C" vacuum-tube amplifiers used in the output stages of radio transmitters.

14.7 For the wave of Prob. 14.1, compute the rms value using the first five terms in the Fourier series in Eq. (14.25). Determine the ratio of this computed rms value to the actual rms value computed by direct integration of the original function. Compute the rms error caused by truncating the series to five nonzero terms.

14.8 Repeat Prob. 14.7 for the wave of Prob. 14.2.

14.9 Repeat Prob. 14.7 for the wave of Prob. 14.3.

14.10 Repeat Prob. 14.7 for the wave of Prob. 14.4.

14.11 The wave of Prob. 14.2 is the voltage applied to a series R-C circuit, with $\omega = 1000$ rad/sec, $R = 2000\ \Omega$, $C = 0.5\ \mu F$, and $V_m = 100$ V. Give the Fourier series equivalent to the current and plot the frequency spectrum of the current.

14.12 An R-L series circuit, with $R = 100\ \Omega$ and $L = 0.5$ H, has a dc ammeter, an ac (rms) ammeter and the current coil of a wattmeter in series; and the voltage coil of the wattmeter and an rms voltmeter are each connected across the network. What will each of the four meters read if the current is

$$i(t) = 2[1 + 0.8 \cos (100t + 30^\circ) + 0.6 \sin (300t - 120^\circ)$$

$$+ 0.4 \cos (500t + 60^\circ)]?$$

14.13 An R-L-C series circuit with $R = 100\ \Omega$, $L = 0.5$ H, and $C = 50\ \mu F$ replaces the R-L series circuit in Prob. 14.12. What will each of the meters read if

$$v(t) = 50[1 + 0.8 \sin 100t + 0.5 \cos 200t + 0.5 \cos 300t]?$$

14.14 The *ripple factor* of a periodic function, $f(t)$ is

$$\gamma = \frac{F_{av}}{F_{eff}} = \frac{F_{dc}}{F_{ac}}.$$

a.   What is the ripple factor of the current of Fig. P.14.3?

b.   Suppose the current of Fig. P.14.3 is that from a source feeding a parallel G-C circuit consisting of 10,000 Ω of resistance in parallel with μF of capacitance. If the fundamental frequency is 60 Hz, what is the ripple factor of the voltage across the G-C combination?

14.15 Double the capacitance in Prob. 14.14 and rework the problem.

14.16 What is the ripple factor (see Prob. 14.14) of the voltage wave of Fig. P.14.4? What is the ripple factor of the current if this voltage is applied to an R-L series circuit consisting of a 5000-Ω resistance and a 2-H inductance? The frequency of the sinusoids whose sections form $v(t)$ is 400 Hz.

14.17 The current of Prob. 14.6 is that of the current source in Fig. P.14.5. The frequency of the periodic current is 10 MHz, $C = 50$ pF, and the "tank circuit" (the R-L-C series-parallel circuit of Fig. P.14.5) is tuned to 10 MHz, at which frequency it has a Q of 300.

a.   Find the ratio of the rms value of all harmonics (fundamental excluded) of $i(t)$ to the rms value of its fundamental component alone.

b. Find the ratio of all harmonics (fundamental excluded) of $v(t)$ to the rms value of its fundamental component alone.

c. Find the ratio of fundamental to third harmonic in both $i(t)$ and $v(t)$.

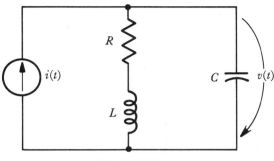

Fig. P.14.5.

14.18 In Prob. 14.17, decrease the capacitance to exactly one-third the value meeting the stated conditions, keeping all other circuit parameters fixed. Find the ratio of fundamental to third harmonic for $v(t)$ and compare the result with that of Prob. 14.17, part (c).

14.19 A certain low-pass filter has the system function

$$\frac{V_2(p)}{V_1(p)} = \frac{\omega_1}{(p + \omega_1)^2}.$$

The input is similar to the square wave of Art. 14.2; specifically, the input voltage is the 50-kHz wave

$$v_1(t) = \begin{cases} 50, & 0 < t < 10^{-5} \\ 0, & 10^{-5} < t < 2 \times 10^{-5}. \end{cases}$$

If $\omega_1 = 300$ krad/sec,

a. Find the frequency spectrum of v_2.

b. Plot one cycle of $v_2(t)$ based on the first four nonzero harmonics.

14.20 Repeat Prob. 14.19 with $\omega_1 = 100$ krad/sec. What is the apparent effect of bandwidth on the distortion introduced by the filter?

14.21 Consider the periodic (after $t = 0$) function of period T,

$$f(t) = \sum_{n=0}^{\infty} f_1(t - nT),$$

where

$$f_1(t) = \begin{cases} 0, & -\infty < t < 0 \\ f(t), & 0 < t < T \\ 0, & T < t < \infty \end{cases}$$

is the equation of the first cycle of the wave. Show that the operational form of $f(t)$ is

$$F(p) = \frac{F_1(p)}{1 - e^{-Tp}},$$

where $F_1(p)$ is the operational form of $f_1(t)$. (Hint: See entry No. 7 in Table 7.2, and recall the properties of the geometric series.)

14.22 Using the results of Prob. 14.21, show that the operational form of the square wave of Eq. (14.1) is

$$F(p) = \frac{1}{p(1 + e^{-\pi p})}$$

and that this function has poles at $p = 0$, $p = \pm j(2n - 1)$, $n = 1, 2, 3, \ldots, \infty$.

14.23 Show that Eq. (8.8), giving one coefficient in Heaviside's expansion theorem, may be extended as follows:

$$K_a = [(p + a)F(p)]_{p=-a} = \left[\frac{A(p)}{\dfrac{dB(p)}{dp}} \right]_{p=-a},$$

where $A(p)$ and $B(p)$ are two polynomials such that

$$F(p) = \frac{A(p)}{B(p)}.$$

Use this result to express the operational form of the square wave in Prob. 14.22 in the form of

$$F(p) = \sum_{m=-\infty}^{\infty} \frac{K_m}{p + p_m},$$

with the K_m and p_m specified, then show that you have arrived at the operational form of the Fourier series derived for the square wave of Fig. 14.1.

14.24 Derive the Fourier series of the wave of Prob. 14.3 using the operational techniques of Probs. 14.21 through 14.23.

14.25 Suppose we have the periodic string of impulses,

$$f(t) = F_o \sum_{n=0}^{\infty} \delta(t - nT).$$

Use the operational techniques of the preceding four problems to show that the Fourier expansion is

$$f(t) = \frac{2}{T} \sum_{n=0}^{\infty} \cos \frac{2\pi}{T} nt.$$

Plot the Fourier spectrum, and graphically add the first four sinusoids to observe how the sum approaches the impulse.

14.26 Approximate the wave of Prob. 14.6 for $t > 0$ with the train of impulses

$$i(t) = t_o I_m \sum_{n=0}^{\infty} \delta\left(t - \frac{2\pi n}{\omega}\right),$$

giving a numerical value for t_o. Repeat Prob. 14.17 using this approximation and the results of Prob. 14.25. Compare the two solutions to Prob. 14.17.

14.27 Find the Fourier transforms of the following functions:

a. $f(t) = 20e^{-3t}u(t)$

b. $f(t) = \begin{cases} Ae^{+at}, & -\infty < t < 0 \\ Ae^{-bt}, & 0 < t < \infty \end{cases}$

c. $f(t) = [A \sin \omega t]\left[u(t) - u\left(t - \frac{\pi}{\omega}\right)\right]$

d. $f(t) = [A \cos \omega t]\left[u\left(t + \frac{\pi}{2\omega}\right) - u\left(t - \frac{\pi}{2\omega}\right)\right].$

14.28 A rectangular voltage pulse, centered at the origin, encloses an area of 1.0 V·sec. Find the Fourier transform if the pulse width is allowed to become infinitesimally small while the enclosed area remains constant. On the basis of these results, what is your conclusion as to the Fourier transform of the unit impulse? Compare the Fourier spectrum with that of Prob. 14.25, discussing the similarities and differences.

14.29 Repeat Prob. 14.19 through part (a) if just the first pulse, occurring between $t = 0$ and $t = T$, of the input voltage is applied.

14.30 Repeat Prob. 14.29 with the filter bandwidth reduced as in Prob. 14.20.

14.31 A rectangular voltage pulse of height V and a width of 0.1 second is applied to an R-C series circuit with $R = 0.5$ MΩ and $C = 10$ μF. Find the Fourier spectrum of the voltage across the capacitor.

14.32 Repeat Prob. 14.31 when the rectangular voltage pulse is replaced by

$$v(t) = 0.1V\delta(t).$$

14.33 Prove that

$$\int_{-\infty}^{\infty} f_1(t) f_2(t)\, dt = \frac{1}{2\pi} \int_{-\infty}^{\infty} F_1(\omega) F_2(-\omega)\, d\omega,$$

and that from this follows *Parceval's theorem*,

$$\int_{-\infty}^{\infty} [f(t)]^2\, dt = \frac{1}{2\pi} \int_{-\infty}^{\infty} |F(\omega)|^2\, d\omega.$$

14.34 The voltage pulse

$$v(t) = \begin{cases} 0, & -\infty < t < -\dfrac{250}{\pi} \\[2mm] 60 \cos 1000t, & -\dfrac{250}{\pi} < t < \dfrac{250}{\pi} \\[2mm] 0, & \dfrac{250}{\pi} < t < \infty \end{cases}$$

is applied to the *R-L* series circuit with $R = 1.0\ \text{k}\Omega$ and $L = 1.0\ \text{H}$. Find $I(\omega)$, then determine the total heat dissipation in the resistor using Parceval's theorem (Prob. 14.33).

14.35 Find the Fourier transform of the gated sinusoid

$$i(t) = [I_m \sin \omega t]\left[u(t) - u\left(t - \frac{6\pi}{\omega}\right) \right].$$

14.36 Write a short essay setting forth the formal similarities and conceptual differences between the operator technique and the Laplace transform approach.

15

Balanced Polyphase Circuits

15.1 INTRODUCTION

When one considers that nearly all the very large blocks of power that turn the wheels of industry are transferred and converted in polyphase systems, it begins to appear that the electrical engineering student should be aware of the special techniques and short cuts that polyphase symmetries allow.

Although in this chapter we shall briefly discuss the n-phase system, our attention will be primarily on the three-phase and two-phase systems. The three-phase network is important because it forms the basic connection today for 60-Hz domestic and industrial power systems and for the 400-Hz power systems in airborne equipment. The two-phase connection is no longer finding any significant use for large power systems, but it is naturally adapted to use with small ac control systems, where the actuating member is often a very small two-phase motor.

The student who has progressed through the preceding material actually has collected all the necessary techniques for solving polyphase circuits, since they are simply special multi-mesh networks. In fact, when the systems are "unbalanced" he will normally need to either revert to these techniques or become familiar with the method of *symmetrical components*, which will not be covered here. However, balanced polyphase circuits are adaptable to short cuts whose great labor-saving potential makes them worthy of special attention.

15.2 BALANCED n-PHASE VARIABLES

Briefly, a set of *balanced n*-phase voltages is a set of the type below:

$$\mathbf{V}_1 = Ve^{j\phi_1}$$

$$\mathbf{V}_2 = Ve^{j(\phi_1 - 2\pi/n)}$$

$$\mathbf{V}_3 = Ve^{j(\phi_1 - 4\pi/n)}$$

$$\vdots$$

$$\mathbf{V}_k = V \exp j\left[\phi_1 - \frac{2(k-1)\pi}{n}\right]$$

$$\vdots$$

$$\mathbf{V}_n = V \exp j\left[\phi_1 - \frac{2(n-1)\pi}{n}\right].$$

(15.1)

These voltages form a radiating set of equal-length phasors appearing as the spokes on a wheel, with an angular displacement of $2\pi/n$ between adjacent spokes, as shown in Fig. 15.1(a). The voltages may be across sources, or loads, or combinations of sources and loads, arranged in a *star* or *mesh* connected as shown in (b) and (c) of Fig. 15.1. Each branch in the star or the mesh constitutes a *phase* of the system. Thus voltage V_k appears in phase k.

Each system may have n lines leaving it. In addition, the star connection may have a line from the *neutral* point at the center of the star, but this line will not carry current in a balanced system. This is because any balanced polyphase system with balanced polyphase forcing functions will have currents, flux densities, and other phase response functions described in a manner analogous to the description of the voltages in Eq. (15.1). Therefore, the neutral current for the star will be the sum of n equally displaced phasors, which must always be zero.

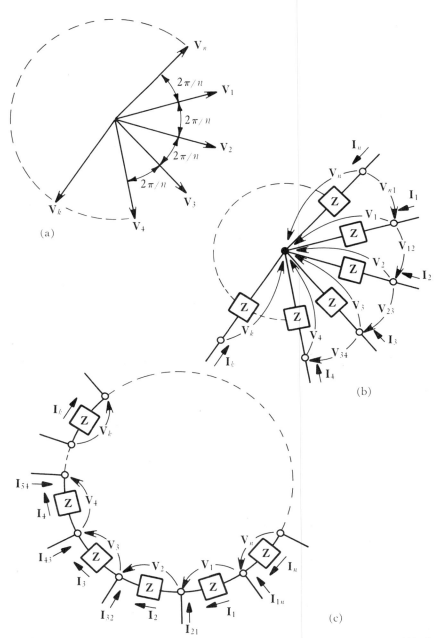

Fig. 15.1 *Balanced n-phase voltages and currents.* (a) *Phasor voltages.* (b) *Star* (c) *Mesh.*

The adjacent line-to-line voltages in the star also form a set of n-phase voltages when taken in sequential order. For example,

$$\mathbf{V}_{12} = \mathbf{V}_1 - \mathbf{V}_2$$

$$= V \exp j\phi_1 \left[1 - \exp\left(-j\frac{2\pi}{n} \right) \right]$$

$$= V \exp j\left(\phi_1 - \frac{\pi}{n} \right) \left[\exp j\frac{\pi}{n} - \exp\left(-j\frac{\pi}{n} \right) \right]$$

$$= j\left(2\sin\frac{\pi}{n} \right) V \exp j\left(\phi_1 - \frac{\pi}{n} \right)$$

$$= \left(2\sin\frac{\pi}{n} \right) V \exp j\left(\phi_1 + \frac{\pi}{2} - \frac{\pi}{n} \right). \tag{15.2a}$$

Similarly,

$$\mathbf{V}_{23} = \left(2\sin\frac{\pi}{n} \right) V \exp j\left(\phi_1 + \frac{\pi}{2} - \frac{\pi}{n} - \frac{2\pi}{n} \right)$$

$$\mathbf{V}_{34} = \left(2\sin\frac{\pi}{n} \right) V \exp j\left(\phi_1 + \frac{\pi}{2} - \frac{\pi}{n} - \frac{4\pi}{n} \right),$$

etc., $\tag{15.2b}$

indicating that the line-to-line voltages form an n-phase set with each member of magnitude $2\sin\pi/n$ times the phase voltage magnitude.

A similar relation will be found to hold between line currents and phase currents in the mesh.

When the k-phase quantity leads the $(k+1)$-phase quantity by $2\pi/n$, as in Eqs. (15.1), the system is said to be *positive sequence*. When the k-phase quantity lags the $(k+1)$-phase quantity, we have a *negative sequence* system.

15.3 DOUBLE-SUBSCRIPT NOTATION

In polyphase systems, there is considerable advantage to be gained from the use of double-subscript notation. This notation eliminates the need for arrows to indicate the directions of voltage drops and currents. It may be briefly described in this way:

In any network branch having end points a and b, the branch current positive from a to b will be called i_{ab} and the voltage drop between a and b and positive from a to b will be called v_{ab}.

This system of notation may be compared with the conventional arrow system by reference to Fig. 15.2. The two networks are identical. The conventional symbols in (a) translated to double-subscript notation for (b) are

$$i = i_{ba} = i_{aA} = i_{AB} = i_{Bb} \tag{15.3a}$$

$$v = v_{ab} = v_{AB}. \tag{15.3b}$$

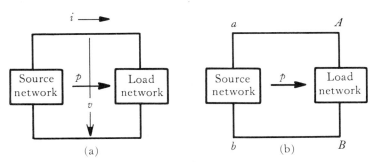

Fig. 15.2 *Illustrating double-subscript notation. (a) Conventional notation. (b) Double-subscript notation.*

Notice that for a load the voltage and current subscripts are in the same order, while for a source they are reversed. This is evident in the instantaneous power expression, where power flow is assumed positive to the right:

$$p = vi = v_{ab}i_{ba} = v_{AB}i_{AB}. \tag{15.3c}$$

15.4 THE BALANCED THREE-PHASE SYSTEM

A balanced three-phase set of voltages has $n = 3$, so that Eqs. (15.1) take the form

$$\left.\begin{aligned}
\mathbf{V}_a &= \mathbf{V}_1 = Ve^{j\phi_v} \\
\mathbf{V}_b &= \mathbf{V}_2 = V \exp j\left(\phi_v - \frac{2\pi}{3}\right) \\
\mathbf{V}_c &= \mathbf{V}_3 = V \exp j\left(\phi_v - \frac{4\pi}{3}\right)
\end{aligned}\right\}, \qquad a\text{-}b\text{-}c \text{ sequence.} \tag{15.4a}$$

Here the letters *a-b-c* replace the numbers 1-2-3 as phase identifiers, in keeping with the most common current usage. The positive sequence is often called the *a-b-c* sequence. This is logical when one remembers that phase diagrams are essentially "snapshots" at $t = 0$ of a set of phasors rotating in the positive angular direction at ω radians per second, but fixed in relation to one another.

Thus a stationary observer will observe the appearance of the rotating three-phase phasors in the *a-b-c* order for the positive sequence.

A negative sequence set of three-phase voltages is similarly said to possess the *a-c-b* sequence. Such a set is

$$\left. \begin{aligned} \mathbf{V}_a &= V e^{j\phi_v} \\ \mathbf{V}_b &= V \exp j\left(\phi_v + \frac{2\pi}{3}\right) \\ \mathbf{V}_c &= V \exp j\left(\phi_v + \frac{4\pi}{3}\right) \end{aligned} \right\}, \qquad \textit{a-c-b} \text{ sequence.} \qquad (15.4b)$$

Voltage sets of the form of Eqs. (15.4) may be either phase voltages or line-to-line voltages. Similarly, current sets of the same form may be either phase currents or line currents. In the following articles, we shall rely on double-subscript notation to distinguish between line and phase quantities.

15.5 THE THREE-PHASE WYE

In three-phase systems, the star connection is, for obvious reasons, more often called the *wye* connection. A wye-connected load is shown in Fig. 15.3(a).

For the load in Fig. 15.3(a), we shall choose positive voltages toward the neutral, *n*, though we could have equally well chosen them outward from the neutral. Then the *a-b-c* sequence three-phase voltages are

$$\mathbf{V}_{an} = V_p e^{j\phi_a} \qquad (15.5a)$$

$$\mathbf{V}_{bn} = V_p e^{j(\phi_a - 2\pi/3)} = \mathbf{V}_{an} e^{-j2\pi/3} \qquad (15.5b)$$

$$\mathbf{V}_{cn} = V_p e^{j(\phi_a - 4\pi/3)} = \mathbf{V}_{an} e^{-j4\pi/3}, \qquad (15.5c)$$

where

$$V_p = \text{magnitude of the phase voltage.} \qquad (15.6)$$

These three phasors are shown in Fig. 15.3(b).

The voltage drop from line *a* to line *b* is the voltage drop from *a* to *n* plus that form *n* to *b*. That is,

$$\begin{aligned} \mathbf{V}_{ab} &= \mathbf{V}_{an} + \mathbf{V}_{nb} \\ &= \mathbf{V}_{an} - \mathbf{V}_{bn} \\ &= V_{an}(1 - e^{-j2\pi/3}) \\ &= \sqrt{3}\, V_{an} e^{j\pi/6} \\ &= \sqrt{3}\, V_p e^{j(\phi_a + \pi/6)} \\ &= V_L e^{j(\phi_a + \pi/6)}, \end{aligned} \qquad (15.7)$$

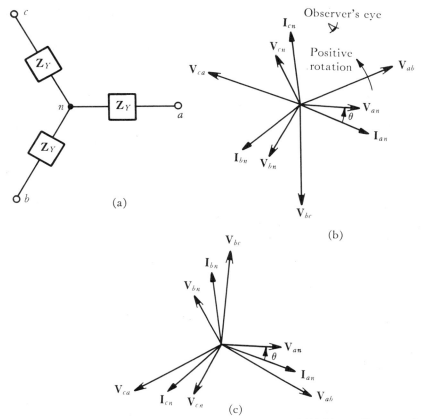

Fig. 15.3 *The wye-connected load. (a) Wye-connected load. (b) Phasor diagram, a-b-c sequence. (c) Phasor diagram, a-c-b sequence.*

where

$$V_L = \text{line-to-line voltage.} \qquad (15.8)$$

Obviously line and phase currents are equal in the wye, so if the subscripts p and L are extended to use with currents in the same sense as with voltages, we note that

$$\left.\begin{array}{l} V_L = \sqrt{3}\,V_p \\ I_L = I_p \end{array}\right\} \qquad \text{for the wye connection.} \qquad (15.9)$$

The phasor line (line-to-line) voltage for the wye is therefore 30° (or $-150°$, depending on subscript order) from an associated phase voltage. These line voltages are also shown in the figure.

Finally, each phase is assumed to be dissipating power as a circuit load, which means that in order to write the power expression without minus signs the current must be assumed positive in the same direction as the positive direction for voltage in that phase. In the phasor diagram, $\mathbf{Z}_Y$ was assumed inductive when the current $\mathbf{I}_{an}$ was shown to lag voltage $\mathbf{V}_{an}$ by the power factor angle θ. Since the system is balanced, a similar situation holds for phases b and c. The three-phase currents then are

$$\mathbf{I}_{an} = I_p \, e^{j(\phi_a - \theta)}, \tag{15.10a}$$

$$\mathbf{I}_{bn} = I_p \, e^{j(\phi_a - \theta - 2\pi/3)} = \mathbf{I}_{an} \, e^{-j2\pi/3}, \tag{15.10b}$$

$$\mathbf{I}_{cn} = I_p \, e^{j(\phi_a - \theta - 4\pi/3)} = \mathbf{I}_{an} \, e^{-j4\pi/3}. \tag{15.10c}$$

The student should get in the habit of checking sequence on his sketches of phasor diagrams in the manner of the observing eye in Fig. 15.3(b). Notice that as the eye observes the appearance of any sequence of first subscripts, or any sequence of second subscripts, they invariably appear in order *a-b-c* for that sequence. On the other hand, the *a-c-b* sequence, shown in Fig. (15.3c), will have any such sequence appear in the *a-c-b* order.

15.6 THE THREE-PHASE DELTA

The three-phase mesh system shown in Fig. (15.4a) is more commonly known as the three-phase delta.

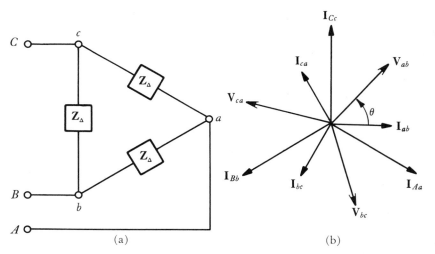

Fig. 15.4 *The delta-connected load. (a) Delta-connected load. (b) Phasor diagram, a-b-c sequence.*

The phase voltages now are also line voltages and may be written, for the
a-b-c sequence, as

$$\mathbf{V}_{ab} = V_p e^{j\phi_{ab}}, \tag{15.11a}$$

$$\mathbf{V}_{bc} = V_p e^{j(\phi_{ab} - 2\pi/3)} = \mathbf{V}_{ab} e^{-j2\pi/3}, \tag{15.11b}$$

$$\mathbf{V}_{ca} = V_p e^{j(\phi_{ab} - 4\pi/3)} = \mathbf{V}_{ab} e^{-j4\pi/3}. \tag{15.11c}$$

Again assuming per-phase inductive power dissipation at power factor
angle θ,

$$\mathbf{I}_{ab} = I_p e^{j(\phi_{ab} - \theta)}, \tag{15.12a}$$

$$\mathbf{I}_{bc} = I_p e^{j(\phi_{ab} - \theta - 2\pi/3)} = \mathbf{I}_{ab} e^{-j2\pi/3}, \tag{15.12b}$$

$$\mathbf{I}_{ca} = I_p e^{j(\phi_{ab} - \theta - 4\pi/3)} = \mathbf{I}_{ab} e^{-j4\pi/3}. \tag{15.12c}$$

The current in the line *A-a* is

$$\begin{aligned}
\mathbf{I}_{Aa} &= \mathbf{I}_{ab} + \mathbf{I}_{ac} \\
&= \mathbf{I}_{ab} - \mathbf{I}_{ca} \\
&= \mathbf{I}_{ab}(1 - e^{-j4\pi/3}) \\
&= \sqrt{3}\, \mathbf{I}_{ab} e^{-j\pi/6} \\
&= \sqrt{3}\, I_p e^{j(\phi_{ab} - \theta - \pi/6)} \\
&= I_L e^{j(\phi_{ab} - \theta - \pi/6)}. \tag{15.13}
\end{aligned}$$

The student should carefully note the phase shift between line and phase
currents and the fact that

$$\left.\begin{aligned} V_L &= V_p \\ I_L &= \sqrt{3}\, I_p \end{aligned}\right\} \quad \text{for the delta connection.} \tag{15.14}$$

15.7 THREE-PHASE VECTOR VOLT-AMPERES

Let $\mathbf{V}_p$ and $\mathbf{I}_p$ be respectively the phasor voltage and current in any
one of the three phases of a wye or delta connection. Then the vector volt-
amperes of that phase will be

$$\begin{aligned}
\mathbf{S}_p &= \mathbf{V}_p \mathbf{I}_p^* \\
&= V_p I_p e^{j\theta}. \tag{15.15}
\end{aligned}$$

The *three-phase vector volt-amperes* will be the combined contribution of all three phases:

$$\begin{aligned}
\mathbf{S} &= 3\mathbf{S}_p \\
&= 3V_p I_p e^{j\theta} \\
&= 3\left(\frac{V_L}{\sqrt{3}}\right) I_L e^{j\theta} \qquad \text{for wye connection} \\
&= 3V_L\left(\frac{I_L}{\sqrt{3}}\right) e^{j\theta} \qquad \text{for delta connection} \\
&= \sqrt{3}\, V_L I_L e^{j\theta} \\
&= \sqrt{3}\, V_L I_L \cos\theta + j\sqrt{3}\, V_L I_L \sin\theta.
\end{aligned} \qquad (15.16)$$

Thus three-phase power is

$$P = 3P_p = \sqrt{3}\, V_L I_L \cos\theta, \qquad (15.17)$$

whereas three-phase reactive volt-amperes are

$$Q = 3Q_p = \sqrt{3}V_L I_L \sin\theta. \qquad (15.18)$$

The student is cautioned about two things in applying these expressions:

1.   They apply only to *balanced* three-phase systems.
2.   The angle θ is the angle between phase voltage and phase current; *it is not the angle between line voltage and line current.*

15.8 POWER MEASUREMENT IN THREE-WIRE SYSTEMS

Reference to Fig. 15.5 will be useful in the discussion of the measurement of power flow down a three-wire transmission system. Part (a) of the figure shows an arbitrary combination of three-terminal source and load networks, which may or may not be balanced three-phase networks.

By KVL,

$$v_{ab} + v_{bc} + v_{ca} = 0,$$

so the voltage between source terminals c and a is thus

$$\begin{aligned}
v_{ca} &= -v_{ab} - v_{bc} \\
&= v_{cb} - v_{ab},
\end{aligned}$$

and, therefore, is fixed when v_{ab} and v_{cb} are chosen. Therefore, there is no loss in generality if only v_{ab} and v_{cb} are assumed across energy sources as in Fig. 15.5(b).

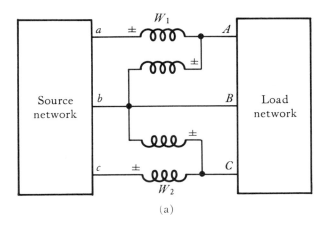

(a)

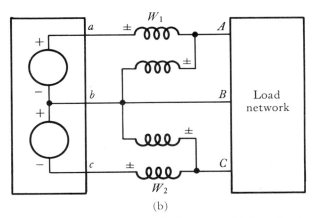

(b)

Fig. 15.5 *Power flow in a three-wire transmission system. (a) Actual system. (b) Source network replaced by a two-generator equivalent.*

The power delivered to the load network is, then, the sum of the powers out of the two sources. That is,

$$p = v_{ab} i_{ba} + v_{cb} i_{bc}$$
$$= v_{ab} i_{aA} + v_{cb} i_{cC}.$$

As the two wattmeter readings are

$$W_1 = [v_{ab} i_{aA}]_{av}$$
$$W_2 = [v_{cb} i_{cC}]_{av},$$

it is clear that the average power for periodic functions is

$$P = W_1 + W_2. \tag{15.19}$$

The expressions for wattmeter indications for sinusoidal variables are

$$W_1 = V_{ab}I_{aA} \cos \phi_1 = V_L I_L \cos \phi_1 \qquad (15.20a)$$

$$W_2 = V_{cb}I_{cC} \cos \phi_2 = V_L I_L \cos \phi_2, \qquad (15.20b)$$

where ϕ_1 and ϕ_2 are the angles between the voltage and current associated with the meter carrying the same tag. The student should carefully note that neither of these is the power-factor angle, θ.

Of course, the two wattmeters may be placed in any pair of the three lines connecting source to load, but the student should have no problem adapting these results to any such pair. In applying these methods, it is extremely important to pay careful attention to meter polarity marks in order to be certain of direction of power flow and of the signs on individual meter readings. When upscale readings result from the polarities shown, power flow is positive to the right. However, it is possible that with these polarities one of the meters will deflect back-scale, and it will be necessary to reverse one of the coils to obtain upscale deflection. Then it will be necessary to record its contribution to right-directed power flow as negative. Should this be the larger of the two readings, with the first meter continuing the polarities shown, it simply means that load power is negative, or that the load is actually acting as a positive source.

15.9 SOME EXAMPLES OF THREE-PHASE COMPUTATIONS

It may be helpful now to illustrate the behavior of a typical three-phase network by means of an example.

EXAMPLE 15.1. In the network of Fig. 15.6(a), the sequence is *a-b-c* and

$$V = 120 \ V; \qquad Z_s = 3 + j5 \ \Omega; \qquad Z_L = 12 + j30 \ \Omega.$$

Find all voltages and currents and the readings of the two wattmeters; determine the three-phase vector volt-amperes, the average power, and reactive volt-amperes of the delta impedances; and sketch the complete phasor diagram showing source and load voltages and currents.

Solution. Note that the generated voltages, in order to satisfy the statement for V_a and the condition of *a-b-c* sequence, must be

1.
$$V_a = 120e^{j0} \ V,$$
$$V_b = 120e^{-j120°} \ V,$$
$$V_c = 120e^{-j240°} \ V.$$

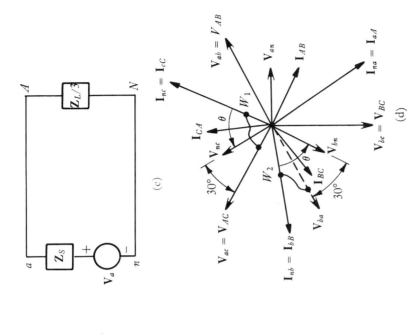

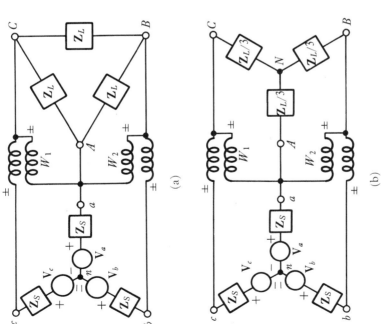

Fig. 15.6 A wye-delta example. (a) Original network. (b) Equivalent wye load. (c) Per-phase network for equivalent wye load. (d) Phasor diagram.

2.   Replace the delta by an equivalent wye, as shown in Fig. 15.6(b).

$$\mathbf{Z}_Y = \frac{\mathbf{Z}_L}{3} = 4 + j10 \ \Omega.$$

3.   Since a neutral conductor connected from n to N will carry no current, n and N are at the same potential, and any phase can be computed separately as a single-phase circuit as shown in Fig. 15.6(c). Thus

$$\mathbf{V}_a = \mathbf{I}_{aA}\left(\mathbf{Z}_S + \frac{\mathbf{Z}_L}{3}\right)$$

and

$$\mathbf{I}_{aA} = \frac{\mathbf{V}_a}{\mathbf{Z}_S + \dfrac{\mathbf{Z}_L}{3}}$$

$$= \frac{120}{3 + j5 + 4 + j10}$$

$$= \frac{120}{7 + j15} = 7.25e^{-j65°} \text{ A.}$$

Also,

$$\mathbf{V}_{an} = \mathbf{V}_{AN} = \mathbf{I}_{aA}\frac{\mathbf{Z}_L}{3}$$

$$= 7.25e^{-j65°}(4 + j10) = 78.0e^{j3.2°} \text{ V.}$$

4.   From the results of (3) and the knowledge of sequence, list all the line voltages and wye-phase voltages.

$$\mathbf{I}_{aA} = \mathbf{I}_{na} = \mathbf{I}_{AN} = 7.25e^{-j65°} \text{ A}$$

$$\mathbf{I}_{bB} = \mathbf{I}_{nb} = \mathbf{I}_{BN} = 7.25e^{j(-65°-120°)} = 7.25e^{-j185°} \text{ A}$$

$$\mathbf{I}_{cC} = \mathbf{I}_{nc} = \mathbf{I}_{CN} = 7.25e^{j(-65°-240°)} = 7.25e^{-j305°} \text{ A}$$

$$\mathbf{V}_{an} = \mathbf{V}_{AN} = 78.0e^{j3.2°} \text{ V}$$

$$\mathbf{V}_{bn} = \mathbf{V}_{BN} = 78.0e^{j(3.2°-120°)} = 78.0e^{-j116.8°} \text{ V}$$

$$\mathbf{V}_{cn} = \mathbf{V}_{CN} = 78.0e^{j(3.2°-240°)} = 78.0e^{-j236.8°} \text{ V.}$$

5.   Although line voltages may be obtained by adding the above phase voltages, we know their magnitudes are $\sqrt{3}$ times the magnitudes of

phase voltages and their angular position is quickly deduced from a sketch of the phasor diagram. For example,

$$\mathbf{V}_{ab} = \mathbf{V}_{AB} = \sqrt{3}\,\mathbf{V}_{an}\,e^{j30°}$$
$$= \sqrt{3}\,(78.0e^{+j3.2°})e^{j30°}$$
$$= 135e^{j33.2°}\ \mathrm{V},$$

and it immediately follows that $\mathbf{V}_{bc}$ and $\mathbf{V}_{ca}$ are respectively 120° and 240° behind this voltage. Thus,

$$\mathbf{V}_{bc} = \mathbf{V}_{BC} = 135e^{+j(33.2°-120°)} = 135e^{-j86.8°}\ \mathrm{V}$$
$$\mathbf{V}_{ca} = \mathbf{V}_{CA} = 135e^{j(33.2°-240°)} = 135e^{-j206.8°}\ \mathrm{V}.$$

6.   A sketch of the phasor diagram shows that the current in phase AB of the delta is

$$\mathbf{I}_{AB} = \frac{\mathbf{I}_{aA}}{\sqrt{3}}\,e^{j30°}$$
$$= \frac{7.25e^{-j65.0°}}{\sqrt{3}}\,e^{j30°} = 4.18e^{-j35°}\ \mathrm{A},$$

and it follows that

$$\mathbf{I}_{BC} = 4.18e^{j(-35°-120°)} = 4.18e^{-j155°}\ \mathrm{A}$$
$$\mathbf{I}_{CA} = 4.18e^{j(-35°-240°)} = 4.18e^{-j275°}\ \mathrm{A}.$$

7.   The wattmeter readings are

$$\begin{aligned}
W_1 &= V_{ca}I_{cC}\cos\phi_1 \\
&= 135(7.25)\cos(-206.8° + 305°) \\
&= 135(7.25)\cos(+98.2°) \\
&= -139.5\ \mathrm{W}
\end{aligned}$$

$$\begin{aligned}
W_2 &= V_{ba}I_{bB}\cos\phi_2 \\
&= 135(7.25)\cos[(-180° + 33.2°) + 185°] \\
&= 135(7.25)\cos(-38.2°) \\
&= 770\ \mathrm{W}.
\end{aligned}$$

8.   The total power into the delta is, by the meter readings

$$P = W_1 + W_2$$
$$= -139.5 + 770 = 630\ \mathrm{W}.$$

We can check this figure by the alternative computation:

$$\mathbf{S} = P + jQ$$
$$= \sqrt{3}\, V_L I_L e^{j\theta}$$
$$= \sqrt{3}\, (135)(7.25)e^{j\underline{12+j30}}$$
$$= 1695 e^{j68.2°}$$
$$= 630 + j\,1570 \text{ VA}$$
$$P = 630 \text{ W (checks above)}$$
$$Q = 1570 \text{ vars.}$$

9.   The phasor diagram is shown in Fig. 15.6(d). Actually, this diagram should be sketched ahead of the analytical work, since it provides an excellent check on the reasonableness of the results. The voltage and current phasors associated with each wattmeter are indicated on the diagram by connection of each pair by a symbolic "string."

A bit of general information useful to the analysis of balanced three-phase circuits can be gained by inspection of the phasor diagram in Fig. 15.6(d). There it can be seen that the voltage associated with the lower-reading watt-meter is out of phase with the associated current by the power factor angle plus the 30° phase difference between line and phase voltage. In the high-reading wattmeter, the voltage is out of phase with the current by the power factor angle minus the 30° phase angle between line and phase voltages. Therefore,

$$W_{\text{(high-reading meter)}} = V_L I_L \cos (|\theta| - 30°) \qquad (15.21a)$$

$$W_{\text{(low-reading meter)}} = V_L I_L \cos (|\theta| + 30°). \qquad (15.21b)$$

Often, in three-phase networks, power is transferred to a complex balanced three-phase network within which there are delta or wye connections or combinations of delta and wye connections. Insofar as the manner in which terminal characteristics of such a network are effected, however, the engineer need not concern himself with whether the network is wye or delta, because any three-terminal network has its equivalent wye and its equivalent delta. Therefore, the engineer may assume it to be wye, or he may assume it to be delta, or he may neglect to consider it either, whichever suits his needs. This is illustrated in the next example.

EXAMPLE 15.2. The balanced three-phase load in Fig. 15.7 constitutes 50 kVA at 440 V and 0.4 pf lag. What will be the meter readings if sequence is *a-b-c*? If sequence is *a-c-b*?

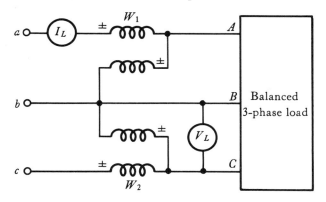

Fig. 15.7 *Circuit for Example 15.2.*

Solution. The vector volt-amperes are

$$\mathbf{S} = 50e^{j\cos^{-1}0.4}$$
$$= 50e^{j66.4°}$$
$$= 20 + j45.8$$
$$= P + jQ \text{ kVA}.$$

Therefore

$$P = 20 \text{ kW} \qquad Q = 45.8 \text{ kvars}.$$

Also

$$\mathbf{S} = 50{,}000e^{j66.4°} = \sqrt{3}\, V_L I_L e^{j66.4°} = \sqrt{3}\,(440)I_L\, e^{j66.4°} \text{ VA}$$

and

$$I_L = \frac{50{,}000}{\sqrt{3}\,(440)} = 65.6 \text{ A}.$$

The two wattmeter readings are

$$W_{\text{(high-reading meter)}} = V_L I_L \cos\left(|\theta| - 30°\right)$$
$$= 440(65.6)\cos\left(66.4° - 30°\right)$$
$$= 28{,}850 \cos\left(36.4°\right)$$
$$= 23{,}200 \text{ W}$$

$$W_{\text{(low-reading meter)}} = V_L I_L \cos\left(|\theta|\right) + 30°)$$
$$= 28{,}850 \cos 96.4°$$
$$= -3200 \text{ W}.$$

Thus the low-reading meter must have either its potential coil or its current coil reversed for an upscale reading.

Now we shall determine which meter is the low-reading meter and which is the high-reading meter. This is most easily done by a sketch of the phasor diagram and is shown for both sequences in Fig. 15.8, assuming a delta load.

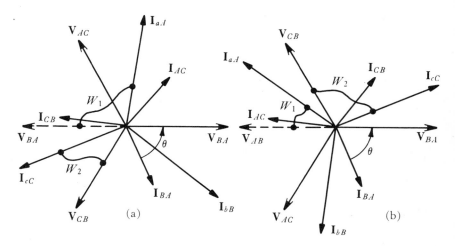

Fig. 15.8 *Phasor diagrams for Example 15.2. (a) a-b-c sequence. (b) a-c-b sequence.*

(It could also have been done assuming a wye load). Reference to these diagrams makes it obvious which is the small-reading meter and that the small-reading meter is indicating a negative value.

Now the meter readings may be listed:

a-b-c Sequence	*a-c-b* Sequence
$V_L = 440$ V	$V_L = 440$ V
$I_L = 65.6$ A	$I_L = 65.6$ A
$W_1 = -3200$ W	$W_1 = 23,200$ W
$W_2 = 23,200$ W	$W_2 = -3200$ W.

15.10 TWO-PHASE SYSTEMS

The two-phase system seems to be an interloper in the balanced polyphase system described in Art. 15.2, since it consists of two equal phasors only 90° apart. This seems at odds with the general case, which would call for two equal phasors 180° apart.

In reality, placing $n = 2$ in the general case yields what is known as the *three-wire* single-phase system in very common use in the distribution of residential and farm power. Such a system is shown in Fig. 15.9, along with

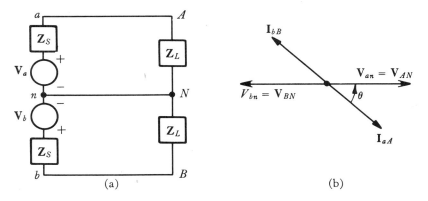

Fig. 15.9 *The balanced three-wire single-phase system.*

its phasor diagram for balanced operation. Under this balanced operation the neutral current is

$$\mathbf{I}_{Nn} = \mathbf{I}_{aA} + \mathbf{I}_{bB} = 0,$$

though it is not unusual for such systems to be unbalanced so that neutral current does flow.

In the United States, three-wire systems feeding residential or farm loads have nominal voltage ratings which make

$$V_{an} = V_{bn} = 120 \text{ V}$$
$$V_{ba} = |\mathbf{V}_{bn} + \mathbf{V}_{na}| = 240 \text{ V}.$$

The line-to-neutral 120-V source is generally used for lighting and light appliance loads, while the 240-V line-to-line source supplies equipment requiring higher power; for example, electric dryers, ranges, water heaters, and heavy-duty single-phase motors. In such applications, the neutral conductor is grounded as a safety precaution insuring that maximum voltage to ground of any part of the system is 120 V.

What is known as "two-phase" is a special case of the four-phase system. With $n = 4$, the general polyphase equations (for voltage) become

$$\mathbf{V}_1 = V_1 e^{j\phi_1}$$
$$\mathbf{V}_2 = V_1 e^{j(\phi_1 - \pi/2)} = -j\mathbf{V}_1$$
$$\mathbf{V}_3 = V_1 e^{j(\phi_1 - \pi)} = -\mathbf{V}_1$$
$$\mathbf{V}_4 = V_1 e^{j(\phi_1 - 3\pi/2)} = j\mathbf{V}_1.$$

The "two-phase" variables may be considered the following combinations of these variables:

$$\mathbf{V}_\alpha = \mathbf{V}_1 - \mathbf{V}_3 = 2V_1 e^{j\phi_1} = V e^{j\phi_\alpha},$$
$$\mathbf{V}_\beta = \mathbf{V}_2 - \mathbf{V}_4 = -j2V_1 e^{j\phi_1} = -jV e^{j\phi_\alpha}.$$

These are of the form

$$\left.\begin{array}{l} \mathbf{V}_\alpha = V e^{j\phi_\alpha} \\ \mathbf{V}_\beta = -jV e^{j\phi_\alpha} = -j\mathbf{V}_\alpha \end{array}\right\} \text{ for positive sequence.} \qquad (15.22a)$$

For the opposite sequence

$$\left.\begin{array}{l} \mathbf{V}_\alpha = V e^{j\phi_\alpha} \\ \mathbf{V}_\beta = +jV e^{j\phi_\alpha} = j\mathbf{V}_\alpha \end{array}\right\} \text{ for negative sequence.} \qquad (15.22b)$$

Similar expressions hold for other circuit variables than voltage.

If $\mathbf{V}_p$ and $\mathbf{I}_p$ are the voltage and current in either phase of the balanced system, the two-phase vector volt-amperes are

$$\begin{aligned} \mathbf{S} &= 2\mathbf{S}_p \\ &= 2\mathbf{V}_p \mathbf{I}_p^* \\ &= 2V_p I_p e^{j\theta} \\ &= 2V_p I_p \cos\theta + j2V_p I_p \sin\theta \\ &= P + jQ. \end{aligned} \qquad (15.23)$$

Thus,

$$P = 2P_p = 2V_p I_p \cos\theta \qquad (15.24)$$
$$Q = 2Q_p = 2V_p I_p \sin\theta, \qquad (15.25)$$

where θ is the power factor angle.

Two-phase systems may be either three-wire or four-wire, as shown in Fig. 15.10 with associated phasor diagram.

It should be noted that the *neutral* wire in the three-wire two-phase system does carry current—more current, in fact, than does a phase itself. This current is designated $\mathbf{I}_{Nn}$ in Fig. 15.10(a).

Two-phase systems have passed into history as a means for transmitting and utilizing large blocks of power, because more copper is required to transmit a given amount of power at a given voltage by two-phase transmission than by three-phase transmission. However, two-phase components continue to be used extensively in the low-power ac control and servo systems. Also, the study of certain classes of rotating machines gains a powerful method of analysis by the method of two-phase symmetrical components, a method

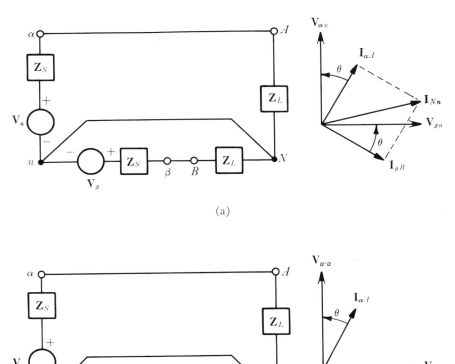

Fig. 15.10 *Two-phase systems.* (a) *Three-wire.* (b) *Four-wire.*

where there is the superposition of the effects of two balanced two-phase systems, one a positive sequence system and the other a negative sequence system.

PROBLEMS

15.1 The coils in Fig. P.15.1 are either separate generator coils or separate transformer secondaries having the following open-circuit terminal voltages:

$$\mathbf{V}_{1'1} = \mathbf{V}_{2'2} = 100e^{j0}$$
$$\mathbf{V}_{3'3} = \mathbf{V}_{4'4} = 100e^{j60°}$$
$$\mathbf{V}_{5'5} = \mathbf{V}_{6'6} = 100e^{-j60°}.$$

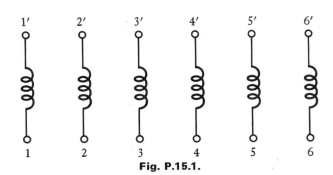

Fig. P.15.1.

Each coil is rated at 10 A. In each case below, show the connections to form the system specified, *using all coils*, and give the rated line and phase currents for each system under balanced conditions.

    a.   A 6-phase star, phase voltage = 100 V.
    b.   A 6-phase mesh, phase voltage = 100 V.
    c.   A 100-V, 3-phase delta source.
    d.   A 200-V, 3-phase delta source.
    e.   A 346-V, 3-phase wye source.
    f.   A 173-V, 3-phase wye source.

15.2 A balanced delta is formed of 20-Ω resistors and balanced 3-phase, *a-b-c* sequence voltages are applied. $V_{ab} = 100 + j0$ V. List the phasor values of all phase and line voltages and currents and compute the total power, reactive volt-amperes, and vector volt-amperes.

15.3 Repeat Prob. 15.2 when the resistors are replaced by three impedances, each one $Z_\Delta = 3 + j4$ Ω.

15.4 Repeat Prob. 15.2 when the resistors are replaced by three capacitors, each having a reactance of magnitude 10.0 Ω.

15.5 Repeat Prob. 15.2 when the resistors are reconnected into a wye on the same source.

15.6 A balanced delta with $Z_\Delta = 5 - j6$ Ω is in parallel with a balanced wye with $Z_Y = 1 + j3$ Ω connected to a balanced 120-V source. Find the total current, the power, and power factor of the combination.

15.7 Equal impedances of $1 + j8$ Ω are in series with the lines to a balanced delta with $Z_\Delta = 2 - j6$ Ω. The combination is supplied by balanced 3-phase voltages of 100 V line-to-line. What are the line current and the terminal voltage at the delta?

15.8 A three-phase, 440-V, 50 hp (shaft rating), 1750–rpm motor has a full-load efficiency of 70 percent and operates with a full-load power factor of 0.7 lag. What current does it draw from the power source?

15.9 The delta of resistors in Prob. 15.2 is replaced by an unbalanced delta with impedances $\mathbf{Z}_{ab} = 20\ \Omega$, $\mathbf{Z}_{bc} = -j20\ \Omega$, and $\mathbf{Z}_{ca} = +j20\ \Omega$. Repeat the computations of Prob. 15.2.

15.10 Repeat Prob. 15.9 after reversing the phase sequence to *a-c-b*.

15.11 List all letter sequences equivalent to specifying the *a-b-c* sequence.

15.12 A certain balanced 3-phase, 240-V load is 1500 volt-amperes at 0.6 pf lagging. Show both the equivalent wye and the equivalent delta to this load. If power is measured by the two-wattmeter method, what will the two wattmeters read?

15.13 The transmission line in Fig. P.15.2 has a line impedance $\mathbf{Z}_T = 1 + j5\ \Omega$. The load consumes 250 kVA at 2400 V line-to-line. Find the line-to-line source voltage when the load pf is:

a.   unity,
b.   0.5 lag,
c.   0.6 lead.

15.14 In Fig. P.15.2, the line impedance is $1 + j5\ \Omega$ and the source voltage is balanced *a-b-c* sequence with $\mathbf{V}_{bc} = 200 + j0$ V. The balanced load is delta connected, with $\mathbf{Z}_\Delta = 33 + j33\ \Omega$. Find:

a.   The phasor values of the load voltages.
b.   The phasor values of the line currents.
c.   The source vector volt-amperes, power, and reactive volt-amperes.
d.   The load vector volt-amperes, power, and reactive volt-amperes.
e.   The efficiency of the transmission line at this load.

15.15 What wye impedance will have the same terminal voltage and current as the delta impedance in Prob. 15.14?

15.16 In Fig. P.15.2, the line impedance is $1 + j5\ \Omega$ and the load is 3.5 kVA at 200 V and 0.6 pf lag. What is the source line-to-line voltage?

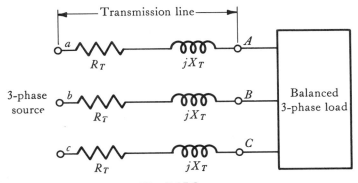

Fig. P.15.2.

15.17 Repeat Prob. 15.16 when the load is 3.5 kVA at unity power factor and 200 V.

15.18 Repeat Prob. 15.16 when the load is 3.5 kVA at 0.6 pf lead.

15.19 The two generators of Fig. P.15.3 are identically constructed 200-kVA machines and are adjusted to have the same open-circuit voltage. Each phase

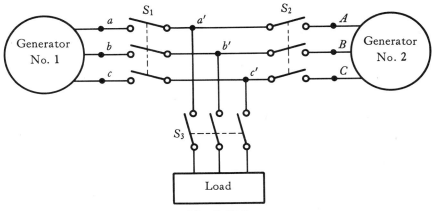

Fig. P.15.3.

consists of a 2400-V ideal source in series with an inductive reactance of 50 Ω. The two machines are to be paralleled by closing switch S_1, then S_2, with S_3 remaining open and the machines being carefully adjusted so that on open circuits $\mathbf{V}_{ab} = \mathbf{V}_{AB} = 2400 + j0$ V. However, the operators are unaware that someone has blundered and machine No. 1 is operating with *a-b-c* sequence while machine No. 2 operates with *a-c-b* sequence.

    a.   What currents will flow when the second switch is closed?

    b.   What percent of rated kVA is each generator handling?

    c.   What currents would have resulted had there been no blunder?

15.20 With all switches closed and *a-b-c* sequence on both machines in Fig. P.15.3, machine No. 1 delivers 200 kVA at 0.7 pf lag through switch S_1 while machine No. 2 delivers 150 kVA at unity pf through S_2. Terminal voltage is 2000 V. What are the vector volt-amperes, the power, the vars, the power factor, and the line current at the load?

15.21 The generated voltages (open-circuit voltages) of the two sources in Fig. P.15.3 are adjustable to give any balanced *a-b-c* sequence of generated voltages. With all switches closed, the load is 200 kVA at 2400 V and 0.707 pf lag. Source No. 1 is to supply all the real power to the load and source No. 2 is to supply all the reactive volt-amperes. To what value must the per-phase generated voltage of each machine be adjusted? What are the line currents to the load and from each source?

15.22 A certain 7200-V, 3-phase load operates at 100 kVA and 0.7 pf lag. It is desired to raise the power factor to unity to avoid the penalty charges by the power supplier for low power factor loads. It is proposed to accomplish this by use of a three-phase capacitor bank. Power capacitor banks are usually rated in kVA and kilovolts.

a.   What must be the rating of the capacitor bank?
b.   Find the line currents with and without the capacitor bank.
c.   Give the voltage rating of each capacitor in the wye bank and the capacitance of each phase.
d.   Repeat (c) for a delta bank.

15.23 Three 2400/120-V, 50-kVA transformers are to be used to form a three-phase bank of transformers. Two-winding power transformers have polarity marks as shown in Fig. P.15.4, where the odd subscripts have the

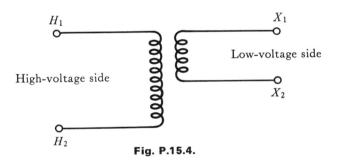

Fig. P.15.4.

same polarity (and, of course, so do the even subscripts) in the sense of the polarity marks of Chapter 13. Assume for the purposes of this problem that the transformers are ideal and that the transformer bank to be formed supplies rated load at rated voltage and 0.6 pf lagging. For each connection specified: draw the connection diagram for the transformers, showing the H and X terminals; find rated primary and secondary line currents and line-to-line voltages; and draw the complete phasor diagram, showing all line and phase voltages and currents identified by double-subscript notation.

a.   Primary in delta, secondary in delta (Δ-Δ).
b.   Primary in delta, secondary in wye (Δ-Y).
c.   Primary in wye, secondary in wye (Y-Y).
d.   Primary in wye, secondary in delta (Y-Δ).

15.24 The power to a certain load is measured by the two-wattmeter method with $W_1 = 1500$ W and $W_2 = 500$ W. Find the total power and reactive volt-amperes.

15.25 In Fig. P.15.5, the voltages $\mathbf{V}_{an1}$, $\mathbf{V}_{bn1}$, and $\mathbf{V}_{cn1}$ form an *a-b-c*, or *positive*, sequence system; the voltages $\mathbf{V}_{an2}$, $\mathbf{V}_{bn2}$, and $\mathbf{V}_{cn2}$ form an *a-c-b*,

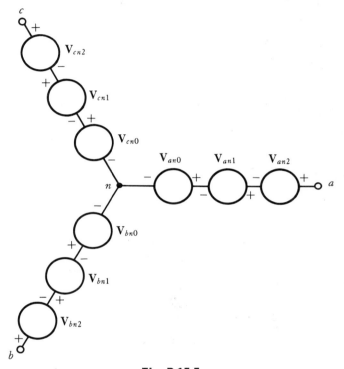

Fig. P.15.5.

or *negative*, sequence system; and the voltages $\mathbf{V}_{an0} = \mathbf{V}_{bn0} = \mathbf{V}_{cn0}$ form the *zero sequence* system similar to a set of three identical single-phase voltages. Find the matrix $\mathscr{A}$ in the expression

$$\begin{bmatrix} \mathbf{V}_{an} \\ \mathbf{V}_{bn} \\ \mathbf{V}_{cn} \end{bmatrix} = \mathscr{A} \begin{bmatrix} \mathbf{V}_{an1} \\ \mathbf{V}_{an2} \\ \mathbf{V}_{an0} \end{bmatrix}$$

relating the unbalanced phase voltages to their balanced *symmetrical components*. Also find $\mathscr{A}^{-1}$.

15.26 In the system of Prob. 15.25, show the matrix listing a set of un-balanced line voltages in terms of symmetrical line-to-line components to be

$$
\begin{bmatrix} V_{ab} \\ V_{bc} \\ V_{ca} \end{bmatrix} = \mathscr{A} \begin{bmatrix} V_{ab1} \\ V_{ab2} \\ V_{ab0} \end{bmatrix} = \mathscr{A}\mathscr{B} \begin{bmatrix} V_{an1} \\ V_{an2} \\ V_{an0} \end{bmatrix},
$$

and show the matrix $\mathscr{B}$ as a 3×3 matrix with numerical values.

15.27 Use the results of Prob. 15.25 to find the symmetric components of the single-phase 3-wire system formed by setting

$$
V_{an} = -V_{bn} = V; \qquad V_{cn} = 0.
$$

Graphically add the resulting three balanced systems to substantiate your answer.

15.28 Use the results of Prob. 15.26 to find the line-to-line symmetrical components of the two-wire single-phase system formed by setting

$$
V_{ab} = -V_{bc} = 0; \qquad V_{ca} = 0.
$$

Graphically add the resulting three balanced systems to substantiate your answer.

15.29 A single-phase, 3-wire, 240/120-V residential wiring system supplies 6 kW of 240-V range load (pure heat), 2000 watts of 120-V lighting at 0.9 pf lag, and 1500 W of 120-V motor load at 0.7 pf lag. The 120-V loads are evenly balanced on the two sides of the neutral. What are the line and neutral currents?

15.30 Repeat Prob. 15.29 when the motor loads are connected from line B to neutral, but lighting loads remain balanced.

15.31 A balanced 2-phase, 3-wire, 200-V system feeds phase impedances of $10 + j20\ \Omega$. What are the three line currents, the power, and the power factor?

15.32 In the system of Fig. 15.10(a), $V_\alpha = 200 + j0$ V, $Z_S = 2 + j6\ \Omega$, and $Z_L = 30 + j40\ \Omega$. Find the two terminal voltages and all currents.

15.33 Repeat Prob. 15.32 when Z_L is changed to $30 - j40\ \Omega$.

15.34 In Fig. P.15.6 the voltages $V_{\alpha1}$ and $V_{\beta1}$ form a balanced α-β, or *positive*, sequence system; and the voltages $V_{\alpha2}$ and $V_{\beta2}$ form a balanced β-α, or *negative*, sequence system. Find the matrix $\mathscr{C}$ in the expression

$$
\begin{bmatrix} V_\alpha \\ V_\beta \end{bmatrix} = \mathscr{C} \begin{bmatrix} V_{\alpha1} \\ V_{\alpha2} \end{bmatrix}
$$

relating the unbalanced phase voltages to their balanced *two-phase symmetrical components*. Also find $\mathscr{C}^{-1}$.

15.35 Use the results of Prob. 15.34 to find the two-phase symmetrical components of the two-wire single-phase system formed by setting

$$
V_\alpha = -V_\beta = V.
$$

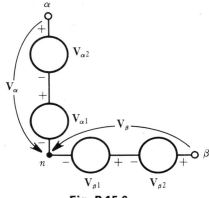

Fig. P.15.6.

Graphically add the resulting two balanced systems to substantiate your answer.

15.36 A 115-V, 2-phase, 400-Hz servomotor, used in automatic control systems, operates with the voltage $V_\alpha = 115 + j0$ volts on its *reference phase* and $V_\beta = -jV_S$ on its *control phase*, the voltage V_S being a variable, $V_S = ks(t)$, where $s(t)$ is some slowly-varying (compared to 400-Hz variations) signal in the system. Find the two-phase symmetrical components, $V_{\alpha 1}$ and $V_{\alpha 2}$ for each of the following:

a. $V_S = 100$ V
b. $V_S = 50$ V
c. $V_S = 0$
d. $V_S = -50$ V
e. $V_S = -100$ V.

15.37 The nature of 3-phase generators is such that all phase quantities have odd symmetry (See Fig. 14.5), but they may not be sinusoidal. Three-phase quantities, sinusoidal or not, obey the following for *a-b-c* sequence, since a three-phase generator treats all phases alike, except in time:

$$f_a(\omega t) = f_a(\omega t)$$

$$f_b(\omega t) = f_a\left(\omega t - \frac{2\pi}{3}\right)$$

$$f_c(\omega t) = f_a\left(\omega t - \frac{4\pi}{3}\right),$$

where ω is the fundamental radian frequency. Prove that the only harmonics which can exist in the currents of a balanced wye with no neutral conductor and in the voltages of a delta are those odd harmonics not divisible by three.

15.38 Prove that in a balanced wye with a neutral, the only currents in the neutral are those harmonics divisible by three, and that this harmonic current is three times the current in each phase due to the same harmonics.

15.39 The three phases of a balanced three-phase generator are being connected into a delta, with just the last connection remaining. The voltage measured between the two leads which will be connected to close the delta is found to be nonzero. Prove that this voltage consists only of those harmonics divisible by three and that this harmonic voltage is three times that of each phase due to the same harmonics.

Appendix

Algebra of Complex Numbers

In electrical engineering, it is customary to set

$$\sqrt{-1} = j$$

rather than to use the symbol i, which is used to indicate imaginary numbers in many mathematics texts but which has so many other uses in the problems of interest to electrical engineers. Some properties of this operator are

$$j^2 = -1, \qquad (A.1a)$$

$$\frac{1}{j} = -j, \qquad (A.1b)$$

$$j^n = (-1)^{n/2}, \qquad (A.1c)$$

$$j^n = (-1)^{n-1/2}j. \qquad (A.1d)$$

Figure A.1 includes an illustration of the complex number

$$z_1 = x_1 + jy_1$$
$$= r_1(\cos\theta_1 + j\sin\theta_1). \qquad (A.2)$$

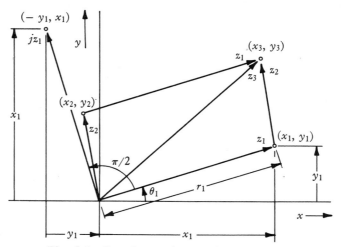

Fig. A.1 *Complex numbers on the complex plane.*

These two forms are the *rectangular* and *trigonometric*, respectively. Notice that from Eqs. (A.1)

$$jz_1 = -y_1 + jx_1$$
$$= r_1(-\sin\theta_1 + j\cos\theta_1)$$
$$= r_1\left[\cos\left(\theta_1 + \frac{\pi}{2}\right) + j\sin\left(\theta + \frac{\pi}{2}\right)\right].$$

The McLaurin series representing the sine and cosine are

$$\sin\theta = \theta - \frac{1}{3!}\theta^3 + \frac{1}{5!}\theta^5 - \frac{1}{7!}\theta^7 + \cdots$$

$$\cos\theta = 1 - \frac{1}{2!}\theta^2 + \frac{1}{4!}\theta^4 - \frac{1}{6!}\theta^6 + \cdots.$$

The McLaurin series for the function $e^{j\theta}$, where e is the base of the natural logarithm, is

$$e^{j\theta} = 1 + j\theta + \frac{j^2}{2!}\theta^2 + \frac{j^3}{3!}\theta^3 + \frac{j^4}{4!}\theta^4 + \frac{j^5}{5!}\theta^5$$

$$+ \frac{j^6}{6!}\theta^6 + \frac{j^7}{7!}\theta^7 + \cdots$$

$$= \left(1 - \frac{1}{2!}\theta^2 + \frac{1}{4!}\theta^4 - \frac{1}{6!}\theta^6 + \cdots\right)$$

$$+ j\left(\theta - \frac{1}{3!}\theta^3 + \frac{1}{5!}\theta^5 - \frac{1}{7!}\theta^7 + \cdots\right).$$

Thus
$$e^{j\theta} = \cos\theta + j\sin\theta, \tag{A.3}$$

and the third form, the *exponential*, of Eq. (A.2) is
$$z_1 = r_1 e^{j\theta_1} = |z_1| e^{j\underline{/z_1}} = \sqrt{x_1^2 + y_1^2}\; e^{j\,\tan^{-1} y_1/x_1}. \tag{A.4}$$

This form expressed the complex number in terms of its *magnitude*, or *modulus*, r_1, and its *angle*, or *argument*, θ_1.

Obviously, from Eq. (A.3)
$$e^{-j\theta} = \cos\theta - j\sin\theta.$$

A simultaneous solution of this equation and Eq. (A.3) leads to the important relationships
$$\cos\theta = \frac{e^{j\theta} + e^{-j\theta}}{2} \tag{A.5a}$$

$$\sin\theta = \frac{e^{j\theta} - e^{-j\theta}}{j2}. \tag{A.5b}$$

The important results of these introductory remarks are summarized in Eqs. (A.3) and (A.4) and the gathering together of the three standard forms of the complex number.

$$z = x + jy \qquad \text{(rectangular form)} \tag{A.6a}$$
$$= r(\cos\theta + j\sin\theta) \qquad \text{(trigonometric form)} \tag{A.6b}$$
$$= re^{j\theta} = r\exp(j\theta) \qquad \text{(exponential form)} \tag{A.6c}$$
$$= \text{Re}(z) + j\,\text{Im}(z), \tag{A.6d}$$

where
$$\text{Re}\,[\ ] = \text{real part of } [\ ], \tag{A.7a}$$
$$\text{Im}\,[\ ] = \text{imaginary part of } [\ ]. \tag{A.7b}$$

For completeness, we add to these the *conjugate* of the complex number, z^*, which is formed by replacing j by $-j$ in z. That is,
$$z^* = x - jy \tag{A.8a}$$
$$= r(\cos\theta - j\sin\theta) \tag{A.8b}$$
$$= re^{-j\theta}. \tag{A.8c}$$

Addition (and Subtraction) of Complex Numbers

The complex number $z_1 = x_1 + jy_1$ is added to the complex number $z_2 = x_2 + jy_2$ as follows:
$$z_1 + z_2 = (x_1 + jy_1) + (x_2 + jy_2)$$
$$= (x_1 + x_2) + j(y_1 + y_2). \tag{A.9}$$

It also follows that

$$z_1 - z_2 = (x_1 - x_2) + j(y_1 - y_2). \tag{A.10}$$

Graphic Display of Complex Numbers

Complex numbers may be displayed graphically on the complex plane or z-plane, on which the abscissa measures the real part of the complex numbers and the ordinate measures the imaginary part, as illustrated in Fig. A.1. There are three ways in which a given number may be characterized on this plane:

1. By the point on the plane located by the real and imaginary parts of the number; for example, the point (x_2, y_2), characterizing the complex number z_2 on Fig. A.1.

2. By a directed line (arrow) from the origin to the point defined by method 1.

3. By a directed line between any two points whose coordinate differences yield the coordinates (as in method 1) of the number. This directed line will always be parallel to and equal in length to the directed line of method 2 and is really an expression of the given complex number as the difference between two other complex numbers. In Fig. A.1, where z_2 is shown in all three representations, $z_2 = z_3 - z_1$.

Multiplication (and Division) of Complex Numbers

The complex numbers z_1 and z_2 are multiplied as follows:

$$\begin{aligned} z_1 z_2 &= (x_1 + jy_1)(x_2 + jy_2) \\ &= (x_1 x_2 - y_1 y_2) + j(x_1 y_2 + y_1 x_2) \end{aligned} \tag{A.11a}$$

or

$$\begin{aligned} z_1 z_2 &= (r_1 e^{j\theta_1})(r_2 e^{j\theta_2}) \\ &= (r_1 r_2) e^{j(\theta_1 + \theta_2)}. \end{aligned} \tag{A.11b}$$

For most practical applications, the second method will be most amenable to rapid slide-rule calculation.

It follows that

$$\begin{aligned} \frac{z_1}{z_2} &= \frac{z_1 z_2^*}{z_2 z_2^*} \\ &= \frac{(x_1 + jy_1)(x_2 - jy_2)}{(x_2 + jy_2)(x_2 - jy_2)} \\ &= \frac{(x_1 x_2 + y_1 y_2) + j(y_1 x_2 - x_1 y_2)}{x_2^2 + y_2^2}, \end{aligned} \tag{A.12a}$$

or, simply,

$$\frac{z_1}{z_2} = \frac{r_1 e^{j\theta_1}}{r_2 e^{j\theta_2}}$$

$$= \frac{r_1}{r_2} e^{j(\theta_1 - \theta_2)}. \tag{A.12b}$$

The latter form is obviously going to be the most convenient for most purposes.

An Important Special Product

An inkling of the usefulness of a special product appeared in the division process above. It will often be useful to recall that

$$z_1 z_2^* = (x_1 + jy_1)(x_2 - jy_2)$$
$$= (x_1 x_2 + y_1 y_2) + j(y_1 x_2 - x_1 y_2) \tag{A.13a}$$

or

$$z_1 z_2^* = (r_1 e^{j\theta_1})(r_2 e^{-j\theta_2})$$
$$= r_1 r_2 e^{j(\theta_1 - \theta_2)}$$
$$= r_1 r_2 \cos(\theta_1 - \theta_2) + j r_1 r_2 \sin(\theta_1 - \theta_2). \tag{A.13b}$$

As a result,

$$r_1 r_2 \cos(\theta_1 - \theta_2) = \text{Re}\,[z_1 z_2^*] \tag{A.14a}$$
$$r_1 r_2 \sin(\theta_1 - \theta_2) = \text{Im}\,[z_1 z_2^*]. \tag{A.14b}$$

Powers and Roots of Complex Numbers

Basic algebra yields quickly the fact that

$$z^n = (re^{j\theta})^n = r^n e^{jn\theta}. \tag{A.15}$$

Also,

$$z^{1/n} = (re^{j\theta})^{1/n}$$
$$= [re^{j(\theta + 2k\pi)}]^{1/n}, \qquad k = 0, 1, 2, \ldots,$$

because

$$re^{j\theta} = re^{j(\theta + 2k\pi)}, \qquad k = 0, 1, 2, \ldots.$$

Therefore,

$$z^{1/n} = r^{1/n} \exp\left(j\frac{(\theta + 2k\pi)}{n}\right), \qquad k = 0, 1, 2, \ldots, n-1, \tag{A.16}$$

where we allow k to range only to $n - 1$ because succeeding values of k would lead to repeating roots obtained at some lower k.

Angular Units

The angle θ appearing in the complex number $z = re^{j\theta}$ has the dimensionless unit, the radian. For example, if the directed-line representation of z is comprised of a line of length 15 at an angle of 60°, then the mathematically correct way to write z is

$$z = 15 \exp\left\{j\left[(60 \text{ degree})\left(\frac{\pi}{180} \frac{\text{radian}}{\text{degree}}\right)\right]\right\} = 15 \exp\left(j\frac{\pi}{3}\right).$$

Strictly speaking, for angles in degrees, one should write

$$z = re^{jk\theta} = 15e^{jk30°},$$

where

$$k = \frac{\pi}{180} \frac{\text{radian}}{\text{degree}}.$$

However, it has long been customary for engineers to write instead

$$z = re^{j\theta} = 15e^{j30°},$$

with the conversion to radians understood. Out of deference to custom, the same notation has been used in this text.

When performing the basic operations of multiplication, division, taking roots, and raising to powers, the conversion constant, k, remains an exponent multiplier and the actual conversion from degrees need never be made, because the multiplier affects the result in exactly the same way as it did the component elements. An example of a case where failing to convert to radians can cause trouble is that of the logarithm as a complex number, where the multiplier ends up as a factor in the imaginary part, not the angle. Here it is absolutely essential that the angle be in radians.

In short, the student should not forget that angles are basically measured in dimensionless "radians," even though they are often shown in "degrees."

Index

581